C0-AWD-348

INTERNATIONAL SERIES OF MONOGRAPHS ON PURE AND APPLIED BIOLOGY

Division: **MODERN TRENDS IN PHYSIOLOGICAL SCIENCES**

GENERAL EDITORS: P. ALEXANDER AND Z. M. BACQ

VOLUME 1

UNITY AND DIVERSITY IN BIOCHEMISTRY

OTHER TITLES IN THE SERIES ON PURE AND APPLIED BIOLOGY

MODERN TRENDS IN PHYSIOLOGICAL SCIENCES DIVISION

Vol. 2. BRACHET—*The Biochemistry of Development*

Vol. 3. GEREBTZOFF—*Cholinesterases*

Vol. 4. BROUHA—*Physiology in Industry*

BIOCHEMISTRY DIVISION

Vol. 1. PITT-RIVERS and TATA—*The Thyroid Hormones*

BOTANY DIVISION

Vol. 1. BOR—*Grasses of Burma, Ceylon, India and Pakistan*

Vol. 2. TURRILL (Ed.)—*Vistas in Botany*

Vol. 3. SHULTES—*Orchids of Trinidad and Tobago*

ZOOLOGY DIVISION

Vol. 1. RAVEN—*An Outline of Developmental Physiology*

Vol. 2. RAVEN—*Morphogenesis: The Analysis of Molluscan Development*

Vol. 3. SAVORY—*Instinctive Living*

Vol. 4. KERKUT—*Implications of Evolution*

Vol. 5. JENKIN—*Animal Hormones*

UNITY AND DIVERSITY IN BIOCHEMISTRY

An Introduction to Chemical Biology

by

MARCEL FLORKIN
University of Liège

Translated from the French by

T. WOOD
University of Sydney

PERGAMON PRESS
OXFORD · LONDON · NEW YORK · PARIS
1960

PERGAMON PRESS LTD.
Headington Hill Hall, Oxford
4 & 5 Fitzroy Square, London W.1.

PERGAMON PRESS INC.
122 East 55th Street, New York 22, N.Y.
P.O. Box 47715, Los Angeles, California

PERGAMON PRESS S.A.R.L.
24 Rue des Écoles, Paris Ve

PERGAMON PRESS G.m.b.H.
Kaiserstrasse 75, Frankfurt am Main

First Published in English 1960

Library of Congress Card Number 58–12669

PRINTED IN GREAT BRITAIN BY THE BAY TREE PRESS, HERTS.

Contents

LIST OF ABBREVIATIONS

ADP	Adenosine diphosphate
AMP	Adenosine monophosphate
ATP	Adenosine triphosphate
DNA	Deoxyribonucleic acid
DPN, DPNH	Diphosphopyridine nucleotide
DPT	Diphosphothiamine
FAD	Flavin adenine dinucleotide
FMN	Flavin mononucleotide
FP	Flavin phosphate
F-6-P	Fructose-6-phosphate
F-1,6-PP	Fructose-1,6-diphosphate
Gal-1-P	Galactose-1-phosphate
G-1-P	Glucose-1-phosphate
G-1,6-PP	Glucose-1,6-diphosphate
G-6-P	Glucose-6-phosphate
HDP	Heptulose diphosphate
HMP	Heptulose monophosphate
LTPP	Lipothiamide-pyrophosphate
PGA	3-Phosphoglyceric acid
PGAD	Phosphoglyceraldehyde dehydrogenase
PRPP	Phosphoribosylpyrophosphate
Ru-P	Ribulose-5-phosphate
Ru-PP	Ribulose diphosphate
TPN, TPNH	Triphosphopyridine nucleotide
UDP	Uridine diphosphate
UDPG	Uridine diphosphate glucose
UMP	Uridine monophosphate
UTP	Uridine triphosphate

TRANSLATOR'S PREFACE

THE translation of Professor Florkin's book has been complicated by the rapid progress of biochemistry in the last few years, necessitating many alterations and additions to the original text, to keep it up to date and to include new material. The subject-matter dealt with in these pages covers a very wide field, and I would crave the indulgence of the reader for any errors due to lack of familiarity with some of the topics discussed. Part of this discussion is at a philosophical level and, although not having had the pleasure of meeting Professor Florkin personally, I have tried to convey as faithfully as possible the ideas and concepts set out in the original text. When in doubt, I have stayed as closely as possible to the phraseology of the original. I have retained the term "biosphere", for example, to describe the total collection of living organisms. Enzyme nomenclature, too, has been a problem, but when in doubt I have used the terms given in Baldwin's *Dynamic Aspects of Biochemistry*, or alternatively, the simplest and most descriptive name for the enzyme. I have endeavoured to write in good concise English and I trust that the result is clear and readable.

TERRY WOOD

INTRODUCTION

In these pages, the reader will find neither a treatise nor a textbook on biochemistry, but a number of essays grouped around ideas of the unity and diversity of organisms in the biochemical sphere. "The manifold and the one" are eternal preoccupations of the human intellect, and we must not be surprised that, from the time biochemistry has been able to gather together a sufficient number of facts, the search for the lowest common denominator of all organisms or a "unity of biochemical plan" has been confused in many minds with the idea of a comparative biochemistry. The latter is a problem which is perhaps more relevant to natural philosphy than to scientific investigation, for we are becoming more and more aware of the extreme diversity of biochemical function arising during cellular differentiation in a single organism, as well as in the multiplicity of species and even of individuals. The biosphere, by which we understand the total amount of living matter, behaves like a chemist of a very special type. All the organic compounds present in the many regions of the biosphere and resulting from its biosynthetic activities have structures lying within certain definite limits. The first part of this book provides a concise catalogue of these structures but is not coincident with the contents of a textbook of organic chemistry provided that the latter is not defined as it was by Berzelius at the beginning of the 19th century, when he wrote that organic chemistry is that section of physiology describing the composition of living things and the chemical reactions going on therein. This definition of organic chemistry is no longer valid today; beginning with the synthesis of a naturally occurring substance, urea, organic chemistry has extended its domain to the synthesis of a tremendous number of non-natural substances. One of the objectives of biochemistry is to define and understand the nature of the collection of compounds composing living matter and to distinguish them from those originating from non-living sources and human inventiveness, all of which are described by the broad generalizations of chemistry.

The biosphere is not only a chemist of a special type, but also one of great antiquity whose methods have been developed over a long period of time since long before there were laboratories of organic chemistry, and are of an efficiency far from being paralleled in these laboratories. This point is developed further in the two essays which make up Parts 2 and 3 of this book with the intention of demonstrating the originality of this organic chemist who has laboured since the dawn of time and comparing his methods with those of the laboratory chemist. The essays making up

Parts 1, 2 and 3 are devoted to general aspects of the biosphere, i.e. to the biochemical facts common to living beings and which constitute their lowest common denominator, or, their "unity of biochemical plan". The cellular theory, as proposed by Theodor Schwann in 1836, taught that organisms are formed not only of cells, of modified cells and cellular products, but that a multicellular organism has two levels of individuality, one on the cellular level and one at the level of the whole organism. In its final perfected form, the cellular theory recognizes that each cell is derived from a pre-exisiting cell. The results of biochemical research have taught us that the manifestations of an underlying biochemical unity are present in each cell, according to a topochemistry briefly described in Part 4. In this context, the "unity of plan" is simply the cellular theory from a biochemical point of view; in the same way as they are *units* of structure, cells are *units* of metabolism. The unity of a structure and cellular metabolism is only another expression of cellular continuity and the persistence in this continuity of a definite collection of genes controlling the synthesis of the collection of enzymes present in each cell. However, no cell is limited by the underlying biochemical unity, for this is only the canvas on to which the cell can embroider the numerous variations constituting its own biological nature, the "unity of plan" remaining an abstraction.

In Part 5 it is only possible to provide a few very brief examples of biochemical variation and biochemical evolution. The few cases quoted will enable the reader to locate some aspects of biochemical variation at the level of cellular differentiation and at the taxonomic level in the same organism. These examples show that the biochemical manifestations of variation are founded on the extension of the general processes of cellular biochemistry and constitute atypical expressions of general metabolic systems, variations on each theme being more or less pronounced but fitting in with general ideas of variation of genotype and biochemical adaptation of the organism to its surroundings.

Part 6 presents the idea of the metabolism of the biosphere as a whole and illustrates how this metabolism, like that of each organism, consists of an entry and an exit of energy and material, but now situated at the frontier between the biosphere and the inorganic world. The metabolism of the biosphere is conditioned by manifestations of biochemical variation, without which life would disappear. In fact, the unity of the biochemical plan of organisms comes down finally to a continuity of the biosphere in time and space and the accompanying biochemical diversity which has appeared as biochemical evolution has progressed with the extension of the biosphere. This extension has only been possible when, by means of new ecosystems, the exchanges between the inorganic surroundings and the biosphere, which are a condition for the survival of the latter, have been maintained.

Biochemistry has provided explanations in many fields of physiology and we can now perceive the preliminary signs of similar progress in a field that up to now has been outside the scope of biochemical explanation—that of electrophysiology. The demystification of biology will be a long and arduous task which is only just beginning. Much work remains to be done before the natural order, natural selection, adaptation, evolutionary tendencies, orthogenesis, morphogenesis, etc., are replaced by a knowledge of the reality underlying these somewhat poetic terms.

The author is conscious of the imperfections of his book and criticisms which could be levelled at it. Nevertheless, perhaps biochemists will find therein reasons for interesting themselves to advantage in biochemical variation and not solely in the unitarian aspects of biochemistry. Perhaps chemists will find reasons for recognizing that although it is true that chemistry is one, and everywhere obeys the same laws, yet the chemist within the living cell has his own special methods which can only be unravelled by means of the experimental study of living material. Perhaps, also, the essays that follow will assist in convincing certain biologists that they are wrong when they assert that the natural realities which we describe by the concepts of species and taxonomic classes no longer exist at the level of the molecular phenomena which is the study of biochemistry. In addition, perhaps, they will also become convinced that the field of the metabolism, of cells, of organisms, and of the biosphere itself, offers a fruitful region for the study of some of the most fundamental problems of biology.

Although unable to flatter himself with unqualified success in an undertaking as difficult as this, the author feels confident of the indulgence of the reader for any omissions or errors he may have committed.

MARCEL FLORKIN

PART ONE

CHAPTER I

THE BIOSPHERE

THE terrestrial globe is surrounded by an *atmosphere* consisting chiefly of nitrogen, oxygen and argon, but containing other elements and such compounds as carbon dioxide.

The distribution of molecules in the atmosphere is of considerable biochemical interest. At altitudes below 20,000 m the average composition shown in Table I is maintained constant by convection currents, but at higher altitudes, due to the different molecular weights of the gases composing the atmosphere, a separation by sedimentation becomes apparent. Beyond 150,000 m, this separation becomes very marked and progressively the atmosphere becomes less dense until finally it fades into the emptiness of interplanetary space. Nearest to the earth is the troposphere, its composition being kept more or less constant at the values shown in Table I, by convection currents. Its thickness varies from 10 to 15,000 m according to the season and the latitude. Above it is the stratosphere, so-called because of the stratification of different gases in order of their molecular weights. The layers of gas are not disturbed by convection currents and there is no appreciable circulation of molecules in a vertical direction. Whilst in the troposphere the temperature decreases with altitude, in the stratosphere it is independent of the latter.

At around 80,000 m is the start of the ionosphere which takes its name from the fact that it is rendered conducting by the ionization phenomena produced by the sun's ultra-violet radiation. The presence of carbon dioxide in the troposphere, as we shall see, is very important despite its low concentration. The presence in the stratosphere of a diffuse layer of ozone, the ozonosphere, is not less important for it prevents the greater part of the sun's ultra-violet radiation from reaching the surface of the earth where it would otherwise soon put an end to all life.

The earth is also surrounded by a *hydrosphere*, a discontinuous layer of water in different physical states which separates the *lithosphere* from the atmosphere and extends into the latter in the form of water vapour.

The hydrosphere is made up of oceans, lakes, rivers, streams, water absorbed by the rocks and by snow and ice. Oceans cover 70% of the earth's surface and their average depth is 3,800 m, and sea water represents approximately 98% of the hydrosphere. The composition of the sea water and its dissolved gases is given in Table II.

TABLE I

Average composition of the troposphere

(from Paneth, completed by Mason, 1952)

	Composition by volume (p.p.m.)	Composition by weight (p.p.m.)	Total mass in geograms (10^{20}g)	Partial pressure (mmHg)
N_2	780,900	755,100	38·648	593·02
O_2	209,500	231,500	11·841	159·52
A	9,300	12,800	0·655	7·144
CO_2	300	460	0·0233	0·228
Ne	18	12·5	0·000636	
He	5·2	0·72	0·000037	
CH_4	2·2	1·2	0·000062	
Kr	1·0	2·9	0·000146	
N_2O	1·0	1·5	0·000077	
H_2	0·5	0·03	0·000002	
Xe	0·08	0·36	0·000018	
O_3[1]	0·01	0·36	0·000031	
				760·00

[1] Variable, increasing with altitude.

TABLE II

Composition of sea water

(mM per litre)

(after Conway, 1943)

Na	478
K	10
Ca	11
Mg	55
Cl	559
SO_4	29
HCO_3	2
PO_4	traces

Gas dissolved in sea water (ml/l)

(after Mason, 1952)

Oxygen	0–9
Nitrogen	8·4–14·5
Total CO_2	34–56
Argon	0·2–0·4

The total of those parts of the lithosphere, the hydrosphere and the atmosphere, in which life is present, is called the *biosphere.* What are its limits? In the direction of interstellar space it is bounded by the ozonosphere, at about 20 km from the ground. Towards the earth's core the boundary is reached very soon at the surface of the continents and is not generally deeper than this by more than 10 m. On the other hand, in the ocean life can be found at depths down to 10,000 m.

No matter to which theory of the earth's origin one subscribes, it seems probable that there was a time when the terrestrial atmosphere consisted almost entirely of nitrogen and carbon dioxide. It is probable that at the beginning of the earth's history the atmosphere just described had been rapidly transformed into a mixture of oxygen and nitrogen, for the study of the rocks does not show the existence of any marked variations, which shows that the composition of the atmosphere has been much as it is now throughout a great part of geological time. For instance, the state of oxidation of pre-Cambrian rocks is not significantly different from that of more recent rocks. The change from an atmosphere of carbon dioxide and nitrogen to one of oxygen and nitrogen is generally considered to be a result of the process of photosynthesis.

In the course of time, considered on a geological timescale, the atmosphere has had various chemical substances added to it: volcanic gases (chiefly CO_2), oxygen resulting from photosynthesis, CO_2 as a result of metabolism and the decay of organic material, helium-4 produced by the radioactivity of uranium and thorium, argon-40 from the decay of potassium-40. (Natural argon contains the isotopes of mass 36, 38 and 40. Only argon-40 is derived from potassium-40. Argon-40 constitutes 99·63% of natural argon. Similarly for helium: only helium-4 is derived from the α rays emitted by several natural isotopes.)

On the other hand, subtraction of certain chemical substances has taken place: loss of oxygen by oxidation of iron, sulphur, manganese, etc., loss of CO_2 through formation of carbon, petroleum and dead organisms, loss of CO_2 in the formation of carbonates, loss of nitrogen by fixation, loss of nitrogen by formation of oxides by electrical or photochemical action, loss of hydrogen and helium due to the weakness of the earth's gravitational field, etc.

The equilibrium between losses and gains which has been obtained is witnessed by the constancy of composition of the atmosphere over extended periods of geological time. In the special case of carbon dioxide the regulatory role of the hydrosphere also plays a part.

Certain geochemists consider that the hydrosphere remained shallow up to the end of the Paleozoic period, so that the oceans as we know them today have a relatively short history. Others say that the volume of the oceans has not changed much since the pre-Cambrian period. Whichever is the case it is generally agreed today that the oceans have not changed appreciably in composition since the Archaean period.

Together with Conway (1943) we may advance four hypotheses to account for the chemical evolution of the oceans.

1. The water results from the condensation of water vapour from the primitive atmosphere whilst the chlorides have been added gradually over the ages (constant volume, volcanic chlorides).

2. Both water and chlorides are the result of an initial condensation (constant volume, constant chloride).

3. The water and the chlorides have been progressively accumulated (both oceans and chlorides of volcanic origin).

4. The chlorides were initially present (metallic chlorides in the surface of the earth), the water being gradually added as a result of volcanic action (volcanic oceans, constant chloride).

At the present time the third hypothesis is the one favoured by geochemists. According to this view the mass of substances dissolved in the sea arises from erosion of the terrestrial crust. The total of these substances is enormous. If all the sea water were evaporated, it would form a layer of salt 153 m thick covering the surface of the continents. Goldschmidt calculates that for each litre of sea water 600 g of igneous rock have been dissolved. In other words, for each square centimetre of the earth's crust, during the formation of the oceans, erosion has removed 160 kg of igneous rock. The greater part of this has gone to form the sedimentary rocks.

The biosphere is chronologically after the lithosphere, the hydrosphere and the atmosphere. Although occupying a portion of all three regions, it is discontinuous and *comprises the total mass of organisms*. This definition is additional to what has already been said about the vital nature of the biosphere, its location and its discontinuous character. The mass of the biosphere is much less than that of the hydrosphere or the atmosphere. According to Rankama and Sahama (1950), the relative weights are as follows :

Hydrosphere	69,100
Atmosphere	300
Biosphere	1

But if the biosphere is quantitatively insignificant, nevertheless it is the centre of considerable chemical activity and it can be calculated that in the course of the last 500 million years, that is since the appearance of the Trilobites, it has "metabolized" a mass of material equal to the total weight of the globe.

One can obtain an idea of the size of the biosphere by calculating the annual production of organically bound carbon per square kilometre of the earth's surface. Riley obtains a figure of 160 metric tons on land and 340 metric tons in the sea. The total annual production of the continents is $20 \pm 5 \times 10^9$ metric tons and that of the sea is $126 \pm 82 \times 10^9$ metric tons, a total of $146 \pm 83 \times 10^9$ metric tons.

The predominant chemical elements in the biosphere are hydrogen, carbon, nitrogen, oxygen and phosphorous. Sodium, magnesium, calcium, potassium, chlorine, sulphur and iron, in addition, are always present in concentrations ranging from 0·05% to 1%. Further elements, although in smaller quantity, are always found in measurable amounts : boron, aluminium, copper, zinc, silicon, gallium, molybdenum, manganese, cobalt and iodine. On occasion other elements may be found in living organisms.

The normal constituents of the biosphere are, with the exception of iodine, members of the first four periods of the periodic table. These are the lighter elements. Now, water makes up a large proportion of the biosphere and it is natural that the elements present in living organisms are those most widely distributed in the earth's crust and whose derivatives are most soluble. The electronegativity of the elements also plays an important part. In a biosphere of a predominantly aqueous nature it is natural that elements of weak electronegativity forming soluble cations are easily absorbed and assimilated. The same applies to elements of very strong electronegativity which give readily soluble anions.

To characterize the quantitative relations existing between the various elements entering into the composition of living things, one can say that if one adds up the amounts present of the following eleven metals and metalloids :

Carbon	Sulphur	Calcium
Hydrogen	Phosphorous	Magnesium
Oxygen	Chlorine	Potassium
Nitrogen		Sodium

then one accounts for almost the total weight of the organism—99·9% in the case of a man. This is one way of saying that the major part of any organism is made up of water, lipids, polysaccharides and proteins, and by chlorides, bicarbonates, phosphates, and sulphates of sodium, potassium, calcium and magnesium. The elements making up these compounds are the lighter elements, and, as already stated, are the most common in the surface of the lithosphere and hydrosphere. They include the elements of very weak and very strong electronegativity. It is not unexpected that they should have an important place in the composition of organisms.

As far as the minor elements are concerned we must guard against limiting the list too closely. Provided that there is at least one atom per cell of a trace element, then a function may be assigned to that element. As the methods of detecting trace elements improve, so does the number of trace elements increase. As our knowledge of biochemistry increases so does the number of trace elements having a known function increase proportionately. All the more reason, therefore, to treat warily any such idea as that of an *element of biochemical importance*.

The lithosphere, the hydrosphere and the biosphere are made up, qualitatively, of the same elements and only differ in the relative proportions of these elements.

REFERENCES

CONWAY, E. J. (1943) The chemical evolution of the ocean. *Proc. Roy. Irish Acad.* (*B*), **48**, 161–212.

LEUTHARDT (1941) Mineralstoffwechsel, *Erg. d. Physiol.*, **44**, 588–655.

MASON, B. (1952) *Principles of Geochemistry*, Wiley, New York.

CHAPTER II

CONSTITUENTS OF THE BIOSPHERE

As LONG as chemistry retained its aura of secrecy and magic; that is, up to the seventeenth century, the study of the chemical compounds making up the biosphere had not even been considered. One may attribute the first step to Van Helmont who, in his work *Ortus medicinae*, published in 1652, described carbonic anhydride as being present in intestinal gases, separated an alkaline substance from blood and attempted to resolve human urine into its constituents. It was necessary to await the development and elaboration of the idea of chemical compounds before Scheele, in 1775, succeeded in isolating uric acid from urinary calculi and Poulletier de la Salle, in 1782, extracted cholesterol from gall-stones with the aid of alcohol.

Following this came the most spectacular period of organic chemistry which saw the establishment of the idea of "radicals" (groups of atoms in the molecule which can be considered as remaining intact throughout a series of reactions, and which can be transferred from one molecule to another without undergoing disruption) and the idea of chemical type (that two substances which possess similar chemical properties have a similar arrangement of their constituent atoms in the molecule). The application of methods capable of isolating substances present in living things without any gross chemical changes taking place resulted in the identification of a large number of these constituents and the list of these increases daily. In 1862, Ernest Wagner, professor at Leipzig, in his *Manual of General Pathology*, stated an important generalization—that, of the material of living substances, apart from water, a large percentage can be divided into three simple organic types which we recognize today as fatty acids, sugars and amino acids. A mushroom, a spinach leaf, a sea urchin egg, the flesh of an oyster, a silk-worm, contain respectively 91·3, 92·3, 77·3, 88·3, and 78·4% of water. The dry residue is made up of these three principal types of compounds to the extent of 94·2% in the mushroom, 72·6% in the spinach leaf, 93·5% in sea urchin egg, 90·5% in oyster flesh and 83·9% in the silk-worm. The spinach leaf contains a somewhat smaller proportion of these organic constituents than the others due to the larger amounts of inorganic material which amounts to 27·2% of the dry weight. The sea urchin egg, on the other hand, contains only 1·5% of inorganic matter, mainly chlorides, sulphates, phosphates and bicarbonates of sodium, potassium, calcium and magnesium. Nevertheless, as stated above, the biosphere contains small amounts of a great number of other elements which are used to good effect.

Organic chemistry began by the study of certain natural carbon derivatives. In the course of its spectacular development during the nineteenth century, it ceased to be a science of naturally occurring compounds and became a science of imaginary molecules in the sense that a molecule not present in nature but synthesized by an organic chemist is a product of his mind and intellect. Nevertheless, a part of organic chemistry forms a whole segment of the natural science of biochemistry—this is the organic chemistry of naturally occurring substances, a field which depends upon the technical skill of the organic chemist, but whose frontiers and content primarily interest the biochemist.

This chapter is only a brief outline, and is not a catalogue of the chemical structures present in the biosphere. In our present state of knowledge it would certainly be premature to think of establishing such a catalogue. It is only necessary for an organic chemist to examine minutely the constituents of such a narrow portion of the biosphere as, for example, the musk gland of the musk-deer (see E. Lederer; Animal odours and perfumes, *Fortschr. Chem. org. Naturstoffe*, 1950, **6**, 87–153), toad parotid gland (V. Deulofeu; The chemistry of the constituents of toad venoms, *Fortschr. Chem. org. Naturstoffe*, 1948, **5**, 241–266), the cell of a mycobacterium (J. Asselineau and E. Lederer; Chimie des lipides bacteriens, *Fortschr. Chem. org. Naturstoffe*, 1953, **10**, 170–273), or the wood of various conifers (H. Erdtman; Chemistry of some heartwood constituents of conifers and their physiological and taxonomic significance, *Prog. org. Chem.*, 1952, **1**, 22–63), for him to obtain an imposing harvest of new molecules. Many molecules among them are merely variations on a general theme and their interest is greater still from the point of view of comparisons between living organisms. At the present time, without stating categorically that they are present in all organisms, we can make a list of types of organic structure most widely and generally distributed.

I. THE THREE PRINCIPAL BIOCHEMICAL STRUCTURES

A. Aliphatic Acids

Aliphatic organic acids are very widely distributed in living things, particularly in the form of fats, hence the name "fatty acids".

The first member of the straight chain saturated series is formic acid

$$H{-}C\begin{matrix}\diagup\!\!\diagup O\\ \diagdown OH\end{matrix}$$

corresponding to methane CH_4, and the first member

of the unsaturated series is acrylic acid, corresponding to propylene, allyl alcohol and acraldehyde (acrolein).

```
                         CH2                     CH2
                         ||                      ||
CH2                      CH  O                   CH  O
||                       |  //                   |  //
CH                       C                       C
|                         \                       \
CH2OH                     OH                      H
```

Allyl alcohol — Acrylic acid — Acraldehyde (Acrolein)

(*a*) *Saturated Fatty Acids*

These are all members of a homologous series of general formula RCOOH, where R represents an aliphatic chain of the type $CH_3(CH_2)_x$ or C_nH_{2n+1}. The lower members are volatile liquids. Those with six to nine carbon atoms are oily liquids. Above ten carbon atoms these substances are solid.

TABLE III

Natural saturated fatty acids $C_nH_{2n}O_2$

Systematic name	Common name	Formula	M.W.
n-Methanoic	Formic	$HCOOH$	46
n-Ethanoic	Acetic	CH_3COOH	60
n-Propanoic	Propionic	C_2H_5COOH	74
n-Butanoic	Butyric	C_3H_7COOH	88
n-Pentanoic	Valeric	C_4H_9COOH	102
n-Hexanoic	Caproic	$C_5H_{11}COOH$	116
n-Octanoic	Caprylic	$C_7H_{15}COOH$	144
n-Decanoic	Capric	$C_9H_{19}COOH$	172
n-Dodecanoic	Lauric	$C_{11}H_{23}COOH$	200
n-Tetradecanoic	Myristic	$C_{13}H_{27}COOH$	228
n-Hexadecanoic	Palmitic	$C_{15}H_{31}COOH$	256
n-Octadecanoic	Stearic	$C_{17}H_{35}COOH$	284
n-Eicosanoic	Arachidic	$C_{19}H_{39}COOH$	312
n-Docosanoic	Behenic	$C_{21}H_{43}COOH$	341
n-Tetracosanoic	Lignoceric	$C_{23}H_{47}COOH$	369
n-Hexacosanoic	Cerotic	$C_{25}H_{51}COOH$	397
n-Octacosanoic	Montanic	$C_{27}H_{55}COOH$	425
n-Triacontanoic	Mellissic	$C_{29}H_{59}COOH$	453
n-Dotriacontanoic	...	$C_{31}H_{63}COOH$	481
n-Tetratriacontanoic	...	$C_{33}H_{67}COOH$	509
n-Hexatriacontanoic	...	$C_{35}H_{71}COOH$	537
n-Octatriacontanoic	...	$C_{37}H_{75}COOH$	564

The lower members are very soluble in water and dissociate weakly; their solubility decreases as the number of carbon atoms increases.

Except for formic acid, propionic acid and valeric acid, the saturated fatty acids generally found in nature are those with *an even number of carbon atoms from 2 to* 38. Table III shows their scientific and common names, their empirical formulae and molecular weights.

(*b*) *Unsaturated Fatty Acids*

The unbranched saturated fatty acids form a perfect homologous series which is represented in nature by the members having an even number of carbon atoms between 2 and 38 (save for formic, propionic and valeric acids) but this is not the case with the unsaturated acids. These acids are made complex by the presence of one or more double bonds which in turn can undergo several types of reaction such as hydrogenation, halogenation, etc.

1. *One Double Bond*

In the same way as the hydrocarbons these acids are named according to the number of carbon atoms they possess, the carboxyl carbon being numbered 1. The presence of a double bond is indicated by the suffix -en, and its position by a numbered prefix, the two numbers indicating which two carbon atoms are joined by the double bond. Thus the acid $C_{18}H_{34}O_2$, commonly known as oleic acid, bears the scientific designation 9 : 10-octadecenoic acid, sometimes abbreviated to 9, octadecenoic acid. It is the most widely distributed in nature, of the monoethenoic acids, but there are several others, *all with an even number of carbon atoms*. The presence of the double bond admits the existence of a *cis* and of a *trans* form. Since nature *only contains the cis forms of the aliphatic acids*, in the field of biochemistry we may consider the prefix *cis* as understood, and therefore omit it.

2. *Two or More Double Bonds*

Fatty acids having two, three, four, five or six double bonds are not unusual in nature. Two of these are particularly widely distributed, they are, linoleic acid, $C_{18}H_{32}O_2$, or 9:10:12:13-octadecadienoic acid, and linolenic acid, $C_{18}H_{30}O_2$ or 9:10:12:13:15:16-octadecatrienoic acid.

(*c*) *Branched Chain Fatty Acids*

Certain fatty acids do not have a linear chain, for example, isovaleric acid, 3-methyl-butanoic acid $CH_3.CH(CH_3).CH_2COOH$. This is the only naturally occurring aliphatic acid (besides formic acid, propionic acid and valeric acid) having an odd number of carbon atoms. Nevertheless, the main chain in it has an even number. In the unsaturated series examples of naturally occurring branched chain acids are more common.

(*d*) *Dibasic and Polybasic Acids*

These play an important part in the chemistry of life. Present in small amounts in animal tissues and bacteria they are present in quantity in vegetable tissues. In both cases they have very important functions.

Only one 1:2 diacid is possible, oxalic acid $COOH.COOH$, an acid which is readily oxidized by permanganate to CO_2 and water. The simplest 1:3 diacid is malonic acid $COOH.CH_2.COOH$, which decomposes at 100°C into acetic acid and CO_2. The 1:4 diacids are represented by succinic acid $COOH.CH_2.CH_2.COOH$. Heat causes their dehydration to form an internal anhydride.

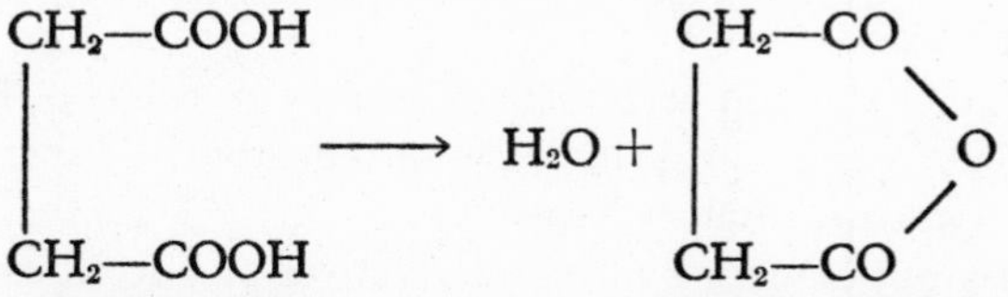

$$\begin{array}{l} CH_2\text{—}COOH \\ \quad | \\ CH_2\text{—}COOH \end{array} \longrightarrow H_2O + \begin{array}{l} CH_2\text{—}CO \\ \quad | \qquad\quad \diagdown \\ \quad | \qquad\qquad O \\ \quad | \qquad\quad \diagup \\ CH_2\text{—}CO \end{array}$$

Succinic acid — Succinic anhydride

Fumaric acid $COOH.CH : CH.COOH$, heated at 140°C in a closed vessel with a little water, is changed into its isomer maleic acid.

$$\begin{array}{c} H\text{—}C\text{—}COOH \\ \| \\ H\text{—}C\text{—}COOH \end{array} \qquad\qquad \begin{array}{c} H\text{—}C\text{—}COOH \\ \| \\ COOH\text{—}CH \end{array}$$

Maleic acid — Fumaric acid

(*e*) *Hydroxy-acids*

Lactic acid $CH_3CHOH.COOH$ is one of the acids most commonly found in nature. When a hydroxy-acid is heated it readily loses water, but the course of the reaction differs according to the relative positions of the carboxyl and hydroxyl groups. If the two groups are in the 1, 2 position, as in lactic acid, they will from a *lactide*

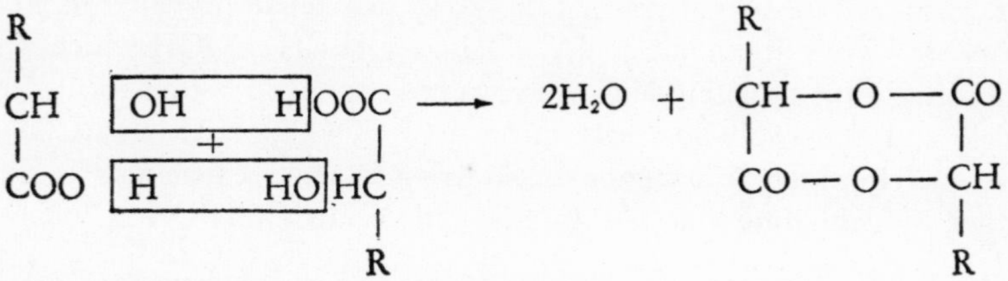

$$\begin{array}{lcl} R & & \\ | & & \\ CH & \boxed{OH \qquad H}OOC & \\ | & + & | \\ COO & \boxed{H \qquad HO}HC & \\ & & | \\ & & R \end{array} \longrightarrow 2H_2O + \begin{array}{ccccc} R & & & & \\ | & & & & \\ CH & \text{—} & O & \text{—} & CO \\ | & & & & | \\ CO & \text{—} & O & \text{—} & CH \\ & & & & | \\ & & & & R \end{array}$$

If the carboxyl and hydroxyl groups are in the 1, 3 position then heating will produce an unsaturated acid :

$$CH_2OH\text{—}CH_2\text{—}COOH \longrightarrow CH_2{=}CH\text{—}COOH + H_2O$$

If the two functional groups are 1, 4 or 1, 5 to each other they will form an internal ester or a lactone.

$$\underset{\text{OH}}{\text{CH}_2}\text{—CH}_2\text{—CH}_2\text{—}\underset{\text{COOH}}{\text{CH}_2} \rightleftharpoons \underset{\text{O}}{\text{CH}_2}\text{—CH}_2\text{—CH}_2\text{—}\underset{\text{CO}}{\text{CH}_2} + H_2O$$

1. *Monohydroxy-monoacids*

These substances frequently appear during the process of the breaking down of cellular nutrients.

The simplest is glycollic acid $CH_2OH.COOH$.

Lactic acid exists as two position isomers, primary or β-lactic acid $CH_2OH.CH_2.COOH$, and secondary or α-lactic acid $CH_3.CHOH.COOH$. This last form possesses an asymmetric carbon atom and therefore exists as a *laevo-* and a *dextro-* rotatory form.

Nature does not contain hydroxy derivatives of butyric acid other than β-hydroxybutyric acid $CH_3.CHOH.CH_2.COOH$. Another interesting monohydroxy-monoacid is hydroxylignoceric acid $C_{22}H_{47}.CHOH.COOH$, an acid found combined in certain cerebrosides.

2. *Polyhydroxy-monoacids*

The simplest is glyceric acid $CH_2OH.CHOH.COOH$. Many others may be readily prepared by oxidation of sugars, particularly the aldoses, whose aldehyde group is more readily oxidizable than the keto group of the ketoses (see p. 24).

3. *Monohydroxy-polyacids*

The simplest is tartronic acid $COOH.CHOH.COOH$, which is a product of the oxidation of glycerol $CH_2OH.CHOH.CH_2OH$, of malonic acid $COOH.CH_2.COOH$ and of tartaric acid.

Two other representatives of this group play an important role in the biosphere. They are, malic acid $COOH.CHOH.CH_2.COOH$ which yields malonic acid on oxidation and when water is removed is transformed into maleic and fumaric acids, and citric acid $COOH.CH_2C(OH).(COOH).CH_2COOH$, which is a monohydroxy-tribasic acid. Citric acid is transformed by dehydration at 175° into aconitic acid $COOH.CH:C(COOH).CH_2.COOH$.

4. *Polyhydroxy-polyacids*

A series of these compounds is present in the biosphere; they are derived from the sugars by oxidation (see p. 24).

(*f*) *Acid Aldehydes*

The simplest is glyoxylic acid COOH.CHO, prepared by reduction of oxalic acid COOH.COOH or oxidation of glycol $CH_2OH.CH_2OH$.

Uronic acids are derived from the aldoses by oxidation of the primary alcohol group to a carboxyl group.

Glucuronic acid is widely distributed in nature, it is the uronic acid derived from glucose.

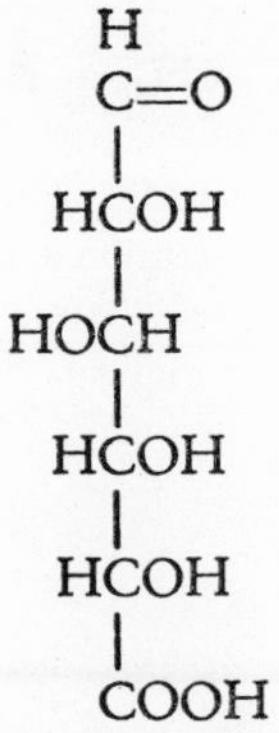

$$\begin{array}{c} H \\ C{=}O \\ | \\ HCOH \\ | \\ HOCH \\ | \\ HCOH \\ | \\ HCOH \\ | \\ COOH \end{array}$$

D-glucuronic acid

(*g*) *Keto-acids*

The monoketo acids are differentiated by the symbols α, β, γ, δ, etc., according to the position of the ketone group relative to the carboxyl group. They can be prepared by oxidizing the corresponding keto-acids or by hydration of a keto-nitrile. For example, pyruvic acid $CH_3.CO.COOH$ is prepared by hydrating $CH_3.CO.CN$. The most important keto-acids in the cell are pyruvic, oxalacetic, α-ketoglutaric and oxalosuccinic, and their decarboxylation is the major source of respiratory carbon dioxide.

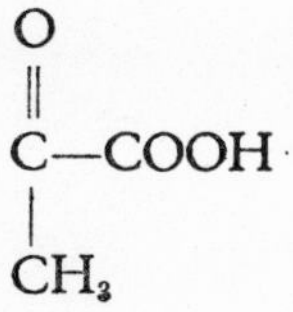

$$\begin{array}{l} O \\ \| \\ C{-}COOH \\ | \\ CH_3 \end{array}$$

pyruvic acid

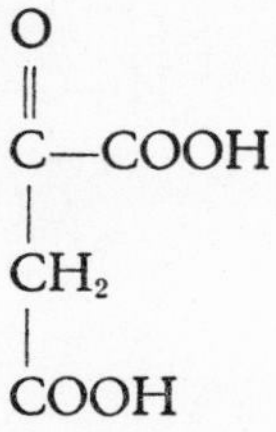

$$\begin{array}{l} O \\ \| \\ C{-}COOH \\ | \\ CH_2 \\ | \\ COOH \end{array}$$

oxalacetic acid

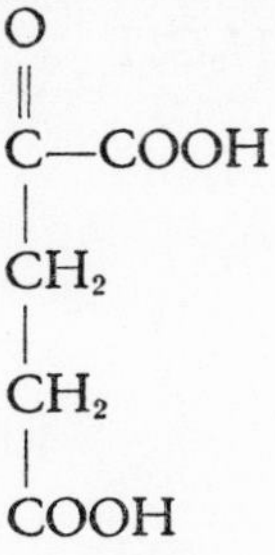

$$\begin{array}{l} O \\ \| \\ C{-}COOH \\ | \\ CH_2 \\ | \\ CH_2 \\ | \\ COOH \end{array}$$

α-ketoglutaric acid

$$\begin{array}{l} \quad O \\ \quad \| \\ \quad C{-}COOH \\ \quad | \\ HC{-}COOH \\ \quad | \\ \quad CH_2 \\ \quad | \\ \quad COOH \end{array}$$

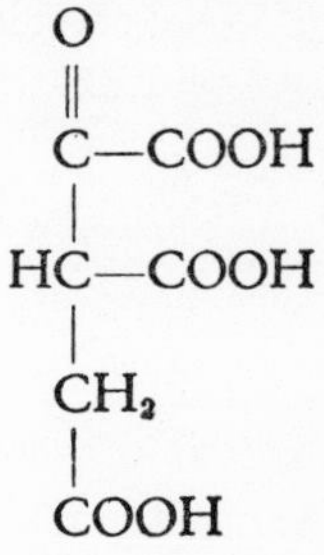

oxalo-succinic acid

The simplest of the β-keto-acids is acetoacetic acid.

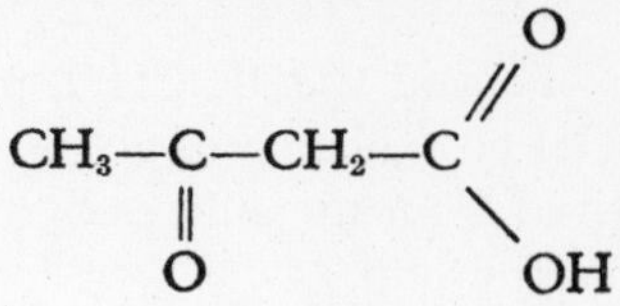

$$CH_3-\underset{\underset{O}{\|}}{C}-CH_2-C\begin{matrix}\diagup\!\!\diagup O\\ \diagdown OH\end{matrix}$$

There are β-keto-acids corresponding to the different fatty acids as shown below :

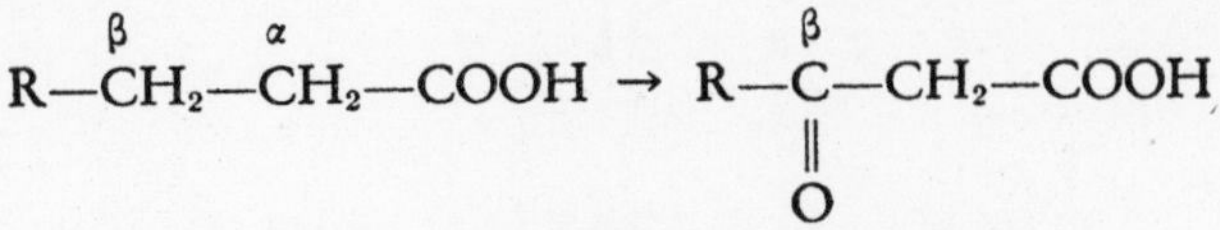

$$R-\overset{\beta}{CH_2}-\overset{\alpha}{CH_2}-COOH \rightarrow R-\underset{\underset{O}{\|}}{\overset{\beta}{C}}-CH_2-COOH$$

The keto-acids can exist in a ketonic or in an enolic form :

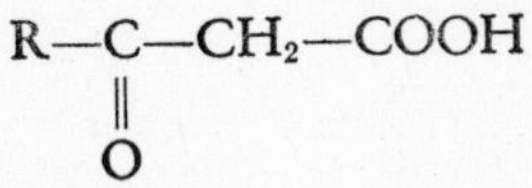

$$R-\underset{\underset{O}{\|}}{C}-CH_2-COOH \qquad R-\underset{\underset{OH}{|}}{C}=CH-COOH$$

ketonic form 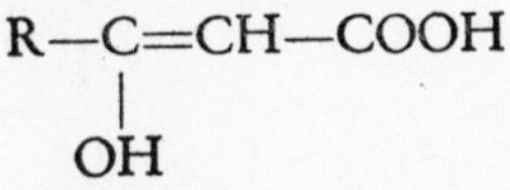 — enolic form

B. The Sugars or "Oses"

These are characterized by the presence of the "ose" grouping :

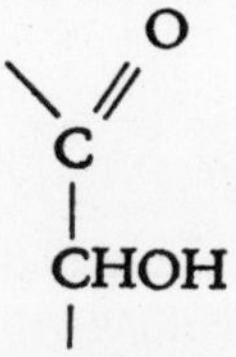

$$\begin{matrix}\diagdown\;\; & \diagup\!\!\diagup O\\ & C\\ & |\\ & CHOH\\ & |\end{matrix}$$

The simplest are those with two carbon atoms, the bioses. For example, glycollic aldehyde, the lowest member of the alcohol-aldehyde series which is obtained by oxidation of glycol :

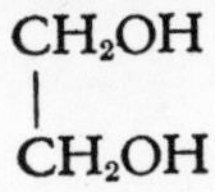

$$\begin{matrix}CH_2OH\\ |\\ CH_2OH\end{matrix} \qquad \begin{matrix}H\diagdown & \diagup\!\!\diagup O\\ & C\\ & |\\ H- & C-H\\ & |\\ & OH\end{matrix}$$

Glycol 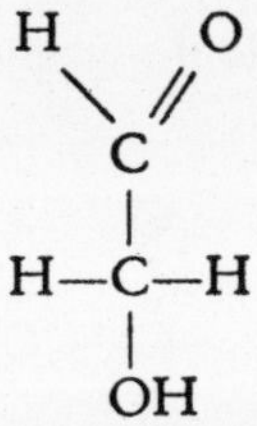 — Glycollic aldehyde

REFERENCES

Marklen, K. S. (1947) *Fatty Acids. Their Chemistry and Physical Properties.* Interscience, New York.

Ralston, A. W. (1948) *Fatty Acids and their Derivatives.* Wiley, New York.

(a) *Aldoses and Ketoses*

Sugars are of two types—aldoses, and ketoses. Amongst the C_3 sugars, for example, there is one ketose, dihydroxyacetone, and one aldose, glyceraldehyde. The latter has an asymmetric carbon atom and exists in two optically active forms.

```
CH2OH            CHO                CHO
|                | (1)              |
C=O            H—C—OH           HO—C—H
|                | (2)              |
CH2OH            CH2OH              CH2OH
                 (3)
```

Dihydroxyacetone — D(+)-Glyceraldehyde — L(−)-Glyceraldehyde

The two forms are designated D and L and the sign inside the parentheses indicates the direction of rotation of the plane of polarized light. By using the procedure of Kiliani (HCN reacts with sugars to form a nitrile-alcohol which on hydrolysis yields an acid having one carbon atom more than the starting material. By reduction of this acid a sugar is obtained having one carbon atom more than the original sugar) one can prepare aldoses higher up the series by inserting between (C-1) and (C-2), either a group of configuration

```
   |                                  |
H—C—OH    or of configuration     HO—C—H.
   |                                  |
```

In this way one obtains four tetroses, or C_4 sugars:

```
   CHO         CHO         CHO          CHO
    |           |           |            |
HO—C—H      H—C—OH     HO—C—H       H—C—OH
    |           |           |            |
 H—C—OH      H—C—OH     HO—C—H      HO—C—H
    |           |           |            |
   CH2OH       CH2OH       CH2OH        CH2OH
```

D-Threose — D-Erythrose — L-Erythrose — L-Threose

The letter D or L preceding the name of the sugar indicates its relationship to one of the parent glyceraldehydes. This is a general rule in sugar terminology.

```
    R              R
    |              |
 H—C—OH        HO—C—H
    |              |
   CH2OH          CH2OH
   D—             L—
```

TABLE IV

Structure of Aldoses

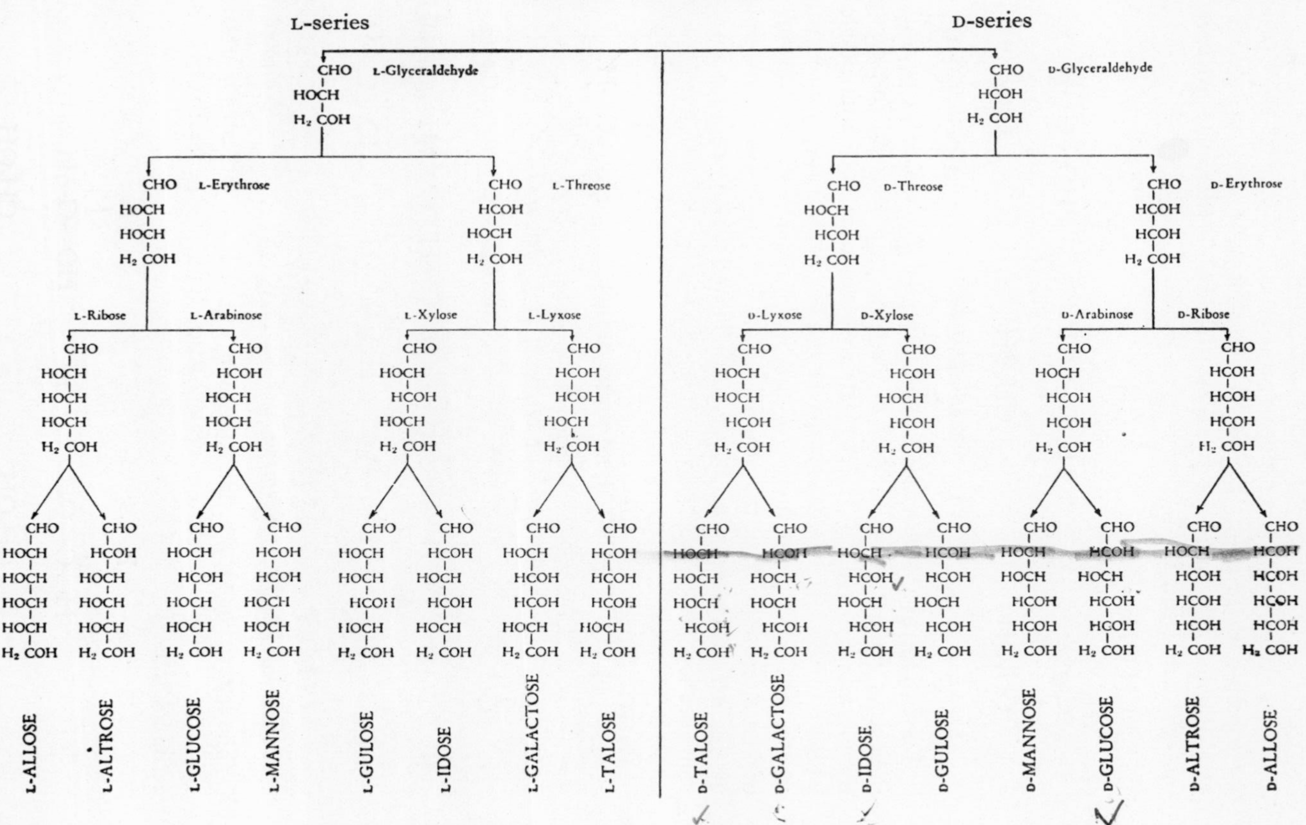

TABLE V

Ketoses (natural and synthetic)

CH_2OH | C=O | CH_2OH	CH_2OH | C=O | HO—C—H | CH_2OH	CH_2OH | C=O | HO—C—H | H—C—OH | CH_2OH	CH_2OH | C=O | H—C—OH | HO—C—H | CH_2OH
Dihydroxy-acetone	**L-Erythrulose**	**D-Xyloketose** **D-Xylulose**	**L-Xyloketose** **L-Xylulose**
CH_2OH | C=O | H—C—OH | H—C—OH | CH_2OH	CH_2OH | C=O | HO—C—H | HO—C—H | CH_2OH	CH_2OH | C=O | HO—C—H | H—C—OH | H—C—OH | CH_2OH	CH_2OH | C=O | H—C—OH | HO—C—H | HO—C—H | CH_2OH
D-Riboketose **D-Ribulose**	**L-Riboketose** **L-Ribulose**	**D-Fructose**	**L-Fructose**
CH_2OH | C=O | H—C—OH | HO—C—H | H—C—OH | CH_2OH	CH_2OH | C=O | HO—C—H | H—C—OH | HO—C—H | CH_2OH	CH_2OH | C=O | HO—C—H | HO—C—H | H—C—OH | CH_2OH	CH_2OH | C=O | HO—C—H | HO—C—H | HO—C—H | CH_2OH
D-Sorbose	**L-Sorbose**	**D-Tagatose**	**L-Psicose**

TABLE V (*continued*)

CH_2OH	CH_2OH	CH_2OH	CH_2OH	CH_2OH
C=O	C=O	C=O	C=O	C=O
HO—C—H	HO—C—H	HO—C—H	H—C—OH	HO—C—H
H—C—OH	HO—C—H	H—C—OH	HO—C—H	H—C—OH
H—C—OH	H—C—OH	H—C—OH	H—C—OH	HO—C—H
H—C—OH	H—C—OH	HO—C—H	H—C—OH	HO—C—H
CH_2OH	CH_2OH	CH_2OH	CH_2OH	CH_2OH
D-Sedoheptose D-Sedoheptulose	D-Manno-ketoheptose D-Manno-heptulose	L-Perseulose L-Galaheptulose	D-Gluco-ketoheptose	L-Gluco-ketoheptose

The direction of rotation is indicated by (+) or (—), as in the following examples : D(—) ribose, D(+) glucose, L(—) glucose, D(—) arabinose.

From the four tetroses, by further syntheses it is possible to obtain eight pentoses, which will be aldopentoses, and from these, sixteen aldohexoses (Table IV). The configuration of the ketoses can be deduced from that of the aldoses, according to whether they derive from D-glyceraldehyde or from L-glyceraldehyde. Table V shows a series of known ketoses, both natural and synthetic.

(*b*) *Cyclic Formulae*

In the above, the sugars have been considered as straight chain molecules, but it has been established that in the crystals of sugars containing more than 4 carbon atoms, cyclic tautomeric forms are present. In solution these sugars exist almost completely as cyclic molecules in equilibrium with small amounts of the straight chain form.

The fact that aldoses having more than 4 carbon atoms do not give certain reactions given by aldehydes is due to their being predominantly in the cyclic form. On the other hand, when a solution of glucose is prepared, the rotatory power of the solution progressively decreases until it reaches a certain value at which it remains constant (mutarotation). This is due to the fact that glucose exists in the form of two cyclic isomers, and that an equilibrium is set up between these two isomers and small amounts of the straight chain form, as shown in the formulae below :

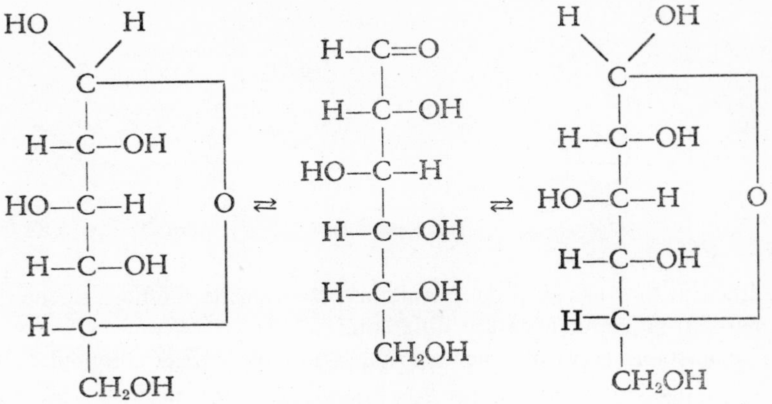

β-D-glucose ⇄ D-glucose chain molecules (traces) ⇄ α-D-glucose

In the above formulae the ring is made up of five carbon atoms and an oxygen atom, but in addition the presence has been demonstrated in solutions of the sugars of molecules in which the ring is made up of four carbon atoms and one oxygen atom, and derivatives of these forms have been prepared. Because these rings correspond to those of furan and pyran, Haworth has proposed a terminology in which the sugars are considered as derivatives of these structures.

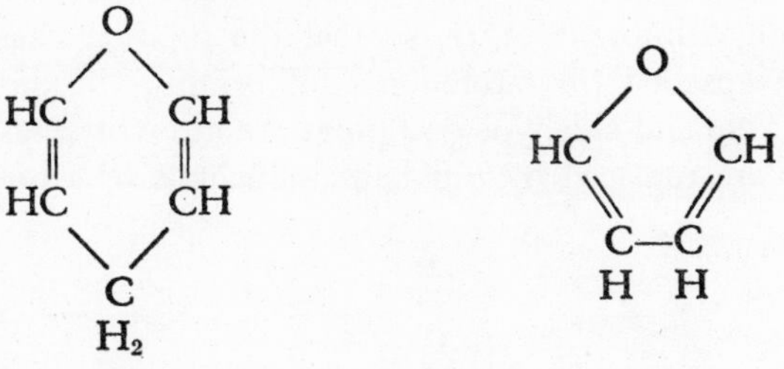

Pyran

Furan

The pyranose and furanose formulae are drawn in perspective looking down on the ring, each of the corners representing a carbon atom.

The atoms whose symbols are written above the ring are situated above the plane of the ring and those whose symbols are written below are situated below the plane of the ring. These formulae contain an asymmetric carbon atom additional to those present in the linear formulae and this is the one which, in D-glucopyranose, for example, is in position 1.

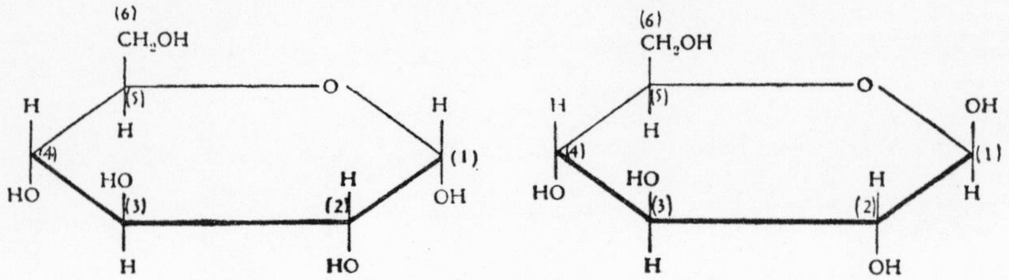

α form D-glucopyranose β form

Although they are both dextrorotatory, the specific rotations of the two forms of D-glucopyranose are different.

The unstable form of glucose is glucofuranose. This compound also exists in the two forms α and β.

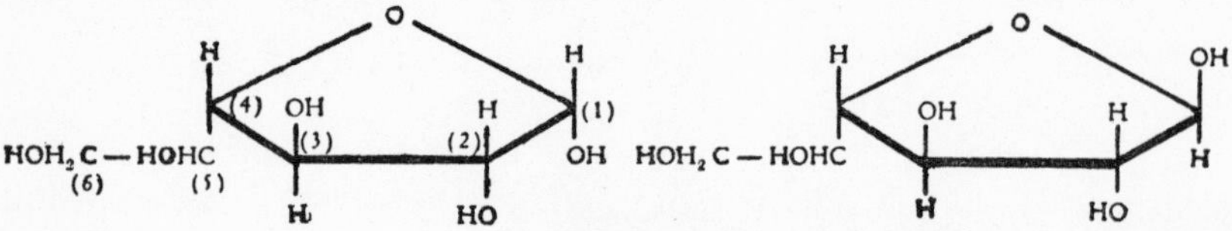

D-glucofuranose

One can prepare crystals of the α form or of the β form of D-glucopyranose. The first will be obtained by crystallization from aqueous solution, and the second by crystallization from pyridine. The two forms are distinguishable by a number of properties, as, for example, their melting point and their specific rotation in a freshly made solution. In solution, one form changes into the other, so that the rotation changes until an equilibrium is reached (mutarotation equilibrium). In the formulae of Haworth, the keto and aldehyde groupings are not written as in the linear formula, they are replaced by a potential-aldehyde or a potential-ketone group.

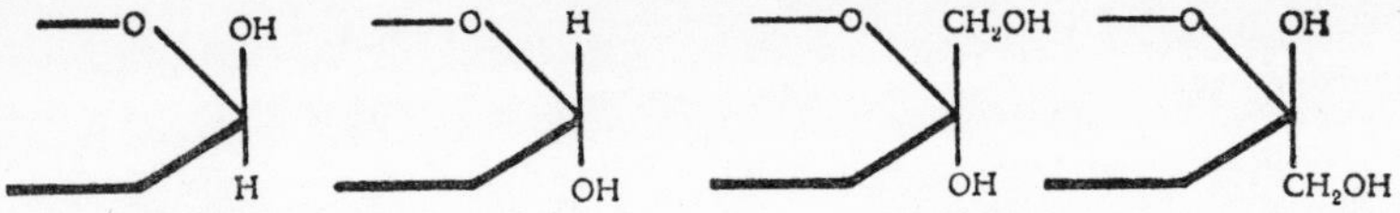

Potential aldehyde group Potential ketone group

The sugars are in effect reducing agents, the same as the aldehydes and ketones, but they do not restore the colour to fuchsin bleached by SO_2.

Haworth's formulae are now generally accepted. They give a clearer idea of the relationship of the various groups than the ordinary cyclic formulae or the linear formulae, although any of the three may be met with.

Haworth's formulae take into account certain properties not immediately apparent when the other formulae are used. For example, the α form of

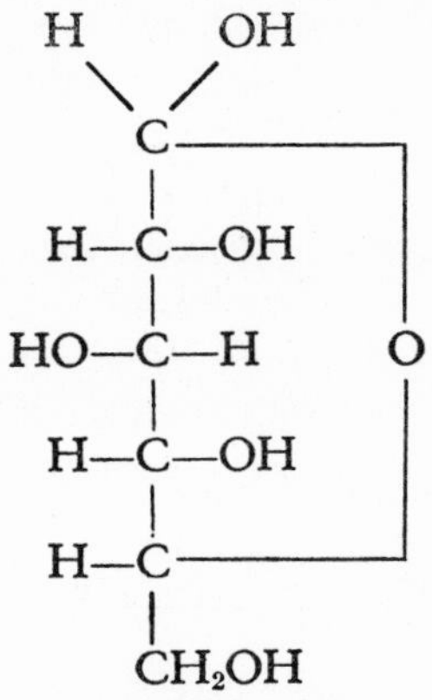

α-D-glucopyranose

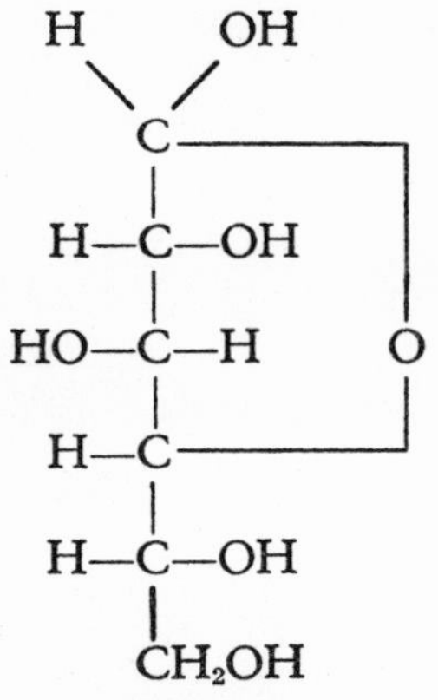

α-D-glucofuranose

D-glucopyranose when heated yields an anhydride, a glucosan formed by elimination of water between the hydroxyl of C-1 and the hydroxyl of C-2:

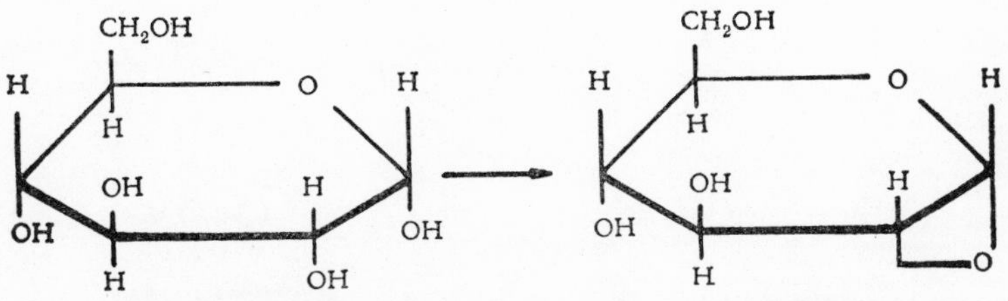

β-D-glucopyranose

glucosan

On the other hand β-D-glucopyranose, under the same conditions, gives a different anhydride, levoglucosan, resulting from the elimination of water between the hydroxyl of C-1 and that of C-6, which is explicable from the closeness of the two carbons in the formulae of Haworth.

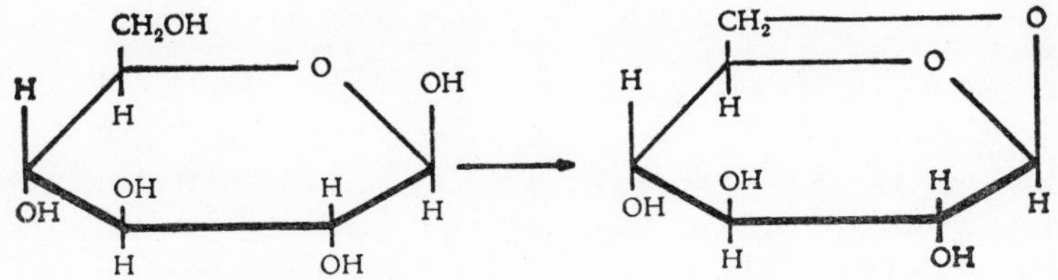

β-D-glucopyranose

levoglucosan

(*c*) *Natural Sugars*

One finds in Nature a selection of sugars, either free or combined. The lower members of this group are a diose, glycollic aldehyde; two trioses, glyceraldehyde and dihydroxy-acetone, and a tetrose, D-erythrose. The pentoses of the biosphere which have been found up to the present are D-xylose, D-ribose, D-ribulose, D-arabinose and L-arabinose. Among the hexoses the commonest is D-glucose. Other aldohexoses in the biosphere are D-mannose, D-galactose and L-galactose. The ketohexose D-fructose is also very common. Two C_7 sugars, sedoheptulose and D-mannoheptulose have also been identified. It is clear that the natural sugars are most often members of the D-series.

(*d*) *Amino Sugars*

Amongst the large number of synthetic compounds two are also of natural origin

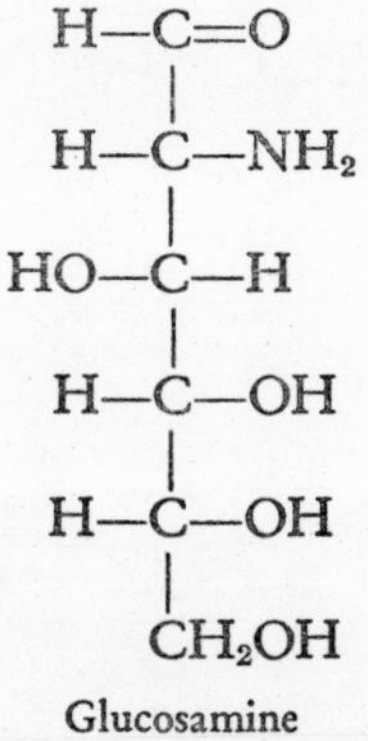

```
   H—C=O                    H—C=O
     |                        |
   H—C—NH2                  H—C—NH2
     |                        |
  HO—C—H                   HO—C—H
     |                        |
   H—C—OH                  HO—C—H
     |                        |
   H—C—OH                   H—C—OH
     |                        |
    CH2OH                    CH2OH
```

Glucosamine (2-desoxy-2-amino-β-D-glucose)

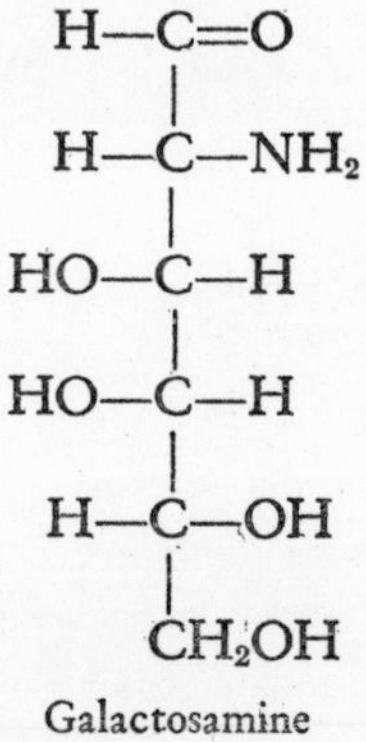

Galactosamine (2-desoxy-2-amino-β-D-galactose)

These are aldohexoses aminated in position 2.

Glucosamine is a constituent of many polysaccharides and mucopolysaccharides, and of chitin. Galactosamine is a constituent of cartilage.

(*e*) *Desoxy-Sugars or "Desoses"*

These are the result of the removal of an oxygen atom from a hydroxyl group. There are a certain number of natural desoses, the principal ones being L-rhamnose, L-fucose and 2-desoxyribose or ribodesose. The desoses give most of the reactions of sugars. They are unstable.

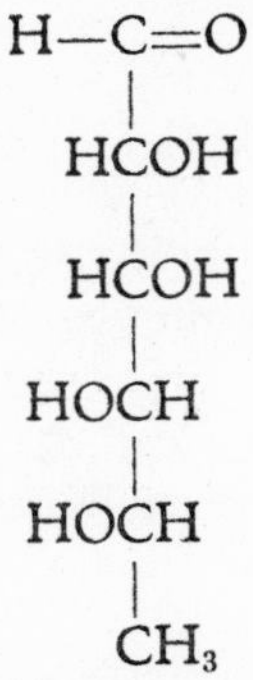

H—C=O
HCOH
HCOH
HOCH
HOCH
CH_3

L-rhamnose
(6-desoxy-L-mannose)

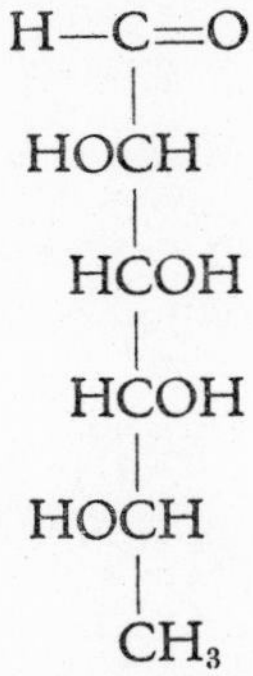

H—C=O
HOCH
HCOH
HCOH
HOCH
CH_3

L-fucose
(6-desoxy-L-galactose)

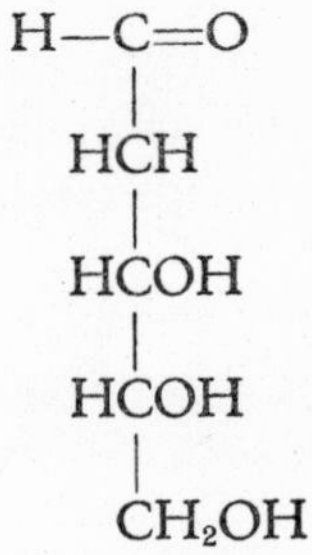

H—C=O
HCH
HCOH
HCOH
CH_2OH

2-desoxyribose

(*f*) *Polyhydroxy Compounds Related to Sugars*

The reduction of ketoses and aldoses produces the corresponding alcohols. The reduction of glyceraldehyde gives glycerol, ribitol arises from ribose and sorbitol is formed from glucose.

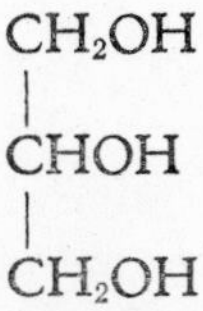

CH_2OH
CHOH
CH_2OH

Glycerol

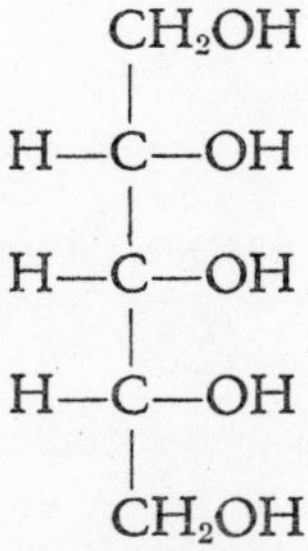

CH_2OH
H—C—OH
H—C—OH
H—C—OH
CH_2OH

Ribitol

CH_2OH
H—C—OH
HO—C—H
H—C—OH
H—C—OH
CH_2OH

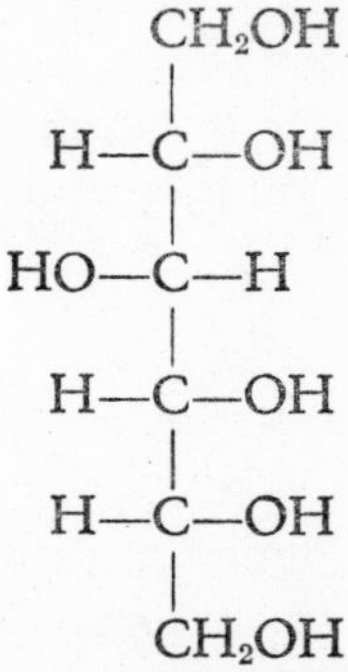

D-sorbitol

The carbocylic alcohols like inositol are similar types of polyalcohol.

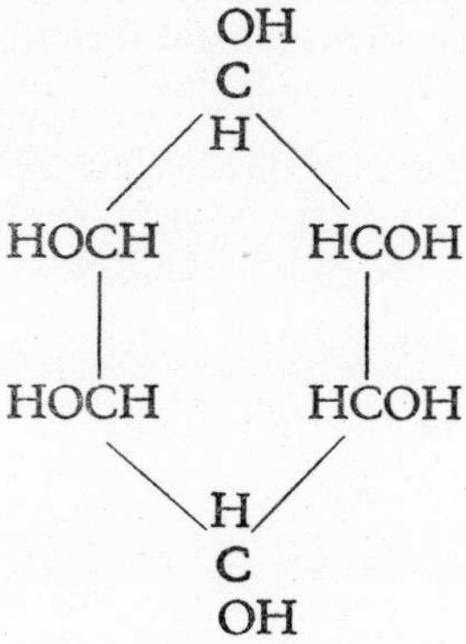

OH
C
H
HOCH HCOH
HOCH HCOH
H
C
OH

Inositol

(*g*) *Oxidation Products of Sugars* (*Monoacidic Polyalcohols, or Polyacids*)

Under controlled conditions oxidation of aldoses can give rise either to aldonic acids resulting from oxidation of the aldehyde group to a carboxyl group, or to uronic acids in which the aldehyde group is preserved and the primary hydroxyl is oxidized to carboxyl, or finally to dicarboxylic acids having a carboxyl at each end. In the case of glucose the following compounds are obtained :

CHO	$COOH$	CHO	$COOH$
|	|	|	|
$(CHOH)_4$	$(CHOH)_4$	$(CHOH)_4$	$(CHOH)_4$
|	|	|	|
CH_2OH	CH_2OH	$COOH$	$COOH$
Glucose (aldose)	Gluconic acid (hexonic acid)	Glucuronic acid (uronic acid)	Saccharic acid (dicarboxylic acid)

Numerous hexonic, uronic and dicarboxylic acids derived from the aldoses are present in nature.

C. Amino Acids

(*a*) *Definition*

The amino acids are defined as substances having a carboxyl and an amino group together in the same molecule. The number of substances falling into this category which organic chemists can synthesize is very great but only a limited number of these compounds are present in the biosphere. The amino acids usually have the amino group in a position α to the carboxyl group, so that their general formula is :

$$\begin{array}{c} NH_2 \\ | \\ R\text{—}CH\text{—}COOH \end{array}$$

REFERENCES

Honeyman, J. (1948) *An Introduction to the Chemistry of Carbohydrates.* Clarendon Press, Oxford.

Pigman, W. W. & Goepp, R. M. (1948) *Chemistry of the Carbohydrates.* Academic Press, New York.

(*b*) *Amino Acids Universally Distributed in Organic Materials*

In all living things which have been studied in this connection, one finds the twenty amino acids listed in Table VI. The natural amino acids can be considered as derivatives of L-serine, related to L-glyceraldehyde.

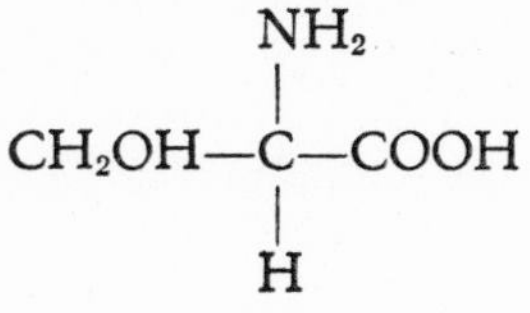

$$CH_2OH-\underset{\substack{|\\H}}{\overset{\substack{NH_2\\|}}{C}}-COOH \qquad\qquad CH_2OH-\underset{\substack{|\\H}}{\overset{\substack{OH\\|}}{C}}-COH$$

L-serine 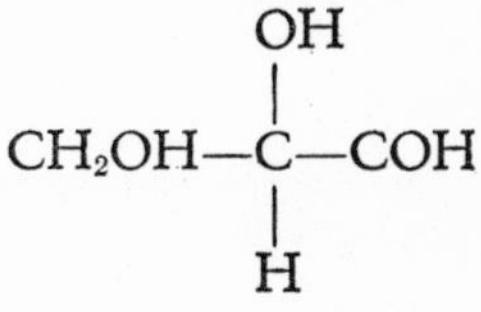 L-glyceraldehyde

(*c*) *Amino Acids Occasionally Found*

Besides the twenty amino acids which are universally distributed in the living organism one finds, here and there, certain special amino acids. Among these are the following:

Hydroxylysine, α,ϵ-diamino-δ-hydroxycaproic acid

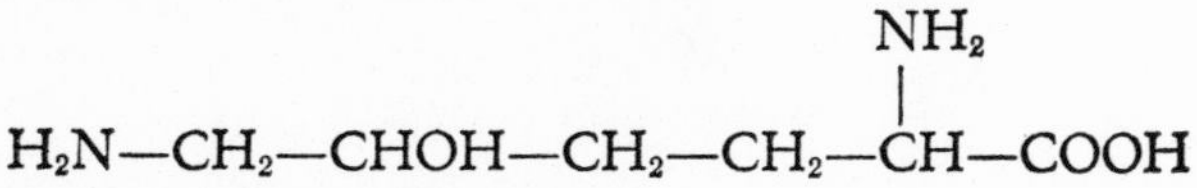

$$H_2N-CH_2-CHOH-CH_2-CH_2-\overset{\substack{NH_2\\|}}{C}H-COOH$$

Ornithine, α,δ-diamino-valeric acid

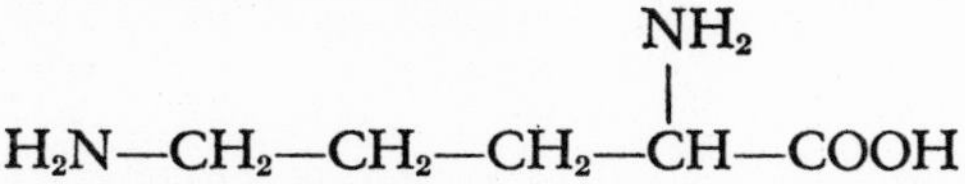

$$H_2N-CH_2-CH_2-CH_2-\overset{\substack{NH_2\\|}}{C}H-COOH$$

β-alanine, β-amino-propionic acid

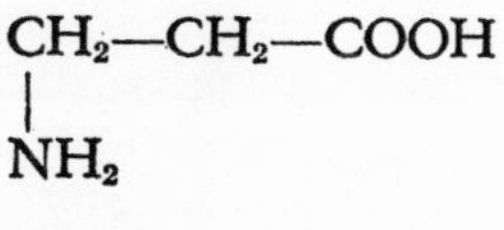

$$\underset{\substack{|\\NH_2}}{CH_2}-CH_2-COOH$$

Citrulline, α-amino-carbamidovaleric acid

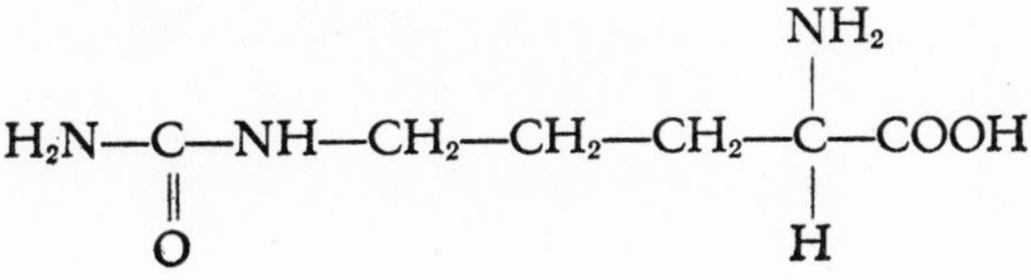

$$H_2N-\underset{\substack{\|\\O}}{C}-NH-CH_2-CH_2-CH_2-\underset{\substack{|\\H}}{\overset{\substack{NH_2\\|}}{C}}-COOH$$

γ-amino-butyric acid

$$H_2N-CH_2-CH_2-CH_2-COOH$$

and several others: octopine, α-aminobutyric acid, djenkolic acid, β-thiolvaline, canavanine, etc.

TABLE VI

α-amino acids $(R-CH(NH_2)-COOH)$

(Symbols indicating the nature of the radical R: aliphatic (Al), aromatic (Ar), heterocyclic (Hc), acidic (A), basic (B), neutral (N), polar (P), feebly polar (FP), non-polar (NP), ionic (I), feebly ionic (FI), non-ionic (NI).)

L (+) Alanine (Ala), α-aminopropionic acid

R = methyl (Al, N, NP, NI) $CH_3-CH(NH_2)-COOH$

L (+) Arginine (Arg), α-amino-δ-guanido-*n*-valeric acid

R = ω-guanido-*n*-propyl (Al, B, P, I)

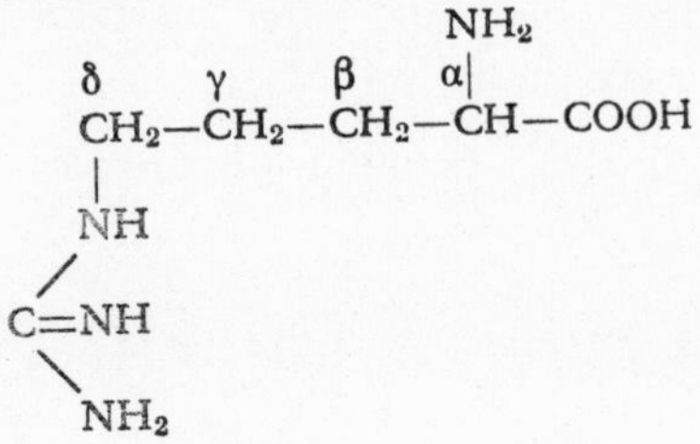

$$\overset{\delta}{CH_2}-\overset{\gamma}{CH_2}-\overset{\beta}{CH_2}-\overset{\alpha}{CH}(NH_2)-COOH$$
$$\delta\text{-}CH_2-NH-C(=NH)-NH_2$$

L (−) Aspartic acid (Asp), α-aminosuccinic acid

R = carboxymethyl (Al, A, P, I) $HOOC-CH_2-CH(NH_2)-COOH$

L (−) Cysteine (CySH), α-amino-β-thiolpropionic acid

R = thiomethyl (Al, N, P, FI) $HS-CH_2-CH(NH_2)-COOH$

L (−) Cystine (CyS), β, β′-dithio-bis (α-aminopropionic acid)

R = dimethyldisulphide (Al, N, NP, NI)

$$S-CH_2-CH(NH_2)-COOH$$
$$|$$
$$S-CH_2-CH(NH_2)-COOH$$

L (+) Glutamic acid (Glu), α-aminoglutaric acid

R = carboxyethyl (Al, A, P, I) $HOOC-CH_2-CH_2-CH(NH_2)-COOH$

TABLE VI (*continued*)

Glycine (Gly), aminoacetic acid

R = H − (Al, N, NP, NI)

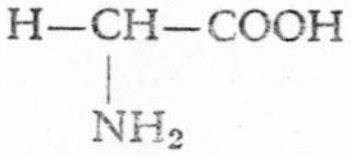

```
H—CH—COOH
   |
   NH2
```

L (−) Histidine (His), α-amino-β(5)-imidazolylpropionic acid

R = imidazolylmethyl (Hc, B, P, I)

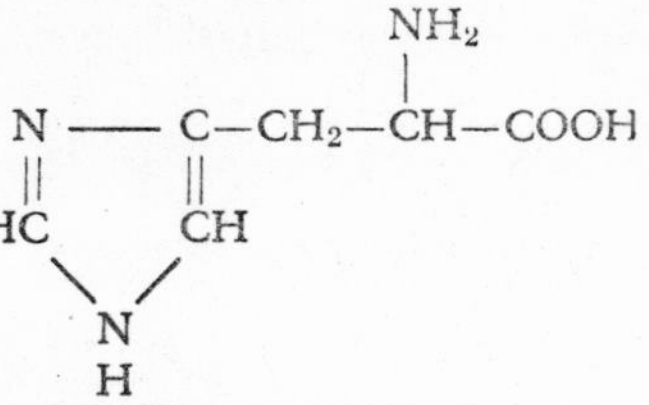

```
                    NH2
                    |
N —— C—CH2—CH—COOH
||   ||
HC   CH
  \ /
   N
   H
```

L (−) Hydroxyproline (Hypro), 4-hydroxypyrrolidine-2-carboxylic acid

R = − (Hc, N, P, NI)

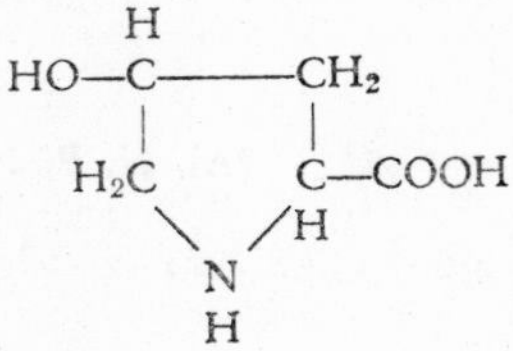

```
     H
HO—C———CH2
   |     |
  H2C    C—COOH
    \   /H
     N
     H
```

L (+) Isoleucine, α-amino-β-methyl-*n*-valeric acid

R = α-methyl-*n*-propyl (Al, N, NP, NI)

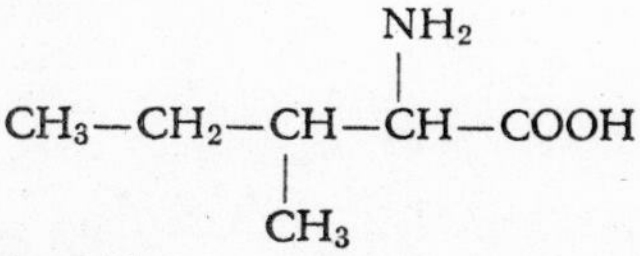

```
                  NH2
                  |
CH3—CH2—CH—CH—COOH
           |
           CH3
```

L (−) Leucine (Leu), α-amino-isocaproic acid

R = isobutyl (Al, N, NP, NI)

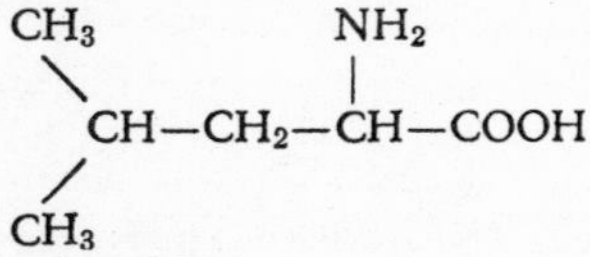

```
CH3          NH2
   \         |
    CH—CH2—CH—COOH
   /
CH3
```

L (+) Lysine (Lys), α-ε-diamino-*n*-caproic acid

R = ω-amino-*n*-butyl (Al, B, P, I)

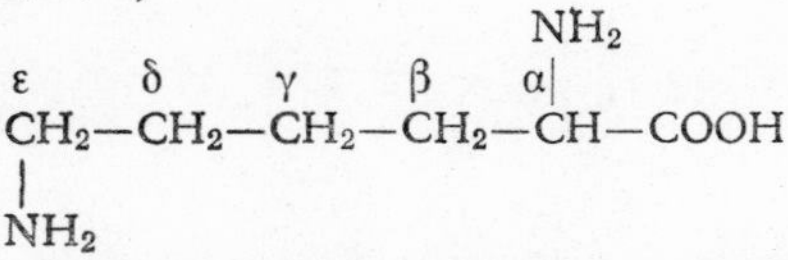

```
                           NH2
 ε      δ      γ      β    α|
CH2—CH2—CH2—CH2—CH—COOH
 |
NH2
```

L (−) Methionine (Met), α-amino-methylthiol-*n*-butyric acid

R = methylthioethyl (Al, N, P, NI)

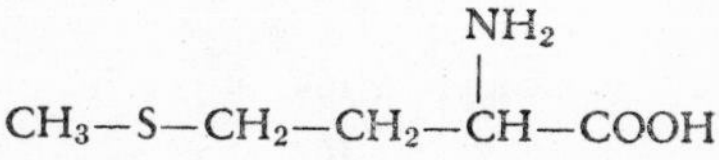

```
                     NH2
                     |
CH3—S—CH2—CH2—CH—COOH
```

TABLE VI (*continued*)

L (+) Phenylalanine (Phe), α-amino-β-phenylpropionic acid

R = benzyl (Ar, N, NP, NI)

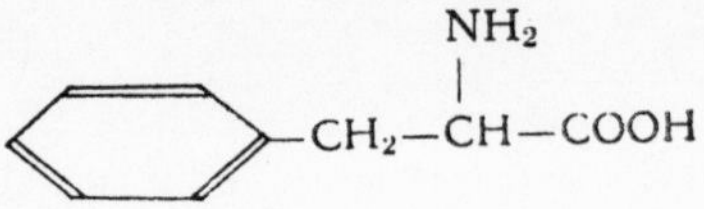

$$C_6H_5{-}CH_2{-}CH(NH_2){-}COOH$$

L (−) Proline (Pro), pyrrolidine-2-carboxylic acid

R = — (Hc, N, NP, NI)

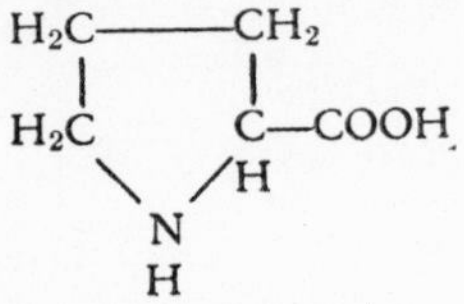

$$H_2C{-}CH_2,\quad H_2C\quad C{-}COOH\ (H),\quad N{-}H \text{ (ring)}$$

L (−) Serine (Ser), α-amino-β-hydroxypropionic acid

R = hydroxymethyl (Al, N, P, NI) $HO{-}CH_2{-}CH(NH_2){-}COOH$

L (−) Threonine (Thr), α-amino-β-hydroxybutyric acid

R = hydroxyethyl (Al, N, P, NI) $CH_3{-}CH(OH){-}CH(NH_2){-}COOH$

L (−) = Tryptophan (Try), α-amino-β(3)-indolepropionic acid

R = skatolyl (Hc, Ar, N, NP, NI)

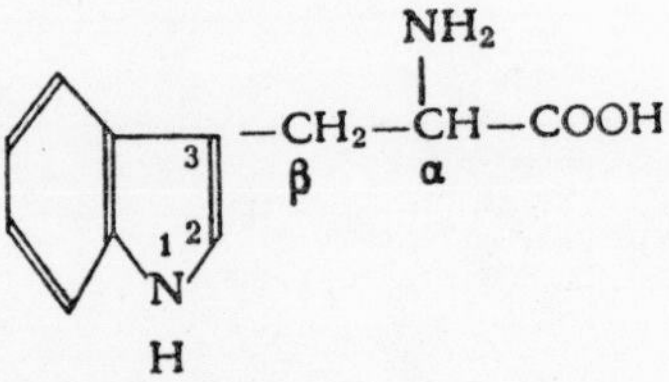

$$\text{indol-3-yl}{-}\underset{\beta}{CH_2}{-}\underset{\alpha}{CH}(NH_2){-}COOH \quad (\text{ring positions } 1\ N{-}H,\ 2,\ 3)$$

L (−) Tyrosine (Tyr), α-amino-β(p-hydroxyphenyl) propionic acid
R = *p*-hydroxybenzyl (Ar, N, FP, FI)

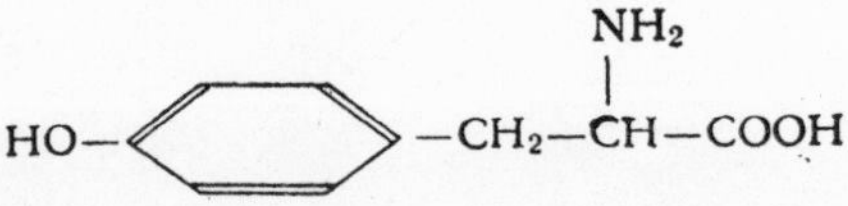

$$HO{-}C_6H_4{-}CH_2{-}CH(NH_2){-}COOH$$

L (−) Valine (Val), α-aminoisovaleric acid

R = isopropyl (Al, N, NP, NI)

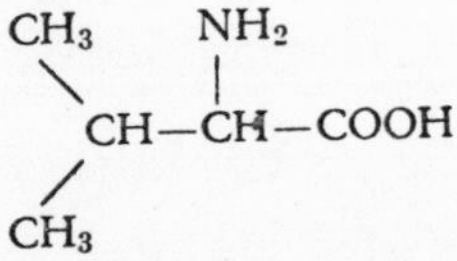

$$(CH_3)_2CH{-}CH(NH_2){-}COOH$$

There are also many iminoacids, such as pipecolic acid, baikiaïne, guvacine, etc.

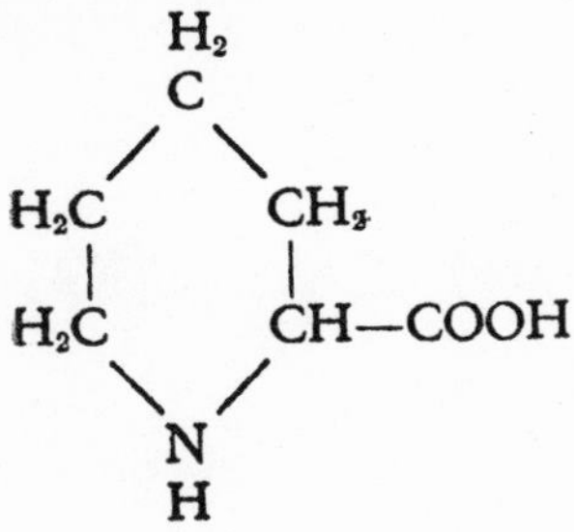

Pipecolic acid

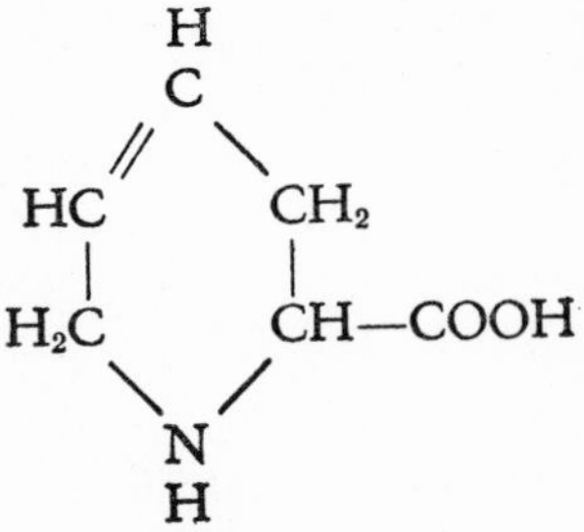

Baikiaïne

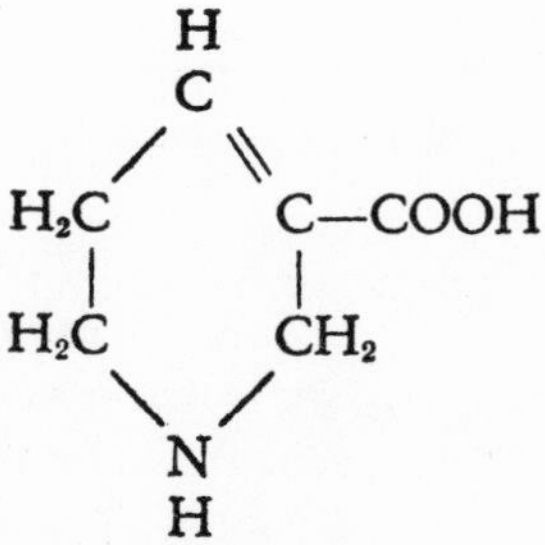

Guvacine

(*d*) *Stereoisomerism*

Whilst the natural sugars are for the most part members of the D-series, the natural amino acids, regardless of their optical activity, belong as a rule to the L-series.

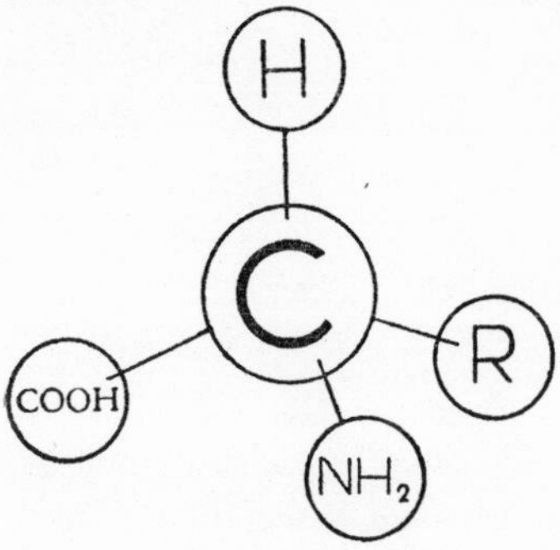

Natural L-form

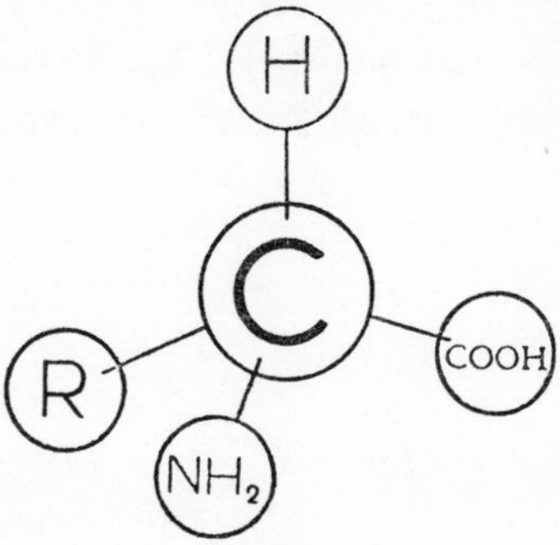

D-form

In addition there are certain amino acids which, in addition to the α carbon atom, contain a second asymmetric carbon (threonine, hydroxyproline, isoleucine, hydroxylysine). These amino acids can theoretically exist in four isomeric forms.

For example in the case of threonine, the four stereoisomers would have the following formulae :

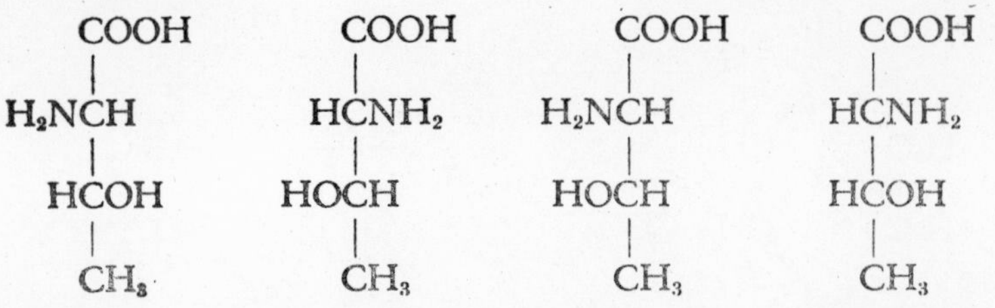

L-threonine	D-threonine	L-allothreonine	D-allothreonine
COOH	COOH	COOH	COOH
H_2NCH	$HCNH_2$	H_2NCH	$HCNH_2$
HCOH	HOCH	HOCH	HCOH
CH_3	CH_3	CH_3	CH_3

The designation L- is reserved for the form found present in proteins, its isomer having opposite configurations on carbon atoms α and β, is distinguished by the prefix D-. The other isomers, which also form a pair of optical isomers, but which are diastereoisomers, are denoted by the prefix allo, as shown in the diagram for threonine. (In the case of cystine, there are also two asymmetric carbon atoms, but since cystine is formed by the union of two molecules of cysteine, then, as in tartaric acid, there are only three isomers : LL, DD and meso, the meso form being optically inactive.)

Although it is true, in general, that the natural amino acids are α-amino acids of the L- series, it sometimes happens that in organisms one encounters stereoisomers of the D- series, for example, D-β-thiolvaline, D-leucine, D-alanine, etc.

II. OTHER CHEMICAL STRUCTURES OF GENERAL INTEREST

A. Terpenes

The terpenes and their derivatives are a group of natural substances related to isoprene C_5H_8.

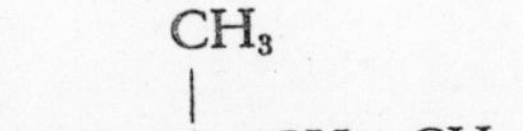

$$
\begin{array}{c}
\quad CH_3 \\
\quad | \\
CH_2{=}C{-}CH{=}CH_2
\end{array}
$$

Isoprene

Isoprene does not exist as such in nature, but it is found in the biosphere in the form of numerous polyisoprenes. These substances may be divided into three groups : the lower terpenes, the carotenoids and the polyterpenes.

REFERENCES

Desnuelle, P. : The general chemistry of amino acids and peptides, *in* H. Neurath & K. Bailey, *The Proteins*, Vol. I, part A, 87–180.

Dunn, M. S. & Rockland, L. B. (1947) The preparation and criteria of purity of the amino acids. *Advanc. Protein Chem.* **3**, 295–382.

(*a*) *Lower Terpenes*

These result from the condensation of two (monoterpenes), three (sesquiterpenes), four (diterpenes), six (triterpenes), or eight (tetraterpenes) isoprene residues. The lower terpenes are widely distributed in the essential oils of many plants. Phytol, an unsaturated alcohol present in the chlorophyll molecule, is a diterpene derivative.

$$\underset{\displaystyle CH_3}{\underset{|}{CH_3{-}CH}}{-}(CH_2)_3{-}\underset{\displaystyle CH_3}{\underset{|}{CH}}{-}(CH_2)_3{-}\underset{\displaystyle CH_3}{\underset{|}{CH}}{-}(CH_2)_3{-}\underset{\displaystyle CH_3}{\underset{|}{C}}{=}CH{-}CH_2OH$$

Phytol

(*b*) *Carotenoids*

1. *Definition*

One of the groups of natural isoprene derivatives is that of the carotenoids—aliphatic or alicyclic pigments whose colours range from yellow to red. According to Karrer, they are derivatives of several isoprene units (often eight) joined together in a manner such that the two methyl groups at the centre of the molecule are 1 : 6 to each other, whilst the remaining lateral methyl groups are in the 1 : 5 positions.

$$-\underset{\displaystyle CH_3}{\underset{|}{C}}{=}CH{-}CH{=}CH{-}\underset{\displaystyle CH_3}{\underset{|}{C}}{=}CH{-}CH{=}\,\vdots\,CH{-}CH{=}\underset{\displaystyle CH_3}{\underset{|}{C}}{-}CH{=}CH{-}CH{=}\underset{\displaystyle CH_3}{\underset{|}{C}}-$$

(1) ⟷ (5)   (1) ⟷ (5)

(1) ⟷ (6)

The chain of conjugated double bonds forms the chromophore system of the carotenoid pigments.

2. *Classification*

There are two classes of natural carotenoids : the carotenoids proper, having a C-40 chain (8 isoprene residues), and the carotenoids possessing less than 40 carbon atoms. The natural carotenoids can be considered as related to lycopene ($C_{40}H_{56}$), the red pigment of the tomato.

$$(CH_3)_2\overset{1}{C}{=}\overset{2}{C}H{-}\overset{3}{C}H_2{-}\overset{4}{C}H_2{-}\overset{5}{C}(CH_3){=}\overset{6}{C}H\overset{7}{C}H{=}\overset{8}{C}H\overset{9}{C}(CH_3){=}\overset{10}{C}H\overset{11}{C}H{=}\overset{12}{C}H\overset{13}{C}(CH_3){=}\overset{14}{C}H\overset{15}{C}H{=}\overset{15'}{C}H\overset{14'}{C}H{=}\overset{13'}{C}(CH_3)\overset{12'}{C}H{=}\overset{11'}{C}H\overset{10'}{C}H{=}\overset{9'}{C}(CH_3)\overset{8'}{C}H{=}\overset{7'}{C}H\overset{6'}{C}H{=}\overset{5'}{C}(CH_3){-}\overset{4'}{C}H_2{-}\overset{3'}{C}H_2{-}\overset{2'}{C}H{=}\overset{1'}{C}(CH_3)_2$$

Lycopene

TABLE VII

Natural carotenoids whose structure is known

(Karrer and Jucker)

```
                                                                                          CH3   CH3
 CH3   CH3                                                                                   \ /
    \ /                                                                                       C
     C          CH3            CH3                 CH3             CH3                         \\
    //          |              |                   |               |                            CH
 CH      CH·CH=CH·C=CHCH=CH·C=CHCH=CHCH=C·CH=CHCH=C·CH=CH·CH       |
 |       ||                                                           ||     CH2
 CH2     C·CH3                                                     H3C·C
    \   /                       Lycopene                                 \  /
     CH2                                                                  CH2
```

```
                                                                                          CH3   CH3
 CH3   CH3                                                                                   \ /
    \ /                                                                                       C
     C          CH3            CH3                 CH3             CH3                       / \
    //          |              |                   |               |                                CH2
 CH      CH·CH=CH·C=CHCH=CH·C=CHCH=CHCH=C·CH=CHCH=C·CH=CH·C          |
 |       ||                                                           ||     CH2
 CH2     C·CH3                                                     H3C·C
    \   /                       γ-Carotene                               \  /
     CH2                                                                  CH2
```

```
                                                                                          CH3   CH3
 CH3   CH3                                                                                   \ /
    \ /                                                                                       C
     C          CH3            CH3                 CH3             CH3                       / \
    / \         |              |                   |               |                            CH2
 CH2     C·CH=CH·C=CHCH=CH·C=CHCH=CHCH=C·CH=CHCH=C·CH=CH·C           |
 |       ||                                                           ||     CH2
 CH2     C·CH3                                                     H3C·C
    \   /                       β-Carotene                               \  /
     CH2                                                                  CH2
```

```
                                                                                          CH3   CH3
 CH3   CH3                                                                                   \ /
    \ /                                                                                       C
     C          CH3            CH3                 CH3             CH3                       / \
    / \         |              |                   |               |                            CH2
 CH2     C·CH=CH·C=CHCH=CH·C=CHCH=CHCH=C·CH=CHCH=C·CH=CH·CH          |
 |       ||                                                           |      CH2
 CH2     C·CH3                                                     H3C·C
    \   /                       α-Carotene                               \\  /
     CH2                                                                  CH
```

```
 CH3   CH3
    \ /
     C                                                                                    CH3   CH3
    / \                                                                                      \ /
 CH2    C=======CH CH3          CH3                CH3             CH3                        C
 |      |       |  |            |                  |               |                         / \
 CH2    C       CH·C=CHCH=CH·C=CHCH=CHCH=C·CH=CHCH=C·CH=CH·C                                        CH2
    \  / |\    /                                                      ||        |
     CH2 | O                                                       H3C·C     CH2
        CH3                                                              \  /
                                                                          CH2
```

Mutatochrome, Citroxanthin

```
CH3   CH3                                                                                   CH3   CH3
  \   /                                                                                       \   /
    C              CH3              CH3                 CH3               CH3                   C
  /   \            |                |                   |                 |                   /   \
CH2    C·CH=CH·C=CHCH=CH·C=CHCH=CHCH=C·CH=CHCH=C·CH=CH·CH    CH2
|      | \                                                                              |     |
|      |   O                                                                      H3C·C     CH2
|      | /                                                                               \\   /
CH2    C                                                                                  CH
  \   / \
   CH2   CH3
```

α-Carotenepoxide

```
CH3   CH3                                                                                   CH3   CH3
  \   /                                                                                       \   /
    C              CH3              CH3                 CH3               CH3                   C
  //                |                |                   |                 |                      \\
CH     CH·CH=CH·C=CHCH=CH·C=CHCH=CHCH=C·CH=CHCH=C·CH=CH·CH     CH
|      ||                                                                              ||      |
CH2    C·CH3                                                                     H3C·C      CHOH
  \   /                                                                                  \   /
   CH2                                                                                    CH2
```

Lycoxanthin

```
CH3   CH3                                                                                   CH3   CH3
  \   /                                                                                       \   /
    C              CH3              CH3                 CH3               CH3                   C
  //                |                |                   |                 |                      \\
CH     CH·CH=CH·C=CHCH=CH·C=CHCH=CHCH=C·CH=CHCH=C·CH=CH·CH     CH
|      ||                                                                              ||      |
HOCH   C·CH3                                                                     H3C·C      CHOH
  \   /                                                                                  \   /
   CH2                                                                                    CH2
```

Lycophyll

```
CH3   CH3                                                                                   CH3   CH3
  \   /                                                                                       \   /
   CH              CH3              CH3                 CH3               CH3                  CH
  /                 |                |                   |                 |                      \
CH2    CH·CH=CH·C=CHCH=CH·C=CHCH=CHCH=C·CH=CHCH=C·CH=CH·CH     CH2
|      ||                                                                              ||      |
H3COC  C·CH3                                                                     H3C·C      COCH3
  \\  /                                                                                  \   //
   CH                                                                                     CH
```

Rhodoviolascin (?)

```
CH3   CH3                                                                                   CH3   CH3
  \   /                                                                                       \   /
    C              CH3              CH3                 CH3               CH3                   C
  /   \            |                |                   |                 |                       \\
CH2    C·CH=CH·C=CHCH=CH·C=CHCH=CHCH=C·CH=CHCH=C·CH=CH·CH     CH
|      |                                                                               ||      |
HOCH   C·CH3                                                                     H3C·C      CH2
  \   /                                                                                  \   /
   CH2                                                                                    CH2
```

Rubixanthin

TABLE VII (*continued*)

```
CH3  CH3                                                                                  CH3  CH3
   C                                                                                          C
CH2  C===CH CH3          CH3               CH3         CH3                                   
HOCH  C     CH·C=CHCH=CH·C=CHCH=CHCH=C·CH=CHCH=C·CH=CH·CH                                      CH
   CH2|  O                                                    H3C·C                        CH2
     CH3                                                                                 CH2
```

Rubichrome

```
CH3  CH3                                                                       CH3  CH3
   C           CH3            CH3            CH3           CH3                     C
CH2  C·CH=CH·C=CHCH=CH·C=CHCH=CHCH=C·CH=CHCH=C·CH=CH·C                              CH2
CH2  C·CH3                                                               H3C·C     CHOH
   CH2                                                                       CH2
```

Cryptoxanthin

```
CH3  CH3                                                                       CH3  CH3
   C           CH3            CH3            CH3           CH3                     CH
CH2  C·CH=CH·C=CHCH=CH·C=CHCH=CHCH=C·CH=CHCH=C·CH=CH·CH                             CH
CH2  C·CH3                                                               H3C·C     CH
   CH2                                                                       CO
```

Myxoxanthin

```
CH3  CH3                                                                       CH3  CH3
   C           CH3            CH3            CH3           CH3                     C
CH2  C·CH=CH·C=CHCH=CH·C=CHCH=CHCH=C·CH=CHCH=C· CH=CH·C                             CH2
CH2  C·CH3                                                               H3C·C     CO
   CH2                                                                       CH2
```

Aphanine (?)

```
CH3  CH3                                                                       CH3  CH3
   C           CH3            CH3            CH3           CH3                     C
CH2  C·CH=CH·C=CHCH=CH·C=CHCH=CHCH=C·CH=CHCH=C· CH=CH·CH                            CH2
HOCH  C·CH3                                                              H3C·C     CHOH
   CH2                                                                       CH2
```

Zeaxanthin

```
CH3  CH3                                                                       CH3  CH3
   C           CH3            CH3            CH3           CH3                     C
CH2  C·CH=CH·C=CHCH=CH· C=CHCH=CHCH=C·CH=CHCH=C· CH=CH·CH                           CH2
HOCH  C·CH3                                                              H3C·C     CHOH
   CH2                                                                       CH
```

Xanthophyll

```
CH3  CH3                                                                                   CH3  CH3
   \ /                                                                                        \ /
    C             CH3              CH2               CH3              CH3                      C
   / \            |                |                 |                |                       / \
CH2   C·CH=CH·C=CHCH=CH·C=CHCH=CHCH=C·CH=CHCH=C·CH=CH·C         CH2
|     |\                                                                ||          |
|     | O                                                            H3C·C         CHOH
|     |/                                                                 \         /
HOCH  C                                                                   CH2
   \ / \
   CH2  CH3
```

Antheraxanthin

```
CH3  CH3                                                                                   CH3  CH3
   \ /                                                                                        \ /
    C             CH3              CH3               CH3              CH3                      C
   / \            |                |                 |                |                       / \
CH2   C·CH=CH·C=CHCH=CH·C=CHCH=CHCH=C·CH=CHCH=C·CH=CH·CH        CH2
|     |\                                                                |           |
|     | O                                                            H3C·C         CHOH
|     |/                                                                 \\        /
HOCH  C                                                                   CH
   \ / \
   CH2  CH3
```

Xanthophyllepoxide

```
CH3  CH3
   \ /                                                                                     CH3  CH3
    C                                                                                         \ /
   / \                             CH3               CH3              CH3                      C
CH2   C=====CH CH3                 |                 |                |                       / \
|     |     |  |
HOCH  C     CH·C=CHCH=CH·C=CHCH=CHCH=C·CH=CHCH= C·CH=CH·CH        CH2
   \ / | \  /                                                           |           |
   CH2 |  O                                                             C          CHOH
      CH3                                                              / \\        /
                                                                    H3C   CH
```

Flavoxanthin, Chrysanthemaxanthin

```
CH3  CH3                                                                                   CH3  CH3
   \ /                                                                                        \ /
    C             CH3              CH3               CH3              CH3                      C
   / \            |                |                 |                |                       / \
CH2   C·CH=CH·C=CHCH=CH·C=CHCH=CHCH=C·CH=CHCH= C·CH=CH·C         CH2
|     |\                                                               /|           |
|     | O                                                             O |           |
HOCH  C/                                                               \|          CHOH
   \ / \                                                                C          /
   CH2  CH3                                                            / \        /
                                                                    H3C   CH2
```

Violaxanthin

```
CH3  CH3                                                                                   CH3  CH3
   \ /                                                                                        \ /
    C                                                                                          C
   / \                             CH3               CH3                                      / \
CH2   C=====CH CH3                 |                 |             H3C CH=====C         CH2
|     |     |  |                                                         |  |      |          |
HOCH  C     CH·C=CHCH=CH·C=CHCH=CHCH=C·CH=CHCH=C·CH      C         CHOH
   \ / | \  /                                                          \  / | \        /
   CH2 |  O                                                              O  |  CH2
      CH3                                                                  H3C
```

Auroxanthin

TABLE VII (*continued*)

```
 CH3   CH3                                                                                   CH3   CH3
   \   /                                                                                       \   /
     C          CH3            CH3                 CH3               CH3                         C
   /   \         |              |                   |                 |                        /   \
CH2    C=CHCH=C·CH=CHCH=C·CH=CHCH=CH·C=CHCH=CH·C=CHCH=C          CH2
 |     |                                                                         |         |
CO     C·CH3                                                                 H3C·C        CO
   \  //                                                                          \\    /
    CH                          Rhodoxanthin                                        CH
```

```
 CH3   CH3                                                                                   CH3   CH3
   \   /                                                                                       \   /
     C          CH3            CH3                 CH3               CH3                         C
   /   \         |              |                   |                 |                        /   \
 CH2    C·CH=CH·C=CHCH=CH·C=CHCH=CHCH= C·CH=CHCH=C·CH=CH·CO     CH2
  |     ||                                                                                      |
HOCH    C·CH3                                                                      H3C·CH2    CHOH
   \   /                                                                                   \   /
    CH2                          Capsanthin                                                 CH2
```

```
 CH3   CH3                                                                                   CH3   CH3
   \   /                                                                                       \   /
     C           CH3            CH3                 CH3               CH3                        C
   /   \          |              |                   |                 |                       /   \
 CH2    CO·CH=CH· C=CHCH=CH·C=CHCH=CHCH= C·CH=CHCH= C·CH=CH·CO      CH2
  |                                                                                             |
HOCH    CH2·CH3                                                                    H3C·CH2    CHOH
   \   /                                                                                   \   /
    CH2                          Capsorubin                                                 CH2
```

```
 CH3   CH3                                                                                   CH3   CH3
   \   /                                                                                       \   /
     C          CH3            CH3                 CH3               CH3                         C
   /   \         |              |                   |                 |                        /   \
 CH2    C·CH=CH·C=CHCH=CH·C=CHCH=CHCH=C·CH=CHCH=C·CH=CH·C          CH2
  |     ||                                                                       ||         |
HOCH    C·CH3                                                                H3C·C        CHOH
   \   /                                                                          \      /
    CO                           Astaxanthin                                        CO
```

```
 CH3   CH3                                                                                   CH3   CH3
   \   /                                                                                       \   /
     C          CH3            CH3                 CH3               CH3                         C
   /   \         |              |                   |                 |                        /   \
CH2    C·CH=CH·C=CHCH=CH·C=CHCH=CHCH=C·CH=CHCH= C·CH=CH·C          CH2
 |     ||                                                                        ||         |
CO     C·CH3                                                                 H3C·C        CO
   \  /                                                                           \      /
    CO                            Astacine                                          CO
```

```
 CH3   CH3
   \   /
     C          CH3            CH3                 CH3               CH3
   /   \         |              |                   |                 |
CH2    C·CH=CH·C=CHCH=CH·C=CHCH=CHCH=C·CH=CHCH=C·CH=CH·CH       COOH
 |     ||                                                                        ||          |
CH2    C·CH3                                                                 H3C·C          CH
   \  /                                                                           \       //
    CH2                       Torularhodin (?)                                      CH
```

```
CH3  CH3
  \ /
   C      OH    CH3           CH3                 CH3
  / \    /      |             |                   |
CH2   C·CH=CH·C=CHCH=CH·C=CHCH=CHCH=C·CH=CH·COOH
|     |
CH2   C·CH3
  \  / \
  CH2   OH
```

Azafrine

```
  CH3  CH3
    \ /
     C            CH3          CH3                CH3           CH3
    / \           |            |                  |             |
  CH2   C·CH=CH·C=CHCH=CH·C=CHCH=CHCH=C·CH=CHCH=C·CHO
  |     ||
HOCH    C·CH3
    \  /
    CH2
```

β-Citraurine

```
         CH3           CH3                CH3           CH3
         |             |                  |             |
HOOC·C=CHCH=CH·C=CHCH=CHCH=C·CH=CHCH=C·COOH
```

Crocetin

```
                 CH3           CH3                CH3           CH3
                 |             |                  |             |
HOOC·CH=CH·C=CHCH=CH·C=CHCH=CHCH=C·CH=CHCH=C·CH=CH·COOCH3
```

Bixin

Cyclization can take place at both ends or at one end of the chain. By oxidative degradation the chain may be shortened. On the other hand, the introduction of various oxygenated groups gives rise to a series of derivatives. The carotenes (carrot, lemon, orange, apricot, etc.) and lycopene (tomato) are hydrocarbons, whilst cryptoxanthin (fruit of Chinese lantern plant, egg yolk, etc.), rubixanthin (berries of the wild rose, etc.), xanthophyll (green and yellow leaves, dandelion flowers, egg yolk, etc.), lutein (pumpkin, many yellow flowers, etc.), zeaxanthin (maize grain, egg yolk, etc.), flavoxanthin (buttercup flowers, etc.), violaxanthin (laburnum flowers, etc.), taraxanthin (dandelion flowers, etc.) and fucoxanthin (algae of the genera *Fucus*, etc.) are alcohols. Similarly, rhodoxanthin (berry of the yew-tree, etc.) is a diketone, capsanthin (red pepper) and capsorubin (red pepper) are hydroxy-ketones and crocetin (saffron or the pigment from *Crocus* pollen, etc.) is an acid. Carotenoid pigments are widely distributed in the biosphere and will be found, no matter whether one examines plants or animals, algae or bacteria.

REFERENCES

DEUEL, H. J. (1951) Carotenoids and related compounds, in *The Lipids*, vol. I, Interscience, New York.

GOODWIN, T. W. (1952), *The Comparative Biochemistry of the Carotinoids*. Chapman and Hall, London.

KARRER, P. & JUCKER, E. (1948) *Carotinoide*. Birkhäuser, Basel.

B. Natural Phenanthrene Derivatives

There are a number of substances occurring naturally that, from the organic chemists' point of view, are related to phenanthrene. This latter substance, $C_{14}H_{10}$, is obtained from coal tar together with anthracene, of which it is an isomer.

Among the phenanthrene derivatives present in the biosphere, one finds many quininoid pigments and a number of alkaloids such as those of the morphine group. But the phenanthrene derivatives most characteristic of living organisms are those in which the phenanthrene nucleus has a cyclopentane ring fused to it.

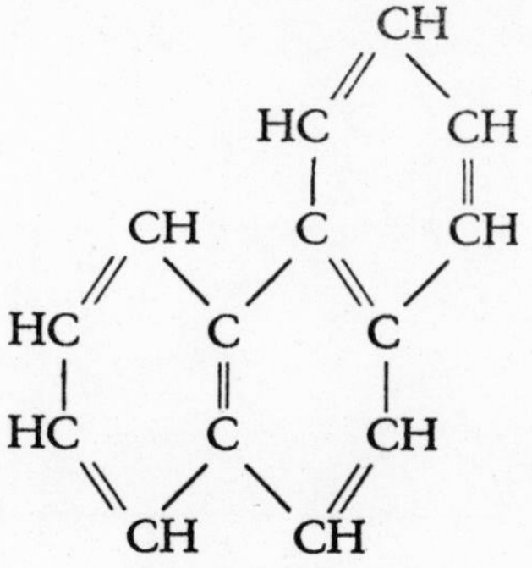

```
                    CH
                  //  \
                HC      CH
                 |      ||
         CH      C      CH
       //  \   /  \\   /
     HC      C      C
     |       ||     |
     HC      C      CH
       \\  /   \  //
         CH      CH
```

Phenanthrene

If a hydrogen atom is added to each carbon of the phenanthrene ring the double bonds disappear and one obtains perhydrophenanthrene.

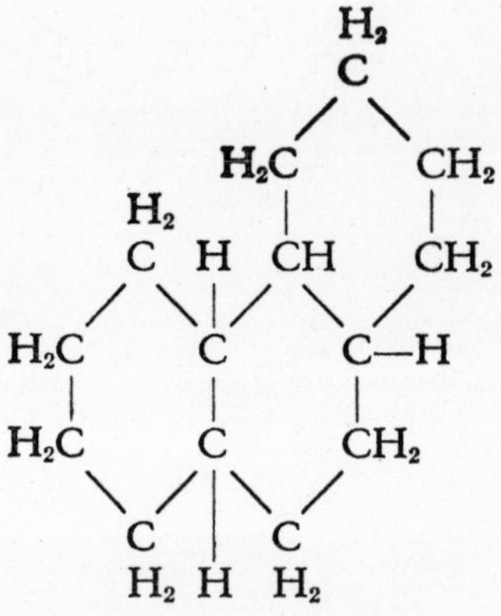

```
               H2
               C
             /   \
          H2C     CH2
     H2    |       |
     C  H  CH     CH2
   /  \ | /   \   /
H2C     C       C—H
 |      |       |
H2C     C       CH2
   \  / | \   /
     C  |   C
     H2 H   H2
```

Perhydrophenanthrene

```
      H2
      C
    /   \
 H2C     CH2
  |       |
 H2C-----CH2
```

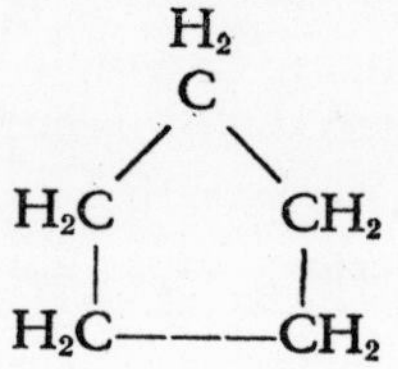

Cyclopentane

Both the structures of cyclopentane and of perhydrophenanthrene are combined in cyclopentanoperhydrophenanthrene, commonly known as sterane.

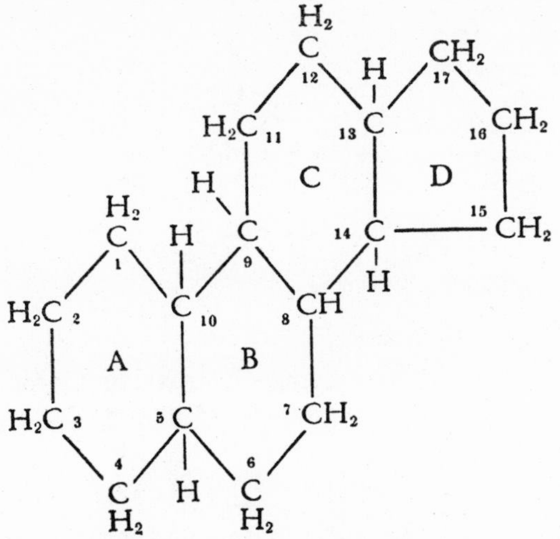

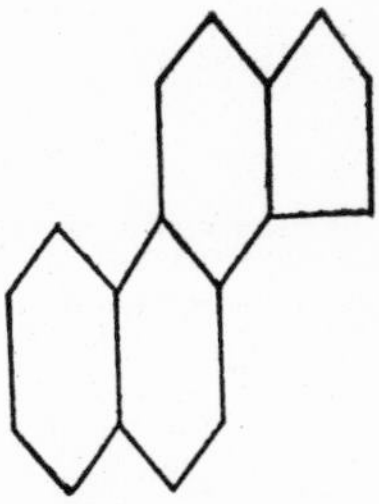

The natural compounds containing this ring, the steroids, are oxygenated, alkyl-substituted derivatives of the hydrocarbon, having the following general formula, where R and R′ vary from compound to compound:

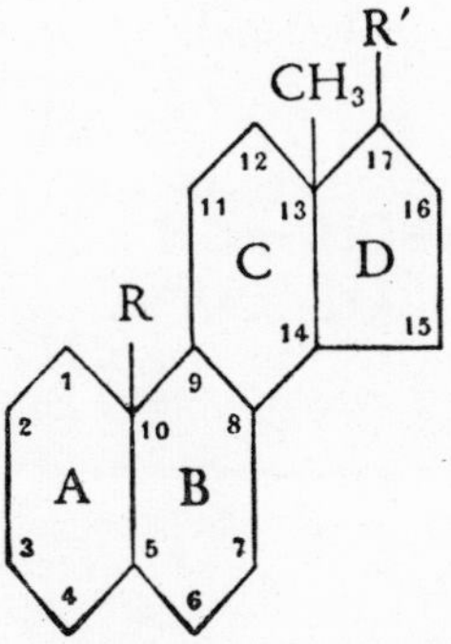

derived from oestrane

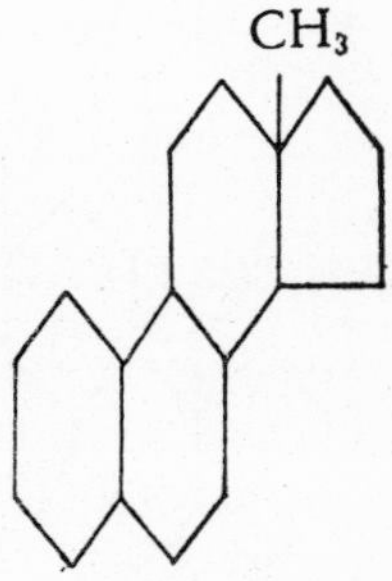

In the biosphere this basic carbon skeleton appears in a series of guises, the most important being the following:

Substituent group R and R′

Cholesterol* $CH_3—CH(CH_3)—(CH_2)_3—CH(CH_3)_2$

* The other sterols have double bonds in the side chain or alkyl substituents.

Bile acids	CH_3	CH_3 —	—CH—$(CH_2)_2$—COOH
Androgenic substances	CH_3	OH or O
Luteal substances	CH_3	Acetyl
Oestrogenic substances (benzene ring)		OH or O

1. *Sterols*

In the biosphere, sterols generally have a single hydroxyl group together with a side chain.

Their general structure

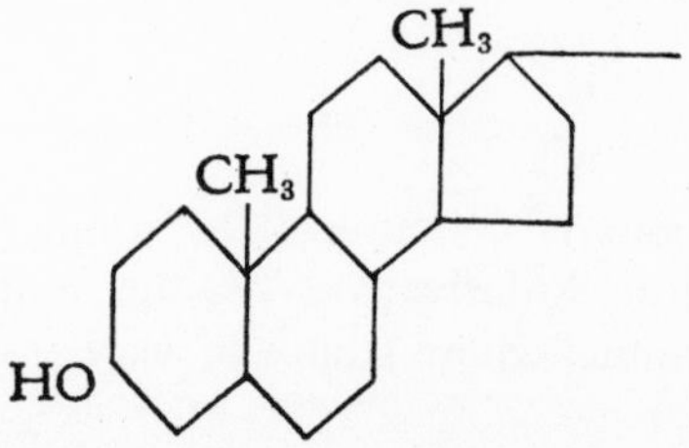

causes them to be classified, from the chemical point of view, as derived from cholestane $C_{27}H_{48}$ or from coprostane (allocholestane).

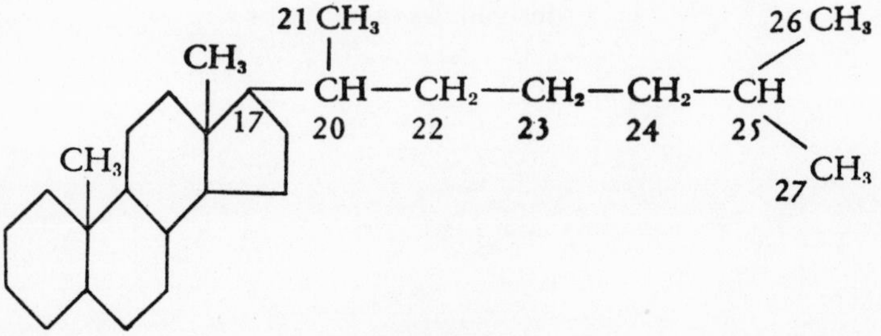

Cholestane

The molecule of cholestane contains eight asymmetric carbon atoms (5, 8, 9, 10, 13, 14, 17, 20) : there are theoretically 256 stereoisomers. If a hydroxyl group is attached to C-3, the number of stereoisomers is raised to 512. Most of the natural isomers differ only in the arrangement of groups in the region of C-3 or C-5. In general, the methyl group on C-10 is situated above the plane of the paper. If, as is generally the case, the hydroxyl group on C-3 is also above the plane of the paper, the isomer is designated *cis* or β. In the inverse case, the compound is called *trans* or α.

When a single bond in cholestane is replaced by a double bond, it becomes a cholestene and the position of the double bond is indicated by the first (in the order of increasing numbers) carbon atom linked by the double bond.

One of the most widely distributed sterols, for example, is cholesterol or 3 (*cis*)-hydroxy-5-cholestene.

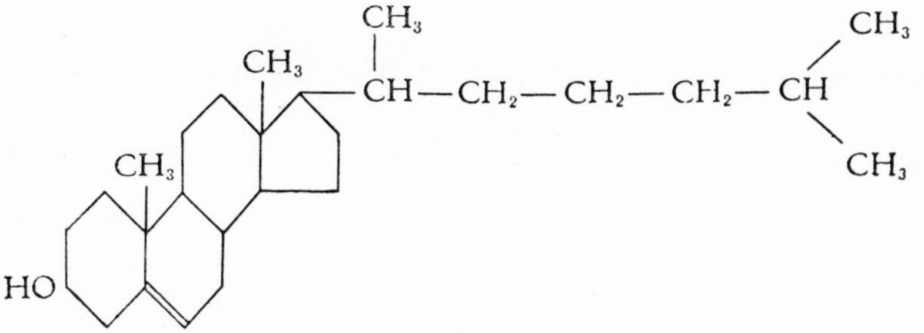

Cholesterol

The numerous sterols in the biosphere differ in the number and position of the double bonds, and in the number of carbon atoms in the side-chain. There are saturated sterols, and sterols having one, two or three double bonds. In the higher animals, cholesterol is the characteristic sterol, but this is not the case for lower animals, in which cholesterol is only one sterol among many.

Ergosterol is the chief sterol in mushrooms, and fucosterol in the brown algae. The higher plants contain complex mixtures of sterols. Bacteria, in general, do not contain sterols, or other steroids.

Werner Bergmann classes the sterols according to their rotatory power, which is intimately related to their structure :

I. [α] greater than −90° — system of conjugated double bonds in ring B.

II. [α] from −30° to −70° — a 5:6 double bond.

III. [α] from −20° to +10° — a 7:8 double bond

IV. [α] from +10° to +30° — saturated ring and side chain (exception : neospongosterol).

V. [α] from +40° to +50° — an 8:9 double bond.

The sterols in group I differ from all the others in one important respect : the conjugated double bonds in ring B confers upon them the property of undergoing molecular rearrangement under the influence of ultra-violet light.

Ergosterol, the chief sterol of mushrooms, belongs to this group, the members of which differ from each other in the side-chain (presence or absence of double bonds, position of methyl and ethyl groups, etc.). Similarly, it is the character of the side-chain which differentiates the sterols of group II (cholesterol, camposterol, clionasterol, etc.).

2. *Bile Acids*

These substances, so named because they were isolated from the bile of vertebrate animals, are cousins to the sterols of group IV and they possess two methyl groups and at least one hydroxyl in the ring system. Their C-5 side-chain ends in a carboxyl group. Cholic acid is an example :

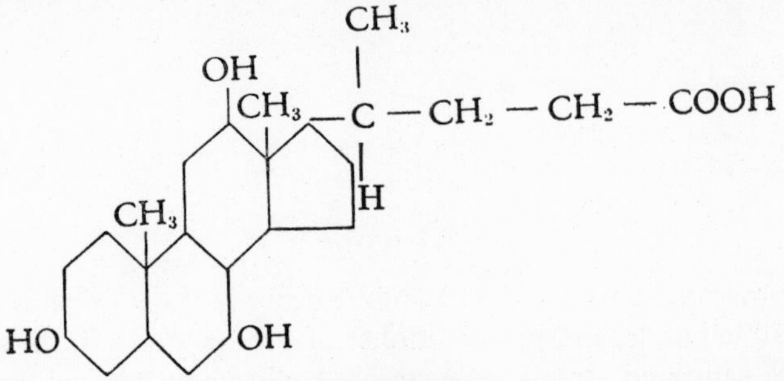

Cholic acid

3. *Other Natural Steroids*

There exist in the biosphere steroids having a chain of only two carbon atoms attached at position 17. These are the 21-carbon steroids. They are derivatives of pregnane. Progesterone and the mammalian adrenocorticosteroids fall into this category.

Other steroids do not have a side-chain attached to carbon 17. They usually carry two methyl groups and are C-19 steroids derived from aetiocholane. Among them are testosterone and those steroids which have a keto group in position 17 and are consequently called 17-ketosteroids; they are often present in mammalian urines.

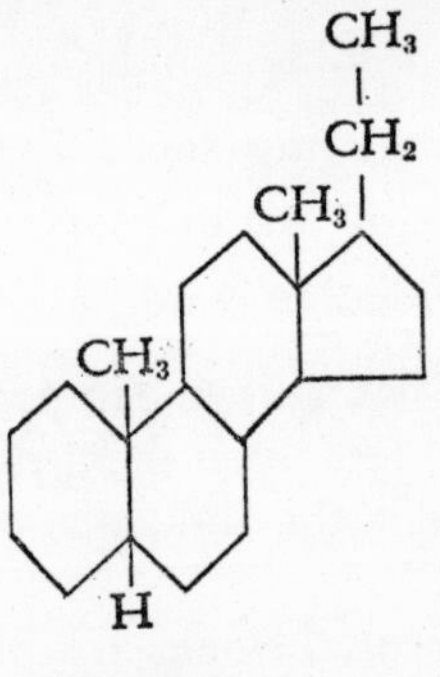

Pregnane

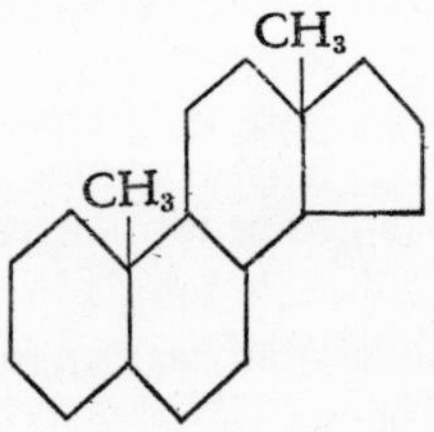

Aetiocholane

Other steroids not possessing a methyl group are the C-18 steroids, derivatives of oestrane. The most interesting of these are the oestrogenic hormones in which ring A is a benzene ring (e.g. oestrone).

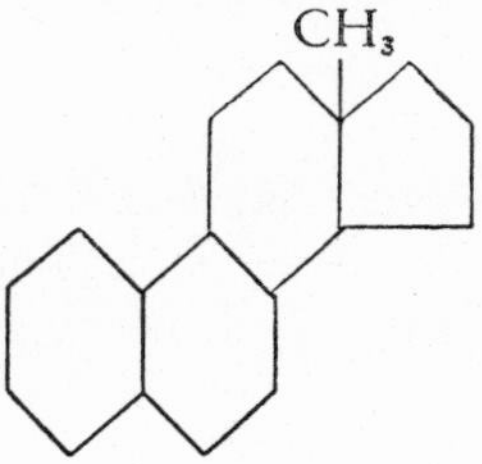

CH_3 CH_3 O HO

Oestrane 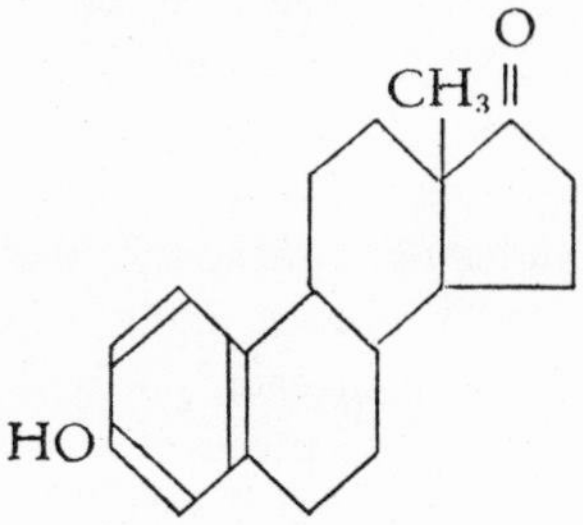 **Oestrone**

C. Natural Heterocyclic Compounds

(a) *Pyrrole Derivatives*

Among the heterocyclic compounds of organic chemistry, those of the pyrrole group present a particular interest to the bicohemist. Pyrrole itself, C_4H_4NH, has been known for over a century as a product of the dry distillation of organic matter. Its biological importance is very great. Suffice it to say that from indole or phenopyrrole are derived indoxyl and

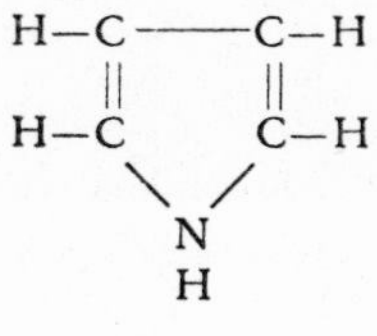

H–C——C–H H–C C–H N H

Pyrrole

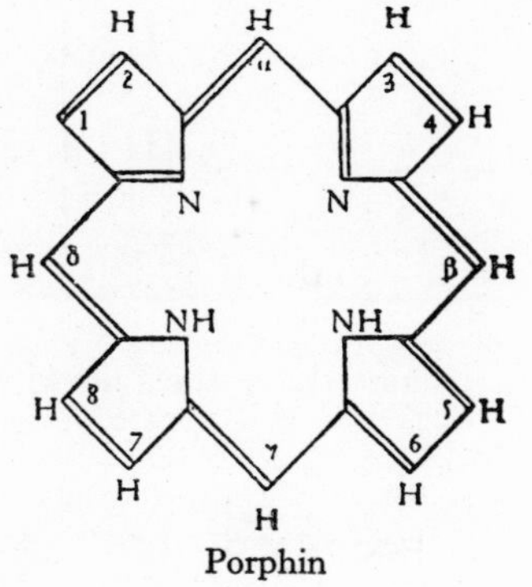

H H H H N N H H NH NH H H H H H H

Porphin

REFERENCES

Bergmann, W (1952). Sterols. *Progress in the Chemistry of Fats and Other Liquids,* 1, Pergamon Press, London & New York.

Fieser, L. & Fieser, M. (1949). *Natural Products Related to Phenanthrene,* 3rd ed., Reinhold (New York).

Heusghem, C. (1950). *Metabolisme et analyse des hormones steroides,* Masson and Desoer, Paris, Liège (*Actualités biochimiques,* No. 14).

indigo, that considerable amounts of pyrrole bases are present in plants, and that tryptophane contains a pyrrole ring. One particular class of pyrrole derivatives, the porphyrins, are of great interest due to their wide distribution both in the free and in the combined state. The porphyrins crystallize readily, have a very high melting point and fluoresce brilliantly in ultra-violet light. Their colouring power is extremely great and spectroscopic analysis allows very small quantities of porphyrins to be detected. They are molecules containing four pyrrole rings and their structure may be represented as based upon a hypothetical tetrapyrrole, porphin, the structure of which in each particular case is modified by the addition of various groups. The position of the double bonds can only be arbitrarily fixed in a structure of this sort.

The four pyrrole rings of porphin and the porphyrins are connected by methyne bridges (= CH —) which are denoted by the Greek letters α, β, γ and δ. The porphyrins are derived from the parent porphin nucleus by replacing the hydrogen atoms on carbons 1 to 8 by various radicals.

The relative positions of the substituent groups can give rise to several isomers. Let us consider, for instance, in one category of porphyrins, the tetramethyl-tetrapropionyl-porphins, also called coproporphyrins. There are four possible isomers corresponding to different positions of the four methyl groups :

I : 1, 3, 5, 7–

II : 1, 4, 5, 8–

III : 1, 3, 5, 8–

IV : 1, 4, 6, 7–

These four isomers have the following structures :

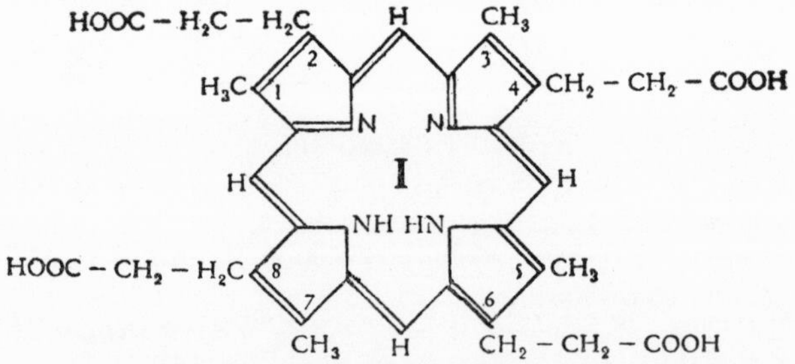

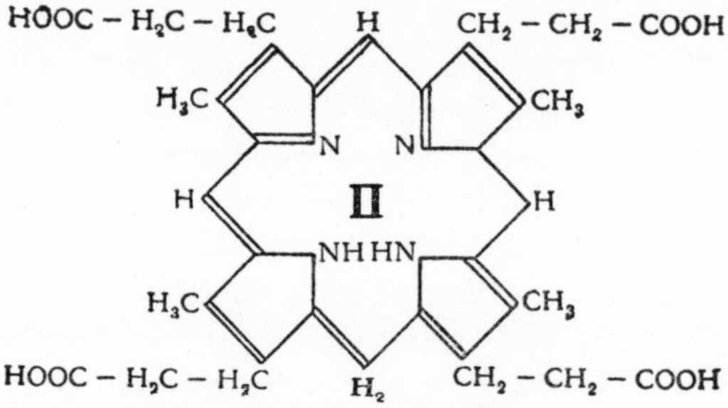

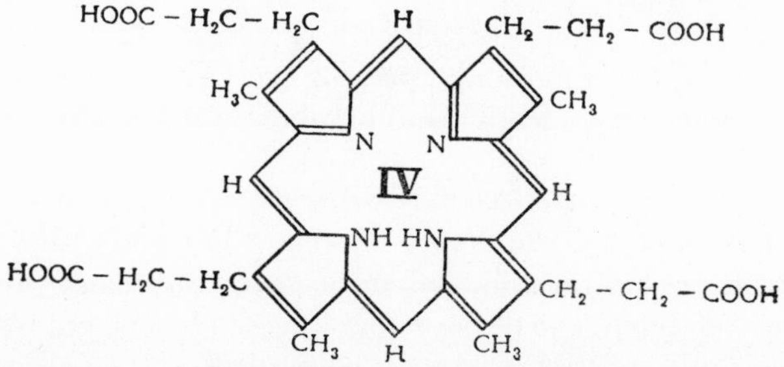

HOOC – H_2C – H_2C H CH_2 – CH_2 – COOH
H_3C CH_3
N N
H H
II
NH HN
H_3C CH_3
HOOC – H_2C – H_2C H_2 CH_2 – CH_2 – COOH

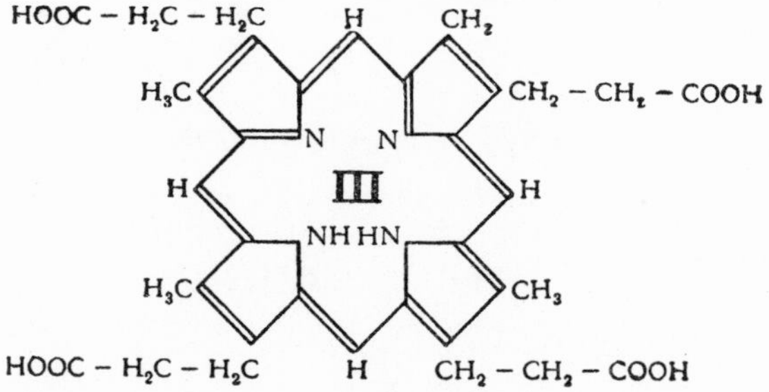

HOOC – H_2C – H_2C H CH_2
H_3C CH_2 – CH_2 – COOH
N N
H H
III
NH HN
H_3C CH_3
HOOC – H_2C – H_2C H CH_2 – CH_2 – COOH

HOOC – H_2C – H_2C H CH_2 – CH_2 – COOH
H_3C CH_3
N N
H H
IV
NH HN
HOOC – H_2C – H_2C CH_2 – CH_2 – COOH
CH_3 H CH_3

Coproporphyrin I is found in yeast, and coproporphyrins I and III have been isolated from faecal matter, from which they take their name.

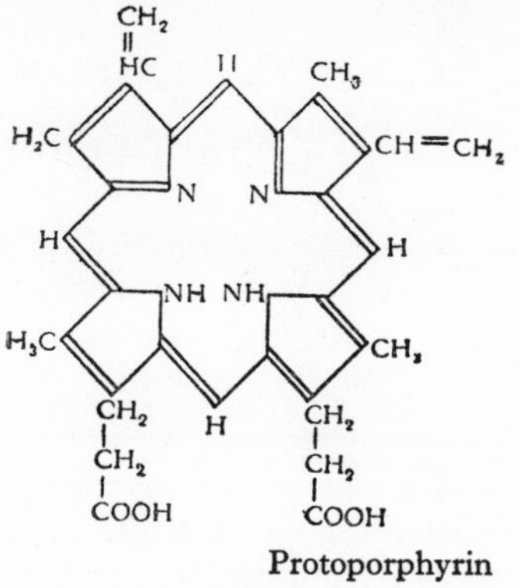

CH_2
||
HC H CH_3
H_3C CH=CH_2
N N
H H
NH NH
H_3C CH_3
CH_2 H CH_2
CH_2 CH_2
COOH COOH

Protoporphyrin

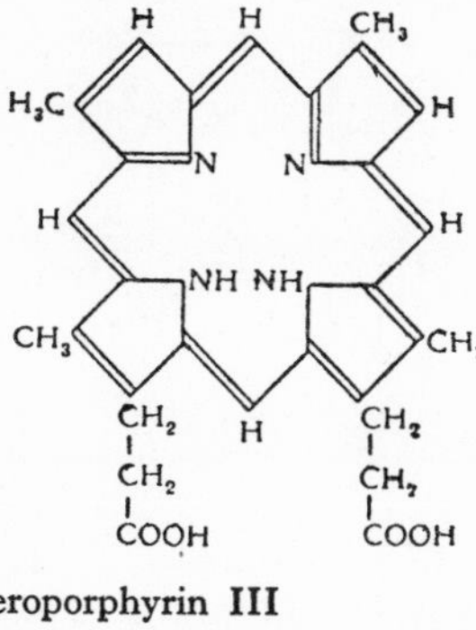

H H CH_3
H_3C H
N N
H H
NH NH
CH_3 CH_3
CH_2 H CH_2
CH_2 CH_2
COOH COOH

Deuteroporphyrin III

In the protoporphyrins, the eight carbon atoms of porphin carry two vinyl groups, four methyl groups and two propionic acid groups. One of the fifteen possible isomers of this structure is protoporphyrin IX or porphin-1:3:5:8-tetramethyl-2:4-divinyl-6:7-dipropionic acid, commonly called protoporphyrin. This is the porphyrin most widely distributed in nature, it is a constituent of haemoglobin, catalase, peroxidase, of cytochrome-*b*, etc. During the course of putrefaction protoporphyrin loses its unsaturated side chains and is transformed into deuteroporphyrin III. On the other hand, it can be derived by a series of operations from coproporphyrin III, another proof of its chemical kinship with the porphyrins of Series III.

(*b*) *Derivatives of Pyrrolidine*

Pyrrolidine is the saturated ring compound corresponding to pyrrole.

```
H2C ——— CH2
 |        |
H2C      CH2
   \    /
     H
     N
```

Pyrrolidine

Its skeleton is found in molecules present everywhere in the biosphere, as in proline, vitamin B_{12}, nicotine and in other alkaloids, etc.

(*c*) *Indole Derivatives*

Indole is the compound whose ring is present in tryptophan. It is also present in the natural auxin α-indolyl-acetic acid, a substance produced at the level of the apical bud and of the young leaves in plants, and transported to the region of the stem when growth takes place.

```
      H
      C
    //  \
  HC     C ——— CH
  |      ||     ||
  HC     C      CH
    \\  /  \   /
      C      N
      H      H
```

Indole

```
      H
      C
    //  \
  HC     C ——— C —CH2COOH
  |      ||    ||
  HC     C     CH
    \\  /  \  /
      C     N
      H     H
```

α-indoyl-acetic acid

(*d*) *Imidazole Derivatives*

The five-membered imidazole ring containing two nitrogen atoms is present in the naturally occurring amino acid, histidine.

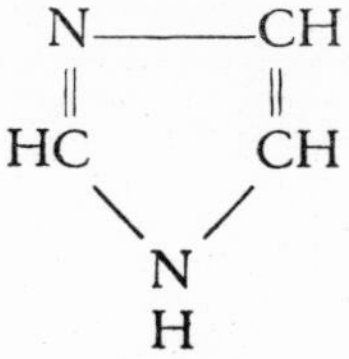

```
N———CH        N———CH
‖      ‖       ‖      ‖
HC      CH     HC      CH
  \    /         \    /
    N              S
    H
```

Imidazole

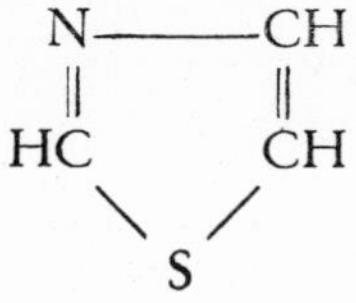

Thiazole

(*e*) *Derivatives of Thiazole*

This five-membered ring, containing both nitrogen and sulphur, together with a pyrimidine ring, forms part of the structure of thiamine pyrophosphate which is an important coenzyme.

(*f*) *Thioctic Acid*

Another important sulphur-containing heterocyclic ring is that of 6:8-dithio-*n*-octanoic acid otherwise known as thioctic or α-lipoic acid.

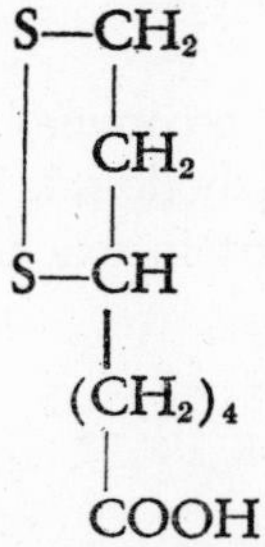

```
S—CH2
|  |
|  CH2
|  |
S—CH
   |
  (CH2)4
   |
  COOH
```

Thioctic acid

This substance, an important coenzyme for oxidative decarboxylation, operates by opening and closing of its ring at the two sulphur atoms.

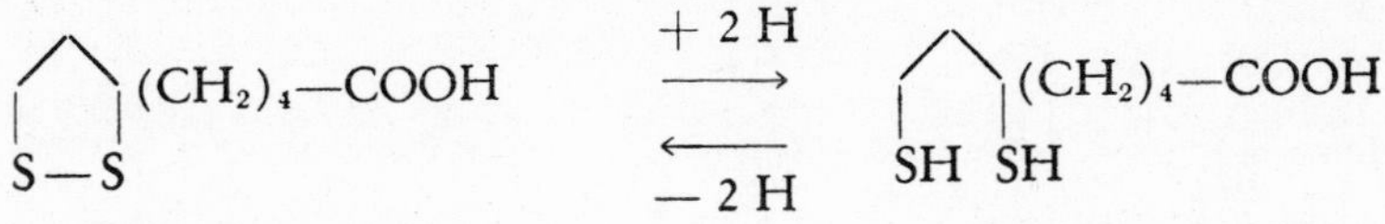

```
 /\                      + 2 H         /\
|  |(CH2)4—COOH        ——————→        |  |(CH2)4—COOH
S—S                    ←——————        SH SH
                         − 2 H
```

Oxidized thioctic acid

Reduced thioctic acid

(*g*) *Derivatives of Six-membered Heterocylic Rings containing Oxygen*

The principal rings in this category are those of pyran, chroman, and flavan. The pyran ring, as has already been stated (p. 19) is the basic skeleton of the sugars in their stable forms.

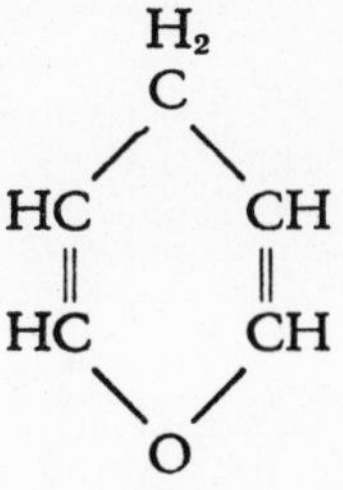

Pyran

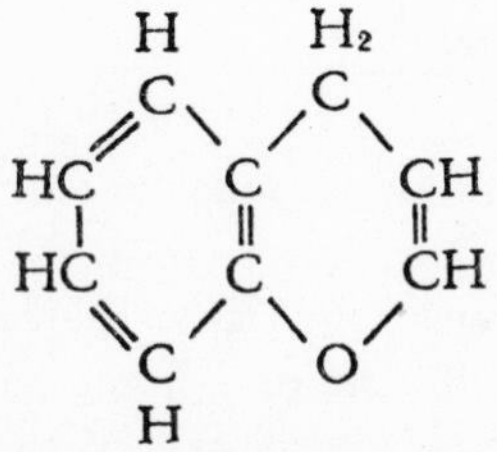

Chroman

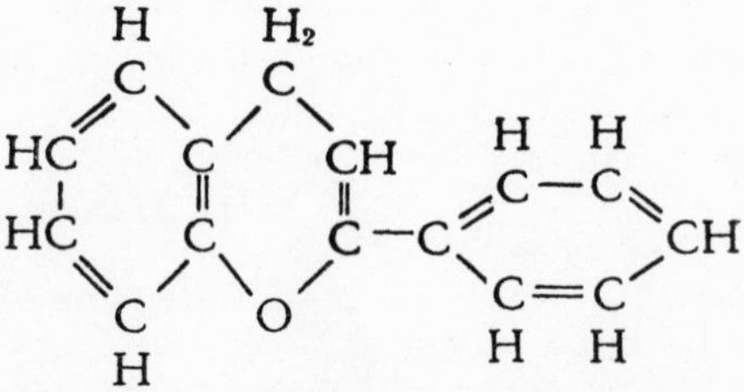

Flavan

Chroman derivatives, called tocopherols, are widely distributed in the biosphere. Although their metabolic role is not yet precisely defined, it is known that they antagonize certain oxidations. The vitamins E are tocopherols.

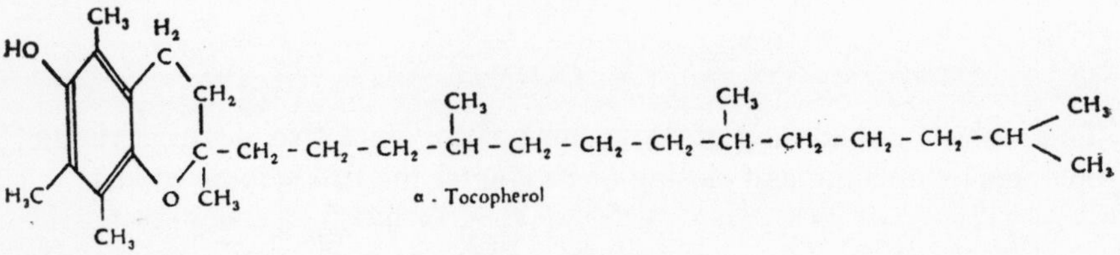

α - Tocopherol

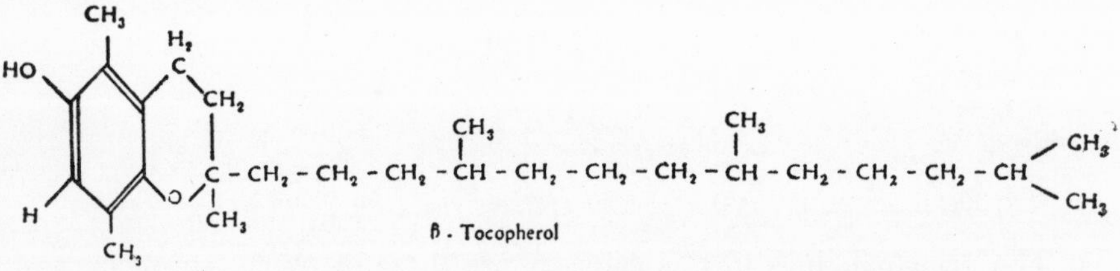

β - Tocopherol

In plants there is a family of yellow pigments, the anthoxanthins, which are derived from the flavan ring, from flavone, flavonol and flavanone.

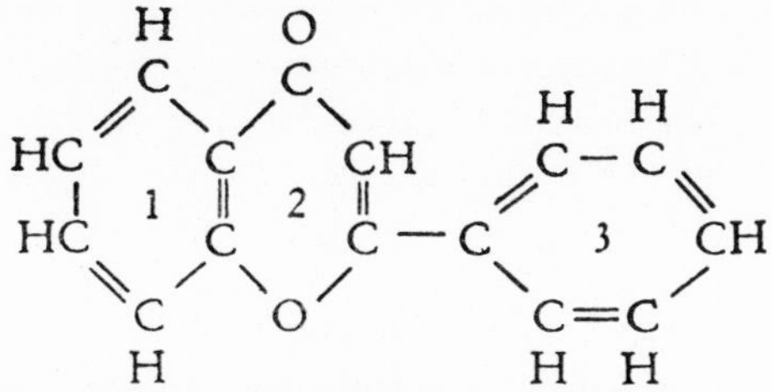

Flavone

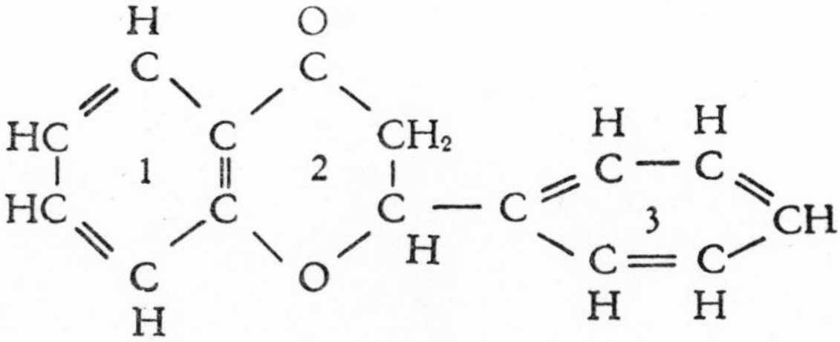

Flavanone

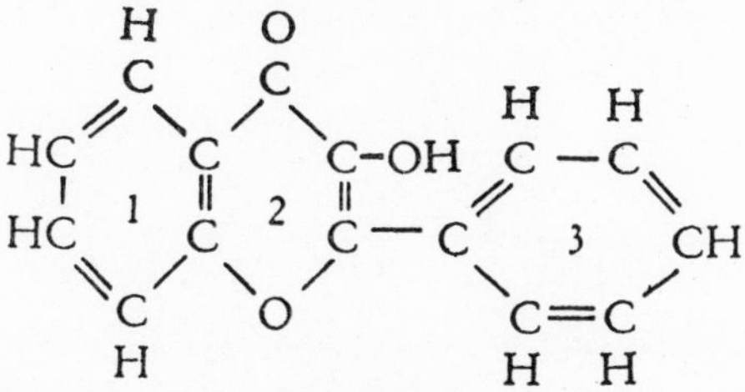

Flavonol

These compounds are generally found in nature in the hydroxyl substituted form, to give such derivatives as quercetin, a flavonol derivative which in combination with glucose (as a glucoside) is to be found in many plants, or hesperitin, a flavanone derivative which is present in the lemon as a glucoside, hesperidin.

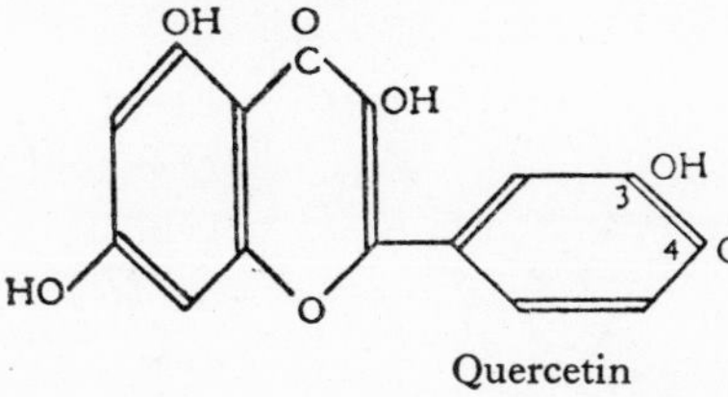

Quercetin

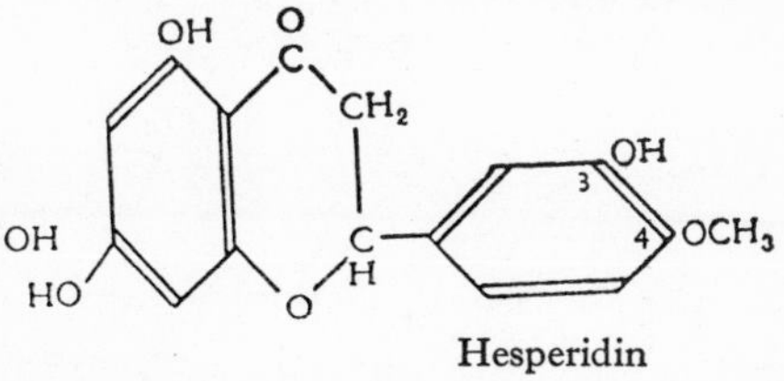

Hesperidin

Substances of this nature have a function in the transfer of metabolic hydrogen in plants. In the process, hydrogen peroxide formed by the combination of hydrogen and oxygen oxidizes the flavone derivative in the presence of peroxidase, and in turn the oxidized flavone oxidizes a molecule of ascorbic acid.

This function is only possessed by derivatives having two hydroxyls in positions 3 and 4 in ring 3, as is the case for quercetin and its glycoside quercitrine, in which the glucose molecule is combined with the hydroxyl group of ring 1. Hesperidin is inactive.

However, in the lemon when it is ripe, a demethylation of hesperidin takes place and eriodictyol is formed and it is the glucoside of this latter substance which is chiefly found in the ripe fruit.

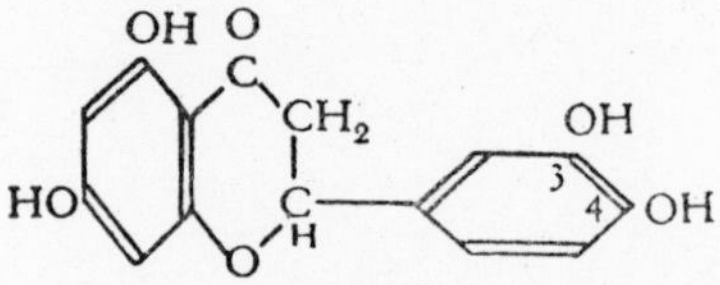

```
    OH O
       C
        CH2            OH
        |             3
HO      C----------     4 OH
      O  H
```

Eriodictyol

The anthocyanins, the blue, red or violet pigments found in many flowers, are glucosides in which there is a six-membered oxygen-containing ring. Their aglucones (non-sugar portion) or anthocyanidins are hydroxylated derivatives of a benzopyrilium nucleus :

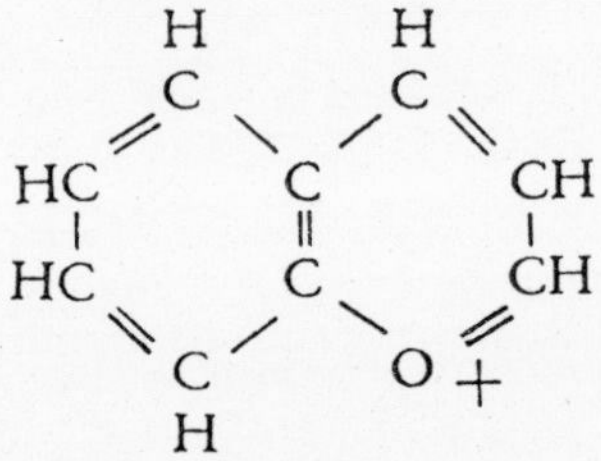

```
        H       H
        C       C
      //  \   /   \\
   HC       C       CH
   |        ||      |
   HC       C       CH
      \\  /   \   //
        C       O+
        H
```

in which oxygen is the central atom of a complex monovalent ion whose coordination number is three. Certain anthocyanidins have a structure similar to that of flavone, for example, this is the case with oenin, the anthocyanidin present in the skin of the black grape.

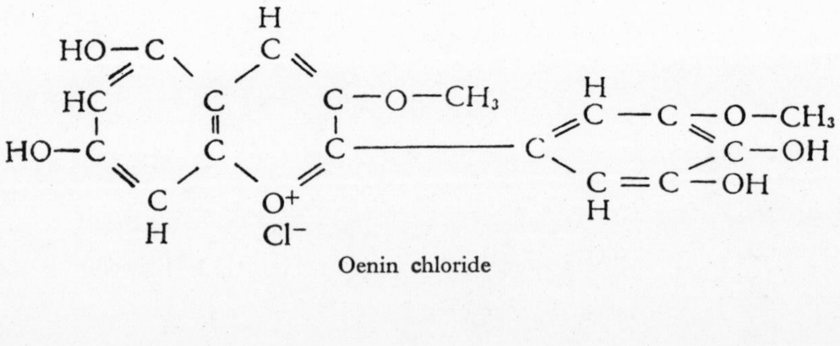

```
               H
   HO—C        C
     //  \   /   \\
   HC      C       C—O—CH3        H
   |       ||      |            //C —C =O—CH3
HO—C       C       C————————————C         \\C—OH
     \\  /   \   //               \ C =C —OH
       C       O+                   H
       H       Cl-
```

Oenin chloride

(*h*) *Pyridine Derivatives*

The simplest six-membered heterocyclic ring containing nitrogen is that of pyridine. It can be prepared by cyclization of ethylallylamine followed by dehydrogenation.

Its formula is :

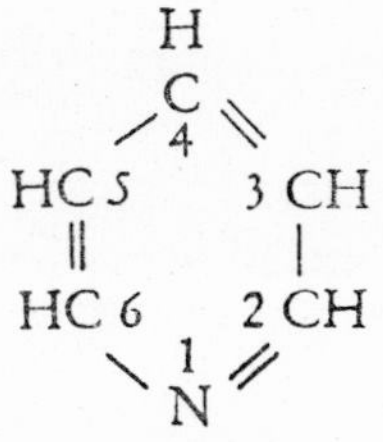

H
C 4
HC 5 3 CH
HC 6 2 CH
1
N

Pyridine

$CH_2{=}CH{-}CH_2{-}NH{-}CH_2{-}CH_3.$

ethylallylamine

It is present in the distillation product of bones and coal. It behaves similarly to the benzene ring with regard to halogenation, nitration and sulphonation, but the reactions are considerably slower. It is the ring present in an important group of alkaloids. This group includes nicotine, present in tobacco leaf in combination with malic and citric acids, and which on oxidation yields nicotinic acid.

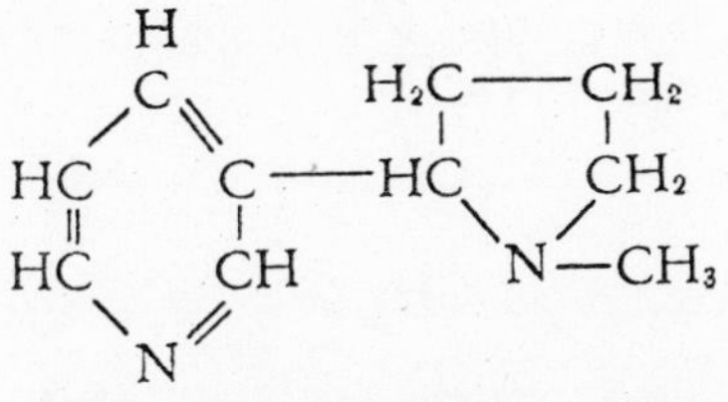

H
C H_2C—CH_2
HC C—HC CH_2
HC CH N—CH_3
N

Nicotine (Methylpyrrolidine-pyridine)

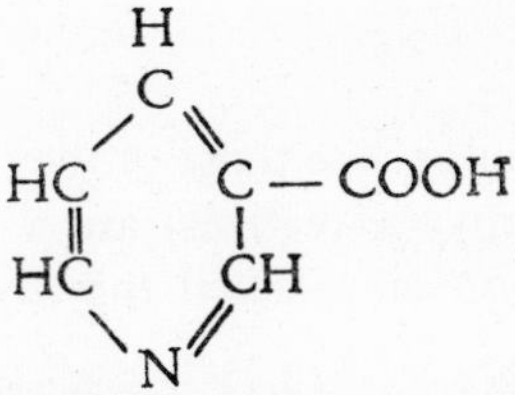

H
C
HC C—COOH
HC CH
N

Nicotinic acid

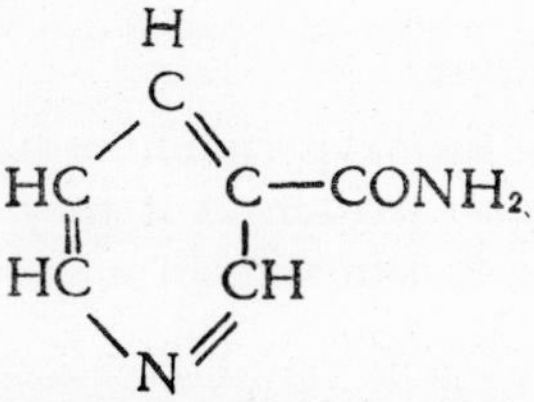

H
C
HC C—$CONH_2$
HC CH
N

Amide of nicotinic acid (Nicotinamide)

The amide of nicotinic acid, or nicotinamide, is a substance of very great biological importance, for it is the active grouping in a whole series of important coenzymes. Another important group of pyridine derivatives comprises pyridoxin (also known as vitamin B_6, being a growth factor for the rat and for certain bacteria), pyridoxal and pyridoxamine. These substances are very widely distributed in nature.

CH_2OH / HOH_2C / OH / CH_3 / N — Pyridoxin (vitamin B_6)

CHO / HOH_2C / OH / CH_3 / N — Pyridoxal

CH_2NH_2 / HOH_2C / OH / CH_3 / N — Pyridoxamine

(i) *Pyrimidine Derivatives*

In pyrimidine there is a heterocyclic ring containing two nitrogen atoms. It is one of three isomeric diamines :

N, HC, N, HC, CH, C, H — Pyridazine

N 1, HC 6, 2 CH, HC 5, 3 N, 4 C, H — Pyrimidine

N, HC, CH, HC, CH, N — Pyrazine

To the organic chemist, pyrimidine derivatives are products of the condensation of urea with certain acids. Barbituric acid or cyclomalonylurea is a member of this group. It is prepared by reacting malonic acid with urea in the presence of $POCl_3$.

$$O{=}C{<}^{NH_2}_{NH_2} + \begin{matrix} COOH \\ | \\ CH_2 \\ | \\ COOH \end{matrix} = \begin{matrix} NH{-}CO \\ | \quad\quad | \\ OC \quad CH_2 \\ | \quad\quad | \\ NH{-}CO \end{matrix} + 2H_2O$$

Urea — Malonic acid — Barbituric acid

1. *Pyrimidines*

Among the oxypyrimidines (their formulae, like those of the oxypurines, may be also written as if they are hydroxyderivatives) are a number of important constituents of nucleic acids, cytosine, uracil and thymine.

N ═ CH (1, 6) / HC 2 5 CH / N —— CH (3, 4)	HN—C=O / O=C CH / HN—CH	HN—C=O / O=C C—CH_3 / HN—CH	N=C—NH_2 / O=C C—H / HN—CH
Pyrimidine	Uracil (2, 6-dioxy-pyrimidine)	Thymine (2, 6-dioxy-5-methyl-pyrimidine)	Cytosine (2-oxy-6-amino-pyrimidine)

2. *Thiamine*

This is the hydrochloride of a molecule formed from a pyrimidine and a thiazole ring. The phosphoric ester of this substance is an important coenzyme.

```
                                      CH3
                                      |
                                      C=C—CH2CH2OH
                                      |    \
         N=C—NH2                      |     S
         |  |                         |    /
   CH3—C  C————CH2————N=C
         ||  ||                      +   H
         N—CH                        Cl⁻
```

Thiamine hydrochloride

(*j*) *Purine Derivatives*

The purine ring results from the condensation of a pyrimidine ring with another heterocyclic ring, imidazole.

```
  N ═ CH             HC — NH \               N ═ CH
  |1  6|             ||        CH            |1  6|    H
 HC2  5CH            HC — N //              HC2  5C — N \
  ||3 4||                                    ||3 4||  7  8 CH
  N — CH                                     N — C — N //
                                                      9
 Pyrimidine          Imidazole               Purine
```

Purine forms salts with acids and compounds with bases, it behaves therefore both as an acid and as a base.

A number of purines are widely utilized in living organisms.

```
        NH2                                  O
       /                                    //
   N=C                                HN—C
   |  |  H                             |  |  H
  HC  C—N \                      NH2—C  C—N \
  ||  ||    CH                         ||  ||    CH
   N—C—N //                            N—C—N //
     Adenine                              Guanine
  (6-aminopurine)                 (2-amino-6-oxypurine)

        O                                    O
       //                                   //
  HN—C                                HN—C
   |  |  H                             |  |  H
  HC  C—N \                        O=C  C—N \
  ||  ||    CH                         |  ||    CH
   N—C—N //                          HN—C—N //
    Hypoxanthine                          Xanthine
   (6-oxypurine)                   (2,6 dioxypurine)
```

(*k*) *Alloxazine Derivatives*

The double heterocyclic ring of lumazine,

```
       N       NH
     / 8 \\   / 1 \
 HC 7      C       2 CO
  ||       |         |
 HC 6      C       3 NH
     \ 5 //  \ 4   /
       N       CO
```

condensed with a benzene ring forms the alloxazine nucleus :

```
       H               H
       C       N       N
    // 8 \   / 9 \\  / 1 \
 HC 7      C       C       2 CO
  |        ||      |         |
 HC 6      C       C       3 NH
    \\ 5 /   \ 10 //  \ 4  /
       CH      N       CO
```

this has been known for over half a century and the method of synthesis by condensation of an aromatic o-diamine with alloxan (Kuhling's sythesis) has also been known for a considerable time.

```
                       H
                       N
                     /   \
  /\ NH2           OC     CO
 |  |          +   |       |        ——> alloxazine  + 2 H2O
  \/ NH2           OC     NH
                     \   /
                       C
                       O
```

It was the great achievement of Richard Kuhn and his fellow workers and then of Karrer and co-workers to show that a very important series of natural substances contained a tautomeric form of alloxazine, isollaoxazine or flavin, a substance which is unstable in the free state.

```
 [     H       H                     ]
       C       N       N
    // 8 \   / 9 \   // 1 \
 HC 7      C       C       2 CO
  |        ||      |         |
 HC 6      C       C       3 NH
    \\ 5 /   \ 10 //  \ 4  /
       C       N       C
 [     H               O             ]
```

Isoalloxazine or Flavin (unstable)

Although unstable in the free state, the ring is present as derivatives in which the hydrogen on the nitrogen atom in position 9 is replaced by a substituent group. The group of these compounds is called "the flavins". One example is lumiflavin (a photoderivate of lactoflavin).

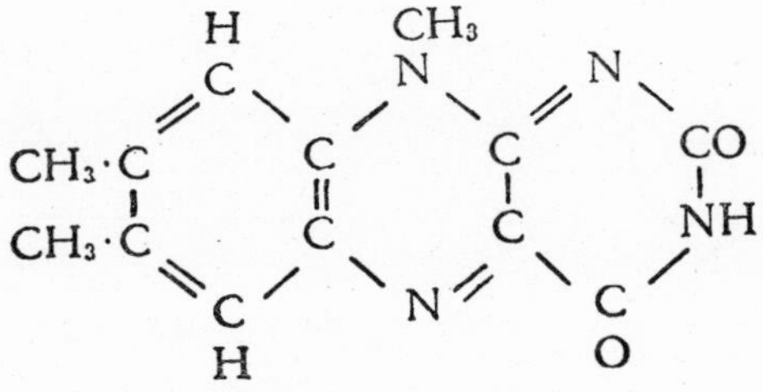

6,7-dimethyl-9-methyl-isoalloxazine or lumiflavin

(*l*) *Pteridine Derivatives*

This heterocyclic ring system arises from the condensation of the pyrimidine and the pyrazine rings.

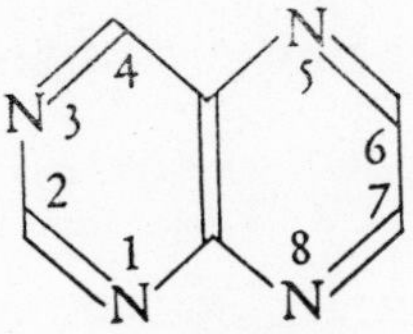

Pteridine

The pteridines are sparingly soluble in water and insoluble in volatile organic solvents. They have a bright fluorescence.

1. *Pterins*

The pteridine nucleus is present everywhere in the biosphere, in the form of a number of derivatives : leucopterin, xanthopterin, erythropterin, etc. Pterins are found, especially, in the wings of butterflies. The fluorescence of tissues is often due to their presence.

2. *Folic Acid*

Also among these derivatives is pteroyl-glutamic acid or folic acid, so called because of its abundant distribution in the leaves of plants. Folic acid is the universal coenzyme for the transfer of C_1 fragments and hence is indispensable for the synthesis of purines and nucleic acids.

2-amino-4-hydroxy -6-methylpterin | para-aminobenzoic acid | glutamic acid

```
          OH
          |
          C       N
        //  \   /   \\
      N       C        C-CH2-N-<C6H4>-C-N-C-CH2-CH2-COOH
      |       ||       |      H        ||  H H
      |       ||       |               O     |
  H2N-C       C        CH                   COOH
        \\  /   \    //
          N       N
```

pteroic acid

pteroylglutamic acid (folic acid)

REFERENCES

BENDICH, A. (1955). Chemistry of purines and pyrimidines, in E. CHARGAFF et J. N. DAVIDSON *The Nucleic Acids*, Vol. I, Academic Press, New York.

LEMBERG, R. (1954). Porphyrins in nature, *Fortschr. Chem. org. Naturstoffe*, XI, 299–349.

SEBRELL, W. H. et HARRIS, R. S. (1954). *The Vitamins*, Vol. III, Academic Press, New York.

WILEY, R. H. (1953). Heterocyclic chemistry, in H. GILMAN, *Organic Chemistry: An Advanced Treatise*, Vol. 4, Wiley, New York.

CHAPTER III

MODES OF LINKAGE BY COVALENT BONDS

I. "OSIDE" LINKAGE

A. Osides

On hydrolysis, osides yield one or more sugars or "oses". They are called holosides if the products of hydrolysis are solely sugars, and heterosides if on hydrolysis substances other than sugars are obtained.

The holosides are designated di-, tri- or tetraholosides according to the number of sugar molecules obtained on hydrolysis.

The heterosides are very abundant in the vegetable kingdom: tannins, ruberythric acid (from the madder plant, hydrolysis liberates glucose and the aglucone, alizarin), anthocyanins (colours of many flowers), digitalis glucosides (gitine, digitonine, digitaline, gitoxine, etc. . . .) cyanogenetic glucosides (whose hydrolysis liberates hydrogen cyanide in addition to a sugar), etc. . . .

The heterosides are called α or β-heterosides according to whether they contain the α or β form of the sugar.

The most interesting osides in the biosphere are the diholosides or disaccharides which are classed as reducing or as non-reducing disaccharides.

(*a*) *Non-Reducing Diholosides*

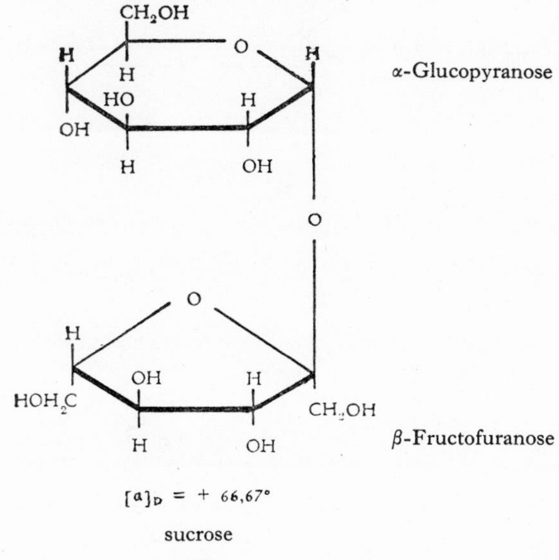

$[\alpha]_D = + 66{,}67°$

sucrose

1. *Sucrose*

This is the sugar of the sugar-cane and sugar-beet. It is present in the tissues and juices of many plants (carrot, beetroot, sweet fruits, sugar-maple juice, sugar-cane, etc. . . .)

In the molecule of sucrose, glucose is present in the α-glucopyranose form and fructose in the β-fructofuranose form. The two sugars are joined by their two reducing groups and as a result sucrose has no reducing properties.

(*b*) *Reducing Diholosides*

1. *Lactose*

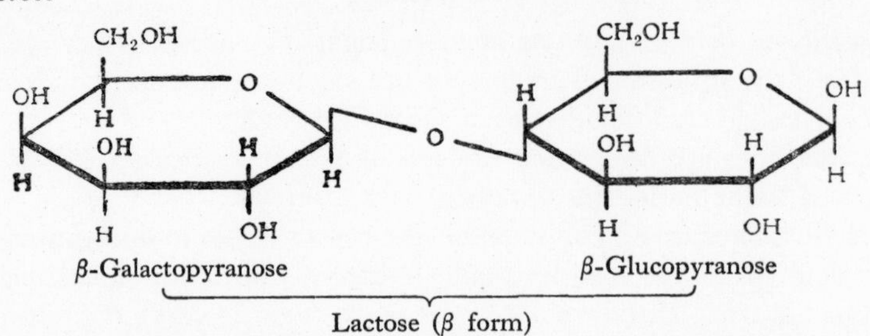

Lactose (β form)

This is milk-sugar, it is present in the milk of all mammals (4% in cows milk, 5–7% in human milk).

Lactose is dextrorotatory, it exists in an α form and in a β form according to the configuration of the remaining free pseudoaldehyde group.

2. *Maltose*

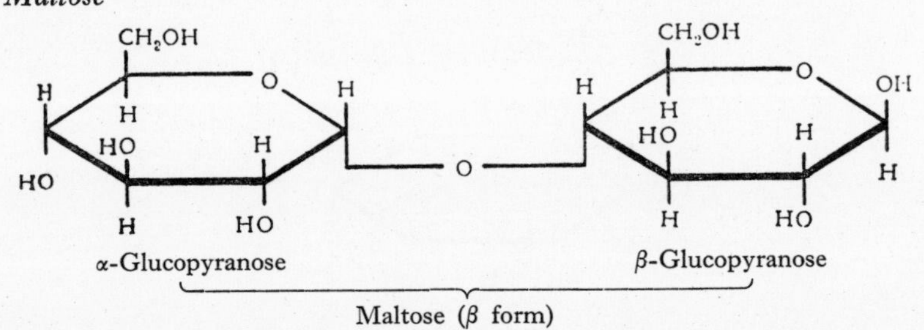

Maltose (β form)

It is obtained when amylase acts on starch or glycogen; it is dextrorotatory.

3. *Cellobiose*

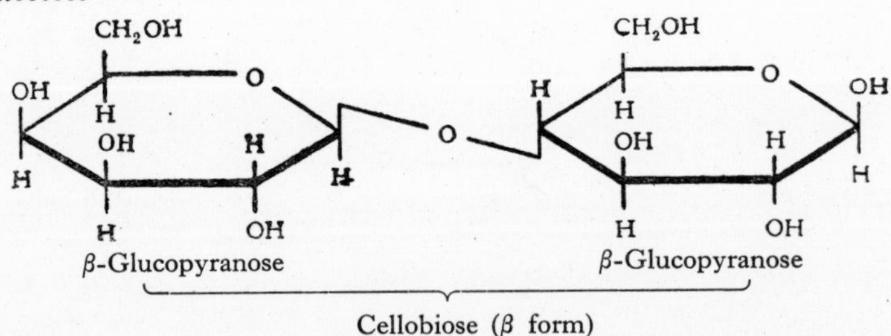

Cellobiose (β form)

It is a product of the hydrolysis of cellulose, like lactose and maltose, it exists in an α and β form.

B. Nucleosides

These substances are the result of the combination of a base (most frequently a purine or pyrimidine base) with a sugar (D-ribose) or desoxy-sugar (desoxyribose) by means of an "oside" bond. Since many of these substances occur in nucleic acids, they are called "nucleosides".

In these compounds the linkage is probably a β-glucoside type of linkage.

```
N=C—NH2
|  |
HC  C—N
||  ||   \\
||  ||    CH
N—C—N   /  ————————— CH ————————
                     |          |
                 H—C—OH         |
                     |          O
                 H—C—OH         |
                     |          |
                   H—C ——————————
                     |
                     CH2OH
```

Adenosine (adenine nucleoside)

```
    HN—CO
     |  |
H2N—C  C—N
    ||  ||  \\
    ||  ||   CH
    N—C—N  /  ———— CH ————————
                   |          |
               H—C—OH         |
                   |          O
               H—C—OH         |
                   |          |
                 H—C ——————————
                   |
                   CH2OH
```

Guanosine (guanine nucleoside)

Among the flavins, or isoalloxazine derivatives, one finds an important natural derivative of this type, it is lactoflavin—more commonly known as riboflavin. Chemically, it is 6,7-dimethyl-9-D-ribityl–isoalloxazine. It is present in a combined state in a large number of animal and vegetable tissues. Like the flavins in general, riboflavin is soluble in water, giving a yellow solution having a yellow-green fluorescence. With heavy metals it forms sparingly soluble salts. When heated, it decomposes at 274°. It is stable to oxidizing agents. Under the influence of light, it is transformed, depending on the conditions, either into lumilactoflavin or lumiflavin (a derivative of isolloxazine, p. 54), or into lumichrome (a derivative of alloxazine). Riboflavin, or vitamin B_2, is not a true nucleoside, since the isoalloxazine in it is not combined with ribose, but with ribitol, the corresponding alcohol.

```
            H               H
            |               |
            C       N       N
          //  \   /   \\  /   \
H3C —C        C       C        CO
     |        ||      |        |
H3C —C        C       C        NH
      \\    /   \   //  \    /
            C       N       C
            |               ||
            H               O
```

Lumichrome

```
                  H
                  |
           HO—C—H       (5′)
                  |
            H—C—OH      (4′)
                  |
            H—C—OH      (3′)
                  |
            H—C—OH      (2′)
                  |
            H—C—H       (1′)
                  |
        H         |
        C         N         N
      //8  \   /  9  \  // 1 \
H3C—C 7       C         C       2 CO
      |       ||        |        |
H3C—C 6       C         C       3 NH
      \\ 5 /    \  10 //  \ 4  /
        C         N         C
        |                   ||
        H                   O
```

6,7-dimethyl-9-D-ribityl-isoalloxazine or vitamin B_2

REFERENCES

Baddiley, J. (1955). Chemistry of nucleosides and nucleotides, in E. Chargaff and J. N. Davidson, *The Nucleic Acids*, Vol. I, pp 137–190 Academic Press, New York.

Pigman, W. W. & Goepp, R. M. (1948) *Chemistry of the Carbohydrates*, Academic Press, New York.

II. ESTER LINKAGE (AND ANHYDRIDE LINKAGE)

A. Ternary Lipides

Lipides are the esters which constitute fats. A distinction is made between ternary lipides, containing only carbon, hydrogen and oxygen, and complex lipides containing in addition phosphorous and nitrogen. These latter compounds are better considered with the other natural phosphate esters.

The ternary lipides can be divided into several types, among which are :

(a) The glycerides, esters of glycerol.

(b) The waxes, ester of higher alcohols.

(c) The sterides, esters of sterols.

(*a*) *Glycerides*

The simple glycerides are those in which the three molecules of acid, which take the place of the H atom in each of the OH groups of glycerol, are identical. The general formula of the simple glycerides is therefore as follows :

$$\begin{array}{l} CH_2—O—OC—R \\ | \\ CH\ —O—OC—R \\ | \\ CH_2—O—OC—R \end{array}$$

In certain other glycerides, the mixed glycerides, the three molecules of fatty acid are not identical, for example in distearopalmitin :

$$\begin{array}{l} CH_2—O—OC—C_{17}H_{35} \\ | \\ CH\ —O—OC—C_{15}H_{31} \\ | \\ CH_2—O—OC—C_{17}H_{35} \end{array}$$

Distearopalmitin

(1 molecule of glycerol + 2 molecules of stearic acid + 1 molecule of palmitic acid)

(*b*) *Waxes*

These are esters of the higher molecular weight fatty acids and monovalent higher alcohols.

Example : cetyl palmitate, the principal constituent of spermaceti (cetyl alcohol = $C_{16}H_{34}O$).

(c) *Sterides*

The sterides are esters of fatty acids and sterols. Lanoline, the fat obtained from wool, is a mixture of cholesterol oleate, palmitate, and stearate.

B. Natural Phosphoric Esters

(a) *Phosphoric Acids*

Orthophosphoric acid, H_3PO_4, possesses three acid groups which ionize, one after the other, as the pH increases.

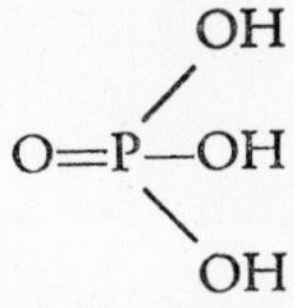

```
      OH
     /
O=P—OH
     \
      OH
```

The first ionization corresponds to a pK of 1·97, so that this group is relatively strongly acidic, and the ionization is complete at a very acid pH, well outside the pH range of biochemical interest. The second acid group (pK = 6·82) is comparable to organic acids in strength. It is this group, when combined with a strong base, which acts as a buffer in the acid-base equilibrium of biological environments. The third acid group is only slightly dissociated, only forming salts in very alkaline solution, outside the biochemical range. Orthophosphoric acid can form phosphoric esters with alcohols. Three types exist : monoesters, diesters and triesters—

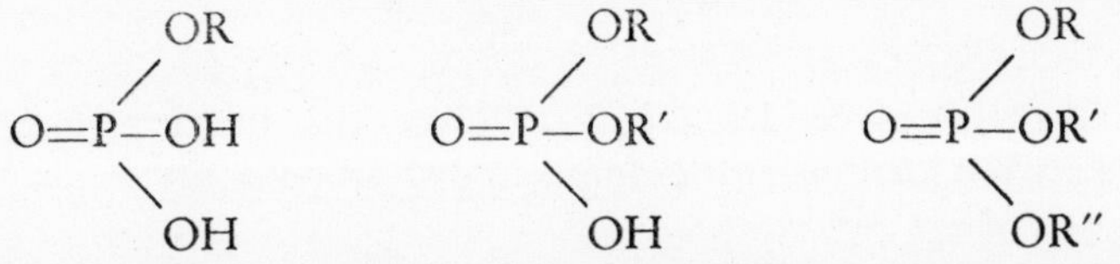

```
      OR              OR              OR
     /               /               /
O=P—OH         O=P—OR'        O=P—OR'
     \               \               \
      OH              OH              OR"
```

In the biosphere, triesters of orthophosphoric acid are unknown, however, this does not exclude the possibility that this binding may be present in certain macromolecules. The diesters of orthophosphoric acid which exist in the biosphere are often mixed esters. Acid or alkaline hydrolysis slowly transforms them into monoesters. Most of the complex lipides are diesters and vitamin B_{12} also falls into this category. The monophosphoric esters of alcohols form a very important biochemical group. The two free acid groups are more strongly acidic than when they were

---

REFERENCES

Deuel, H. J. Jr. (1951) *The Lipids. Their Chemistry and Biochemistry*, Vol. I : *Chemistry*. Inter-science, New York.

Hilditch, T. P. (1947). *The Chemical Constitution of Natural Fats*, 2nd ed., Chapman and Hall, London.

Lovern, J. A. (1955). *The Chemistry of Lipids of Biochemical Significance*. Methuen, London.

present in orthophosphoric acid alone, so that these substances are stronger acids than phosphoric acid itself. When phosphoric acid is liberated from these esters and regains its three acid groups there is no appreciable change in the reaction of the medium. Among the monoesters of orthophosphoric acid, we might mention glucose-6-phosphate, α-glycerophosphoric acid and fructose-6-phosphate.

Orthophosphoric acid may be esterified, not only with alcohol groups, but also with the pseudoaldehyde groups of sugars. Aldose derivatives in which the reducing group of the sugar is combined with orthophosphoric acid are very important in cell-chemistry. Sugar-1-phosphates are in this category; their general formula is as follows :

$$PO_3H_2-O-\underset{H}{C}-(CHOH)_n-CH-R$$

(with an O bridge linking the C and CH atoms)

R=H
or CH_2OH

They are very easily hydrolysed in strongly acid solution. The sugar-1-phosphates of furanose sugars are more acid-labile than those of the pyranose form.

Phosphoric acid also forms esters with enols, the most interesting of these is phosphopyruvic acid, in which the enolized pyruvic acid is combined with H_3PO_4. Very acid-labile and very alkaline-labile, it is readily split by oxidizing agents liberating phosphoric acid.

Phosphoamides are also phosphoric acid esters. Their general formula is:

$$(HO)_2P(=O)-N(R)(R')$$

Phosphoamides of the phosphoguanidine type are very acid- and alkaline-labile and their rate of acid hydrolysis is increased by molybdic acid. Phosphoarginine and phosphocreatine are phosphoamides.

Orthophosphoric acid can associate with other molecules of the same acid by means of anhydride linkages to form polyphosphoric acids, notably pyrophosphoric and triphosphoric acids.

Pyrophosphoric acid is made up of two molecules of ortho-phosphoric acid.

$$(HO)_2P(=O)-O-P(=O)(OH)_2$$

It is very stable in alkaline solution, but not in acid solution. A large number of important biochemical structures are derived from pyrophosphate, similarly triphosphoric acid also plays an important role in biochemical energetics in the form of its derivatives, adenosinetriphosphate (ATP) and uridinetriphosphate (UTP).

(*b*) *Phosphoric Esters of Glycerol and Glyceric Acid*

The monophosphoric ester of glycerol, or glycero-phosphoric acid, exists in the two isomeric forms α and β:

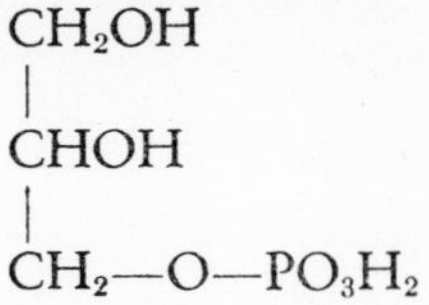

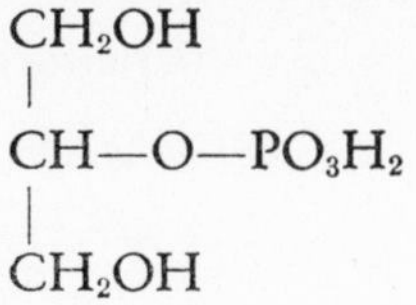

$$\begin{array}{l} CH_2OH \\ | \\ CHOH \\ | \\ CH_2{-}O{-}PO_3H_2 \\ \quad\alpha \end{array} \qquad\qquad \begin{array}{l} CH_2OH \\ | \\ CH{-}O{-}PO_3H_2 \\ | \\ CH_2OH \\ \quad\beta \end{array}$$

Glycerophosphoric acids

and corresponding to these are the monophosphoric esters of glyceric acid, α and β phosphoglyceric acids.

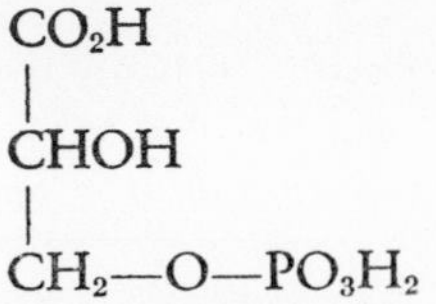

$$\begin{array}{l} CO_2H \\ | \\ CHOH \\ | \\ CH_2{-}O{-}PO_3H_2 \\ \quad 3 \text{ or } \beta \end{array} \qquad\qquad \begin{array}{l} CO_2H \\ | \\ CH{-}O{-}PO_3H_2 \\ | \\ CH_2OH \\ \quad 2 \text{ or } \alpha \end{array}$$

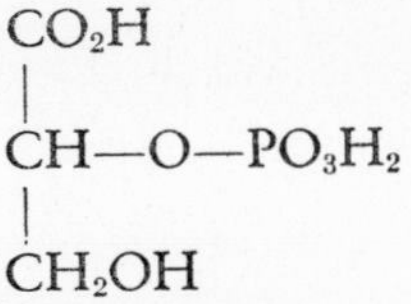

Closely related to the above acids is phosphorylated pyruvic acid (phosphoenolpyruvic acid):

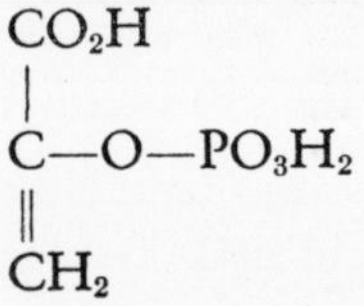

$$\begin{array}{l} CO_2H \\ | \\ C{-}O{-}PO_3H_2 \\ \| \\ CH_2 \end{array}$$

(*c*) *Triosephosphates*

Phosphodihydroxyacetone $CH_2OH\text{-}CO\text{-}CH_2O\text{-}PO_3H_2$ is a triose ester a triosephosphate. Another member of the same class is its isomeric aldehyde, phosphoglyceraldehyde or 3-glyceraldehyde-phosphoric acid:

$$CHO{-}CHOH{-}CH_2{-}O{-}PO(OH)_2$$

These two triosephosphates, unlike the hexose phosphates, are easily hydrolysed by alkali.

(*d*) *Phosphorylated Sugars*

1. *Ribose phosphates*

The ribose phosphate normally present in cells is β-D-ribose-1-phosphate; it is very acid-labile. Desoxyribose-1-phosphate is even more unstable in acid solution; at pH 4·0 at room temperature, it is 50% hydrolysed in 15 minutes. It is hydrolysed in the course of estimations of "inorganic phosphate" and is consequently often measured as such.

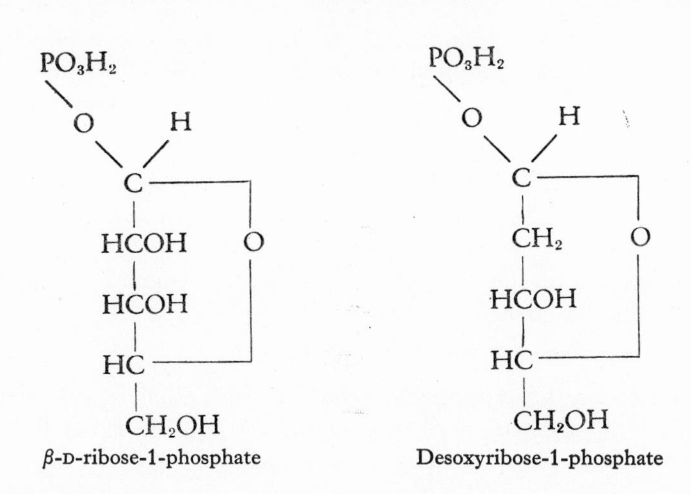

β-D-ribose-1-phosphate   Desoxyribose-1-phosphate

2. *Hexose phosphates*

(*a*) α-D-*glucose*-1-*phosphate* (*Cori ester*)—This ester is reducing and is stable to alkali, on hydrolysis glucose is liberated.

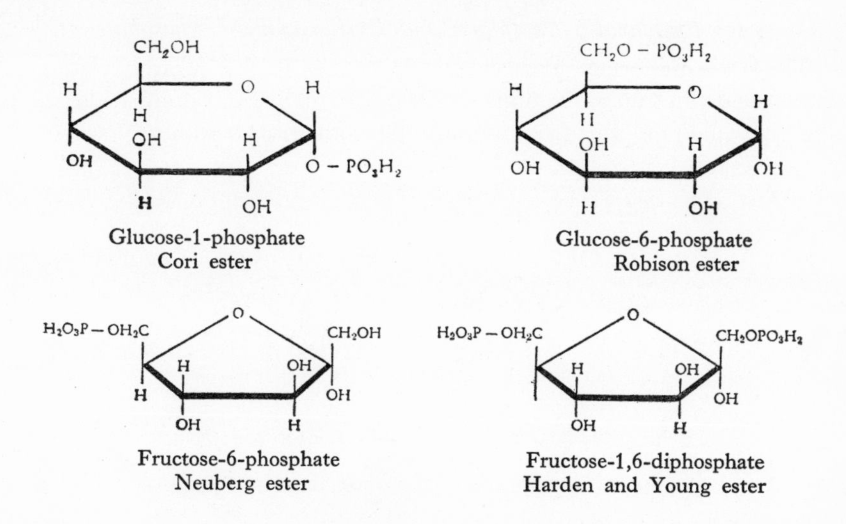

Glucose-1-phosphate
Cori ester

Glucose-6-phosphate
Robison ester

Fructose-6-phosphate
Neuberg ester

Fructose-1,6-diphosphate
Harden and Young ester

(*b*) *Glucose*-6-*phosphate* (*Robison ester*)—Although the existence of this ester had been known since 1914 from experiments on yeast carried out by Harden and Robison, it was not until 1931 that Robison and King succeeded in obtaining it in the pure state.

(*c*) *Glucose*-1,6-*diphosphate*—This ester, which is a coenzyme in glycolysis, was isolated by Leloir from yeast after incubation with phosphate and glucose.

(*d*) *Fructose*-1-*phosphate* (*Robison ester*)—Hydrolysis of fructose-1, 6-diphosphate by phosphatases, gives equal amounts of fructose-1-phosphate and fructose-6-phosphate. Fructose-1-phosphate has been isolated from liver and been found in the intestine during the intestinal absorption of fructose.

(*e*) *Fructose*-6-*phosphate* (*Neuberg ester*)—Fructofuranose-6-phosphate was first prepared by partial hydrolysis of fructose-1, 6-diphosphate and later isolated from the products of alcoholic fermentation. In normal acid, at 100°, the phosphate group in position 1 is split off about a dozen times more rapidly than the group in position 6.

(*f*) *Fructose*-1,6-*diphosphate* (*Harden and Young ester*)—Fructofuranose-1, 6-diphosphate in alkaline solution (0·2N NaOH) at 100° liberates the whole of its phosphate in three minutes.

(*g*) *Other phosphorylated sugars and their derivatives present in the biosphere*—Such compounds are galactose-1-phosphate, ribitol phosphate, sedoheptulose phosphate, gluconic acid phosphoric ester, etc.

(*e*) *Pyridoxal*-5-*Phosphate and Pyridoxamine*-5-*Phosphate*

These are important coenzymes, the former in the decarboxylation of amino acids, in transaminations, deamination of hydroxyaminoacids and in the removal of sulphur from amino acids containing sulphur.

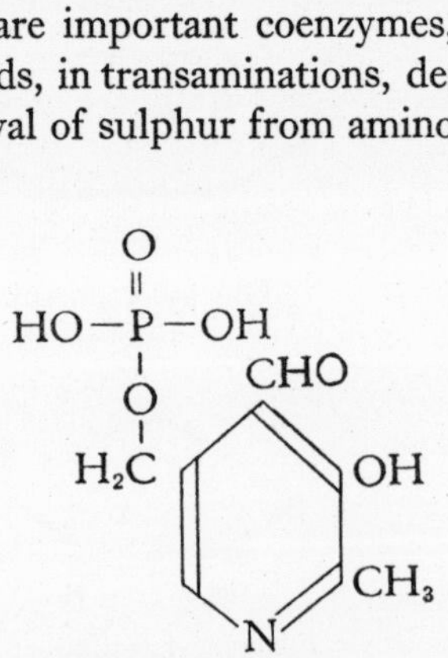

O
||
HO—P—OH
|
O
|
H_2C — ring with CHO, OH, CH_3, N

Pyridoxal-5-phosphate

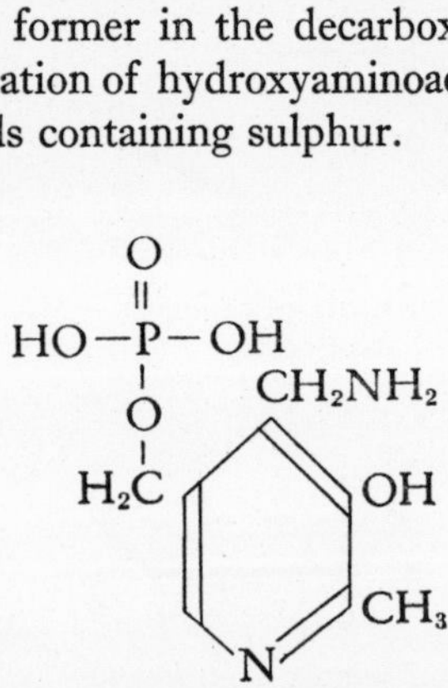

O
||
HO—P—OH
|
O
|
H_2C — ring with CH_2NH_2, OH, CH_3, N

Pyridoxamine-5-phosphate

(*f*) *Thiamine Pyrophosphate* (*Cocarboxylase, Diphosphothiamine, DPT*)

Thiamine, being basic, gives a series of salts and esters.

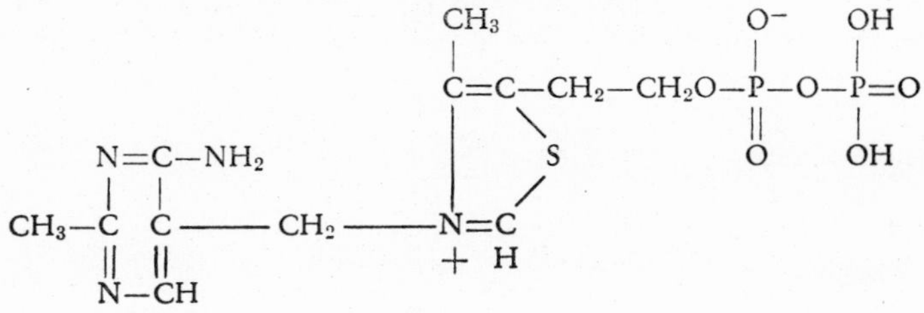

```
                                CH3                 O-    OH
                                |                   |     |
                                C=C—CH2—CH2O—P—O—P=O
                                |   \                ||    |
          N=C—NH2              |    S               O     OH
          |   |                 |   /
   CH3—C   C ——— CH2 ——— N=C
          ||  ||                +  H
          N—CH
```

The most important ester is the product of the reaction between pyrophosphoric acid and the hydroxyl of the thiazole ring. This ester is the coenzyme for carboxylase and for the decarboxylation of a series of α-keto-acids.

(*g*) *Nucleotides*

These are the phosphoric esters of nucleosides.

1. *Mononucleotides*

(*a*) *Adenosine mono- and poly- phosphates*—In most cells these compounds act as coenzymes in the transport of phosphate groups.

Adenosine triphosphate (ATP) was isolated from muscle by Lohmann in 1928. The three terminal phosphate groups of ATP are joined by two anhydride bonds. Removal of the terminal phosphate gives adenosine diphosphate (ADP), and of the next phosphate leaves adenosine monophosphate (AMP) or adenylic acid.

The adenosine phosphates (AMP, ADP, ATP) are relatively unstable in solution. At 100° in dilute acid the two anhydride bonds of ATP are split but the ester linkage remains intact. In AMP the esterification of the adenosine is on C-5′ of the sugar whilst in other nucleotides (coenzyme A, triphosphopyridine-nucleotide) other carbon atoms are involved.

In the molecules of adenosine polyphosphates, one of the phosphoric acid residues is linked to the nucleoside by an ester bond but the phosphoric acid residues among themselves are joined by an anhydride bond much less stable than the ester bond. As we shall see the hydrolysis of anhydride linkages plays an important part in biochemical energetics on account of their strongly exergonic nature.

(*b*) *Uridine phosphates*—These mononucleotides have been demonstrated in yeast and in animal liver. They are coenzymes for the reaction galactose-1-P $\leftrightarrows$ glucose-1-P, and for the formation of sucrose from glucose and fructose. As with the adenosine phosphates, a uridine-5′-triphosphate

(UTP), a uridine-5′-diphosphate (UDP) and a uridine-5′-monophosphate (UMP), exist.

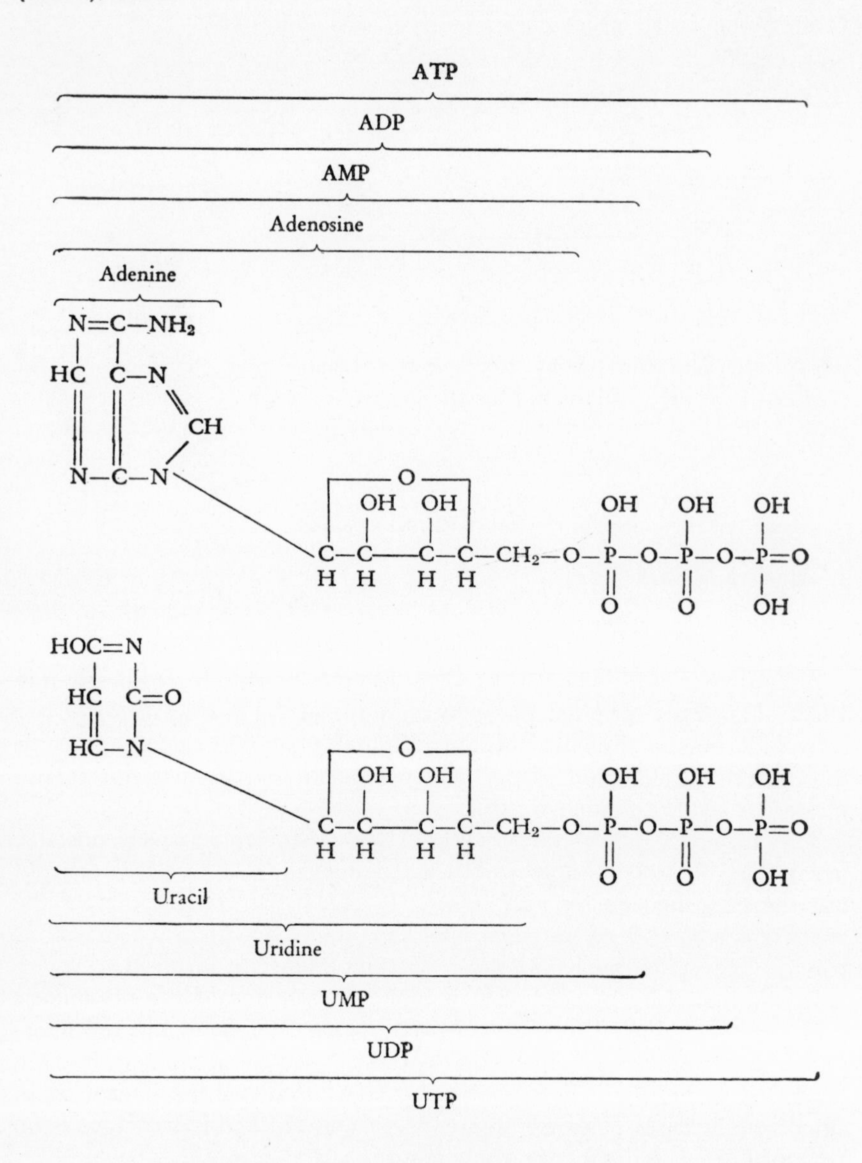

(*c*) *Uridine diphosphate glucose* (*UDPG*)—This nucleotide is the coenzyme of the isomerase which transforms galactose-1-P into glucose-1-P. It was discovered by Leloir, and has been isolated both from yeast and from animal tissues so that it appears to be of general importance. A whole series of compounds exists, with structures similar to UDPG, in which the glucose is replaced by other substances such as acetylglucosamine, for example.

```
HOC=N
 |   |
HC   C=O
 ||  |
HC—N                                              CH2OH
     |                                              |
     HC ———┐                                        HC ———┐
     |     |                                        |     |
     HCOH  |                                        HCOH  |
     |     O                                        |     O
     HCOH  |                                      HOCH    |
     |     |                                        |     |
     HC ———┘                                        HCOH  |
     |                                              |     |
     CH2            OH            OH                HC ———┘
     |              |             |                 |
     O ———————————— P ——— O ——— P ——————————————— O
                    ||            ||
                    O             O
```

UDPG

(*d*) *Flavin monophosphate*—This is commonly called flavin mononucleotide (FMN) but this is incorrect since it is a compound of phosphoric acid with riboflavin which is not a true nucleotide. The phosphate is attached at the 5′ position of the ribityl residue. Flavin mononucleotide is the coenzyme of L-amino oxidase and of the TPNH→O_2 transhydrogenase.

```
               OH  OH  OH            O
               |   |   |             |
         CH2 — C — C — C — CH2 — O — P — OH
          |    |   |   |             |
          |    H   H   H             OH
          |
          N        N
H3C                    =O

H3C                    NH
          N
               O
```

(*e*) *Nicotinamide mononucleotide*—

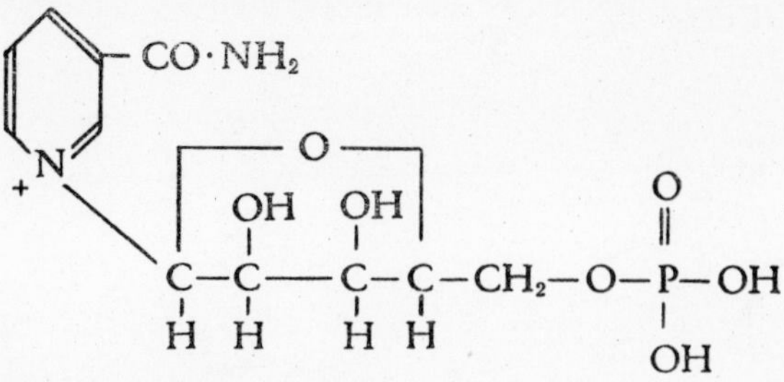

```
   (pyridine ring)—CO·NH2
        +N
          \      ┌──────── O ────────┐                O
           \     │   OH     OH       │                ‖
            \    │   |      |        │                
             C — C ——— C — C — CH2 — O — P — OH
             |   |     |   |                   |
             H   H     H   H                   OH
```

This has been isolated from yeast.

2. *Dinucleotides*

(*a*) *Diphosphopyridine-nucleotide* (*DPN*) *and triphosphopyridine-nucleotide* (*TPN*)—Diphosphopyridine nucleotide (DPN, coenzyme I, codehydrogenase I, cozymase), an important coenzyme of general utility, contains the heterocyclic bases adenine and nicotinamide and two molecules of D-ribose. The two component nucleotides are joined by a pyrophosphate bridge. A related compound, also widely distributed in the biosphere, only differs from the above substance by having an additional phosphate residue esterified at C-2′ of the ribose molecule attached to adenine. This substance is known as triphosphopyridine nucleotide (TPN, coenzyme II, Co II or codehydrogenase II).

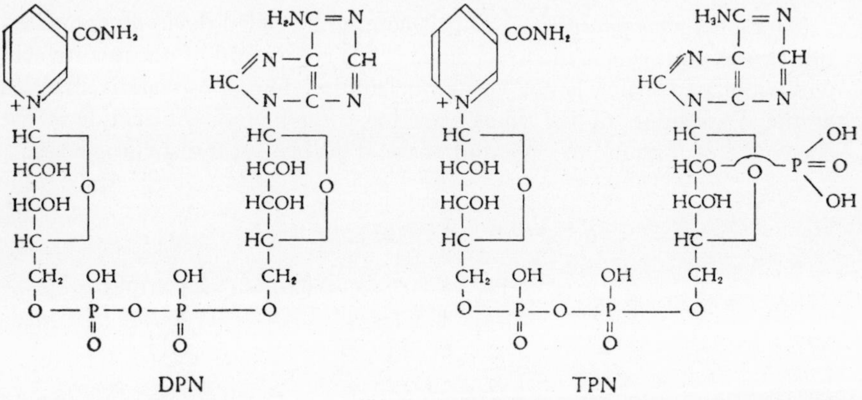

```
(pyridine)CONH2        H2NC = N               (pyridine)CONH2        H3NC = N
                          |   |                                          |   |
                       ∕N—C   CH                                      ∕N—C   CH
                    HC    ‖   ‖                                    HC    ‖   ‖
+N                     \N—C—N                  +N                     \N—C—N
 |                        |                     |                        |
HC ──┐                 HC ──┐                  HC ──┐                 HC ──┐        OH
 |   │                  |   │                   |   │                  |   │       /
HCOH │                 HCOH │                  HCOH │                 HCO— O —P = O
 |   O                  |   O                   |   O                  |   │       \
HCOH │                 HCOH │                  HCOH │                 HCOH │        OH
 |   │                  |   │                   |   │                  |   │
HC ──┘                 HC ──┘                  HC ──┘                 HC ──┘
 |                      |                       |                      |
CH2  OH      OH        CH2                     CH2  OH      OH        CH2
 |   |       |          |                       |   |       |          |
 O — P — O — P ———————— O                       O — P — O — P ———————— O
     ‖       ‖                                      ‖       ‖
     O       O                                      O       O

            DPN                                            TPN
```

The pyridine nucleotides and their barium salts are very soluble in water. The oxidized forms are written DPN^+ or TPN^+. DPN^+ has two phosphate residues bearing two primary acidic groups, whilst TPN^+, has three primary acid groups and, in addition, a secondary group.

Reversible reduction of the pyridine ring transforms DPN^+ into the reduced dinucleotide DPNH and, similarly, for TPN^+.

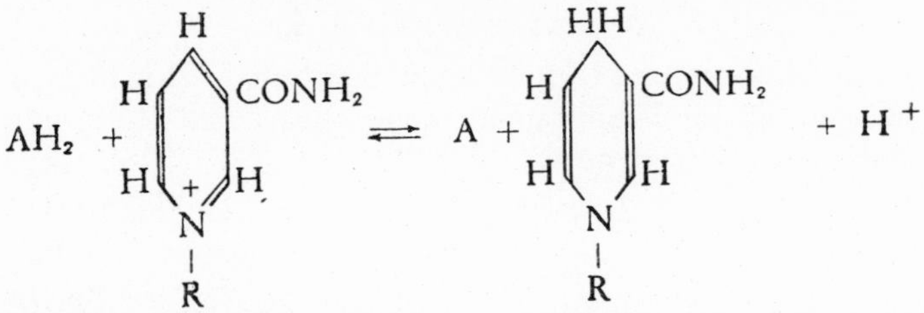

$$AH_2 + \text{(pyridinium ring: H, H, CONH}_2\text{, H, H, } \overset{+}{N}\text{–R)} \rightleftharpoons A + \text{(dihydropyridine ring: HH, H, CONH}_2\text{, H, H, N–R)} + H^+$$

A stoichiometric transfer of hydrogen takes place, from the substrate to the coenzyme, with the liberation of one equivalent of acid. In effect, a highly basic quaternary nitrogen atom is transformed into a feebly basic ternary nitrogen. The reduction takes place, as can be seen from the formula, in the para position of the pyridine ring.

(*b*) *Flavin adenine dinucleotide* (*FAD*)—Like FMN, FAD is a pseudo-nucleotide containing adenylic acid joined via a pyrophosphate linkage to FMN.

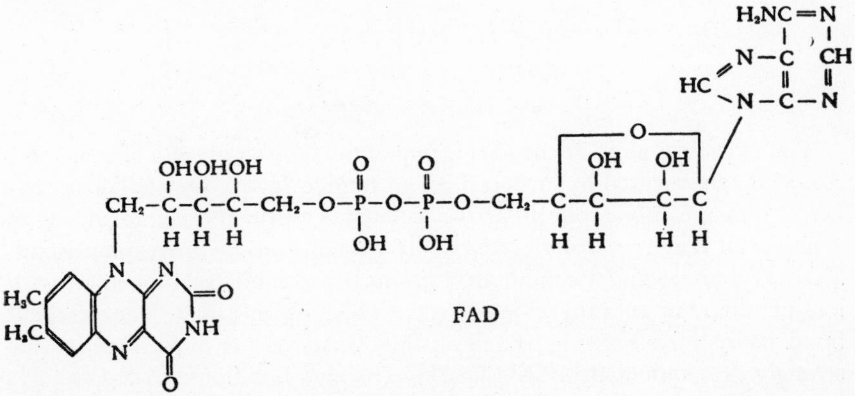

$$\text{(H}_3\text{C, H}_3\text{C-isoalloxazine, N}_{10}\text{)}-CH_2-\underset{H}{\overset{OH}{C}}-\underset{H}{\overset{OH}{C}}-\underset{H}{\overset{OH}{C}}-CH_2-O-\underset{OH}{\overset{O}{\overset{\|}{P}}}-O-\underset{OH}{\overset{O}{\overset{\|}{P}}}-O-CH_2-\underset{H}{C}-\underset{H}{\overset{OH}{C}}-\underset{H}{\overset{OH}{C}}-\underset{H}{C}\text{(–O–ring)}-\text{adenine (}H_2NC{=}N,\ N{-}C,\ CH,\ HC,\ N{-}C{-}N\text{)}$$

FAD

It is the coenzyme of xanthine oxidase, aldehyde oxidase and other aerobic dehydrogenases. Like riboflavin and FMN, FAD is universally present in the biosphere. It is reddish-yellow in colour but, like FMN and riboflavin, its solutions are a yellow-green.

The formula above is that of the oxidized dinucleotide, reduction takes place in the isoalloxazine ring as follows :

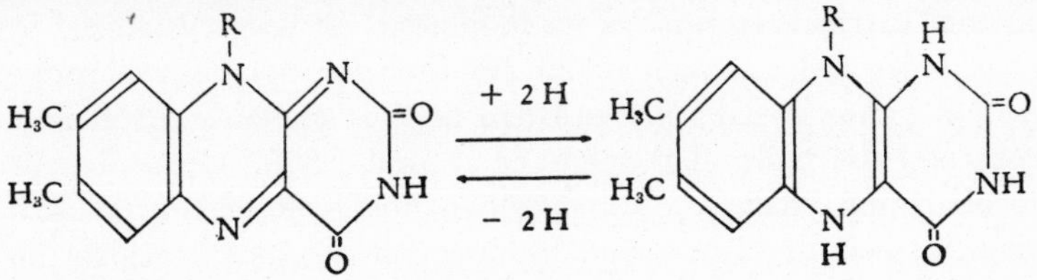

$$\text{(H}_3\text{C, H}_3\text{C-isoalloxazine, N–R, N, =O, NH, O, N)} \underset{-\ 2H}{\overset{+\ 2H}{\rightleftharpoons}} \text{(H}_3\text{C, H}_3\text{C-dihydroisoalloxazine, N–R, NH, =O, NH, O, NH)}$$

(*h*) *Coenzyme A* (*Co A*)

This essential compound is universally distributed. It is formed by the joining of adenosine-3, 5-diphosphate, pantothenic acid-4′-phosphate and thioethanolamine (cysteamine).

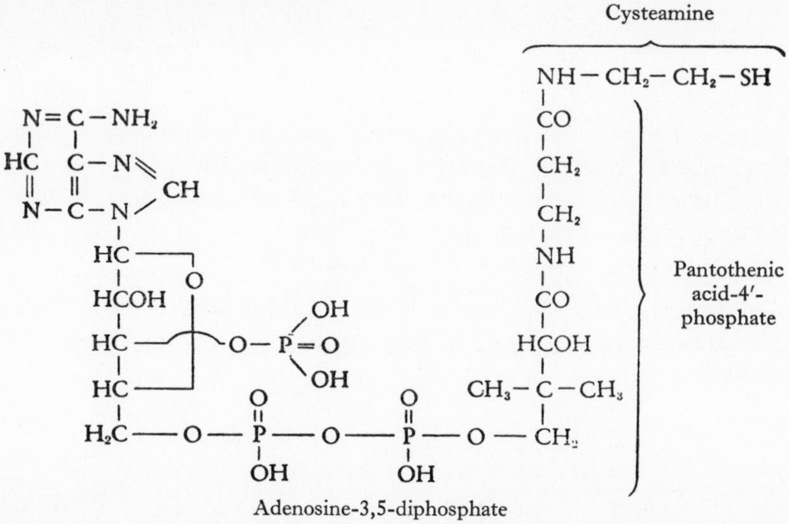

```
                                                    Cysteamine
                                          ___________________________
                                          NH − CH2 − CH2 − SH
                                          |
 N=C−NH2                                  CO
 |  |                                     |
 HC  C−N\                                 CH2
 ||  ||   CH                              |
 N−C−N/                                   CH2
     |                                    |
     HC ———┐                              NH
     |     O                              |                  Pantothenic
     HCOH  |        OH                    CO                   acid-4′-
     |     |       /                      |                    phosphate
     HC ———┼—O— P=O                      HCOH
     |     |       \                      |
     HC ———┘        OH     O          CH3−C−CH3
     |             ||      ||             |
     H2C — O — P — O — P — O — CH2
               |          |
               OH         OH
          Adenosine-3,5-diphosphate
```

The hydrogen atom of the -SH group at the cysteamine end of coenzyme A may be substituted by an acetyl group to give "active acetate" or acetyl-Co A. The metabolic role of "active acetate" is a primary one, for it acts as a universal donor of acetyl groups. It contains an acylmercaptan bond, a carboxyl group and a sulphhydryl group being condensed together, with loss of water, in an anhydride linkage. This is a so-called "energy-rich" bond, its hydrolysis setting free about 16,000 calories per mole. Despite this strongly exergonic hydrolysis, the acylmercaptan bond of CoA-S-CO-CH_3 is very stable in aqueous solution at physiological pH's. It is only in the presence of specific enzyme catalysts that the bond is hydrolysed.

(*i*) *Cyanocobalamin* (*Vitamin* B_{12})

Cyanocobalamin is widely distributed in living organisms; it is found in bacteria, in algae and in animal tissues, but it does not appear to be present in the green leaves of plants. For man, it is an important vitamin, being one of the "extrinsic factors" of haemopoiesis. It was crystallized in 1948; the crystals are dark red, melt at 320° and their solution has well pronounced absorption bands at 278, 361 and 550 mμ. It contains cobalt and phosphorous and the molecular weight is around 1,500. On acid hydrolysis, cyanocobalamin yields 5,6-dimethylbenzimidazole, ribofuranose, phosphoric acid, 1-amino-2-propanol and a cobalt complex in which the metal is surrounded by a hexacarboxylic acid, formed by the association of four pyrrolidine rings modified by the inclusion of a conjugated system of double bonds. The molecule contains six primary amide groups and one secondary group joining the aminopropanol residue to the propionic acid group of ring D.

Cyanocobalamin is a phosphoric diester in which the free acid function is neutralized by the positive charge on the cobalt.

Cyanocobalamin, then, is the result of combination of adenosinemono-phosphoric acid with a pyrrolidine chromogen via 1-amino-2-propanol.

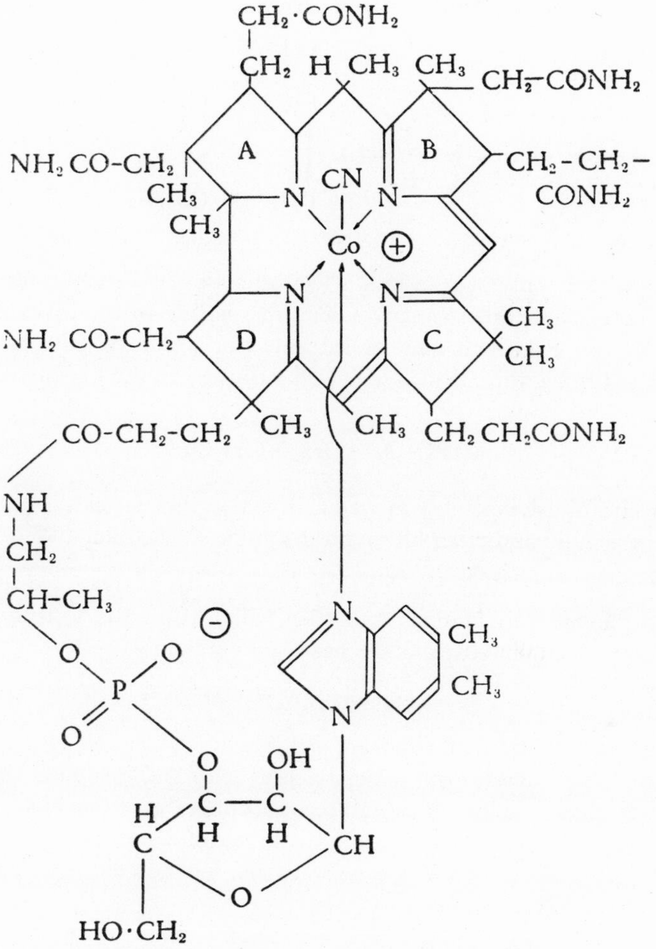

Cyanocobalamin (Formula of Todd *et al.*)

(*j*) *Complex Lipides*

Most of the complex lipides are diesters of orthophosphoric acid. Those not belonging to this category will be described with those that do. The fact that the complex lipides described here are extremely widely distributed in the biosphere, confers upon them the status of fundamental cellular constituents.

1. *Glycerophosphatides*

(*a*) *Lecithins or phosphatidylcholines*—Lecithins are esters of phosphorylcholine with glycerol which is esterified in the remaining two positions by fatty acids. Two isomers are possible according to whether the binding is with the α carbon or the β carbon of the glycerol.

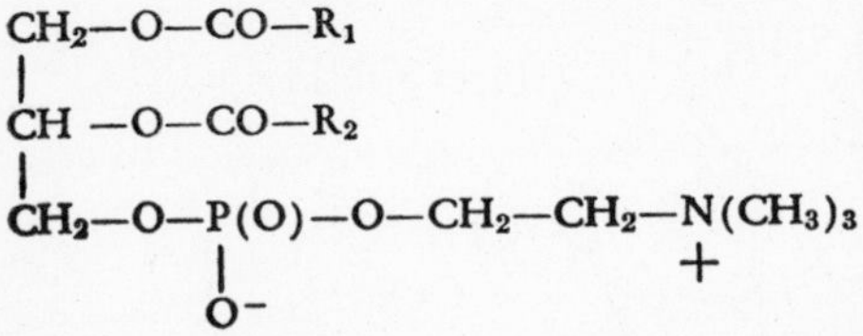

$$\begin{array}{l} CH_2-O-CO-R_1 \\ | \\ CH-O-CO-R_2 \\ | \\ CH_2-O-P(O)-O-CH_2-CH_2-\overset{+}{N}(CH_3)_3 \\ \qquad\quad | \\ \qquad\quad O^- \end{array}$$

α-lecithin

$$\begin{array}{l} CH_2-O-CO-R_1 \\ | \\ CH-O-P(O)-O-CH_2-CH_2-\overset{+}{N}(CH_3)_3 \\ | \qquad\quad | \\ | \qquad\quad O^- \\ | \\ CH_2-O-CO-R_2 \end{array}$$

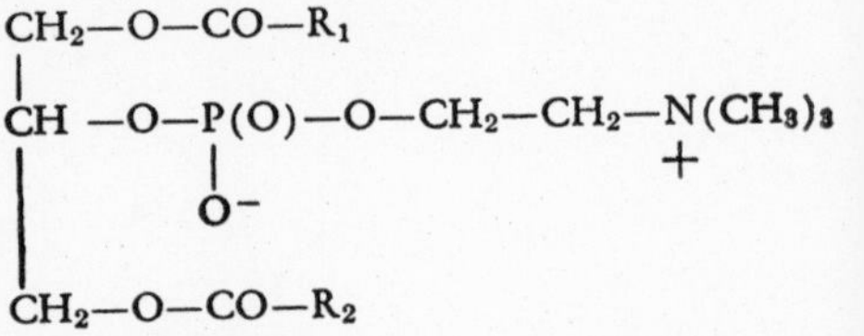

β-lecithin

Living matter only synthesizes α-lecithins which are to be found in all cells. The existence of so many α-lecithins is due to the diversity of the groups R_1 and R_2 which may be saturated or unsaturated. Choline, the base present in lecithin, is also widely distributed in the biosphere :

$$(CH_3)_3\overset{+}{N}-CH_2-CH_2OH$$

The lecithins are insoluble in water, in which they swell up, but they are soluble in alcohol and ether although insoluble in acetone.

(*b*) *Cephalins or phosphatidylethanolamines*—Cephalins are diacylglycerylphosphorylethanolamines and they differ from the lecithins by the substitution of choline by another base, aminoethanol.

$$NH_2\cdot CH_2-CH_2OH$$

In the pure state, cephalins are soluble in methanol, ethanol, ether, petroleum ether, chloroform, glacial acetic acid, and insoluble in acetone, but when mixed with other glycerophosphatides (phosphatidylserine, plasmalogens, etc.) they are insoluble in alcohol. It is likely that the natural cephalins are of the α type, but this has not yet been completely proved.

(*c*) *Phosphatidylserine*—These glycerophosphatides are soluble in chloroform but are less soluble in ethanol or methanol and this allows their isolation. Serine is the base which takes the place of choline, and the phosphatidylserines have the following structure:

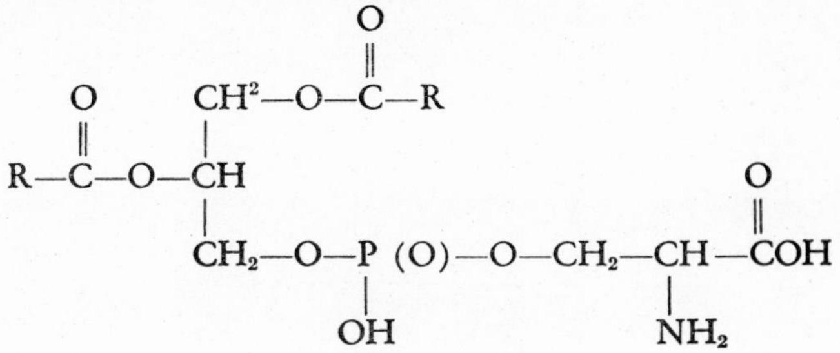

```
                         O
                         ‖
  O       CH²—O—C—R
  ‖        |
R—C—O—CH                                  O
           |                               ‖
          CH₂—O—P (O)—O—CH₂—CH—COH
                   |                  |
                  OH                 NH₂
```

L—phosphatidylserine

(*d*) *Plasmalogens or acetalphosphatides*—In the pure state, the acetalphosphatides are soluble in alcohol, glacial acetic acid and chloroform, sparingly soluble in benzene, and insoluble in acetone and ether. They are derivatives in which an aldehyde group is condensed with two hydroxyls of glycerol to form an acetal (a *gem*-diether). The third glycerol hydroxyl is esterified with an aminoethanol-phosphate residue.

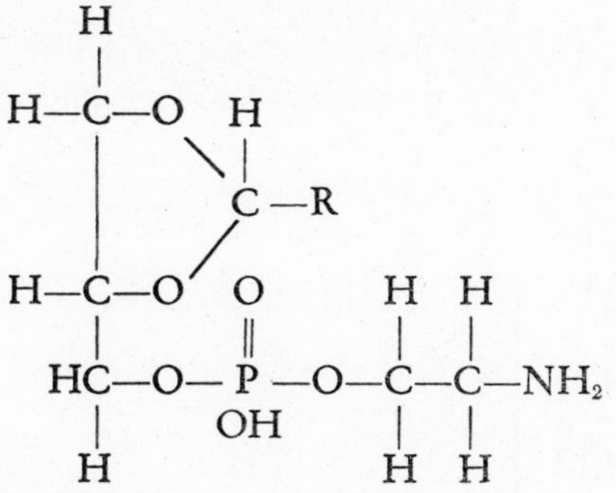

```
      H
      |
   H—C—O  H
      |     \ |
      |       C—R
      |     /
   H—C—O   O        H  H
      |      ‖        |  |
   HC—O— P —O—C—C—NH₂
      |     OH       |  |
      H              H  H
```

2. *Phosphoinositides*

These complex lipides containing inositol are numerous and little is known about them.

3. *Sphingolipides*

In these complex lipides the alcohol is not glycerol but sphingosine, a C_{18} aminoalcohol.

$$CH_3—(CH_2)_{12}—CH{=}CH—CH(OH)—CH(NH_2)—CH_2OH$$

Sphingosine

(*a*) *Sphingomyelins or phosphosphingosides*—The pure crystalline sphingomyelins are insoluble in ether and acetone, but soluble in benzene, hot ethanol and hot ethyl acetate. They are emulsifiable with water.

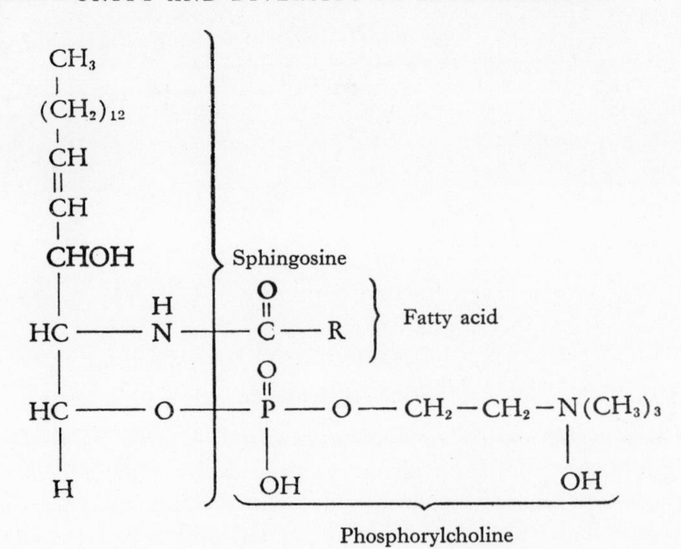

General formula of the sphingomyelins

(*b*) *Cerebrosides*—On hydrolysis these substances give sphingosine, fatty acids and galactose. They are essential constituents of all cells (animal, vegetable and fungi).

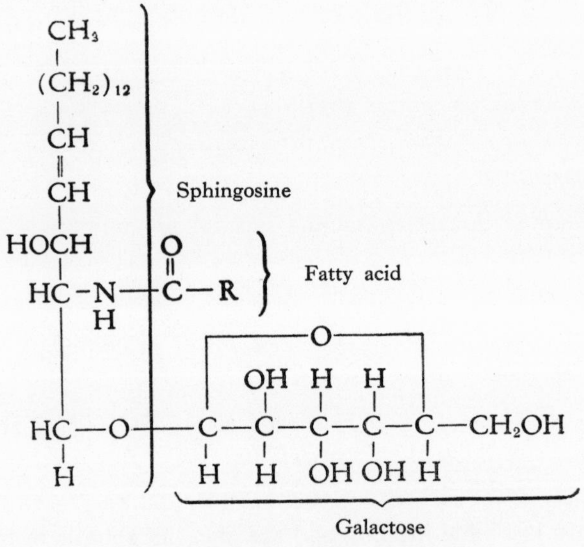

```
    CH3
    |
    (CH2)12
    |
    CH
    ||
    CH                Sphingosine
    |
  HOCH       O
    |        ||
   HC-N------C-R      Fatty acid
    |  H
    |        ┌─────────O─────────┐
    |        |  OH   H    H      |
    |        |  |    |    |      |
   HC-O------C--C----C----C------C--CH2OH
    |        |  |    |    |      |
    H        H  H    OH   OH     H
             └────── Galactose ──────┘
```

General formula of the cerebrosides

III. PEPTIDE BOND

The peptide bond is an amide linkage resulting from the reaction of a carboxyl group with an amino group, with the elimination of water. Peptides are the result of joining two or more amino acids by the peptide linkage. Example :

$$2\ \underset{\displaystyle NH_2}{CH_3\text{—}\underset{|}{CH}\text{—}COOH} \longrightarrow CH_3\text{—}\underset{|}{CH}\text{—}COOH + H_2O$$

$$NH\text{—}CO\text{—}\underset{\displaystyle \overset{|}{NH_2}}{CH}\text{—}CH_3$$

Alanylalanine
(a dipeptide)

A. Synthetic Peptides

The synthesis of peptides is of great interest, for, as we shall see, the synthesis of an important natural polypeptide has confirmed the structure assigned to it.

The most important synthetic method at the present time is that of Bergmann and Zervas. It is based upon the fact that carbobenzoxy- ($C_6H_5CH_2OCO$-) derivatives of amino acids may be split by catalytic hydrogenation.

Among other recent methods, we may quote the conversion of amino acids into mixed anhydrides with carbonic acid; these latter compounds react with an amino group to form a peptide bond. Similarly, carbobenzoxy-amino acid anhydrides react readily with other amino acids.

B. Natural Peptides

(*a*) *Glutathione, Anserine, Carnosine*

Glutathione, a tripeptide found in animal and vegetable cells, has been known for a long time.

REFERENCES

Celmer, W. D. & Carter, H. E. (1952). Chemistry of phosphatides and cerebrosides. *Physiol. Rev.*, **32**, 167–196.

Kenner, G. W. (1951). The chemistry of nucleotides. *Fortschr. Chem. org. Naturstoffe*, **8**, 96-145.

Leloir, L. F. (1951). Sugar phosphates. *Fortschr. Chem. org. Naturstoffe*, **8**, 47–95.

Singer, T. P. & Kearney, E. K. (1954). Chemistry, metabolism and scope of action of the pyridine nucleotide coenzymes. *Advances in Enzymology* 15, 79–139.

Todd, A. R. (1953). The nucleotides : Some recent chemical research and its biological implications. *Harvey Lectures*, **47**, 1–20.

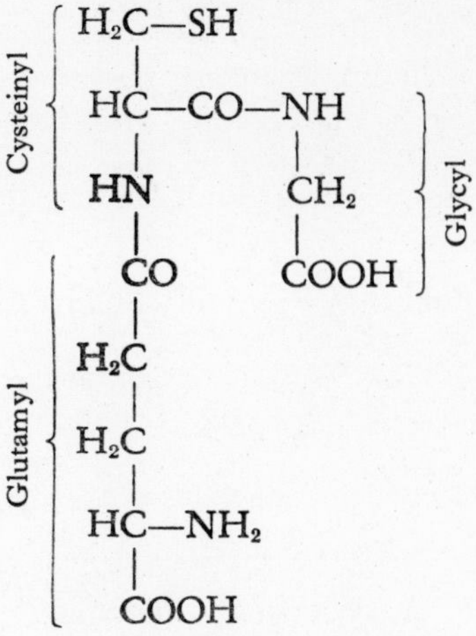

```
             ⎧  H2C—SH
             ⎪    |
 Cysteinyl   ⎨  HC—CO—NH         ⎫
             ⎪    |     |        ⎪
             ⎩  HN      CH2      ⎬ Glycyl
                  |     |        ⎪
             ⎧    CO    COOH     ⎭
             ⎪    |
             ⎪  H2C
             ⎪    |
 Glutamyl    ⎨  H2C
             ⎪    |
             ⎪  HC—NH2
             ⎪    |
             ⎩    COOH
```

Reduced form of glutathione

Glutathione is a tripeptide made up of cysteine, glutamic acid and glycine, it exists in two forms, reduced (or thiol form) and oxidized (disulphide form), or dehydrogenated glutathione.

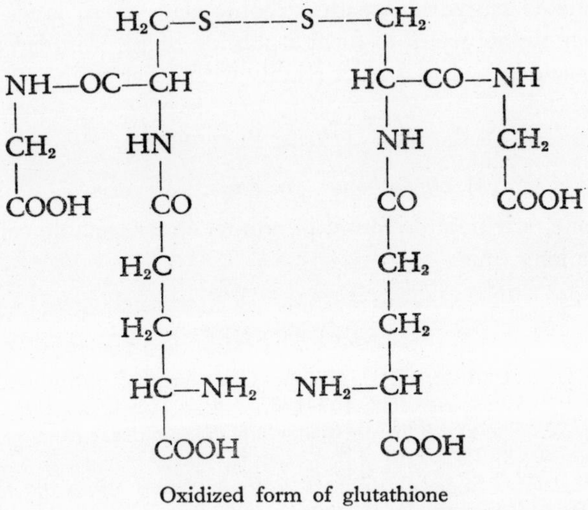

```
           H2C—S————S———CH2
              |          |
NH—OC—CH                 HC—CO—NH
|       |                |      |
CH2     HN               NH     CH2
|       |                |      |
COOH    CO               CO     COOH
        |                |
        H2C              CH2
        |                |
        H2C              CH2
        |                |
        HC—NH2    NH2—CH
        |                |
        COOH             COOH
```

Oxidized form of glutathione

Carnosine or β-alanyl-L-histidine is another natural peptide, present in vertebrate muscle accompanied by its methyl derivative, anserine.

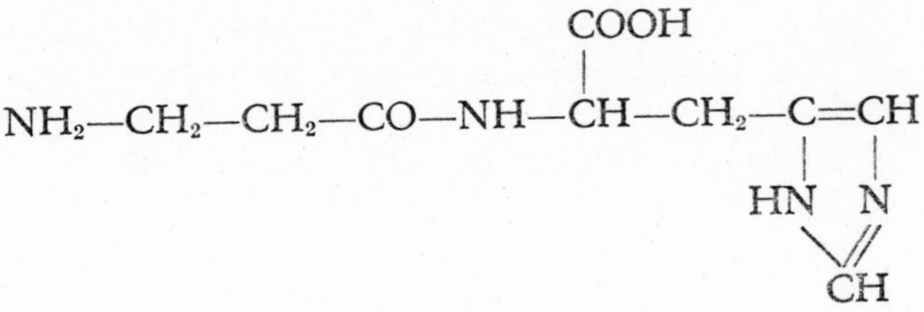

```
                                  COOH
                                  |
NH2—CH2—CH2—CO—NH—CH—CH2—C=CH
                                          |    |
                                         HN   N
                                           \ //
                                            CH
```

Carnosine

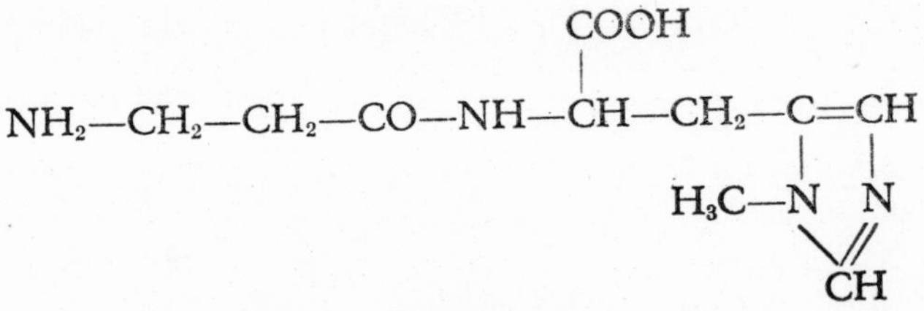

```
                                  COOH
                                  |
NH2—CH2—CH2—CO—NH—CH—CH2—C=CH
                                          |    |
                                   H3C—N   N
                                           \ //
                                            CH
```

Anserine

β-alanine, which is present in carnosine and anserine, is not a constituent of proteins, but one finds it in other natural substances such as pantothenic acid, which is a dihydroxy-dimethyl-butyryl-β-alanine.

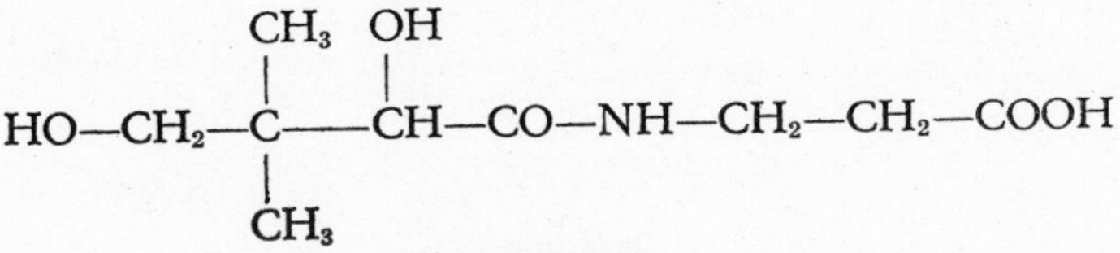

```
              CH3  OH
              |    |
HO—CH2—C——CH—CO—NH—CH2—CH2—COOH
              |
              CH3
```

Pantothenic acid

Interest in natural peptides has greatly increased during the last few years since a great number of antibiotics have been found to be polypeptides.

(*b*) *Antibiotics*

Many antibiotics are peptides which are produced by microorganisms and possess antibacterial properties.

The gramicidines produced by *Bacillus brevis*, for example, are cyclic peptides having a molecular weight around 400, and containing chiefly L-trytophane and D-leucine together with smaller amounts of D-valine, L-valine, L-alanine, glycine and ethanolamine. One of the characteristics of natural antibiotic peptides is that one finds in their structure amino acids which are never present in proteins, or the D-stereoisomers of the natural L-forms present in proteins.

The tyrocidines are antibiotic peptides produced at the same time as the gramicidines. Among their amino acids are L-ornithine and D-phenylalanine. The penicillins, produced by moulds of the genus *Penicillium*, are derived from a dipeptide, α-formylglycyl-D-penicillamine.

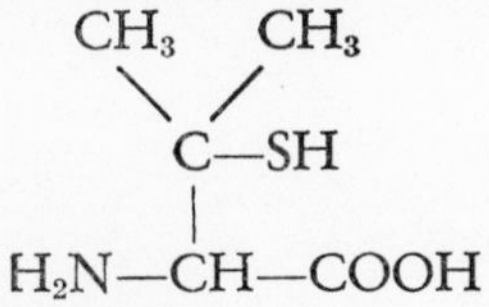

$$H_2N-CH(C(CH_3)_2SH)-COOH$$

Penicillamine

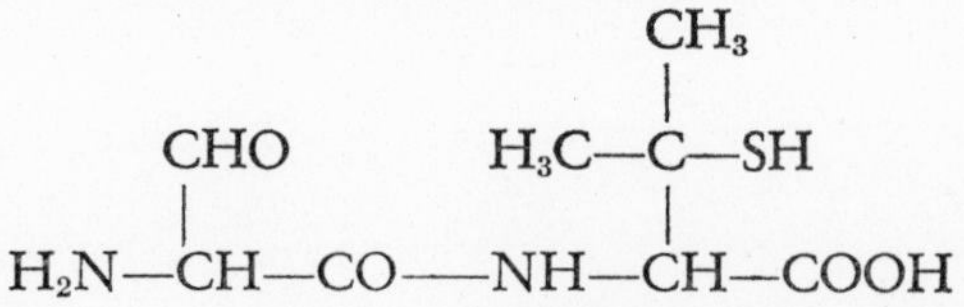

$$H_2N-CH(CHO)-CO-NH-CH(C(CH_3)_2SH)-COOH$$

α-formylglycyl-D-penicillamine

In penicillin G, for example, the penicillamine is cyclized into a thiazolidine ring by reaction of the aldehyde group (formyl radical) with the thiol and NH groups.

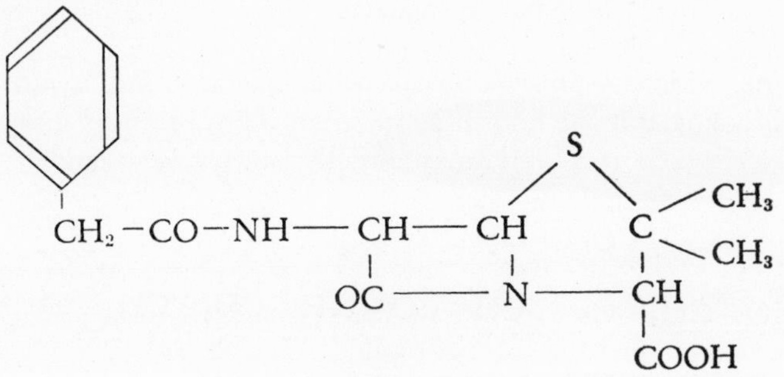

$$C_6H_5-CH_2-CO-NH-CH-CH(S)-C(CH_3)_2-CH(COOH)-N(-CO-)$$

Penicillin G

In other penicillins the benzene ring of penicillin G is replaced by other groups.

(*c*) *Phalloidin*

The poison present in the fungus most commonly responsible for cases of poisoning, *Amanita phalloides*, is a peptide known as phalloidin. On hydrolysis, it gives cystine and alanine, but, in addition, allohydroxy-L-proline, a diastereoisomer of the form of proline found in proteins.

(*d*) *Peptide Hormones*

The peptide type of structure is frequently employed for the chemical transmission of messages by means of hormones. An example is provided by the two hormones of the posterior hypophysis of vertebrates, oxytocin and vasopressin. These two polypeptides have been extracted from the gland itself, by rather a drastic treatment such that it still remains debatable

```
                        OH
                        |
                        C
                      /   \\
                   HC       CH
                   ||       |
                   HC       CH     CH3
                     \     //      |
                        C        H2C      CH3
                        |           \    /
                       CH2            CH
       NH2 O            |      O      |
        |  ||           |      ||     |
CH2—CH—C —NH—CH—C—NH—CH
|                 Tyr           Ileu  |
S                                     C=O
| Cys                                 |
S                     Asp (NH2)       NH
|              O                 O    |
|              ||                ||   |
CH2—CH—NH—C—CH—NH—C—CH—CH2—CH2—CONH2
                    |
     C=O            CH2           Glu (NH2)
     |              |
     |              CONH2
     |
H2C—N   Pro  O             Leu  O           Gly (NH2)
|     \      ||                 ||
|        CH—C—NH—CH—C—NH—CH2—CONH2
|     /                  |
H2C—C                    CH2
    H2                   |
                         CH
                        /  \
                     H3C    CH3
```

Beef oxytocin

whether they circulate in the animal in the free or in the combined states. Oxytocin and vasopressin are both octapeptides whose structures have been confirmed by synthesis—no mean performance for a molecule of this degree of complexity. This magnificent piece of work was carried out in the laboratories of du Vigneaud in New York, Fromageot in Paris and Tuppy in Vienna.

```
                               OH
                               |                   H
                               C                   C
                             /  \\               //  \
                          HC      CH        HC        CH
                          ||      |         |         ||
                          HC      CH        HC        CH
                             \  //             \\  /
                               C                   C
                               |                   |
                               CH2                 CH2
          NH2  O               |         O         |
          |    ||              |         ||        |
CH2—CH—C—NH—CH—C—NH—CH
|                   Tyr                  Phe       |
S                                                  C=O
| Cys                                              |
S                            Asp (NH2)             NH
|                       O                O         |
|                       ||               ||        |
CH2—CH—NH—C—CH—NH—C—CH—CH2—CH2—CONH2
     |                  |                   Glu (NH2)
     C=O                CH2
     |                  |
     |                  CONH2
     |
H2C—N   Pro   O         Arg   O        Gly (NH2)
|      \      ||              ||
|       CH—C—NH—CH—C—NH—CH2—CONH2
|      /                |
H2C—C                   CH2
    H2                  |
                        CH2
                        |
                        CH2
                        |
                        NH
                        |
                        C
                      //  \
                    HN     NH2
```

Beef vasopressin

REFERENCES

BRICAS, E. and FROMAGEOT, Cl. (1953). Naturally occurring peptides, *Advances in Protein Chemistry*, **8**, 1–25.

DESNUELLE, P. (1953). The general chemistry of amino acids and peptides, *in* NEURATH, H. & BAILEY, K., *The Proteins*, Vol. I, part A, 87–180, Academic Press, New York.

FRUTON, J.S. (1949). The synthesis of peptides, *Advances in Protein Chemistry*, **5**, 1–83.

CHAPTER IV

MACROMOLECULES

THE knowledge of the various typical types of chemical structure which have been identified in the biosphere, and of the principal linkages which join them, still leaves us in a region where the essential identity of all organisms may be distinguished. There is no more difference between a molecule of coenzyme A isolated from a bacterium and one prepared from animal tissue than there is between two molecules of sodium chloride. When covalency forces operate in a volume within the limits of a few cubic angstroms to a few thousand cubic angstroms, we are still in the world of simple molecules, or molecules joined together in the compounds described in Chapter III : this is the region in which organisms are identical. This truth has long intrigued biochemists, whose desire to understand the chemistry of life on a molecular scale has not prevented consideration of the great diversity of living things. The advent of the chemistry of macromolecules introduced into biochemistry the idea of specificity, which up till then was lacking.

Macromolecules are defined as chemical compounds whose molecular weight is above 10,000 and in which covalent forces are effective in all the available space. This more or less arbitrary boundary corresponds approximately to molecular sizes above which the solution of these particles takes on the so-called "colloidal" properties. But we are still dealing with chemical molecules, even though these very large molecules cannot pass through ordinary membranes. Their constituent atoms, like the compounds described in Chapter III, are united mainly by covalencies.

As soon as one arrives in the world of macromolecular chemistry, one must be careful to distinguish between the chemical molecular weight and the physical molecular weight. The chemical molecular weight is the sum of the weights of the atoms joined by covalencies, in the smallest particle of that compound. The physical molecular weight is the weight of the particle actually present in a gas or in a solution. An example, taken from Staudinger, will illustrate this difference. The chemical molecular weight of stearic acid $C_{18}H_{36}O_2$ is 284; the determination of the freezing point depression in benzene reveals a physical molecular weight of 568. This result is explained by the fact that the molecules of stearic acid, in which the atoms are united by covalencies, are associated in pairs by the action of residual valencies. The chemical molecular weight is certainly equal to

284, for derivatives of stearic acid, such as the esters, contain the radical $C_{18}H_{35}O$-. (Radical = residue, group, grouping = aggregate of atoms, which survive from one compound to another = residue of a molecule when one or several atoms are removed. If an H atom is removed from water H—O—H, the hydroxyl radical —OH remains. If an H atom is removed from ammonia H—N—H, the amidogen radical —N—H remains.) The idea of chemical molecular weight is derived from the idea of a radical. When the chemical molecular weight is below 10,000 but is not equal to the physical molecular weight, then one is dealing with molecules associated in "micelles", as is the case with colloidal solutions of soaps. When the chemical molecular weight, being above 10,000, is the same as the physical molecular weight, then we are dealing with a solution of macromolecules. When, however, the chemical molecular weight is above 10,000 but is less than the physical molecular weight then these molecules are associated by residual valencies. In every case, the physical molecular weight is either equal to, or greater than, the chemical molecular weight.

These polymers or macromolecules are made up of monomeric residues by covalencies at two or more points. The natural macromolecules are generally made up of long chains of such radicals joined by covalencies; these chains may also be joined by a small number of side-chains, also covalent in nature, such that the resulting structure takes the form of a three-dimensional network.

The idea that proteins, cellulose, starch, etc., are polymers, that is that they are made up of smaller units linked by covalencies, is not modern. It dates at least from 1871, when the idea was clearly set out in a paper by Hlaziwetz and Habermann. Unfortunately, these compounds were classed by Graham among his "colloids", and there was for a long time confusion between macromolecules and true colloids, in which the molecules are linked by residual valencies. It was Staudinger who was responsible for putting biochemists on to the right track once more when he showed that the "colloidal" properties of solutions of macromolecules persisted whatever the solvent, contrary to what is observed with micelles resulting from the association of small molecules by secondary valencies. Staudinger also demonstrated that the transformation of macromolecules into their derivatives does not suppress their "colloidal" properties.

Among the macromolecules we find the same classes of organic compounds as with simple molecules; but, particularly important, the number of isomers is very much greater with these larger molecules.

The chemical structures described in Chapters II and III have been established by organic chemists, not only by means of analysis, but also with the additional control furnished by synthesis. In the case of naturally occurring macromolecules, synthesis is not yet possible for the chemist (although Fraenkel-Conrat, after separating the nucleic acid from the protein, has succeeded in recombining them to reform the macromolecule of tobacco mosaic virus), so that it is not possible to say that any macromolecule in the biosphere is known in all its details. Nevertheless, the study of synthetic polymers has greatly aided the understanding of natural polymers.

I. POLYSACCHARIDES

Polysaccharides are very widely distributed in the biosphere, being employed as a structural material (cellulose, xylan, chitin, etc.) and as a form for storing the monomers (starch, glycogen, inulin, galactogen, etc.).

The polysaccharide molecule is formed by the association, by means of oside bonds, of a large number (n) of sugar molecules. The uronic acids are associated into polyuronides in the same way as the sugars form polysaccharides.

$$n(C_6H_{12}O_6) - n\ H_{20} = (C_6H_{10}O_5)n$$

D-glucose cellulose

$$n(C_5H_9O_5.COOH) - n\ H_{20} = (C_5H_7O_4.COOH)_n$$

D-mannuronic acid

A. Holopolysaccharides

(a) *Polysugars or Polyoses*

1. *Hexosans*

(*a*) *Cellulose*—The name "cellulose" is given to mixtures of homologous polymers which give a quantitative yield of D-glucopyranose when hydrolysed in strong acid. Cellulose is the most abundant structural material in plants. It is also found in many bacteria and even in certain groups of animals, such as the Tunicates.

Cellulose is present in the pure state in the hairs of the cottonseed. Complete acid hydrolysis of cellulose by strong, concentrated mineral acids gives D-glucopyranose in quantitative amounts. Careful partial hydrolysis in the presence of acetic anhydride and sulphuric acid (acetolysis) gives molecules of cellobiose (4-D-glucopyranose-β-D-glucopyranoside) and trisaccharides which can be hydrolysed by the enzyme emulsin. Hence, it

REFERENCES

Frey-Wyssling, A. 1957. *Macromolecules in Cell Structure*. Harvard University Press, Cambridge, Mass., U.S.A.

Meyer, K. H. (1942). *Natural and Synthetic High Polymers*. Interscience, New York.

Staudinger, H. (1947). *Makromolekulare Chemie und Biologie*. Wepf, Bale.

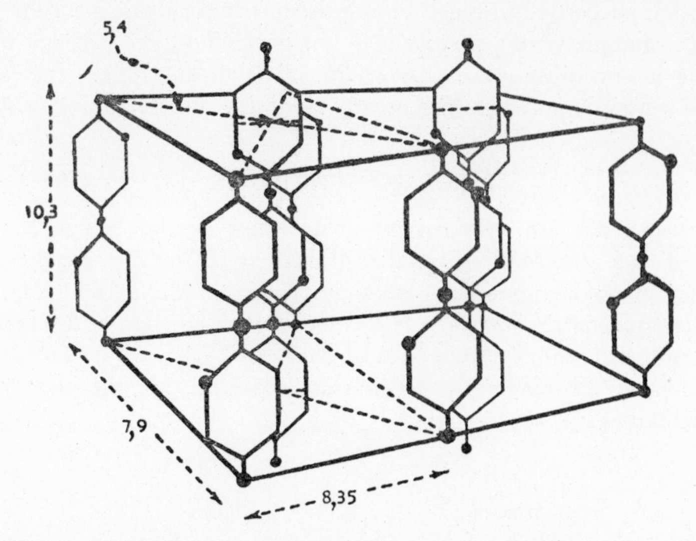

FIG. 1 (Meyer and Mark)—The dimensions are shown in Ångstrom units. The black dots represent the oxygen atoms of the pyranose rings.

seems clear that cellulose contains only 1:4-β-linkages. Hydrolysis of methylated cellulose yields 2:3:4:6-tetramethyl-glucopyranose and 2:3:6-trimethylglucopyranose. Methylation followed by hydrolysis never gives any dimethylglucose, so the chain must be a straight one. The chain differs in length according to the source of the cellulose, and the values obtained range between 1400 and 10,000 glucose units. The lay-out of atoms is such that each cellobiose residue has the dimensions shown in Fig. 5.

The cellobiose chains, arranged in the network illustrated by Fig. 1, are grouped in bundles, the cellulose *micelles*, which are about 50Å thick and at least 500Å long. The grouping of these micelles as they exist in structures where the crystallites are parallel is shown in Fig. 2.

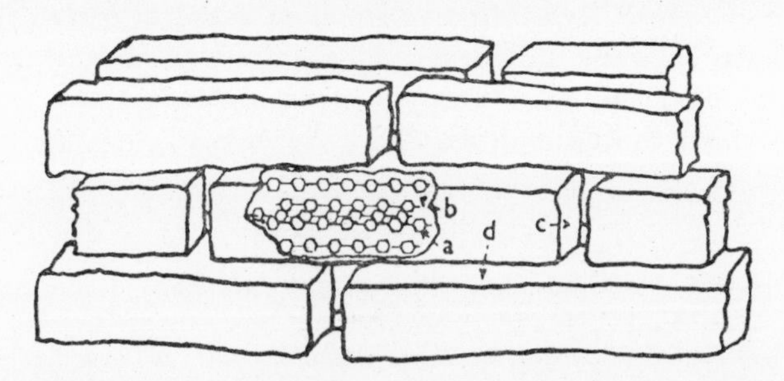

FIG. 2 (Seifriz)—Orientation of the micelles in a block of cellulose

Sometimes, the micelles may be randomly oriented as, for example, in cellophane (Fig. 3).

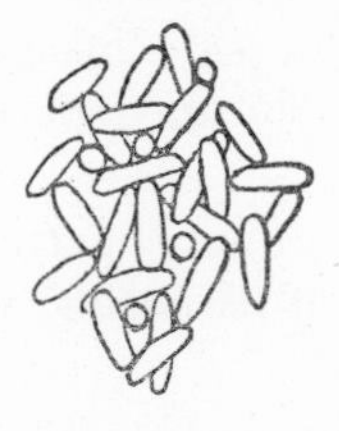

FIG. 3 (Mark)—Orientation of cellulose micelles in cellophane.

(*b*) *Starch*—The most abundant reserve of carbohydrate in plants and in microorganisms is starch, which on hydrolysis is transformed quantitatively into D-glucose. In the starch molecule the glucose molecules are associated by 1:4-α-glucoside linkages. From most starches two constituents may be isolated :

(1) a straight-chain polysaccharide called amylose which is coloured blue by iodine. It consists of straight chains of variable length in which the glucose units are linked by 1:4-linkages and the number of units in each chain varies from 100 to 2000.

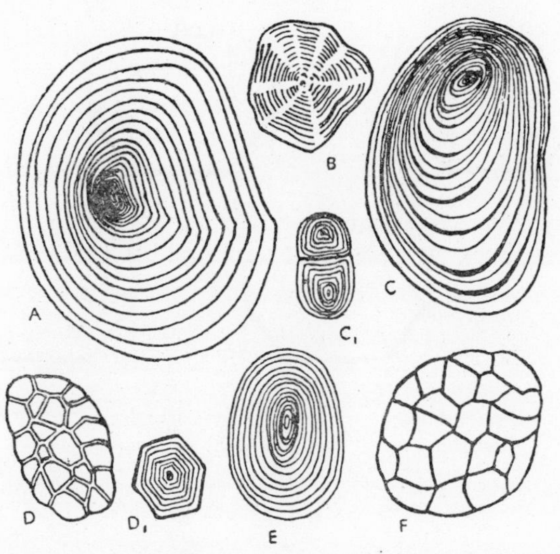

FIG. 4 (Miller)—Different types of starch granule. A, from the haricot bean; B, from maize; C and C_1, from potatoes (C, simple granule; C_1, composite granule); D and D_1, rice grains (D, whole of the composite grain; D_1, one of the constituents of the grain at a higher magnification); E, wheat grain; F, composite grain from oats. Note that each elementary granule (A, B, C, C_1, D_1, E) has a number of concentric striations around an initial point, the hilum.

(2) a highly branched polysaccharide, amylopectin, which is coloured violet by iodine. The smaller side-chains are attached to the main branches by 1:6-α-linkages (isomaltose). The side-chains themselves, like the main chain, are built up of 1:4-α-glucoside linkages.

Certain starches contain only amylopectin. This is the case for the starches from maize and rice.

When a starch is made up of amylopectin and amylose, the proportion of the latter, like the length of its chains, varies according to the source.

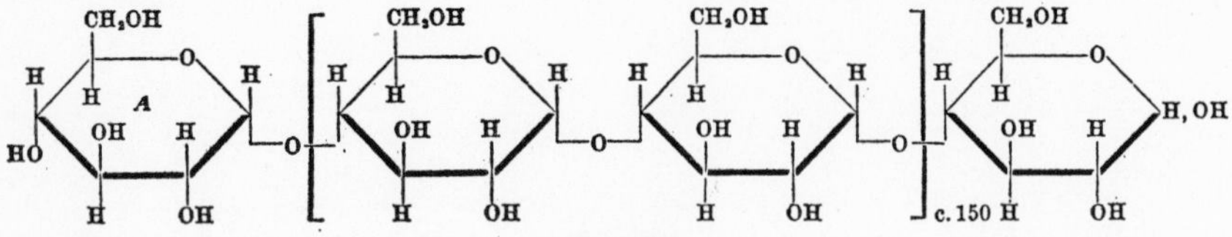

AMYLOSE

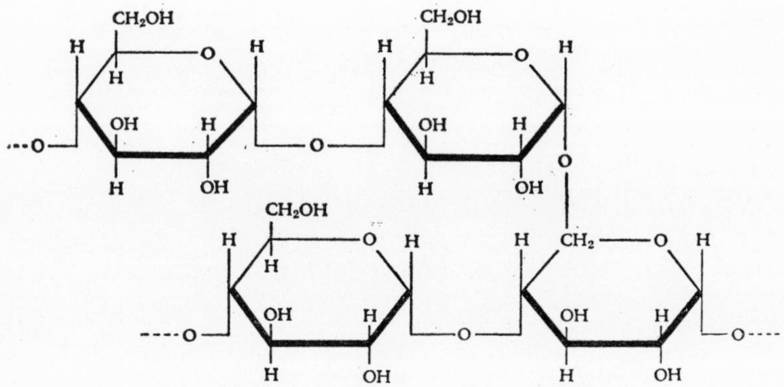

Branching by 1 : 6-α-linkages in amylopectin

(*c*) *Glycogen*—Glycogen, the major carbohydrate reserve in animals, is a branched polysaccharide similar to amylopectin. It is made up of D-glucose units. It is coloured brown by iodine and is water soluble (15 to 20%). Glycogen is more highly branched than amylopectin and, consequently, it contains a greater proportion of 1:6-α-glucoside linkages.

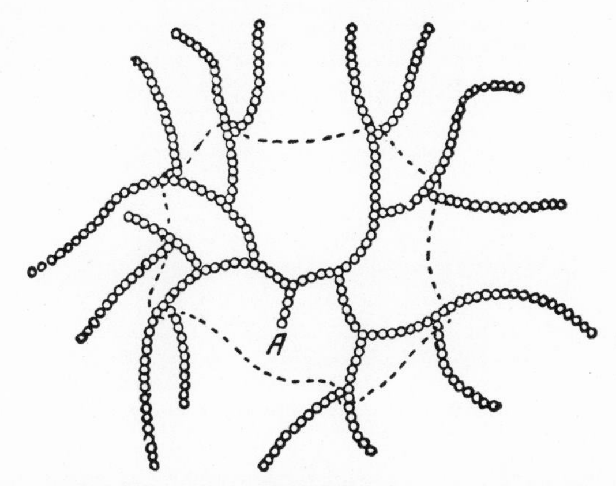

FIG. 5 (Meyer and Bernfeld)—Structure of amylopectin.
o = a glucose residue. A = a reducing group. The dotted line shows the limit of hydrolysis brought about by β-amylase attacking the macromolecule at its surface.

(*d*) *Other polyglucoses*—One finds in the biosphere a great variety of these; a few are given below:

Lichenin from lichens (straight chain; 30% of 1:3-α; 70% of 1:4-α)
Laminarin in the *Laminaria* (straight chain; 1:3-β; an average of 20 residues)

Polyglucoses of *Betabacterium vermiforme* (1:6-α; 25 residues)

Polyglucoses of *Phytomonas tumefaciens* (1:2-β; 22 residues)

Polyglucoses of the cellular skeleton of yeast (36 residues)

Polyglucoses of *Leuconostoc mesenteroides* (3–24 residues)

Polyglucoses of *Leuconostoc dextranicum* (straight chain; 1:6-α; 200–500 residues)

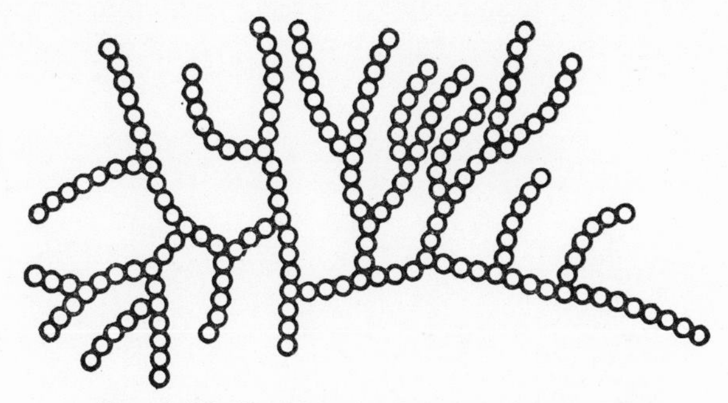

FIG. 6 (K. H. Meyer)—Structure of glycogen.

(*e*) *Galactans*—They are frequently found in plants; in the wood, in the seeds and elsewhere. The galactan of lupin seeds is constructed on the 1:4-β principle, and is made up of about 120 galactose units.

(*f*) *Mannans*—These are often present in wood, especially of conifers, and they are difficult to separate out. The mannans of pine and spruce are built of mannose molecules joined in straight chains of about 200 residues. The mannan of yeast, on the other hand, is highly branched and is not homogeneous. The number of molecules of mannose in these chains varies from 90 to 830.

(*g*) *Fructosans* (*Levans*)—The inulin found in the tubers of many of the Compositae is a linear molecule containing about 30 D-fructose residues, interspersed with about 6% of D-glucose units. Plants contain a multitude of other fructosans (asparagosine, graminine, triticine, etc.) and so also do bacteria. Unlike other fructosans, those in bacteria are highly branched molecules.

2. *Pentosans*

(*a*) *Xylans*—Xylans are present in the lignified membranes of plants. They are branched molecules made up of D-xylose units.

(*b*) *Other pentosans*—Plants contain many other types among which araban may be mentioned.

(*b*) *Polyuronides*

The units here are uronic acids. The most numerous group is that of the "pectic substances" or "pectin", in which the principal constituent is pectic acid—a chain of D-galacturonic acid molecules united chiefly by 1:4-α-linkages. The pectins are not at all homogeneous and certain of their constituents are still ill-defined.

Another polyuronide is alginic acid, present in marine algae and formed of chains of about one hundred units of D-mannuronic acid, joined together by 1:4-β-glucoside linkages.

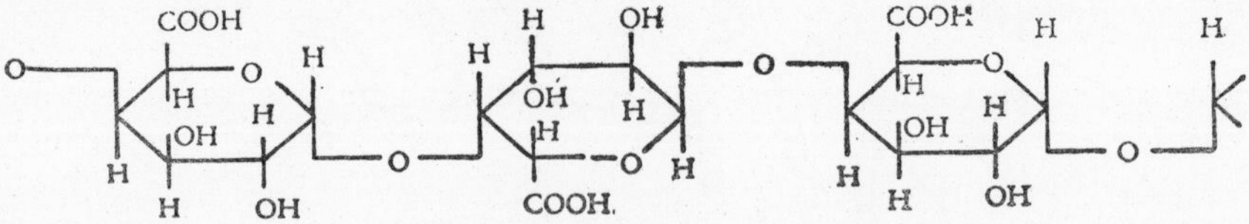

Pectic acid (polygalacturonic acid)

(*c*) *Polyglucosamines*

Chitin, a constituent of fungi and of the exoskeleton of arthropods, falls into this category.

Hydrolysis with boiling acids gives glucosamine and acetic acid in equivalent amounts. A more careful hydrolysis with chitinase gives as the sole product N-acetylglucosamine, that is, glucosamine acetylated at its amino group.

It has been possible to isolate from the products of a mild hydrolysis a disaccharide, chitobiose, identical with cellobiose except that C-2 of each glucose unit bears an amino group.

(a) Cellulose (b) Chitin $R = CH_3CO—$ (acetyl)

B. Heteropolysaccharides

(*a*) *Gums and Mucilages*

It is difficult to make any definite distinction between these two classes of macromolecules. Gums, which exude from bark in the form of "gum arabic", are salts of heteropolyuronides. Mucilages, like that from linseed, swell in water. In both cases we are dealing with highly complex branched molecules containing several sugars. For example, in gum arabic, arabinose, galactose, rhamnose, glucuronic acid, etc., are all present, whilst in the mucilage of the plaintain seed the following substances have been detected : galacturonic acid, rhamnose, galactose, arabinose, xylose, etc.

(*b*) *Mucopolysaccharides*

These polysaccharides are invariably associated with amounts of protein which, although they are small, are always present and are by no means negligible.

1. *Hyaluronic acid*

This polysaccharide is very widely distributed, both in the free form and as salt-like compounds with proteins. It is the inter-cellular cement in animals.

Hyaluronic acid is a complex polysaccharide containing equivalent amounts of D-glucosamine, D-glucuronic acid and acetic acid combined with glucosamine in the form of N-acetyl-D-glucosamine.

2. *Bacterial polysaccharides*

(*a*) *Pneumococcal*—These polysaccharides control the immunological type specificity of the pneumococci by their presence in the bacterial capsule. Their constituents are D-glucose, D-glucuronic acid, aldobionic acids and amino sugars. The proportions of each vary from one type to another and certain constituents may be missing.

Examples of constituents which have been identified :

Type I. Galacturonic acid and an acetylhexosamine.

Type II. D-Glucose, D-glucuronic acid, L-rhamnose.

Type III. D-Glucose and D-glucuronic acid.

Type IV. N-Acetylhexosamine, D-glucose.

(*b*) *Of other microorganisms*—Mucopolysaccharides of numerous microorganisms have recently been studied. The luteose of *Pencillium luteum*, for example, is a poly-D-glucose in which the glucoside bonds are of the 1:6-β type. The complex antigen has been isolated from the typhus bacterium, *Eberthella typhosa*, it is a complex chain of sixty hexose units, with 50% of D-glucose, 25% of D-mannose and 25% of D-galactose. Tuberculin, the medium from the concentrated culture of *Mycobacterium tuberculosis*, contains a polysaccharide in which there is D-arabinose, D-mannose and D-galactose together with a little D-glucosamine. In the mucopolysaccharide of *Corynebacterium diptheriae* there are D-galactose, amino sugars and pentoses.

Several mucopolysaccharides have been isolated from *Penicillium charlesii* cultivated on D-glucose. Mannocarolose, one of these products, is a mannan having a straight chain with 1:6 linkages, whilst galactocarolose, from the same source, is a straight chain galactan containing 1:5 linkages.

3. *Blood group polysaccharides*

These are mostly polysaccharide in nature, but their molecules also contain such substances as amino acids.

The substance of Group A, a branched molecule, contains L-fucose, D-glucosamine, D-galactose and D-mannose. Very little is yet known about the polysaccharides of the other blood groups.

C. Polysaccharide Sulphuric Esters, or Mucoitinsulphates

1. *Heparin*

Heparin is the sulphuric ester of a polysaccharide containing D-glucuronic acid and D-glucosamine.

2. *Chondroitin sulphate*

This is the sulphuric ester of a polysaccharide whose main constituents are D-glucuronic acid and N-acetylchondrosamine. The hyalin cartilage of vertebrates is a compound of chondroitin sulphate and a protein, the binding being between the -COOH and —SO_3H groups of the chondroitin sulphate and the -NH_2 groups of the protein.

3. *Mucoitin sulphate*

It is similar to the above compound except that chondrosamine is replaced by D-glucosamine. It is present in many animal tissues.

II. PROTEINS

Proteins are macromolecules which on hydrolysis yield a mixture of amino acids. Whatever their origin, they are always made up of a selection of the 20 amino acids described previously (p. 24). These acids are of the L-configuration and joined together chiefly by peptide bonds. The various properties of the proteins depend upon the number of amino acid residues forming the peptide chain, on the nature of the amino acids, the order in which they are assembled, the branching of their chains and on the configuration of the folding which results from the free rotation of the parts of the peptide chains about certain bonds.

A. Classification

Proteins are divided into two main types : fibrous proteins and soluble or globular proteins. Most fibrous proteins are insoluble in aqueous solvents. Although they do not crystallize, they contain crystalline regions. They are formed from long molecules arranged more or less rectilinearly

---

REFERENCES

Evans, T. H. & Hibbert, H. (1946). Bacterial polysaccharides, *Advanc. Carbohyd. Chem.*, **2**, 204–234.

Greenwood, C. T. (1952). The size and shape of some polysaccharide molecules, *Advanc. Carbohyd. Chem.*, **7**, 290–332.

Kabal, E. A. (1956). *Blood Group Substances*. Academic Press, New York.

Manners, D. J. (1957). The molecular structure of glycogens, *Advanc. Carbohyd. Chem.*, **12**, 262–298.

McIlroy, R. J. (1948). *The Chemistry of Polysaccharides*, Arnold, London.

Mori, T. (1953). Seaweed polysaccharides, *Advanc. Carbohyd. Chem.*, **8**, 316–350.

Pigman, W. (1951). *The Carbohydrates*. Academic Press, New York.

Stacey, M. (1946). The chemistry of mucopolysaccharides and mucoproteins, *Advanc. Carbohyd. Chem.*, **2**, 162-203.

and more or less parallel to the axis of the fibre. The structural proteins fall into this class. Their molecular weights are very high but hard to define since they are generally insoluble.

By contrast, the molecular weights of the globular proteins are definite (between 10,000 and several million) and their molecules are more or less spherical. Most often they may be crystallized and they are soluble in aqueous solvents (water or aqueous solutions of salts, acids, bases or alcohols, depending on the particular protein). They may be denatured. Active substances like enzymes, hormones, etc., belong to this class.

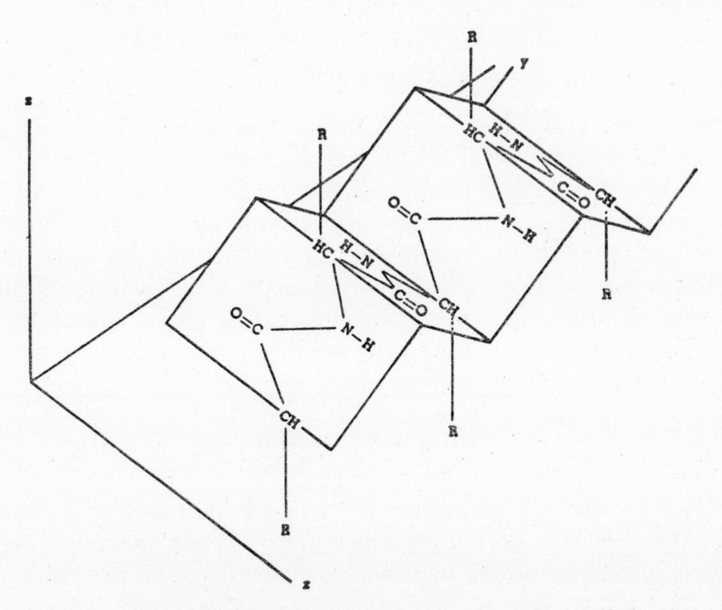

FIG. 7 (Springall)—Polypeptide ribbon in zig-zag form (β form)

The fibrous proteins have many similarities to the synthetic polymers. The latter are not very soluble and give infra-red absorption spectra and X-ray diffraction spectra very similar to those obtained from the fibrous proteins. The globular proteins do not resemble synthetic polypeptides. However, complete denaturation transforms them into substances similar to polypeptides.

(*a*) *Fibrous Proteins*

Organisms often employ fibrous proteins for supporting material. This is most particularly the case in animals, for plants delegate the same function preferentially to polysaccharides. Among the fibrous proteins are the collagen of connective tissue, myosin of muscles, fibrin present in blood clots, keratin and epidermin of vertebrate skin, the gorgonins of coral, the conchiolines of mollusc shells, the sclerotins of the teguments of arthropods, etc.

Apart from the determination of their amino acids, fibrous proteins have chiefly been studied by X-ray diffraction methods. Astbury, applying the results obtained by this method, classifies fibrous proteins into two groups : the k-m-e-f group (keratin-myosin-epidermin-fibrin) and the collagen group.

X-ray diffraction spectra show that stretched fibres of keratin (β-keratin) are formed by the repetition of units 3·3 Å in length, a figure very near the calculated length (3·6 Å) for the distance —NHCHCO—. The amino acid

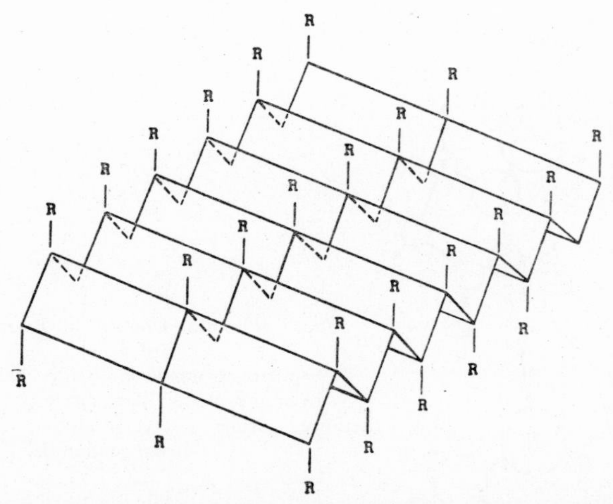

FIG. 8 (Springall)—A sheet of polypeptide ribbons in zig-zag form (β form).

side-chains project on alternate sides of the main chain. The peptide chains in β-keratin are separated by a distance of 9.7 Å. This distance is near that calculated for the longest side chain of an amino acid such as arginine (8·4 Å).

Unstretched keratin (α-keratin) gives a different X-ray pattern. Fibrous proteins of the k-m-e-f group give patterns similar to either that of α-keratin or of β-keratin, whilst the fibrous proteins of the collagen group give patterns of another type.

The most generally (but not unanimously) accepted view is that the β form of the k-m-e-f group corresponds to a zig-zag structure (Figs. 7 and 8), and the α form of the k-m-e-f group and the collagen group represents a helical twisting, the axis of this twist corresponding to the fibre axis. The most generally accepted helical structure is that in which there are 3·69 amino acid residues per turn (Fig. 9). In certain fibrous proteins the polypeptide chains with the α-helical structure are arranged in parallel with each other. In other proteins they are themselves associated in threads in which the polypeptide chains are twisted together (Fig. 10).

(*b*) *Globular Proteins*

A profound study of the many globular proteins has been carried out over the last few years, information being obtained from the study of osmotic pressure, diffusion, viscosity, sedimentation, electrophoresis, light

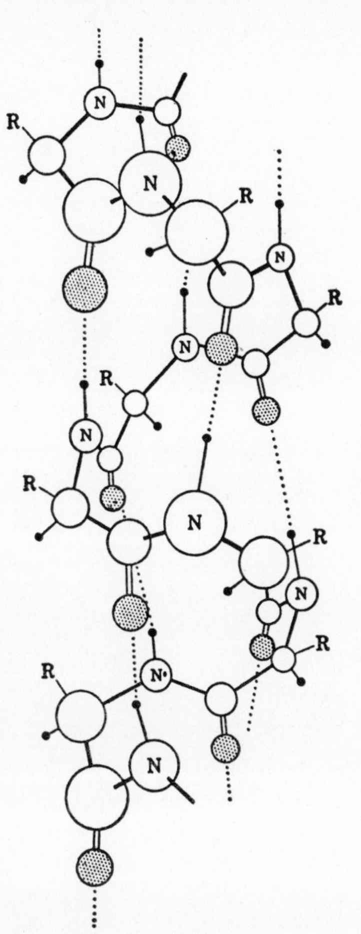

FIG. 9 (Pauling, Corey and Branson)—Portion of α-helix.
N = nitrogen atom; R = side chain; black dots = hydrogen atoms; blank circles = carbon atoms; dotted circles = oxygen atoms; dotted lines = hydrogen bonds.

diffraction, birefringence of flow, dielectric properties, infra-red absorption, X-ray diffraction and by the use of the electron microscope. This imposing array of techniques has provided an immense amount of data the systemization of which remains almost impossible. Certain general conclusions, however, may be drawn from these results.

(a) Molecular weights

The molecular weights of globular proteins lie between 10,000 and several million. Several attempts to arrange these molecular weights into groups (Svedberg; Bergmann and Neumann) have not stood the test of time, and one is forced to admit that the laws governing the molecular weights of proteins are still unknown to us.

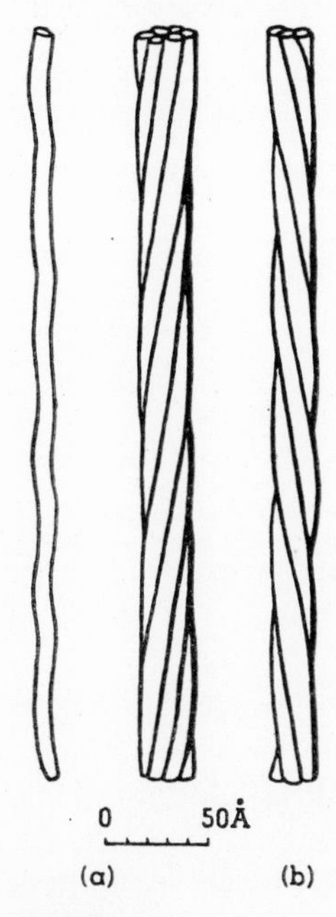

FIG. 10 (Pauling and Corey)—Forms in which α-helical polypeptide chains may be twisted together. An AB_6 bundle (six chains rolled around a seventh : this is the structure of the keratin found in hair and nails) or a D_3 cord (three rolled chains).

(b) Shape

This is sometimes visible in the electron microscope, as is the case for haemocyanin (Fig. 11). In other cases, measurement of physical constants permits the dimensions of the protein molecule to be calculated approximately. Thus, beef insulin (M.W. $= 12 \times 10^3$) is a right prism 44 Å long, 26 Å wide and 20 Å thick, whilst tobacco mosaic virus (M.W. $= 4 \times 10^7$) is a rod 2980 Å long by 150 Å in diameter.

(c) Structure

From the sum total of the evidence it appears that the globular proteins have a structure similar to the α form of the k-m-e-f group of the fibrous proteins, that is, a helical twist with 3·6 residues per turn or 18 residues per 5 turns. However, this does not explain the compactness of the globular proteins. It appears that the polypeptide ribbons are bunched into compact globules and held by lateral linkages between the chains.

The flexibility required for this bunched state, as Neurath has suggested, may be obtained by the presence of an amino acid such as glycine, which is without side chains to prevent free rotation. Or, in Pauling's opinion, proline may be a point of flexibility since, when part of the peptide structure, it does not possess an NH group, does not form hydrogen bonds N-H . . . O, and retains full liberty of bending.

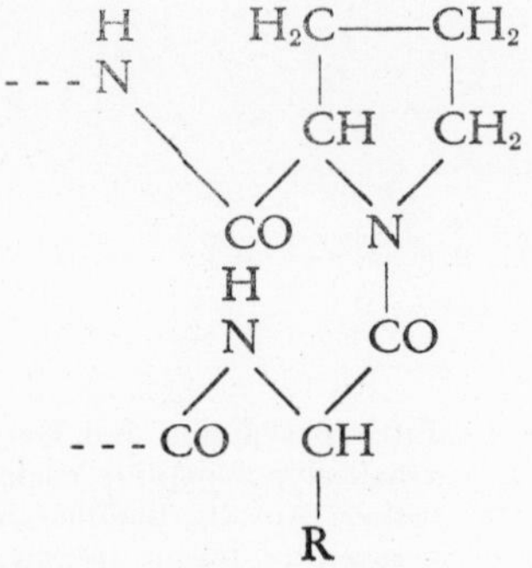

```
       H      H2C——CH2
   - - - N        |      |
          \      CH   CH2
           \    /  \  /
            CO      N
            H       |
            N       CO
           / \    /
   - - - CO    CH
                |
                R
```

Diagram showing the possibility of a change in direction of the peptide chain at a proline residue.

(*d*) *Denaturation*

The globular proteins can undergo denaturation, a process which is often irreversible, but is not well defined; it may result from the action of many and diverse agents (urea, alcohol, detergents, ultrasonic vibrations, etc.) and is revealed by a decrease in solubility, an increase in viscosity, the appearance of free —SH groups, etc. Denaturation is characterized by a very high temperature coefficient, which implies a high degree of order in the molecule of native protein.

On the other hand, the enthalpy (—ΔH, heat liberated at constant pressure) is low, indicating little change at the level of covalent bonds. Denaturation appears to be a sort of collapse of a highly ordered and specific arrangement. The result is a poorly ordered mixture of polypeptides.

All these observations lead us to consider a globular protein as a highly ordered three-dimensional structure of polypeptide layers of the α-k-m-e-f configuration (probably containing 3·6 residues per turn) bunched into a globular mass and maintained thus by linkages between side-chains and by relatively weak hydrogen bonds. In the region of a polar group having a spare hydrogen atom, there is an attraction for the negative charges of neighbouring molecules. In two neighbouring peptide chains, a peptide hydrogen may form a bridge with a pair of electrons on an oxygen atom of the other chain.

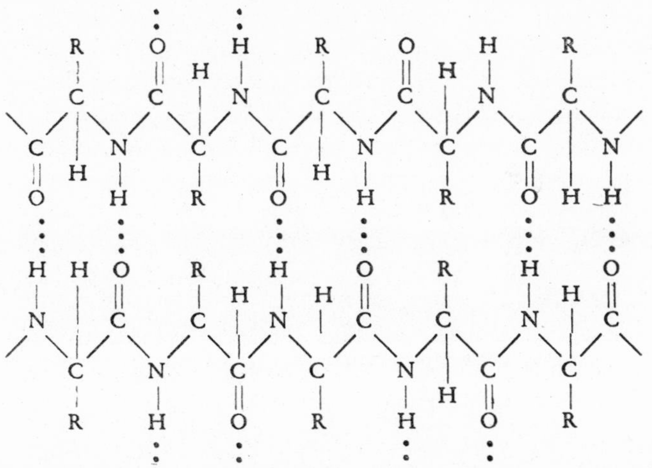

```
                 :         :
     R           O         H         R         O         H         R
     |           ||    H   |         |         ||    H   |         |
     C           C     |   N         C         C     |   N         C
  \ / | \      / \ | /   \       / | \       / \ | /   \       / | \  /
   C  |  N         C         C   |  N          C         C   |  N
   || H  |         |         ||  H  |          |         ||  |  |
   O     H         R         O      H          R         O   H  H
   :     :                   :      :                    :      :
   :     :                   :      :                    :      :
   H  H  O         R         H      O          R         H      O
   |  |  ||        |    H    |  H   ||         |         |   H  ||
   N  |  C         C    |    N  |   C          C         N   |  C
  / \ | /  \      /  \  | /    \   /  \      / | \      /  \ | /  \
     C       N         C         C       N   |   C         C
     |       |         ||        |       |   H   ||        |
     R       H         O         R       H       O         R
             :         :                 :       :
```

The formation of hydrogen bridges is an expression of the tendency possessed by hydrogen atoms to share the electrons of an oxygen atom.

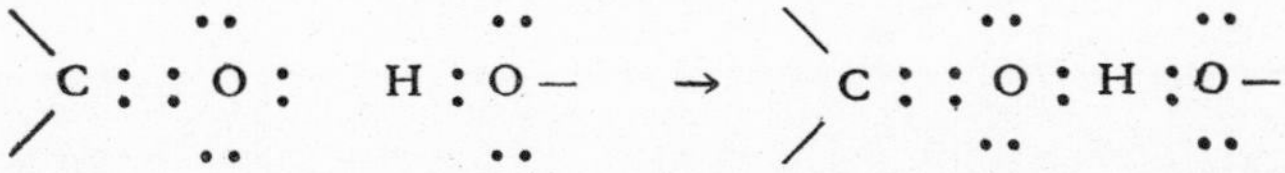

```
\       ..         ..              \        ..      ..
 C : : O :     H : O —      →       C : : O : H : O —
/       ..         ..              /        ..      ..
```

Hydrogen bonds may also be formed between hydrogen and nitrogen atoms between -OH of tyrosine and free -COOH groups, and also between amides

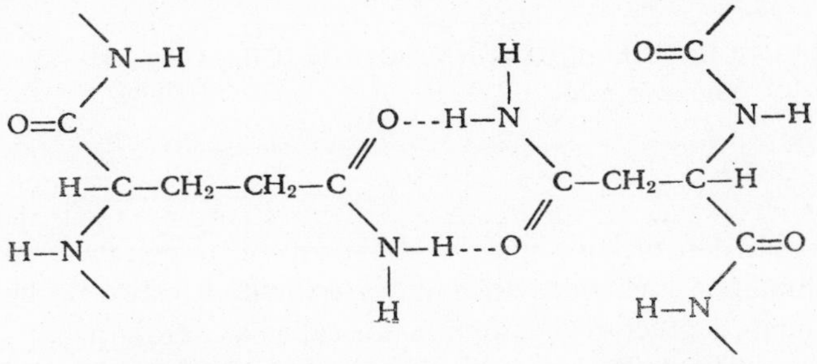

```
       \                                                /
        N—H                         H             O=C
       /                            |                 \
  O=C                         O---H—N                  N—H
      \                      //      \                /
   H—C—CH₂—CH₂—C                      C—CH₂—C—H
      /                      \       //                \
  H—N                         N—H---O                   C=O
      \                       |                        /
                              H                     H—N
                                                       \
```

Glutamine Asparagine

Other bridges between polypeptides are of the disulphide type (covalent), or of a salt-like nature (non-covalent, electro-valent).

We have said that the shape of the globular proteins depends upon relatively weak secondary bonds. On raising the temperature, thermal agitation of the molecules may be sufficient to break these secondary bonds. Mineral salts and urea, by polarizing the water molecules around their molecules or their ions, cause dehydration of the globular macromolecule thus modifying the electrical field of force around it and changes in shape result. Acids and bases, by modifying the ionization of basic and acidic groups, also modify the electric field and the shape of the macromolecule. Heavy metals, which form coordination complexes with certain groups, act in the same way. In many cases this denaturation and change in shape is accompanied by a tendency to pass into a fibrous state and at the same time certain functional groups which were hidden in the interior of the molecule are revealed. The uncovering of these groups certainly plays a part in the tendency displayed by denatured proteins to form aggregates. The formation of these aggregates and the accompanying decrease in solubility are facilitated at the isoelectric point since then nothing prevents the molecules from coming together.

Denaturation may be irreversible. This is the case when important changes in structure have taken place altering the geometry of the electric field of the globular molecule.

```
     /                                                            \
O=C                                                                C=O
    \                                                             /
     C-CH2-----------S-----------S-----------CH2-C
    /                                                  \
H-N                                                     N-H
    \                                                  /
     C=O                                           O=C
    /                                                  \
R-C-H                                                   H-C-R
    \                                                  /
     N-H                                           H-N
    /                                                  \
O=C                                                     C=O
    \                                                  /
  H-C-CH2-CH2-COO-···NH3-C-NH-CH2-CH2-CH2-C-H
   /    Glutamic acid       ||         Arginine       \
HN                          NH                         C=O
   \                                                  /
    C=O
   /
```

Irreversible denaturation may be accompanied by polymerization and a fall in solubility. The appearance of a precipitate is called flocculation; if the precipitate is practically insoluble it is called a coagulum.

Denaturation may be reversible, if the changes in structure are slight. When the initial conditions are restored, the electrostatic field reestablishes the original shape of the globular molecule.

B. The Nature and Positions of the Constituent Amino Acids in the Protein

(a) *Nitrogen and Sulphur Content*

One of the present tasks of biochemistry is the determination of the order in which the amino acids are assembled in the protein polypeptide chains and the description of the structure of that protein. It is first of all necessary to know the total protein nitrogen (around 16%) and the total sulphur (around 2%); when the different amino acids have been determined these figures allow one to check that the sum of these amino acids accounts completely for the composition of the protein.

(b) Titration

The reactive groups of the protein may be determined by titration, with acids and dilute alkalies when dealing with acid or basic groups, and by means of silver nitrate, iodine, etc., when dealing with thiol groups.

The potentiometric titration of a protein in aqueous solution with an acid or dilute alkali is carried out by measuring the change in pH which results from the addition of a known amount of the acid or base to the isoionic protein. The isoionic state exists when the number of protons attached to the basic groups (e.g. $-NH_2 + H^+ \rightarrow -NH^+_3$) is equal to the number of protons removed from the acidic groups (e.g. $-COOH \rightarrow -COO^- + H^+$). If there are no other ions apart from protons fixed on to the protein, then the isoionic state coincides with the isoelectric state, defined by charge O. The results of the titration are expressed in terms of change in pH/unit of acid added and change in pH/unit of base added. Figure 12 shows the dissociation curve of the protein.

There are quite a number of ionizing groups present in proteins :

α-COOH the terminal group of polypeptide chains;

β-COOH or γ-COOH of aspartic or glutamic acid;

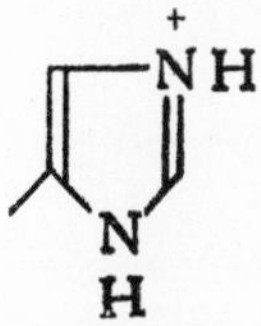

$\overset{+}{N}H$ of histidine;
N
H

α-NH^+_3 the terminal group of polypeptide chains;
ϵ-NH^+_3 of lysine;

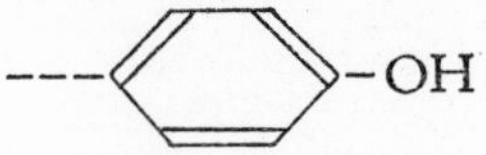

---⬡—OH of tyrosine;

--- SH of cysteine;

---NH
\
$C{=}\overset{+}{N}H_2$ of arginine.
/
H_2N

When the pH is very acid, around 1·0, for example, all these groups are in the undissociated state. At pH 14·0, they are all completely dissociated. As one passes from pH 1·0 to pH 14·0 each ionizing group will dissociate over a particular pH range corresponding to its pK value. Figure 13 illustrates this. In Fig. 12, three regions, labelled *a*, *b* and *c*, may be distinguished, in which a slight change in pH has had a marked effect on the number of protons combined with the protein. Referring to Fig. 13, we can see that region *a* corresponds to the dissociation of terminal free-carboxyl groups, and region *b* to that of the dissociable groups of histidine and terminal α-amino groups. Region *c* corresponds to the dissociation of the groups of lysine, tyrosine, cysteine and arginine. To investigate the question further and resolve the complexities of regions *b* and *c* it is necessary

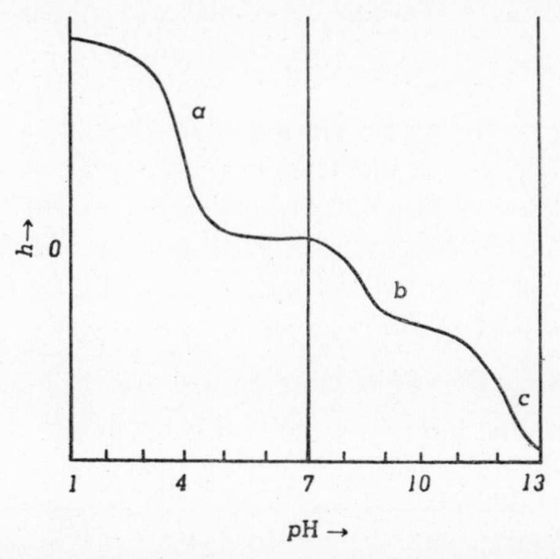

FIG. 12 (Springall)—Titration curve of a protein. Abscissae: pH values. Ordinates: the number *h* of protons added or subtracted, starting from the isoionic state, to give these pH values in aqueous solution. These values of *h* are obtained from the number of equivalents necessary to bring the solvent to the same pH.

to mask one or other of the groups. Thus, free amino groups may be reacted with formol or removed by enzymatic deamination, etc. The complete and often arduous analysis of the titration curve of a protein gives us information about the amount of arginine, histidine and lysine in that protein, and also the total number of free carboxyl and α-amino groups. Knowing the number of primary amide groups (from the amount of ammonia in the hydrolysed protein—see later) and the amount of aspartic and glutamic acids, it is possible to calculate the number of carboxyl groups not involved in peptide bonds. If the number of free carboxyls and the number of free amino groups are known some idea may be obtained of the number of polypeptide chains present in the protein molecule.

(*c*) *Composition of the Hydrolysate*

When the titration of the native protein has been carried out the amino acid composition is determined. Hydrolysis gives a mixture of amino acids and ammonia. The latter derives from the amide groups of glutamine and asparagine, but it may also be an artefact arising from the breakdown of certain amino acids during the hydrolysis. Since the average molecular weight of the amino acids is 110, then complete hydrolysis of a protein of molecular weight 36,000 will produce around 300 molecules of amino acids of 20 different kinds. It is evident that the analysis of this hydrolysate is a formidable problem whose solution was a notable achievement. The methods used are numerous: specific precipitation of some groups of amino acids (for example by phosphotungstic acid in the case of cystine, arginine, histidine and lysine); precipitation of the amino acid directly

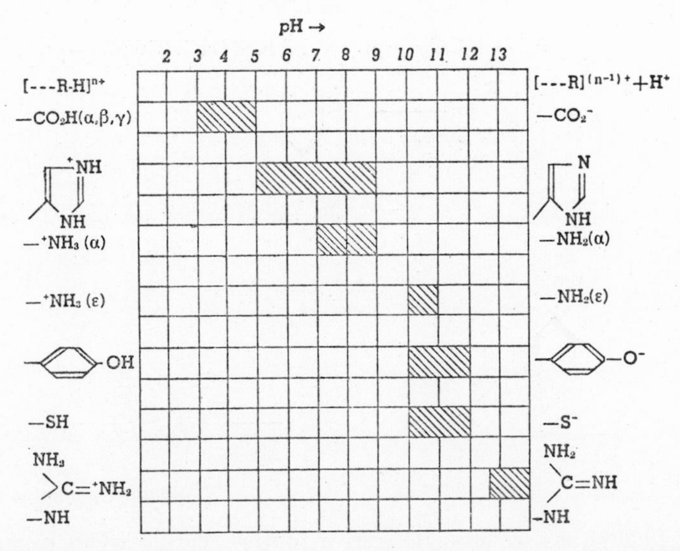

FIG. 13 (Springall)—Dissociation constants of the different groups—R-H. The dashed areas indicate the pH range in which dissociation takes place when the pH increases.

(proline by ammonium rhodanilate); colorimetric methods; isotope dilution methods; enzymatic methods (for example, measurement of CO_2 liberated by a specific decarboxylase); microbiological methods—depending on the fact that for a certain strain a certain amino acid is indispensable for growth, the latter may be measured (for example, in the lactic acid bacteria by the production of acid) and is proportional to the concentration of the amino acid; chromatographic methods, etc.

Table IX shows the amino acid composition of a collection of proteins whose analysis is complete or almost complete. As can be seen, such a table does not permit any useful conclusion to be drawn from it. Thus attention is focussed on the sequence of the amino acids in the protein polypeptide chains.

(*d*) *Determination of the Amino Acid Sequence*

A number of methods allow the removal of an amino acid residue from the N-terminal end of a polypeptide terminal residue :

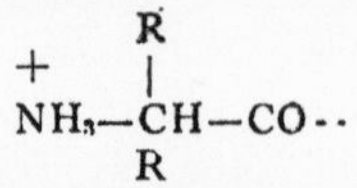

$$\overset{+}{NH_3}-\underset{R}{\overset{R}{\overset{|}{C}}}H-CO\cdots$$

Such a method is that of Edman (1950) in which phenylisothiocyanate in pyridine at pH 9·0 is used. The principle is as follows :

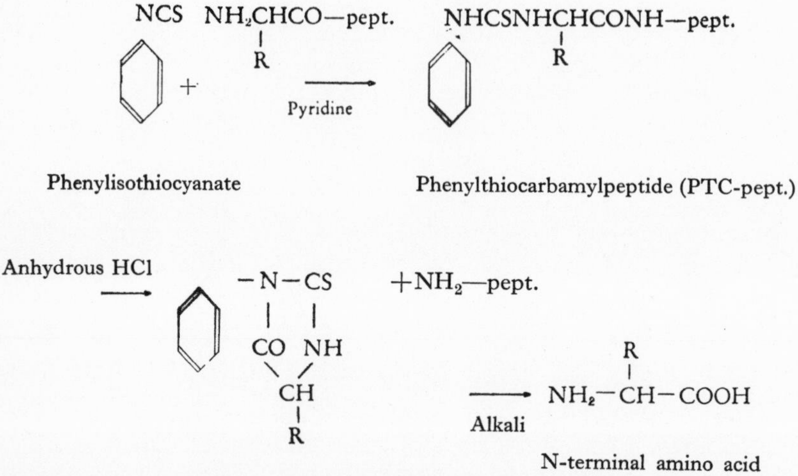

$$C_6H_5NCS + NH_2\underset{R}{\underset{|}{C}}HCO-\text{pept.} \xrightarrow{\text{Pyridine}} C_6H_5NHCSNH\underset{R}{\underset{|}{C}}HCONH-\text{pept.}$$

Phenylisothiocyanate

Phenylthiocarbamylpeptide (PTC-pept.)

Anhydrous HCl ⟶ C_6H_5—N—CS, CO NH, CH, R (ring: N–CS, CO–NH, joined through CH–R) $+NH_2$—pept.

⟶ (Alkali) $NH_2-\underset{|}{\overset{R}{C}}H-COOH$

N-terminal amino acid

The phenylthiocarbamyl derivative of the peptide when treated with anhydrous HC1 gives the phenylthiohydantoin of the N-terminal amino acid which, when treated with $Ba(OH)_2$ in alkaline solution, liberates this terminal amino acid.

This method is applied to the polypeptides obtained from proteins by various means. It is possible to remove the N-terminal amino acids one after the other and identify them while still keeping the rest of the chain intact for a further shortening and further identification of the amino acids obtained. There are also methods which allow amino acid residues to be chopped off from the C-terminal end of the chain.

To obtain these polypeptides from the protein, it may be hydrolysed carefully with a 10 N mixture of hydrochloric and acetic acids for several days at 37°, or hydrolysed with alkali or by the action of enzymes.

A witness to the success of these methods is the determination, by Sanger, of the amino acid sequence of a part (fraction B, one of the two

TABLE IX.—*Composition of proteins*

(Taken from Springall, 1954)

(*Moles of amino acid in* 10^5*g. of protein*)

	β-Lactoglobulin	Ovalbumin	Conalbumin	Human serum albumin	Beef serum albumin	Human haemoglobin	Human haemoglobin in sickle-cell anaemia	Horse haemoglobin	Ferritin	Insulin	Lactogenic hormone
Gly.	20	40·6	76·0	21	24	64·6	64·9	74·8	45·3	57·4	53
Ala.	72	75·5	49·5	—	70	114·5	114·1	83·2	21·4	50·5	—
Val.	48·9	60·2	70·1	66	50	91·1	89·4	77·8	36·8	66·2	50
Leu.	118	70·2	67·1	84	94	115·0	110·7	117·6	145·9	100·9	93
ILeu.	45	53·5	38·2	13	20	15·7	14·5	0	10·7	21·1	55
Pro.	46·9	31·3	42·6	44·4	41	38·2	37·6	33·9	13·1	22	54
Phe.	23·9	46·4	34·5	47·3	40	46·4	45·8	46·6	37·0	49	25
Cy-S	19·1	4·3	31·7	46·4	54	—	—	3·8	14·2	104	26
Cy-SH	9·2	11·2	—	5·8	—	—	—	6·4	—	0	—
Met.	21·5	35·0	13·4	8·7	5	9·3	9·6	6·7	12·7	0	29
Try.	9·3	5·0	14·7	1	3	7·3	7·9	8·3	5·9	0	6
Arg.	16·5	32·9	43·7	35·7	34	18·9	19·7	21·0	52·3	17·6	49
His.	10·2	15·2	16·8	22·6	26	54·4	54·7	56·2	31·0	31·7	29
Lys.	77·5	43·2	68·5	84·3	88	66·0	66·2	58·3	53·4	17·2	36
Asp.	85·9	70	100·0	78·2	82	82·9	86·1	79·9	51·1	51·1	101
Glu.	146·5	112·2	80·9	118·6	104	48·8	49·2	57·9	117·1	125·1	96
Ser.	38·7	33·9	60·0	35·3	40	48·1	51·7	55·0	—	49·9	63
Thr.	43·4	34	49·6	42·0	49	49·1	50·4	36·6	36·1	17·5	40
Tyr.	20·6	20·3	24·0	26·0	28	16·5	16·6	16·7	27·6	72·0	26
Total	852	796	881	781	852	887	889	839	712	854	823

	Corticotropic hormone	Ribonuclease	Chymotrypsinogen	Pepsin	Aldolase	Triosephosphate dehydrogenase	Dephosphorylase	Lysozyme	Fibrinogen	Tropomyosin	Fibroin of the silk from *Bombyx mori*
Gly.	66·4	17·3	70·6	85·3	74·9	81·1	52·0	76·0	74·7	—	581
Ala.	—	—	—	—	96·3	75·4	53·8	65·2	41·5	98·8	334
Val.	29·1	62·3	86·2	60·6	63·2	102·7	62·4	41·0	35·4	26·7	30·8
Leu.	59·5	0	79·3	79·3	87·7	51·9	80·2	52·6	54·2	119·0	7·0
ILeu.	23·7	23·6	43·5	82·3	60·3	69·4	49·7	39·7	36·7	—	8·4
Pro.	71·3	31·3	51·3	43·4	49·7	32·0	40·9	12·2	49·5	11·3	6·4
Phe.	24·2	21·8	21·8	38·7	18·5	33·7	37·6	18·8	27·9	27·9	20·4
Cy-S	60·0	54·2	27·5	13·6	9·3	9·1	3·6	66·6	19·0	6·3	—
Cy-SH	—	5	10·7	4·1	—	—	—	—	3·3	—	—
Met.	8·3	29·7	8·2	11·4	7·9	18·1	18·1	14·1	17·1	18·8	—
Try.	—	0	27·3	11·6	11·3	10·0	9·8	51·9	16·0	0	—
Arg.	49·5	29·6	16·2	5·7	36·4	30·1	66·7	73·0	44·8	44·8	6·3
His.	9·3	27·2	7·9	5·8	27·2	32·3	21·3	6·5	17·1	5·5	2·3
Lys.	34·3	71·1	54·7	6·2	65·4	64·6	43·9	39·0	63·0	107·4	4·7
Asp.	50·4	106·4	84·8	120·2	73·0	93·4	79·0	136·9	98·5	68·4	20·8
Glu.	106·1	88·3	61·2	89·9	77·7	32·5	92·6	29·3	98·7	223·6	14·7
Ser.	57·1	114·2	108·5	116·1	69·5	71·1	36·2	63·8	66·3	41·7	154·3
Thr.	26·9	75·6	95·7	80·6	62·9	61·1	36·9	46·2	51·7	24·4	13·5
Tyr.	13·3	43·8	16·3	46·9	29·3	25·2	32·6	18·7	5·5	17·2	70·7
Total	689	801	871	893	920	893	824	851	846	842	1,275

TABLE X

Peptides identified in hydrolysates of fraction B of oxidized insulin (Sanger)

Dipeptides in acid and alkaline hydrolysates	Phe.Val Glu. His. CySO$_3$H.Gly His.Leu Glu.Ala CySO$_3$H.Gly Arg.Gly Lys.Ala Val.Asp His. Leu Leu.Val Ala.Leu Leu.Val Gly.Glu Gly.Phe Thr. Pro. Asp.Glu Leu.CySO$_3$H Ser.His Val.Glu Val.CySO$_3$H Glu.Arg
Tripeptides in acid and alkaline hydrolysates	Phe.Val.Asp Leu.CySO$_3$H.Gly Val.Glu.Ala Tyr.Leu.Val. Gly.Glu.Arg Pro.Lys.Ala Glu. His. Leu Ser.His.Leu Val.CySO$_3$H.Gly Val.Asp.Glu Leu.Val.Glu Leu.Val.CySO$_3$H His. Leu.CySO$_3$H Ala.Leu Tyr
Higher peptides in acid and alkaline hydrolysates	Phe.Val.Asp.Glu Ser.His.Leu.Val Tyr.Leu.Val.CySO$_3$H Thr.Pro.Lys.Ala His. Leu.CyCO$_3$H.Gly Leu.Val.Glu.Ala Leu.Val.CySO$_3$H.Gly Glu. His. Leu.CySO$_3$H Ser.His.Leu.Val.Glu. His.Leu.Val.Glu Ser.His.Leu.Val.Glu.Ala
Sequences deduced from above	Phe.Val.Asp.Glu. His. Leu.CySO$_3$H.Gly Tyr.Leu.Val.CySO$_3$H.Gly Thr.Pro.Lys.Ala Gly.Glu.Arg.
Peptides in peptic hydrolysates	Ser.His.Leu.Val.Glu.Ala Phe.Val.Asp.Glu. His. Leu.CySO$_3$H.Gly. Ser.His.Leu Leu.Val.CySO$_3$H.Gly.Glu.Arg.Gly.Phe Tyr.Thr.Pro.Lys.Ala Val.Glu.Ala.Leu His. Leu.CySO$_3$H.Gly. Ser.His.Leu
Peptides in chymotrypsin hydrolysates	Phe.Val.Asp.Glu. His. Leu.CySO$_3$H.Gly. Ser.His.Leu.Val.Glu.Ala.Leu.Tyr Tyr.Thr.Pro.Lys.Ala Leu.Val.CySO$_3$H.Gly.Glu.Arg.Gly.Phe.Phe
Peptides in trypsin hydrolysates	Gly.Phe.Phe.Tyr.Thr.Pro.Lys Ala
Structure of fraction B	Phe.Val.Asp.Glu. His. Leu.(CyS—).Gly. Ser.His.Leu.Val.Glu.Ala.Leu.Tyr.Leu.Val.(CyS—). Gly.Glu.Arg. Gly.Phe.Phe. Tyr.Thr.Pro.Lys.Ala

polypeptide chains joined by disulphide bridges) of the insulin molecule. Table X shows the amino acid sequence, as determined by Sanger, in a series of polypeptides separated from fraction B of insulin. Sanger has demonstrated that the only possible sequence corresponding to these many peptides is that shown at the bottom of the table.

III. NUCLEOPROTEINS

The nucleoproteins are macromolecules formed by the union of proteins and nucleic acids. The nucleic acids themselves are polymers of nucleotides. The complete hydrolysis of the nucleic acids separated from nucleoproteins gives phosphoric acid, purines and pyrimidines (six members of these two groups have been identified up to the present time), and two furanose sugars. These latter are, either D-ribose (ribonucleic acids) or 2-desoxy-D-ribose (desoxyribonucleic acids). They have either two or three -OH groups available for esterification. The number of possible nucleotides entering into the composition of nucleic acids is, therefore, very great. The purines, adenine and guanine, enter into the composition of all nucleic acids. Among the pyrimidines, cytosine is present in all the nucleic acids. Besides these purines and the pyrimidine which are always present, one finds uracil in ribonucleic acids, and thymine and 5-methylcytosine in desoxyribonucleic acids. Analysis of the nucleic acids reveals that they are polymers of nucleotides. However, we are still far from knowing the nature of the complex mixture of polynucleotides which make up each nucleic acid. The little that is known at the present time is due to a combination of the results of chemical hydrolysis and step-wise degradation by means of enzymes.

A. Properties of the Two Types of Nucleic Acid

(*a*) *Ribonucleic Acids* (*RNA*)

These complex mixtures contain only four bases : adenine, guanine, cytosine and uracil. The relative proportion of each of these bases does not differ appreciably from unity. Considering that this is not the case for the

REFERENCES

Edsall, J. T. (1958). *Aspects actuels de la biochimie des acides amins et des proteines*. Masson, Paris.

Fox, S. & Foster, J. F. (1957). *Protein Chemistry*. Wiley, New York.

Neuberger, A. (1958). *Symposium on Protein Structure*. Methuen, London.

Neurath, H. & Bailey, K. (1953–1955) *The Proteins. Chemistry, Biological Activity, and Methods.* (A collaborative work by many specialists in this field, it is both the most comprehensive and the most modern text book available.) 4 vols. Academic Press, New York.

Springall, H. D. (1954). *The Structural Chemistry of Proteins.* (More concise than the above, it gives a clear and constructive account of the methods and results of the chemical study of protein structure.) Butterworths, London.

polynucleotide chains isolated from ribonucleic acids, this is an indication of the complexity of what is customarily called a "ribonucleic" acid. The nucleosides entering into the composition of the ribonucleic acid from yeast are β-D-ribofuranosides in which adenine and guanine are linked at N-9 and cytosine and uracil at N-3. It appears that ribose is always the sugar present in what were formerly known as pentose-nucleic acids and they can, therefore, be named ribonucleic acids.

The internucleotide bond which is predominant in the ribonucleic acids is the phosphoric ester bridge between C-3′ and C-5′ of two adjacent nucleotides.

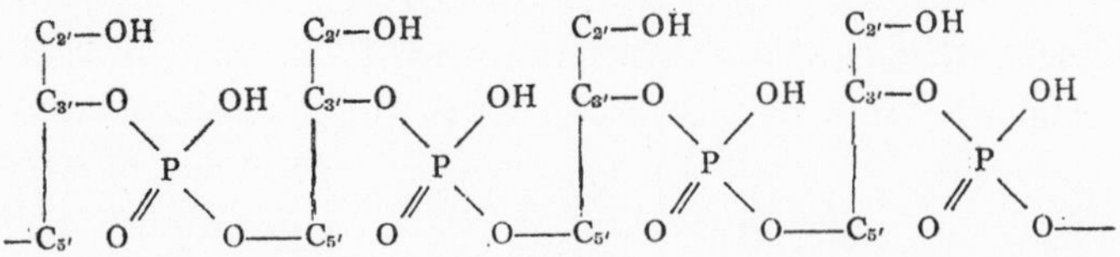

```
  C2'—OH              C2'—OH              C2'—OH              C2'—OH
  |                   |                   |                   |
  C3'—O        OH     C3'—O        OH     C3'—O        OH     C3'—O        OH
  |     \     /       |     \     /       |     \     /       |     \     /
  |        P          |        P          |        P          |        P
  |     //    \       |     //    \       |     //    \       |     //    \
—C5'  O        O——————C5'  O        O——————C5'  O        O——————C5'  O        O——
```

In such a scheme, —C-2′—C-3′—C-5′— represents a nucleotide residue. The presence of an -OH on C-2′ explains how, by analogy with the results obtained with mononucleotide esters, the alkaline degradation proceeds through the intermediate formation of a cyclic structure in which nucleoside-2′, -3′ cyclic phosphates are formed by cleavage of the C-5′—O—P bond, as shown above.

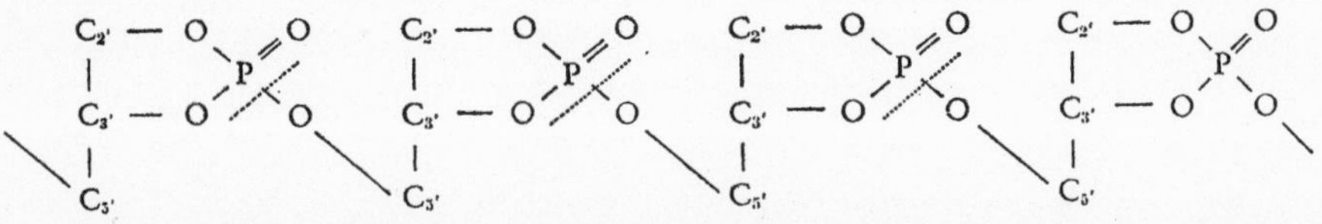

```
   C2' — O     O      C2' — O     O      C2' — O     O      C2' — O     O
   |      \  //       |      \  //       |      \  //       |      \  //
   |        P         |        P         |        P         |        P
   |      /  \        |      /  \        |      /  \        |      /  \
   C3' — O    O       C3' — O    O       C3' — O    O       C3' — O    O
\  |           \      |           \      |           \      |           \
 \ C5'          \     C5'          \     C5'          \     C5'
```

The isolation of ribonucleic acids is difficult which makes the determination of their structure and composition difficult also. However it can be shown that the ribonucleic acid of animals differs from that of yeast, and that the ribonucleic acids from different organs of the same species are less alike than are those from a given organ obtained from several species. Unlike the desoxyribonucleic acids, the ribonucleic acids differ not only from species to species but also from tissue to tissue in the same species. Moreover, the ribonucleic acids of the nucleus differ from that of the cytoplasm, and external conditions also cause variations.

(b) *Desoxyribonucleic Acids* (*DNA*)

The desoxyribonucleic acids which do not have an -OH group on C-2′, differ from the ribonucleic acids in possessing a more stable internucleotide bond. Although the linkage is between C-3′ and C-5′ of adjacent sugar molecules, the cyclization described above for the ribonucleic acids is impossible, which gives the desoxyribonucleic acids a very great stability. Their general structure is the following :

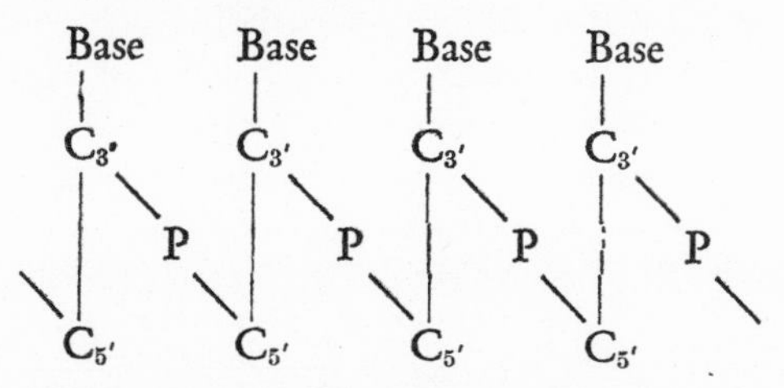

The concept of the helical structure of the desoxyribonucleic acids was first suggested by Pauling and Corey (1953), following research by the X-ray diffraction method. A helical structure which accounts more fully for the experimental facts has been proposed by Watson and Crick (1953) (Fig. 14). It consists of two helical chains rolled around the same axis. The two chains are twisted in parallel but the order of the atoms is inverse. The purines and pyrimidines are directed to the interior and the phosphate to the outside. Along the helix a nucleotide occupies a distance of

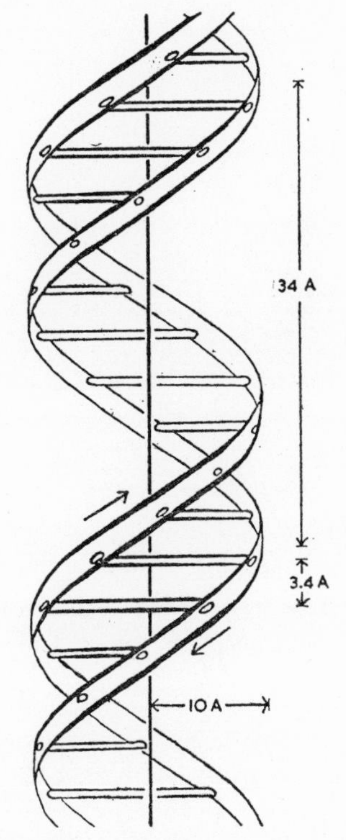

Fig. 14 (Watson and Crick)—Helical structure of desoxyribonucleic acid.

3·4 Å, and the repeating unit which is made up of ten nucleotides occupies 34 Å. The angle between two adjacent nucleotides in the same chain is 36°. The purine and pyrimidine bases, being directed to the interior, are perpendicular to the axis of the helix. They are associated in pairs, one from each chain by means of hydrogen bonds.

As there is not enough room to allow two purines end to end, and since two pyrimidines would form too short a bridge, the only possible linkages

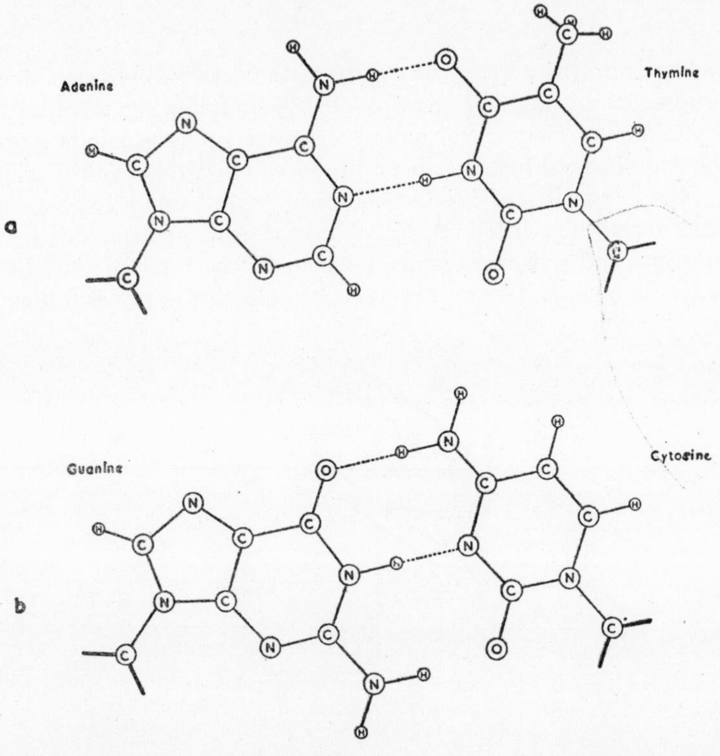

FIG. 15 (Watson and Crick)—Hydrogen bonds compatible with the formula of Watson and Crick.

are adenine-thymine and guanine-cytosine linkages. The shape of these links is represented in Fig. 15.

The desoxyribonucleic are more stable than the ribonucleic acids and, consequently, a greater number of results have been obtained in determinations of their molecular weight. They are very elongated, threadlike molecules, whose molecular weight is in the region of six million.

The composition of the desoxyribonucleic acids varies from one species to another, but their composition appears to be the same in different organs and does not appear to be influenced by the environment.

B. The Nucleoproteins

The nucleoproteins of the nuclei of trout, salmon and herring spe made up almost entirely of protamine and desoxyribonucleic acid. The nucleoproteins of thymus are made up of desoxyribonucleic acid (40%), ribonucleic acid (1–2%), histones and non-basic proteins. The cellular nuclei contain chiefly desoxyribonucleic acid but, in addition, there is a little ribonucleic acid (in the nucleolus and chromosomes). The cytoplasmic nucleoproteins in general contain only ribonucleic acid associated with proteins which do not have the basic properties of those joined to desoxyribonucleic acid. But the reproductive cell of animals (oocytes) contain desoxyribonucleic acid in the cytoplasm. The desoxyribonucleic acid of the chromosomes is combined with histones, protamines, and a protein of the usual type, which is referred to as *residual protein.*

Protamines not possessing primary amino groups are associated with DNA by a salt linkage, and this is also the case for the histones. Separation takes place when an extraction is made with solutions of high ionic strength. The protamines and histones are very heterogeneous. The residual protein, unlike the histones, contains tryptophan.

IV. METALLOPROTEINS

The metalloprotein structure is one which is widely and diversely employed in the chemistry of living cells.

A. Metalloproteins in which the Metal is Bound to the Protein Through the Intermediary of Another Structure

(*a*) *Haemoproteins*

Iron possesses 26 electrons distributed among 4 shells (K, L, M, N). The K and L shells are saturated and contain 2 and 8 electrons respectively, all of which are paired; the N shell contains 2 paired electrons; the M shell contains 14 electrons. The M shell has 1 *s* orbital, 3 *p* orbitals and 5 *d* orbitals; the energy level of the *s* orbital is below that of the *p* orbitals which is less than that of the *d* orbitals. Each orbital can contain 0, 1 or 2 electrons; in the last case the two electrons have opposite spins and their magnetic effects cancel out (paired electrons). First of all, the electrons

REFERENCES

Brachet, J. (1952). *Le rôle des acides nucléiques dans la vie de la cellule et de l'embryon,* Masson, Paris and Liège, Desoer, (Actualités biochimiques, No 16).

Chargaff, E. & Davidson, J. N. (1955). *The Nucleic Acids. Chemistry and Biology.* 2 vols. Academic Press, New York. (The collective effort of leading workers in this field. This work contains full information and a constructive discussion of the subject.)

fill the orbitals which have the lowest energy level, so that in iron, the *s* and *p* orbitals of the M shell are saturated, making 8 electrons in all (4 pairs). The 6 remaining electrons are in *d* orbitals and they tend to occupy as many of these as possible : one orbital contains two paired electrons and the four others each contain one unpaired electron. So iron possesses 4 unpaired electrons.

Each unpaired electron, on account of its spin, behaves as a small magnet : it becomes oriented in a magnetic field so as to oppose the field. Measurements of magnetic susceptibility allow the number of unpaired electrons to be determined. Substances which, like iron, contain unpaired electrons are said to be paramagnetic and those which contain only paired electrons are called diamagnetic.

The valency electrons are usually those in the outer shell. However, in the case of iron, the energy level of the *d* orbitals of the M shell is almost the same as the energy level of the *s* orbitals of the N shell, so that the *d* orbitals of the M shell take part in the formation of iron complexes.

The iron atom loses two electrons and becomes a ferrous ion; the two electrons which are lost are two paired electrons of the *s* orbital of the N shell; the ferrous ion then, like iron itself, contains 4 unpaired electrons.

The loss of an additional electron to give the ferric ion is at the expense of the six electrons in the *d* orbital of shell M; the 5 remaining electrons redistribute themselves among the 5 *d* orbitals and ferric iron contains 5 unpaired electrons.

In ferrous or ferric coordination complexes containing covalent links, the complexing groups bring two electrons per bond. Four electrons can be introduced into the *d* orbitals of the M shell (saturating them in the case of ferrous complexes and leaving one unpaired electron in the case of ferric complexes) and 8 other electrons will be required to saturate the *s* and *p* orbitals of the N shell, conferring upon this shell the very stable octet structure. It can be seen that the coordination number of the ferrous ion, as well as that of the ferric ion, is 6: two bonds established through the M shell (*d* orbitals) and 4 bonds through the N shell (*s* and *p* orbitals) of the ion. These hybrid bonds (hybrid, because two electronic shells are involved) are denoted by the symbols d^2sp^3. The complex has the form of an octahedron with the centre occupied by the ion; the coordination linkages which are covalent (2 shared electrons per bond) are directed towards the 6 corners.

1. *Haems*

The porphyrin molecule can combine with heavy-metal ions such as ferrous, ferric, cupric ions, etc.

Haem refers to the ferro-porphyrin which results from the combination of a porphyrin with a ferrous ion :

$$\text{porphyrin} + Fe^{++} \rightleftarrows \text{ferro-porphyrin} + 2H^+$$

It is obvious that the reaction is pH-sensitive, in acid solution the compound is completely dissociated. The loss of the two protons from the porphyrin molecule leaves behind two negative charges which, by means of the system of conjugated double bonds, are distributed by resonance over the four nitrogen atoms.

The ferrous ion is paramagnetic; it has 4 unpaired electrons. Likewise, the haem molecule is also paramagnetic and measurements of magnetic susceptibility have shown that, like the ferrous ion, it has 4 unpaired electrons; this shows that the nitrogen atoms of the porphyrin bound to the ferrous ion do not share any electrons with it; the bond is ionic. In the

Protohaem

ferro-porphyrin complex, the ferrous ion has a coordination number of 6 : in the complex, it retains two water molecules by means of ion-dipole bonds. The 6 bonds of the complex are, therefore, electrostatic in nature.

Ferro-porphyrin can be represented :

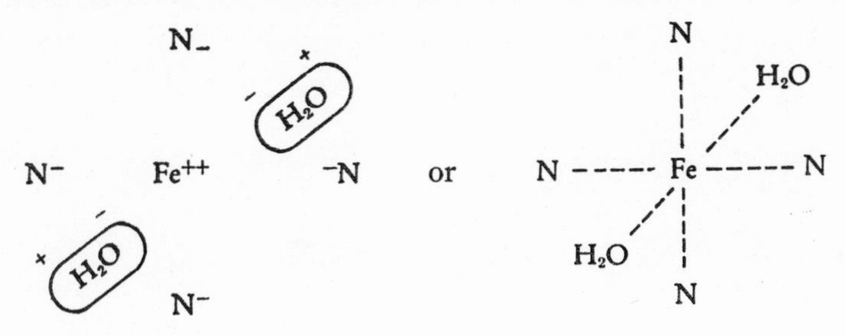

2. *Haemochromogens*

The water molecules in the ferro-porphyrins are readily replaced by nitrogen bases; the name "haemochromogens" is given to the new complexes so formed.

This substitution reaction is accompanied by a complete rearrangement of the structure of the complex. Measurements of susceptibility now indicate that the haemochromogen no longer possesses any unpaired electrons : it is diamagnetic. The two molecules of nitrogen base and the four porphyrin nitrogen atoms have shared their electrons (12 in all) with the ferrous ion; there are no remaining unpaired electrons and the 6 coordination bonds of the complex are covalent (d^2sp^3). The haemochromogen has the shape of an octahedron with the ferrous ion at the centre and the nitrogen atoms at the 6 corners. The 4 nitrogen atoms of the porphyrin molecule are in the same plane. The structure of the haemochromogens is exactly the same as that of the ferrocyanide ion, Fe $(CN)_6$, which is also diamagnetic.

A haemochromogen can be written thus :

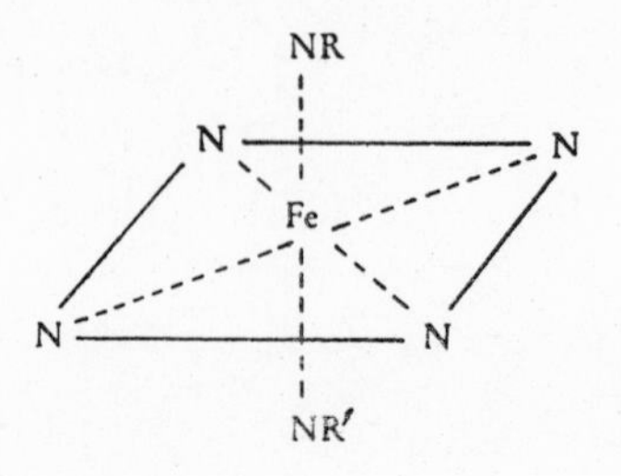

3. *Haematins and parahaematins*

Oxidation of the ferrous ion of haem gives rise to a ferri-porphyrin which is given the name "haematin". An oxygen molecule can bring about this oxidation.

The ferric ion has 5 unpaired electrons. Ferri-porphyrin also possesses 5 unpaired electrons; hence all the bonds in the complex are of an electrostatic character. The complex, in which the ferric ion has a coordination number of 6, can be represented thus :

```
        N                                      N
        |    OH                                |      H2O
        |   /                                  |     /
        |  /                                 + |    /
N ------Fe ------ N   +   H+   ⇄   N ------ Fe ------ N
       /|                                   /|
      / |                                  / |
  H2O   |                              H2O   |
        N                                    N
```

The equilibrium depends upon the pH; addition of HC1 will displace it to the right with the formation of the chloride of ferri-porphyrin which can be represented as a mixture of the two forms in the following equilibrium :

$$\left[\begin{array}{c} N \\ N - \overset{+}{Fe}(H_2O)_2 - N \\ N \end{array}\right] Cl \rightleftharpoons \begin{array}{c} N \\ N - Fe(Cl)(H_2O) - N \\ N \end{array} + H_2O$$

Oxidation of the ferrous ion of a haemochromogen to a ferric ion will give rise to a parahaematin. One may also obtain a parahaematin by the combination of a ferri-porphyrin with nitrogen bases; however, the affinity of ferri-porphyrins for nitrogen bases is much less than that of the ferro-porphyrins. The parahaematins are slightly paramagnetic; they possess 1 unpaired electron; the 6 coordination linkages of the complex are covalent (d^2sp^3) as in the ferricyanide ion, $Fe(CN)_6$, which also has an unpaired electron. Parahaematin has an octahedral form and can be written so :

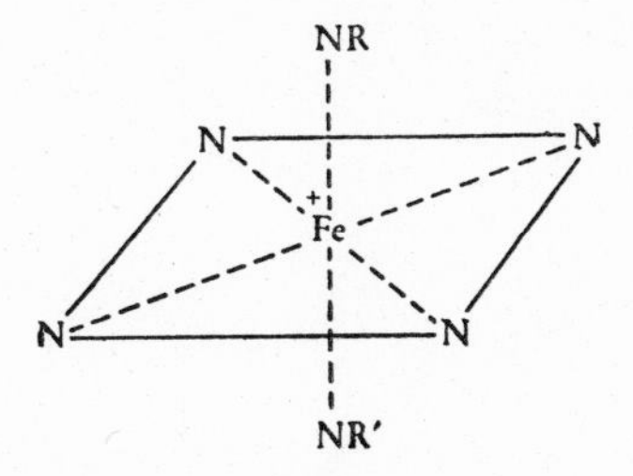

4. *Haemoglobin*

Combination of globin with a haem gives a haemochromogen of a particular type : the ferrous ion retains all its 4 unpaired electrons so that all the linkages in the complex are electrostatic in nature.

Haemoglobin results from the union of protohaem and globin. The linkage between the globin and the haem is between the ferrous ion and the two imidazole groups of histidine residues in the globin, the latter replace the two water molecules in the ferro-porphyrin.

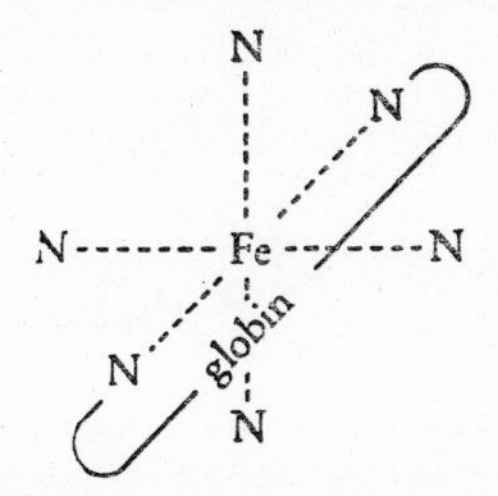

In the complex, haemoglobin, oxygen or carbon monoxide can displace one of the imidazole groups; there is a consequent redistribution of electrons (bringing 12 electrons to the ferrous ion) with formation of

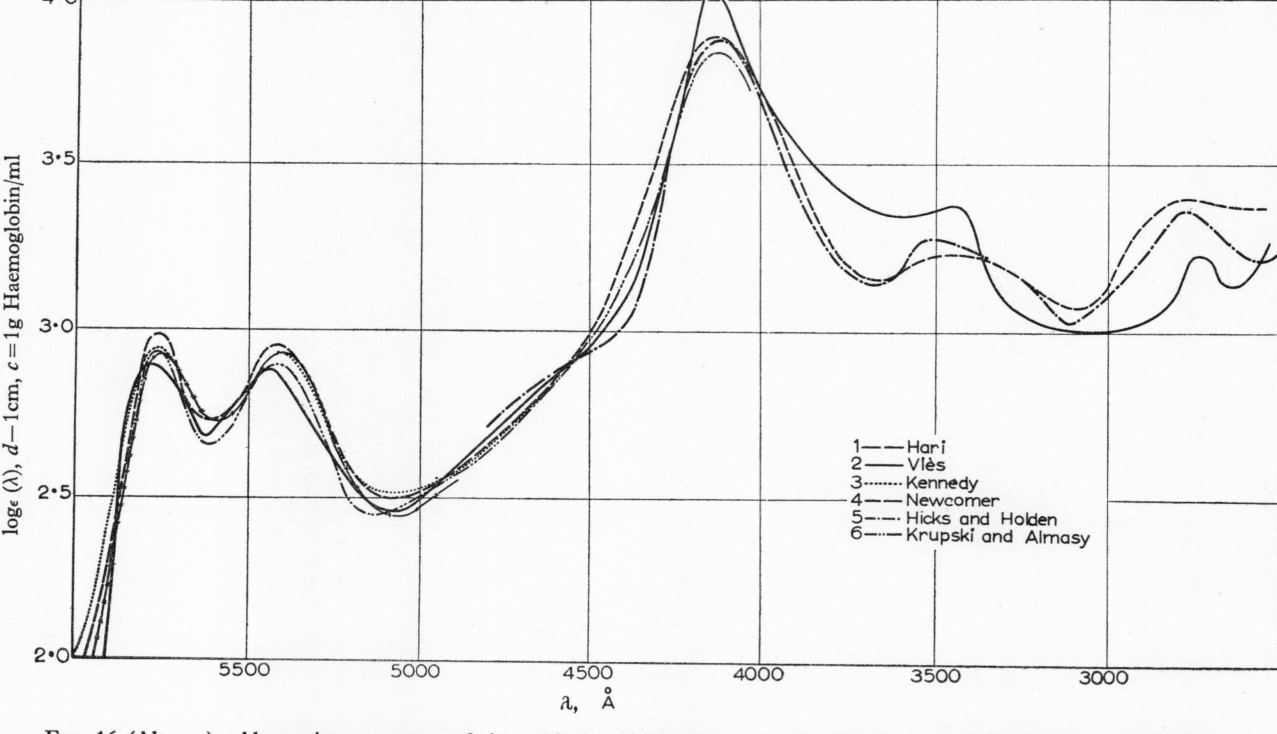

FIG. 16 (Almasy)—Absorption spectrum of the oxyhaemoglobin from human blood as determined by different workers.

6 coordinate covalent bonds (d^2sp^3) and the appearance of the octahedral structure. Oxyhaemoglobin and carboxyhaemoglobin are diamagnetic (same structure as that of the ferrocyanide ion). The detachment of one of the imidazole groups from the complex and the transformation of the ionic bond of the other group into a covalent bond, brings about a change in the pK of the two imidazole groups thus explaining the Haldane effect (change in the isoelectric point of haemoglobin at the moment of its oxygenation).

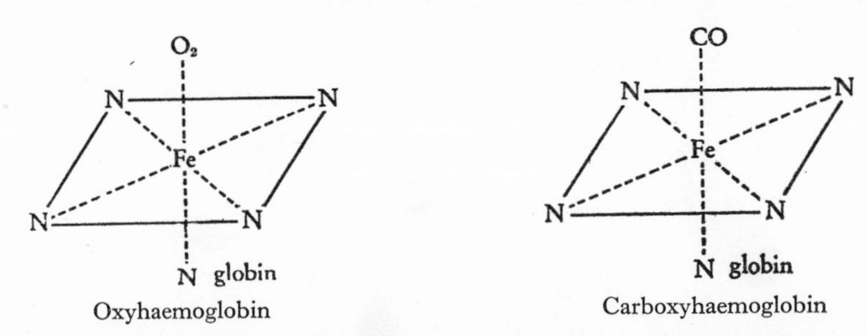

Oxyhaemoglobin Carboxyhaemoglobin

Haemoglobin can be oxidized to methaemoglobin or ferrihaemoglobin by oxidizing agents other than oxygen. Methaemoglobin is a parahaematin of a special type since it contains 5 unpaired electrons, therefore all the bonds in the complex are electrovalent.

Haemoglobin possesses the unique property of complexing reversibly with molecular oxygen instead of being oxidized by it to ferrihaemoglobin. It is endowed with this property by the globin which forms with ferro-porphyrin a complex, which is rather unusual since, unlike other haemo-chromogens, it is paramagnetic.

The characteristics of the binding of protohaem with a special type of protein confers on haemoglobin the property used by organisms in many ways—that of being reversibly oxygenated and deoxygenated without change in the valency of the iron, which remains in the ferrous state.

Oxyhaemoglobin, like the other haemochromogens, has two absorption bands in the visible range, in addition to the Soret band which is situated in the ultra-violet (Fig. 16). Deoxygenation transforms the two-band spectrum into a one-band spectrum.

5. *Chlorocruorin*

Chlorocruorin, which acts as an oxygen carrier in certain types of Annelids, is a derivative of chlorocruorohaem. This latter substance is the haem of chlorocruoroporphyrin or Spirographis-porphyrin (from the name of the worm (*Spirographis*) whose blood is most commonly used as a source of chlorocruorin) (porphin-1,3,5,8-tetramethyl-2-formyl-4-vinyl-6,7- propionic acid). In fact, it is derived from protoporphyrin by oxidation of the vinyl group at position 2.

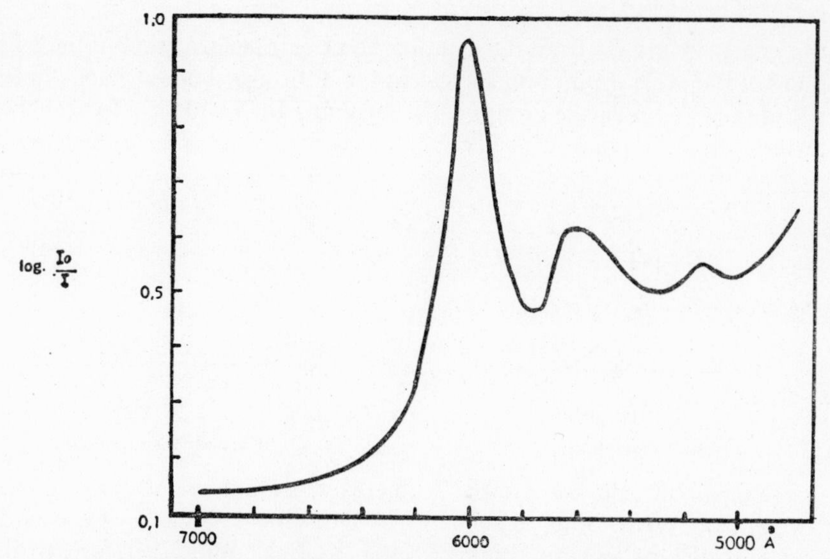

FIG. 19 (Roche and Fox)—Visible spectrum of oxychlorocruorin.

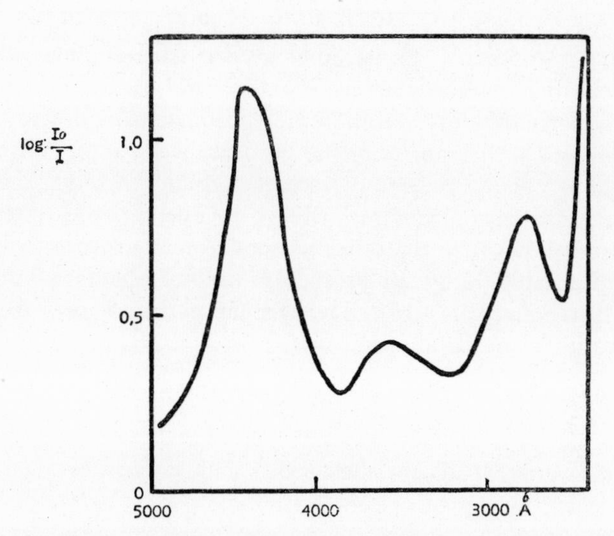

FIG. 20 (Roche and Fox)—Ultraviolet spectrum of chlorocruorin.

6. *Cytochromes*

These pigments are haemoproteins and are found in all cells which respire. The form of the haem-protein linkage, in this case, does not allow oxygen to be involved in the complex, but there is a reversible oxidation and reduction of iron. The cytochromes show the typical two-banded absorption spectrum of the haemochromogens when their iron is in the ferrous state. Since each haemochromogen is characterized by a particular position of these bands in the visible region, Keilin has been able to detect

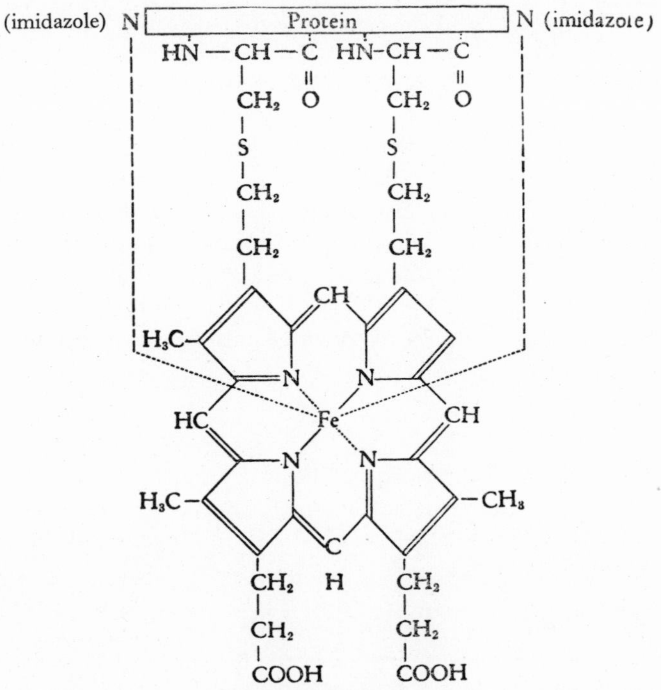

Reduced cytochrome-*c*

the presence in cells of three cytochromes which he called *a*, *b* and *c*, and which are characterized by the positions of the absorption bands of their reduced forms. Cytochrome-*c* has been isolated. It has been shown to be present in all aerobic cells. The protein part of cytochrome-*c* is rich in basic amino acids, particularly in lysine.

The haem of cytochrome-*c* is derived from protophorphyrin, two vinyl groups being reduced and bound as thioethers to cysteine residues on the rest of the molecule. The side-chains of the protein are believed to be attached to the β carbon of the vinyl groups, but this has not yet been completely proved. But, certainly, the α carbon is the point of binding to the sulphur atom. The imidazole nitrogen atoms of the two histidine residues are firmly attached to the iron, they take the place of the two water molecules in the haem complex.

Of the *a* and *b* cytochromes little is known save that the haem of cytochrome-*a* is similar to that in chlorocruorin and that the haem of cytochrome-*b* is protohaem. Cytochrome-*a* is not autoxidizable (modification of the valency of the iron by the action of molecular oxygen) whilst cytochrome-*b* is. It has been possible to identify three new haemochromogens whose spectra are similar to the spectrum of cytochrome -*a*; these are cytochromes-a_1, -a_2 and -a_3. Cytochromes-a_1 and -a_2 replace cytochrome-*a* in certain bacteria where this latter substance is missing. Cytochrome-a_3 is identical with cytochrome-oxidase, otherwise known as Warburg's respiratory enzyme. In the ferrous state it is autoxidizable, that is, it is oxidized to the ferric state by molecular oxygen. Cytochrome-*a*, which is not autoxidizable, is oxidized by cytochrome-a_3 (cytochrome-oxidase).

Molecular oxygen oxidizes ferrous cytochrome-a_3 to the ferric state. An electron is lost by the iron (which becomes trivalent) and passes to oxygen. Then the ferricytochrome-a_3 receives an electron from ferrocytochrome-*a* (which becomes ferri-) and is reconverted into ferrocytochrome-a_3.

$$2\,Fe^{++}\ (\text{cyt. } a) + 2\,Fe^{+++}\ (\text{cyt. } a_3) \rightarrow$$

$$2\,Fe^{+++}\ (\text{cyt. } a) + 2\,Fe^{++}\ (\text{cyt. } a_3)$$

$$2\,Fe^{++}\ (\text{cyt. } a_3) + O_2 + 2\,H^+ \rightarrow 2\,Fe^{+++}\ (\text{cyt. } a_3) + H_2O.$$

7. *Hydroperoxidases*

In these haemoproteins the iron is in the ferric state and remains in this state. The reaction catalysed by the hydroperoxidase enzymes is the following:

$$AH_2 + H_2O_2 \rightarrow A + 2H_2O$$

(A = a phenol, ascorbic acid, etc.)

These enzymes can be divided into two groups: the peroxidases and the catalases. The peroxidases are principally to be found in plants, but they have been discovered in milk and in leucocytes. The catalytic action of peroxidase has been elucidated by B. Chance. He showed that when H_2O_2 is added to the peroxidase, a primary addition product is formed which is green. This enzyme-substrate complex is transformed into a pale red compound.

$$\text{Per Fe}^{+++}\text{OH} + \text{HOOR} \rightleftarrows \text{Per Fe}^{+++}\text{OOR} + H_2O$$
(brown) (green)

$$\text{Per Fe}^{+++}\text{OOR} \rightleftarrows \text{Per Fe}^{+++}\text{OOR}$$
(green) (pale-red)

$$\text{Per Fe}^{+++}\text{OOR} + AH_2 \rightarrow \text{Per Fe}^{+++}\text{OH} + \text{ROH} + \text{A}$$

Another hydroperoxidase is catalase. This is a particular type of peroxidase which can decompose hydrogen peroxide in the absence of a second substrate :

$$2\ H_2O_2 \rightarrow 2\ H_2O + O_2$$

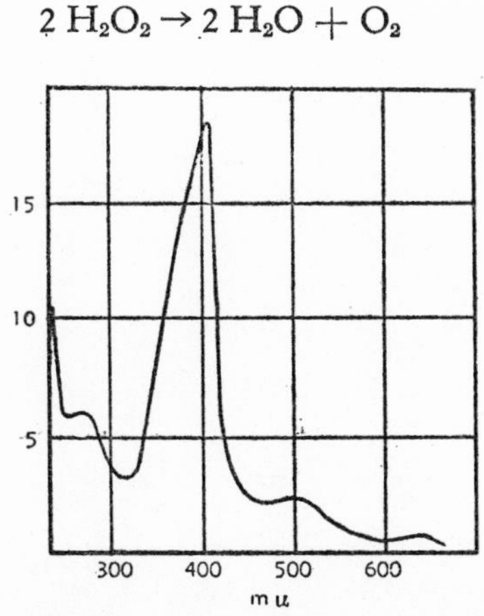

FIG. 21 (H. Theorell)—Absorption spectrum of crystalline peroxidase.

(*b*) *Chlorophylls and Chlorophyll-proteins*

Chlorophylls-*a* and *b* are extracted from leaves by acetone, along with other pigments. The addition of an equal volume of petroleum ether and a small amount of water, to this extract, removes most of the chlorophyll. From this petroleum ether solution it is possible, by extraction with aqueous methanol, to remove most of the xanthophyll and a little of the chlorophyll-*b*. Extracting with water several times, in this way, one finishes by precipitating the chlorophyll, which is collected on a filter and its two constituents separated, by utilizing the fact that chlorophyll-*a* is more soluble in petroleum ether, and chlorophyll-*b* is more soluble in methyl alcohol.

The chlorophylls are methylphytol esters of the chlorophyllines, which are the corresponding acids. These are neutral substances containing magnesium in a non-ionic form. A hydrolase, called for this reason chlorophyllase, splits off from chlorophylls a C-20 (with one double bond) aliphatic alcohol which is a diterpene derivative named phytol (see p. 31).

When the phytol is separated from a chlorophyll in acetone solution, the green compound remaining is a chlorophylline.

The formula below shows that the chlorophylls are magnesium complexes of a modified porphin structure, isomeric with protoporphyrin. Chlorophyll-*a* and chlorophyll-*b* are present in green plants and the green algae. Chlorophyll-*b* differs from chlorophyll-*a* by replacement of a methyl group in position 3 by a formyl group. The structures of chlorophylls *c* and *d* are still not completely known. The brown algae contain chlorophylls *a* and *c*, and the red algae chlorophylls *a* and *d*.

Bacteriochlorophyll, which is present in the purple bacteria, differs from chlorophyll-*a* in two respects :

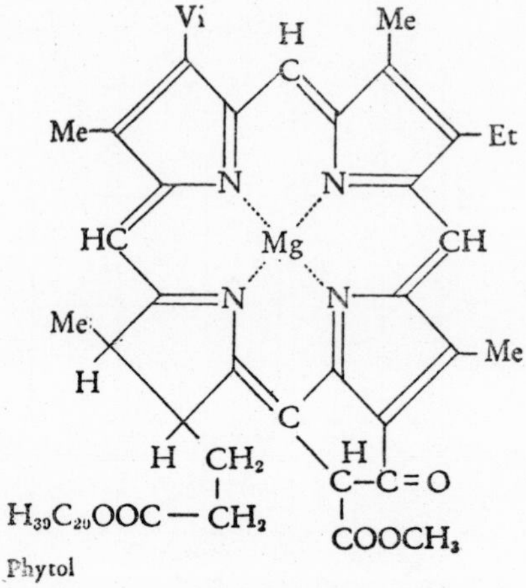

Chlorophyll-*a*

the replacement of a vinyl group by acetyl, and the reduction of ring II to a dihydropyrrol structure.

If the magnesium is removed from chlorophyll, a phaeophytin is left, and if, in addition, the phytol is removed then the remaining fragment is named a "phaeophorbide", and has the same structure as porphyrin, apart from the presence of two extra hydrogen atoms and a resulting redistribution of double bonds.

In the *grana* of leaves, the chlorophylls are associated with proteins to form complex macromolecules whose nature is still obscure.

(*c*) *Metalloflavoproteins*

Flavin phosphate (FP) or flavin mononucleotide (FMN) (see p. 69) exist in combination with protein, in a macromolecular form which bears the name "old yellow enzyme", thus called because others have since been isolated from yeast and other types of cell. The "old yellow enzyme" plays a catalytic role in the oxidation of glucose-6-phosphate. Another macromolecule of the same type is the "new yellow enzyme" in which the flavin is flavin-adenine dinucleotide (FAD), and which plays a similar catalytic role to the "old yellow enzyme", the two being present in the same cells. Corresponding to the flavoproteins there is a whole series of metalloflavoproteins resulting from the chelation of copper, iron or molybdenum.

B. Metalloproteins in which the Metal is Bound Directly to the Protein

In proteins, the carboxyl and amino groups are, for the most part, combined in peptide linkages, so that it is chiefly the polar side chains which form complexes with metals. If we refer back to Fig. 13, we have a list of side chains of this type. They are those whose pK is below 10. Those groups whose pK is above 10 are such strong bases that they cannot form bonds with metals.

Most protein molecules, then, have many points where complexes may be formed with metals. Among these metals it is worthwhile to distinguish those which appear to be coordinated strongly and by many different polar side-chains : such are mercury, silver, copper and zinc. The alkaline earth metals, like calcium, seem to be bound primarily by free carboxyl groups, or, in the phosphoproteins such as casein, by phosphate groups.

The most abundant metals in the biosphere (Na, K, Ca, Mg), which are bound strongly to proteins, are those whose internal electronic levels are full whilst the external ones are not. They have the very stable electronic structure found in the rare gases. They therefore bind to functional groups by electrostatic attraction whilst the transition elements tend to use their incompletely filled inner orbits to form covalent bonds.

(*a*) *Proteins Binding Copper*

As in the case of the association of a haem and a protein, the nature of which association controls the different properties and functions of the macromolecule, macromolecules of proteins and copper differ from each other, both in their properties and in their functions. Examples of this type of association are the phenolases and the haemocyanins.

1. *Phenolase* (*phenol oxidase*)

This molecule of protein and copper has a double function, as a catalyst in the *o*-hydroxylation of phenols and in the dehydrogenation of *o*-diphenols.

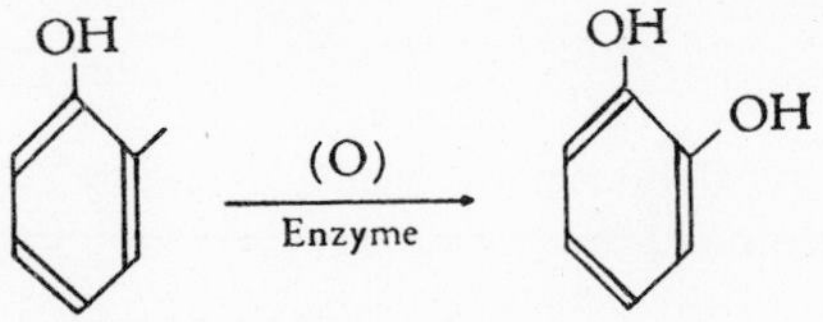

OH → (O) Enzyme → OH, OH

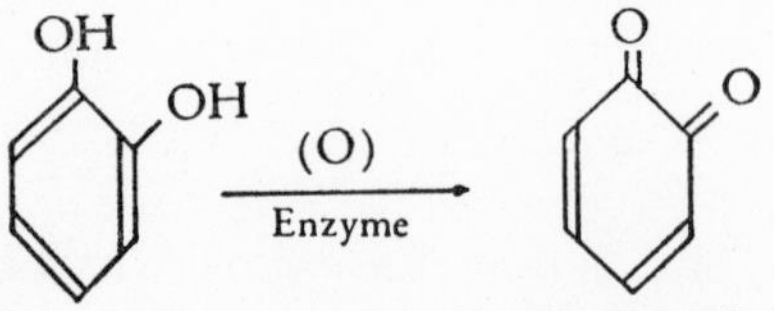

OH, OH → (O) Enzyme → O, O

Similarly, phenolase oxidizes *o*- and *p*- polyphenols.

In the course of these reactions, cupric copper of the phenolase is reduced to cuprous copper which is again oxidized by oxygen.

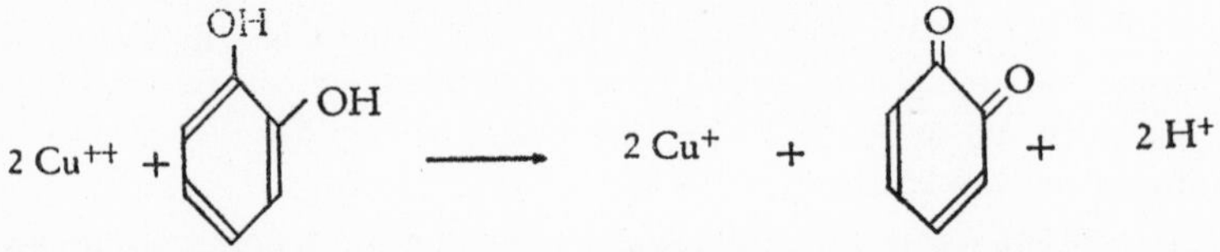

$$2\,Cu^{++} + \text{(OH, OH)} \longrightarrow 2\,Cu^{+} + \text{(O, O)} + 2\,H^{+}$$

$$2\,Cu^{+} + 2\,H^{+} + 1/2\,O_2 \rightarrow 2\,Cu^{++} + H_2O$$

There are many uses made of the properties of the cupriprotein phenolase, both in plants and in animals : respiration, biosynthesis, scelerotization of cuticles, pigmentation, etc.

2. *Haemocyanins*

These cuproproteins are oxygen carriers found in certain animals belonging to the mollusc and arthropod families. They are blue in the oxygenated state and colourless in the reduced state. The spectrum of haemocyanin is very similar to that of any copper-protein in which cupric copper is bound to an -SH group.

The absorption spectra of oxyhaemocyanin in the visible and ultraviolet regions (Figs. 23 and 24) can be superimposed on the spectra of copper-serum albumin in which the copper is attached to a sulphhydryl group.

(*b*) *Proteins Binding Iron*

Examples of this widely distributed type of compound are the haemerythrins, ferritin and transferrin.

1. *Haemerythrins*

These are large molecules of protein and iron in which the iron, according to Klotz and Klotz, appears to be partly ferrous and partly ferric. The haemerythrins which can be oxygenated like the haemoglobins, chlorocruorins and the haemocyanins, like these substances, function as oxygen

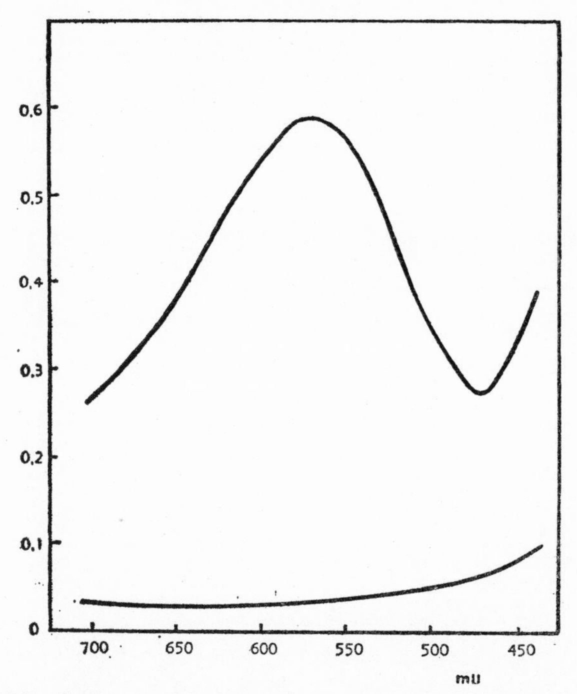

FIG. 23 (Redfield)—Spectrum of the haemocyanin of a gastropod (*Busycon canaliculatum* in the visible region. Upper curve : oxyhaemocyanin. Lower curve : reduced haemocyanin)

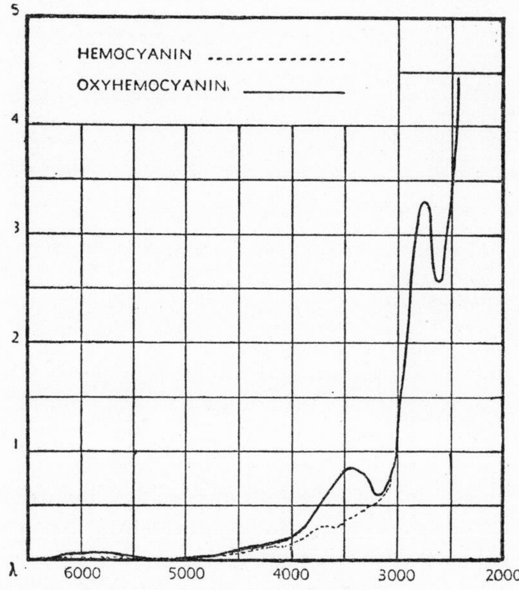

FIG. 24 (Roche)—Absorption spectrum of the haemocyanin from the snail.

carriers. This use is characteristic of a group of animals, the sipunculids. The absorption spectra of the haemerythrins are analogous to those of the haemocyanins. Like the latter, they do not show the absorption characteristics of haem derivatives that we have noted in the case of the haemoglobins, cytochromes and hydroperoxidases. Oxyhaemerythrin is wine-red whilst haemerythrin is colourless. The spectrum of oxyhaemerythrin is like that of ferriproteins. The iron of haemerythrin, like the copper of haemocyanin, appears to be attached to an -SH group.

2. *Ferritin*

Ferritin is a compound of a protein with an iron hydroxide whose formula is $[(FeOOH)_8.(FeOPO_3H_2)]$. In certain organisms, and particularly in mammals, it serves as a means of storing iron in organs such as the liver and spleen.

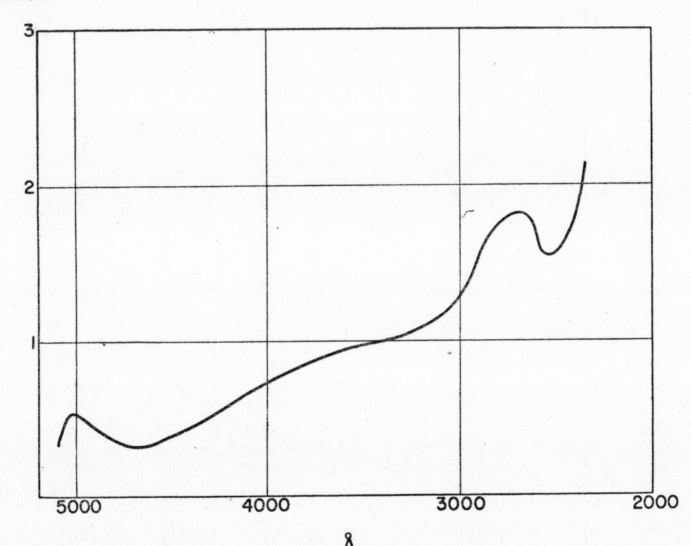

FIG. 26 (Florkin)—Absorption spectrum of the haemerythrin from *Sipunculus nudus*.

3. *Transferrin* (*siderophilin*)

In the blood plasma of mammals there is present a β-pseudo-globulin called transferrin or siderophilin, and which at a definite point in its molecule forms an iron complex. This protein, whose molecular weight is in the region of 90,000, makes up about 3% by weight of the plasma proteins. The iron is complexed by it in the ferric form and only in the presence of CO_2. When the level of iron in the plasma is at its normal value, which in man is 129γ/100 ml., the transferrin is saturated to the extent of 30% of the maximum amount of iron which it can carry. The same protein can also fix copper.

V. LIPOPROTEINS

The lipoproteins are macromolecules that are complexes of proteins with simple or complex lipides. Complexes of steroids and their esters and carotenoids and their esters with proteins are generally classed under this heading.

Lipoproteins are very widely distributed in the biosphere. They are very large and very unstable macromolecules. They are found in all parts of the cell. Certain authors maintain that the chlorophyll-proteins are really chlorophyll-lipoproteins. Whatever the truth of this, the study of lipoproteins has not progressed far.

One of these substances, however, has been the subject of much exhaustive study; this is the lipoprotein of mammalian blood plasma. It is a very complex macromolecule made up of complex lipides, cholesterol, cholesterol esters and polypeptide chains.

REFERENCES

GURD, F. R. N. (1954). *Chemical Specificity in Biological Interactions.* (A collection of papers read by various authors, the principal theme being the formation of complexes of proteins with metals and with other molecules.) Academic Press, New York.

LEMBERG, R. and LEGGE, J. W. (1949). *Hematin Compounds and Bile Pigments.* Inter-science, New York.

WYMAN, J., Jr. (1948). Heme proteins. *Adv. Protein Chem.*, **4**, 407–531.

PART TWO

ENZYMES AND BIOCHEMICAL ENERGETICS

CHAPTER I

GENERAL PRINCIPLES OF BIOCHEMICAL ENERGETICS

I. FREE ENERGY

A. Free Energy and Work

The first law of thermodynamics states that the total amount of energy in a system does not change when the different forms of this energy (chemical, mechanical, thermal, electrical, etc.) are converted from one to the other. If a system receives a certain quantity of energy ΔE, from outside, then the outside loses the same amount $\Delta E'$ and in all the systems together taking part in the exchange, the total energy change is zero :

$$\Delta E = - \Delta E'$$

Let us consider, for example, a system in the gaseous state. On receiving from its surroundings an amount of heat Q, it will expand and in doing so will perform work W, contributing to the energy of the surroundings :

$$\Delta E = Q - W$$

But if the system we are considering is unable to perform external work, as would be the case in a container of constant volume in which an endothermic reaction is occurring whose energy is supplied by the surroundings in the form of heat, then, we have

$$\Delta E = Q$$

The reactions studied in the laboratory are not of the type just described. They generally take place at atmospheric pressure, that is, with a change of volume. Let us consider again the above reaction, only this time allowing the pressure to remain constant, which implies that the volume changes and work is done on the surroundings. The system will receive the heat Q from the outside and whilst the endothermic reaction is taking place the reaction mixture will undergo a change in volume performing positive or negative work. The change in heat content of the whole system under consideration is measured by the amount of heat Q, which is divided into that part which brings about a change in the energy of the reacting system and another part equal to the work which has been performed.

$$\Delta H = Q = \Delta E + P\Delta V$$

(variation in heat content)

In fact, if the pressure P remains constant, and the increase in volume is ΔV, then the work which has been done is equal to $P\Delta V$. Since we have selected an endothermic reaction, ΔH has a positive value. Its value would have been negative if an exothermic reaction had been chosen.

At 20° and 1 atmosphere, ΔH in the case of the combustion of glucose ($C_6H_{12}O_6 + 6O_2 \rightarrow 6H_2O + 6CO_2$) has a value of $-673,000$ calories per mole of glucose (heat of combustion), whilst in the case of a mole of palmitic acid ($C_{16}H_{32}O_2 + 23O_2 \rightarrow 16CO_2 + 16H_2O$) its value is $-2,380,000$ calories.

If we place in a calorimeter, at a temperature of 15° (one calorie = the amount of heat required to raise the temperature of a gram of water from 14·5° to 15·5°), zinc, mercurous sulphate and water in the molar proportions in accordance with the following equation :

$$Zn + Hg_2SO_4 + 7H_2O \rightarrow ZnSO_4.7H_2O + 2Hg$$

we obtain the products indicated and we can measure a ΔH value of $-82,000$ calories.

However, if we assemble the same components into a battery at 15° and 1 atmosphere so that it functions perfectly reversibly, the electrical energy obtained is only equivalent to 66,000 calories. The term *free energy* (ΔF) is given to the maximum work which is obtainable from a chemical reaction taking place under completely reversible conditions at constant temperature and pressure. In the case of the reaction between zinc, mercurous sulphate and water, $\Delta H - \Delta F = (-82,000) - (-66,000) = -16,000$ cal/mole.

This represents the energy which is lost (in the form of heat) during the reaction. Although the first law of thermodynamics states that there is a definite relation between work and heat, it says nothing about the work which can be obtained from a given amount of heat. It says only that the total amount of energy does not change.

The second law of thermodynamics states that there are definite restrictions on the transformation of heat into work. The weight which furnishes a clock with its mechanical energy descends by a spontaneous process. It is possible, at constant temperature, by the introduction of external work, to cause the weight to be raised again, but one cannot reverse this spontaneous process by supplying heat at constant temperature. In natural spontaneous processes, a part of the energy liberated is not used to perform work at constant temperature and pressure. This fraction, which is not used isothermally, divided by the absolute temperature T, is the increase in entropy (ΔS). All spontaneous processes are accompanied by an increase in entropy. Such a process is the diffusion of a substance in solution from a concentrated solution to a less concentrated solution. The increase in entropy which accompanies such a process can be considered as the result of passing from one state to another with an increase in disorder, or, if one prefers, a decrease of the ordered state.

To illustrate more clearly the difference between $-\Delta H$ and $-\Delta F$, that is, between the heat liberated by a reaction and the maximum possible work which can be done by that reaction, we may consider molecules as containing two different types of energy. One is an ordered energy : it unites the atoms to each other by primary or secondary valency bonds. It is this energy which can do work. The other is of a disordered nature (vibrational, rotational and translational). What primarily interests the biochemist is work, chemical or otherwise, obtainable from a reaction. If the reaction takes place with liberation of a great deal of useful energy, then work may be done.

It can be seen that it is ΔF which we wish to know. But it should be noted that ΔF does not depend solely on the nature of the chemical reaction. It also depends on the concentrations of the reactants, and the direction of the reaction will also depend on these concentrations. It would not be practicable to compile tables of ΔF for all concentrations, so its value is determined under defined conditions : liquids or solids in the pure state, gas at a pressure of 1 atmosphere, solutions at 0·1M, temperature 25°. Concentrations thus defined are assigned a value of unity and, from the ΔF° value thus defined, it is possible to calculate values of ΔF for other conditions.

The use of ΔF values is limited, as far as the biochemist is concerned. Pardee compares the information they give with that given to a car-driver by a map showing contour lines but no roads. The driver, knowing the power of his engine, can deduce whether he can, or cannot, climb the slope between two points. No information is given him as to the road to take.

B. Free Energy and the Equilibrium Constant

Under given conditions of temperature, pH, etc., each of the chemical reactions occurring in the organism is in a stationary state of dynamic equilibrium (see later). An organism of a given species, given age, and under specified conditions, has a definite composition. Undoubtedly, in a species, the compositions of two individuals show differences, but these differences are much smaller between individuals of one species than between individuals belonging to different genera, and less still, when different families, classes or orders, are considered.

A reversible reaction is usually written thus :

$$A + B \rightleftarrows C + D$$

According to the law of mass action, the velocity of the reaction between A and B is proportional to the product of the active masses of these two compounds, and the reaction velocity from left to right is written :

$$\nu_1 = K_1(A)\,(B)$$

whilst that from right to left is :

$$\nu_2 = K_2(C)\,(D)$$

At equilibrium, when $v_1 = v_2$, $k_1(A)\,(B)$ is equal to $k_2(C)\,(D)$ and the equilibrium constant of the reversible reaction is written :

$$K = \frac{(C)\,(D)}{(A)\,(B)}$$

We can represent a reversible reaction by using small letters for the number of moles of each reactant.

$$aA + bB \rightleftarrows cC + dD$$

The relation between the free energy change and the equilibrium constant is given by the equation

$$\Delta F = -RT \ln K + RT \ln \frac{(C)^c(D)^d}{(A)^a(B)^b}$$

K is the equilibrium constant, that is, the ratio between the product $(C)^c(D)^d$ and the product $(A)^a(B)^b$ under conditions of thermodynamic equilibrium. The second term permits ΔF to be calculated for different activities. If these latter are equal to unity, the second term disappears and we have

$$\Delta F^\circ = -RT \ln K$$

In common logarithms, and replacing the gas constant R by its value (1·987 cal/degree/mole),

$$-\Delta F^\circ = 4{\cdot}575\ T \log K$$

C. Free Energy and Electromotive Force

It is known that one can obtain work from certain chemical reactions by constructing a cell. The maximum work ΔF can be obtained from a direct and precise measurement, that of the E.M.F. of the cell. The voltage E is proportional to the work done for each electron transferred and if it is known, ΔF can be calculated from the equation

$$\Delta F = -n\mathbf{F}E$$

in which n represents the number of electrons transported in the reaction and **F** is the Faraday constant.

In oxidation–reduction reactions, as we shall see, the measurement of E.M.F. provides invaluable information about the free energy of numerous biochemical reactions.

D. Sources of Free Energy

The organisms in Nature obtain their vital energy from two main free energy sources. One is situated in the biosphere itself, it is the covalent energy of the organism's food and depends upon the properties of the external electronic orbits of the constituent atoms.

The other is outside the biosphere : it is nuclear energy coming into it in the form of light.

Ordinary hydrogen has a nucleus made up of a single proton around which a single electron revolves.

The atom of ordinary helium has two protons and two neutrons in the nucleus and two external electrons. If we take the exact masses of a proton and a neutron, add them together and multiply by two, we obtain a figure of 4·03304 units. But, if we measure the mass of the helium nucleus, we shall obtain 4·00279. Between the calculated and the measured value there is a difference of 0·03025 units, equivalent to an energy value of 28·2 MeV (millions of electron volts). This is the energy of binding the mass lost in order to keep together such particles as the protons which, because of their extremely small size, develop considerable forces of repulsion.

Since this binding energy is 0 in the hydrogen atom and is equal to 28·2 MeV in the helium atom, the transformation of a hydrogen atom into a helium atom will liberate 28·2 MeV. This is what happens in the centre of the sun which, because of its considerable diameter (1,392,000 km or 109 times the diameter of the earth), has a resulting gravitational field strong enough to retain its hydrogen which forms 99% of its weight. The centre of the sun has a temperature of 20,000,000° C and is under a pressure of several tens of thousands of atmospheres, so that the kinetic energy of the hydrogen atoms is sufficient for collisions between them to bring about nuclear reactions. The sun converts hydrogen atoms into helium atoms by means of a cyclic process in which carbon acts as a catalyst. It is this nuclear energy which reaches the biosphere in the form of heat and various forms of radiation, in particular those which are utilized by organisms containing chlorophyll.

However, a great many organisms use sources of non-nuclear energy. This energy is derived from the change in energy level of electrons during the atomic rearrangements which accompany the changes in structure of nutrient molecules, and those which accompany oxido-reduction reactions. These changes in potential are expressed in electron-volts (1 electron-volt = the kinetic energy acquired by a particle carrying the charge on an electron when accelerated by a potential of one volt). The commonly used unit is a million times greater (MeV). The energy corresponding to an electron-volt is equal to $1{\cdot}60207 \pm 0.00007 \times 10^{-12}$ ergs. The energy in calories per mole corresponding to one electron-volt per molecule $= 23{\cdot}05285 \pm 3{\cdot}2$ cal/mole).

II ENERGY COUPLING

Exergonic reactions are the only reactions which can occur in the biosphere. It is, therefore, necessary to explain by what mechanism cells perform numerous biosyntheses where the resulting molecules have an energy content higher than that of their starting materials.

In the cell, the energy of a chemical bond can be transferred to another bond by only one possible mechanism, that in which two separate reactions have one substance common to both. The transfer of energy is accomplished by utilizing part of the free energy of an exergonic reaction to bring about a reaction which, by itself, would be endergonic and would not, therefore, otherwise take place.

Consider the following endergonic reaction :

$$\text{(I) } A \rightarrow B$$

$(K_1 = 0{\cdot}01,\ \Delta F^\circ = +2{,}470 \text{ cal.})$ $\left(\text{at equilibrium } \begin{matrix} A \rightleftarrows B \\ 100 \quad 1 \end{matrix}\right)$

We are given the value of the equilibrium constant and the reaction will be at equilibrium when the concentration of A is a hundred times that of B, and it will not take place from left to right except when the concentration of B is less than one per cent of that of A. If the concentration of B is greater than one per cent of that of A, the reaction will take place from right to left.

Now, consider the exergonic reaction :

$$\text{(II) } B \rightarrow C$$

$(K_2 = 1000,\ \Delta F^\circ = -4110 \text{ cal.})$ $\left(\text{at equilibrium } \begin{matrix} B \rightleftarrows C \\ 1 \quad 1000 \end{matrix}\right)$

It will take place from left to right until C is a 1000 times more concentrated than B.

Now let us suppose that the two reactions occur simultaneously. Reaction II will continuously remove the product of reaction I, and this reaction, endergonic when the ratio $[B]/[A]$ is greater than 1/100, will become exergonic and, consequently, will proceed from left to right, when the concentration of B becomes sufficiently small for the ratio $[B]/[A]$ to fall below 1/100. For the combined reaction, $\Delta F = (2470 - 4110) = -1370$ cal). The overall reaction is therefore exergonic.

The exergonic reaction II causes B to disappear. As B disappears, the ΔF of reaction II becomes progressively smaller in absolute value, whilst the ΔF of reaction I approaches zero (the reaction becomes less and less endergonic). When the ΔF of I becomes negative (because $[B]$ is sufficiently small), the two reactions proceed in the direction $A \rightarrow B \rightarrow C$ up to the time when the two ΔF values become equal to 0, which is the point of final equilibrium.

III. ENERGY-RICH BONDS

It is to Lipmann (1941) that we owe the classification of the phosphorylated compounds which occur in Nature, into two types—those possessing a bond whose hydrolysis is accompanied by a considerable release of free energy, and those which yield much less energy. The bonds which are "energy-rich" from the point of view of the release of free energy by hydrolysis are, in fact, for the physical-chemist, weak bonds, being rapidly and easily broken, whilst those bonds which release little free energy on hydrolysis are stronger and more difficult to hydrolyse. When the different types of phosphoric esters were listed in the first part of this book (p. 62), we noted the existence of bonds of the acid anhydride type, resulting from the union of two molecules of acid with elimination of a molecule of water. These bonds are hydrolysed with the release of large amounts of energy as can be seen, for example, when acetic anhydride is mixed with water: the reaction takes place with a considerable increase in temperature.

The most important type of acid anhydride in biochemistry is that between two molecules of phosphoric acid, as exemplified by the two terminal bonds of ATP (p. 67), but the pyrophosphate bond is not the only type of energy-rich bond as can be seen from Table XI. Mixed anhydrides of carboxylic and phosphoric acids (acyl-phosphates), phosphorylated enol groups (enolphosphates), phosphorylated guanidine groups (guanidine phosphates), compounds of sulphhydryl groups with phosphoric or carboxylic acids (thioesters or thiophosphates), all these types of compound are energy-rich.

How does one explain this release of large amounts of free energy when an energy-rich bond is hydrolysed? As far as the pyrophosphate linkage is concerned, one of the reasons is that in pyrophosphate the number of resonating structures is much smaller than in inorganic phosphate. Also, in the pyrophosphate molecule there are several like charges close to each other and their reciprocal repulsion is balanced by a certain amount of energy which is set free on hydrolysis. Moreover, the neutralization of the acid groups liberated on hydrolysis is also productive of energy. Considerations of a like character can explain the liberation of energy which accompanies hydrolysis of the acyl-phosphate and guanidine-phosphate bonds, but they cannot explain this in the case of the phosphoenolpyruvate bond. In this case, one of the sources of the energy is the transformation of the enol form of pyruvic acid into the keto form.

The formation of glycogen from glucose is an example of an apparently endergonic reaction which is, in fact, made exergonic by the mediation of a molecule having an energy-rich bond, ATP, which acts by phosphorylating one of the reactants :—

$$\text{glucose} + (\text{glycogen})_n \rightarrow (\text{glycogen})_{n+1} + H_2O \qquad \Delta F^\circ = +5{,}000 \text{ cal}$$

The reaction can be split up into the following stages :

$$\text{glucose} + \text{ATP} \rightarrow \text{G-6-P} + \text{ADP} + H^+ \qquad \Delta F^\circ = -8{,}000 \text{ cal}$$
$$\text{G-6-P} \rightarrow \text{G-1-P} \qquad \Delta F^\circ = +1{,}800 \text{ cal}$$
$$\text{G-1-P} + (\text{glycogen})_n \rightarrow (\text{glycogen})_{n+1} + H_3PO_4 \qquad \Delta F^\circ = +\ 200 \text{ cal}$$

The sum of these reactions leads to the following :

$$\text{glucose} + (\text{glycogen})_n + \text{ATP} \rightarrow (\text{glycogen})_{n+1} + \text{ADP} + H_3PO_4 + H^+ \qquad \Delta F^\circ = -6{,}000 \text{ cal}$$

IV. THE PHOSPHATE CYCLE

Research carried out during recent years has revealed that the energy stored in food which is broken down during cellular metabolism is gradually liberated in "packets" of energy which can be stored and utilized at a later date. The direct oxidation of glucose by oxygen :

$$6O_2 + C_6H_{12}O_6 \rightarrow 6CO_2 + 6H_2O \quad \Delta F^\circ = -686{,}000 \text{ cal}$$

will release a considerable amount of energy in the form of heat, that is to say, in a non-utilizable form. But, as Pardee has remarked, one does not start a car by putting a match to the petrol tank.

The energy economy of living organisms rests on the fact that anaerobic and aerobic metabolism can give rise to energy-rich bonds, which can be stored as energy-rich bonds of ATP and this energy can be used by the cell to do various forms of work including the chemical work of biosynthesis.

V. BIOLOGICAL OXIDO-REDUCTIONS AND THE GENERATION OF ENERGY-RICH BONDS

Energy-rich bonds are generated by the conduction of certain definite electrons along definite channels. During this passage of electrons their energy level is lowered and energy-rich bonds are formed at their expense. So an organism is an electro-chemical machine whose structure is that of a special type of electronic conductor.

A. Oxido-Reduction Potentials

Consider a solution of ferric chloride. In this solution there are Fe^{+++} ions, Cl^- ions and water molecules. The solution is stable, however it is capable of accepting electrons with the conversion of Fe^{+++} to Fe^{++} : we can say that it has a certain (negative) electron pressure. We can measure this pressure, provided that we have a reference system which we can place together with the solution in an electric circuit. Let us place in the ferric

TABLE XI

Free energy liberated in the hydrolysis of various bonds

Bonds		*Kilocals/mole* (negative values)
Ester linkage	R—C(=O)—O—R′ ; R—O—PO_3H_2	2.0 - 4.0
Oside linkage	H, OR, C	4.8
Peptide linkage	R—C(=O)—NH—R′	3.0
Pyrophosphate	R—P(=O)(OH)—O~P(=O)(OH)—R′	12.0
Guanidinephosphate	R—NH—C(=NH)—NH~PO_3H_2	14.0
Enolphosphate	R=C(H)—O~PO_3H_2	16.0
Acylphosphate	R—C(=O)—O~PO_3H_2	16.0
Thioester	R—C(=O)~SR	16.0
Thiophosphate	R—S~PO_3H_2	ca. 16.0

chloride solution an electrode made of a noble metal (platinum, for example) at whose surface no chemical reaction occurs. By means of an agar bridge, we can connect the solution with another solution capable of giving or receiving electrons. In this solution we will also place a platinum electrode and we will join the two electrodes by a wire together with a potentiometer in the circuit. If the *electron pressures* of the two solutions are different there will be an *electron flow* which will be revealed by the passage of an electric current. If we know the electron pressure of the reference solution, and measure the potential difference and direction of flow of the current, then we have a basis on which to calculate the electron pressure of the first solution. As a reference solution we may take what is commonly known as the *normal hydrogen electrode*, that is, a normal solution of hydrochloric acid saturated with hydrogen gas. The e.m.f. of the system is measured with a potentiometer. The electron pressure (which depends upon the ratio between the concentrations of the oxidized and reduced substance) is called the *oxidation-reduction* (or redox) *potential* (E). The relation between E and the concentrations of the oxidized substance and the reduced substance is given by the equation :

$$E = E_o + \frac{RT}{nF} \ln \frac{\text{(oxidized form)}}{\text{(reduced form)}}$$

in which,

R is the gas constant;

T is the absolute temperature;

n is the number of electrons involved when the substance passes from the oxidized to the reduced state (for $Fe^{+++} \rightleftarrows Fe^{++}$, $n = 1$);

E_o is a special constant for each particular system.

Furthermore, ln signifies log to the base e and F is the Faraday ($F =$ 96,500 J, and since 1 cal $= 4{\cdot}18$ J, $F = 23{,}098$ cal).

If the concentration of the oxidized form (Ox) is equal to the concentration of the reduced form (Red),

$$(Ox) = (Red) \text{ and } \ln \frac{(Ox)}{(Red)} = 0.$$

$$E = E_o + \frac{RT}{F} \times 0 = E_o.$$

To measure E_o, it is only necessary to measure E when $(Ox) = (Red)$. E_o is termed the standard oxidation-reduction potential, it is the potential which is measured against the hydrogen electrode at the pH of a normal solution of HCl (pH $= 0$, since log $1 = 0$). It has become customary to state the potential at, or around, pH 7·0 and this standard potential is designated by the symbol E_o'.

In Table XII is listed a series of E_o' values for a number of systems important biochemically. If system A is characterized by a higher (or less negative) value of E than system B, then B can serve as a reducing system for system A, and A as an oxidizing system for B.

We have seen (p. 134) that there is a definite relation between the change in free energy ΔF and electromotive force E, and that by means of the following equation it is possible to calculate the electrical work accompanying the formation of a mole of reaction-product.

$$\Delta F = -nFE$$

Let us now consider, inside a cell, the oxidation (or dehydrogenation) of lactate to pyruvate, the proton and the electron of the hydrogen, or the electron alone, being conducted through several intermediates as far as cytochrome-*c*. Let us also suppose that the pyruvate and lactate are present at equal concentrations and that the cytochrome-*c* is 50% reduced and 50% oxidized. The number of intermediates does not matter. E'_o for the lactate-pyruvate system = 0·180 at pH 7·0; at the same pH, for the system cytochrome-*c* (Ox)/cytochrome-*c* (Red), E'_o = 0·262. Since both systems are 50% reduced, $E = E'_o$ for both,

$$\text{and } \Delta E = 0{\cdot}442 \text{ volts}$$

whence $-\Delta F = 2 \times 96{,}500 \times 0{\cdot}442 = 85{,}500 \text{ J} = 20{,}500 \text{ cal.}$

So that the energy liberated by the oxidation of a mole of lactate by a mole of cytochrome-*c* under the specified conditions is 20,500 calories. Johnson calculates that this amount of energy would be sufficient to keep a 100 W lamp alight for 14 min.

TABLE XII

Some oxidation-reduction potentials

System	Temp.	pH	E_ol (volts)
α-ketoglutarate-succinate		7·0	−0·600
Acetaldehyde-acetate		7·0	−0·468
H⁺-hydrogen	All. temps.	0·0	−0·060
Coenzyme I	30	7·0	−0·282
Lactate-pyruvate	35	7·01	−0.180
Malate-oxaloacetate	38	7·0	−0·102
Succinate-maleate	37	7·0	−0·094
Cytochrome-*b*	20	7·4	−0·04
Succinate-fumarate		7·0	0·00
Cytochrome-*c*		7·0	+0·262
Cytochrome-*a*	20	7·4	+0·29

B. Formation of Energy-rich Bonds during Oxidation-reduction Reactions

Although the passage of electrons, either from one point to another in the same molecule, or by a conductor made up of a series of systems of higher and higher oxidation potential, is accompanied by a change in free energy, these free energies, like that resulting from the direct oxidation of glucose, are not in a form which can be used by the cell. These free energies will be degraded into heat and lost to the cell unless some mechanism exists to store them in the form of energy-rich bonds of ATP, the universal source of cellular work.

It is, therefore, important now to consider this mechanism—the coupling of electron transfer and phosphorylation. There are two aspects to be considered : phosphorylation at substrate level and phosphorylation during the transfer of electrons through a series of intermediates.

(*a*) *Phosphorylation at Substrate Level*

An example of this type of genesis of pyrophosphate linkages is furnished by the oxidation of phosphoglyceraldehyde to 1,3-diphosphoglyceric acid, an oxidation which occurs during glycolysis.

Phosphoglyceraldehyde dehydrogenase (PGAD) is the enzyme catalysing the oxidation (anaerobic) of phosphoglyceraldehyde which takes place with an internal redistribution of electrons and the accumulation of 16,000 calories in the acyl–phosphate bond. The enzyme, whose coenzyme is

$$\begin{array}{l} C(=O)H \\ | \\ CHOH \\ | \\ CH_2OPO(OH)_2 \end{array} + DPN^{+} + H_3PO_4 \rightleftharpoons \begin{array}{l} C(=O)O{\sim}PO(OH)_2 \\ | \\ CHOH \\ | \\ CH_2OPO(OH)_2 \end{array} + DPNH$$

Phosphoglyceryldehyde 1,3-diphosphoglyceric acid

DPN, has been crystallized. It is poor in cysteine but rich in basic amino acids. Near to an —SH group on the surface of the enzyme protein molecule there is attached a molecule of the coenzyme DPN^+. An addition complex is formed between the —SH grouping and the —N = C— of DPN^+. When phosphoglyceraldehyde is added, this bond is broken and an energy rich thioester is formed and at the same time the DPN^+ is reduced to DPNH. A phosphate residue which is also attached to the protein molecule takes the place of the thiol group and the energy of the thioester bond is transferred to the acyl-phosphate bond. 1,3-diphosphoglyceric acid subsequently detaches itself from the protein molecule.

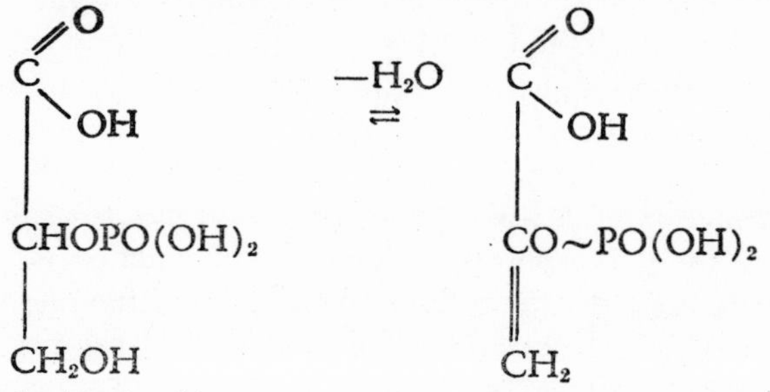

$$\begin{array}{c} C(=O)OH \\ | \\ CHOPO(OH)_2 \\ | \\ CH_2OH \end{array} \quad \underset{\rightleftharpoons}{-H_2O} \quad \begin{array}{c} C(=O)OH \\ | \\ CO{\sim}PO(OH)_2 \\ \| \\ CH_2 \end{array}$$

2-phosphoglyceric acid — phosphoenolpyruvic acid

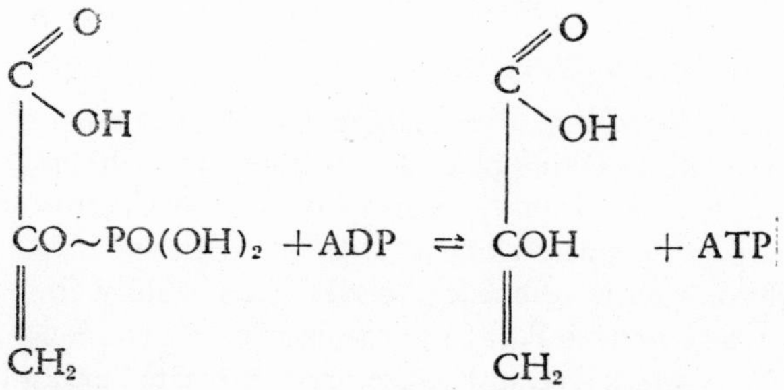

$$\begin{array}{c} C(=O)OH \\ | \\ CO{\sim}PO(OH)_2 \\ \| \\ CH_2 \end{array} + ADP \rightleftharpoons \begin{array}{c} C(=O)OH \\ | \\ COH \\ \| \\ CH_2 \end{array} + ATP$$

phosphoenolpyruvic acid — pyruvic acid (enolic form)

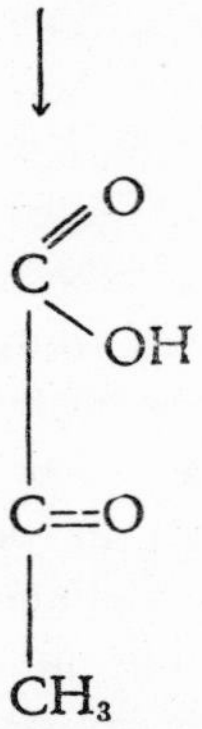

$$\downarrow$$

$$\begin{array}{c} C(=O)OH \\ | \\ C{=}O \\ | \\ CH_3 \end{array}$$

pyruvic acid (ketonic form)

This reaction can only continue till all the substrate is used up, if the reaction product, which is 1,3-diphosphoglyceric acid, is removed from the solution; in the cell, this acid then reacts with ADP, converting it into ATP; the energy-rich anhydride bond then disappears from the 1,3-diphosphoglyceric acid and reappears in ATP. 1,3-diphosphoglyceric acid + ADP ⇄ 3-phosphoglycericid + ATP.

This transfer of energy of the energy-rich acyl-phosphate bond to the energy-rich pyrophosphate bond is catalysed by a highly specific enzyme, 3-phosphoglyceric phosphokinase; this enzyme, also, has been crystallized.

An example of the transformation of an ordinary phosphate ester into an energy-rich phosphate is provided by another reaction of the glycolysis chain : the conversion of 2-phosphoglyceric acid into phosphoenolpyruvic acid followed by a transphosphorylation. The reaction (a dehydration), catalysed by enolase, results in the redistribution of the internal energy of the molecule with concentration of around 16,000 calories in the enol-phosphate bond.

The rapid transfer of this energy-rich phosphate to ADP with formation of ATP is brought about by pyruvic phosphokinase.

(*b*) *Phosphorylation in the Respiratory Chain*

As we have just seen, the formation of $\sim$P bonds is coupled with oxidation-reductions taking place at substrate level. Others may be formed in a way which depends on the energy liberated by electrons removed from the substrate as they pass along a series of carriers of increasing potential until finally oxygen is reached. Acetyl-CoA resulting from a number of metabolic reactions (see Part 3) is oxidized by a common pathway in the presence of oxygen. Here, unlike the previously cited examples taken from anaerobic glycolysis, the phosphorylations which yield pyrophosphate bonds are not coupled to oxidation-reductions at substrate level. This concept is based on a number of experimental findings. The quantitative study of this process was initiated by Belitzer in 1939. As we shall see, during the respiratory cycle which transforms substrates into CO_2 and H_2O, a series of dehydrogenations occur. If each of these dehydrogen-ations was accompanied by a phosphorylation of the substrate, then for each of these a molecule of phosphate would be removed from the solution and an atom of oxygen would be consumed (P/O would be equal to 1). Now, Belitzer calculated the ratio P/O and obtained values greater than unity. This expresses the fact that for each pair of electrons (or of electrons accompanied by protons) transferred to oxygen several phosphorylations occur. Theoretically there is nothing very astonishing about this since when we defined oxidation-reduction potentials we showed that when lactate is dehydrogenated to pyruvate, the transfer of electrons or hydrogen atoms (electron + proton) to oxygen liberates much more energy than is required for the formation of an energy-rich pyrophosphate bond.

Belitzer put forward the following hypothesis, which has been confirmed by numerous observations : the reaction producing the energy which is coupled to phosphorylation is the oxidation of the carrier, which was reduced directly by the electrons of the substrate by a second carrier of higher oxidation-reduction potential; the carrier of the highest oxidation-reduction potential is, of course, oxygen itself.

This coupling of phosphorylations to oxidation-reduction during respiration makes up the dynamo which transforms the energy of electron transfer into energy-rich bonds of ATP. Without this coupling this energy would be lost in the form of heat, and, in fact, a part of it is lost in this way. We shall leave a detailed discussion of this aspect of energy until we come to study the particular reactions involved.

VI. THE CELLULAR DYNAMO

The preceding has given us some idea of the lay-out of the cellular machine and the function of its "dynamo" (Fig. 27). Details will be studied later. This scheme is of general application for the provision of energy to the living cell from the packets of chemical energy in the form of cellular nutrients. However, there is another way of obtaining energy—by utilizing the energy of the sun to perform biosynthesis. This dynamo functions by coverting electromagnetic energy into chemical energy, but at the present time its mode of operation is not so well understood as the chemical energy dynamo described above.

However, even if not generally accepted, the scheme proposed by Calvin is of interest. The first stage of photosynthesis, is the conversion of water into a reducing substance and half a molecule of oxygen :

$$H_2O \xrightarrow{hv} 2[H] + \tfrac{1}{2}O_2$$

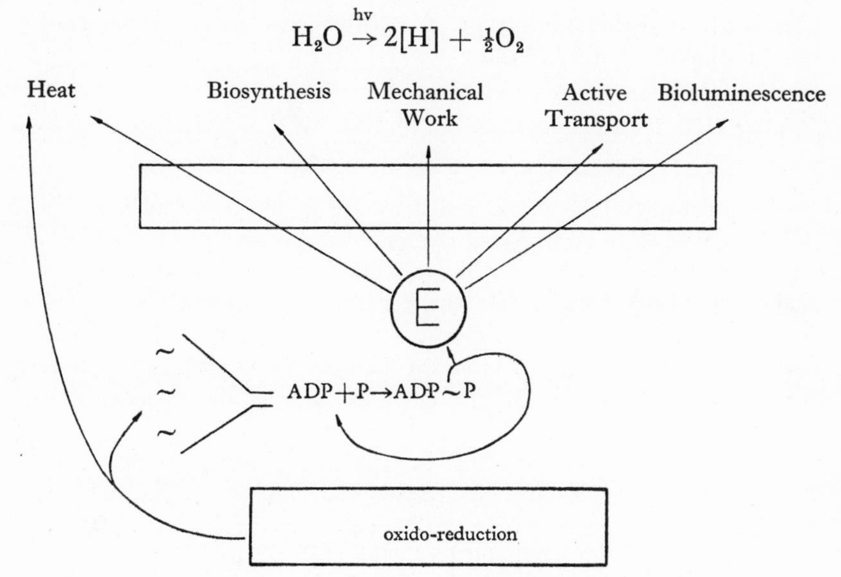

FIG. 27—General lay-out of the cellular dynamo (modified from Lipmann)

In Calvin's view, in the organized and oriented system containing chlorophyll, absorption of light liberates an electron. As depicted in Fig. 28, water is on one side of the photobattery and the disulphide form of thioctic acid on the other. Electrons move towards the thioctic acid layer and the sites which are left empty are immediately filled up by electrons coming

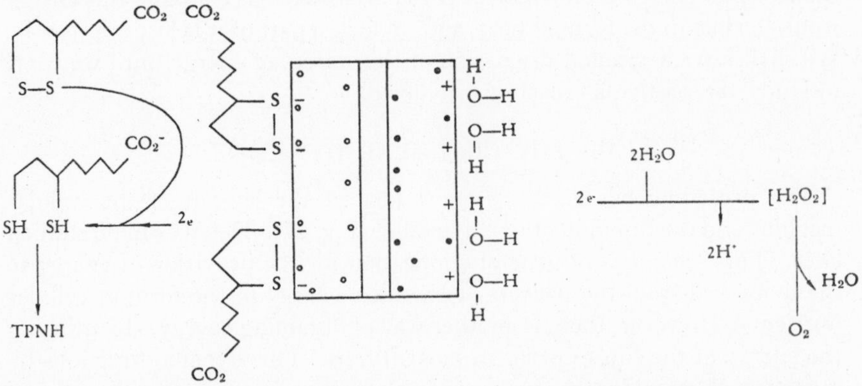

FIG. 28 (after Calvin)—The role of thioctic acid in the first stage of photosynthesis.

from the water molecules. In particular, this photobattery produces a high concentration of TPNH.

For the moment, the scheme in Fig. 28 is sufficient to illustrate the fact that the energy-transformer at the primary stage of photosynthesis is different from the chemical type of transformer. Later, we shall return to the question of photosynthesis.

VII. THE PYROPHOSPHATE BOND AND CELLULAR WORK

The pyrophosphate bonds of ATP are the coins which pay for the performance of cellular work, and there are as many examples of their use in this way as there are types of dynamic biochemical reaction.

A very common type of cellular work is the transport of a molecule against the concentration gradient, for example, the transport of glucose from a region where its concentration is low, through a membrane, to a region where the concentration of glucose is higher. Such a case is represented in Fig. 29. On the left-hand side of the membrane, corresponding to the low concentration of glucose, the glucose is phosphorylated in the presence of hexokinase at the expense of a molecule of ATP and G-6-P is formed. The presence of this molecule, which diffuses freely in the thickness of the membrane, does not prevent the diffusion of glucose to continue through the left-hand face. On the right-hand side, this ester is hydrolysed in the presence of a phosphatase, regenerating glucose and liberating inorganic phosphate; the concentration of glucose on this side of the membrane is above that existing on the right of the membrane; so the glucose diffuses to the right of the membrane. The membrane is made up of cells and its thickness is the same as these cells. Thus, the free energy of a pyrophosphate bond is used for each molecule of glucose transported, and it is converted into work done against the concentration gradient.

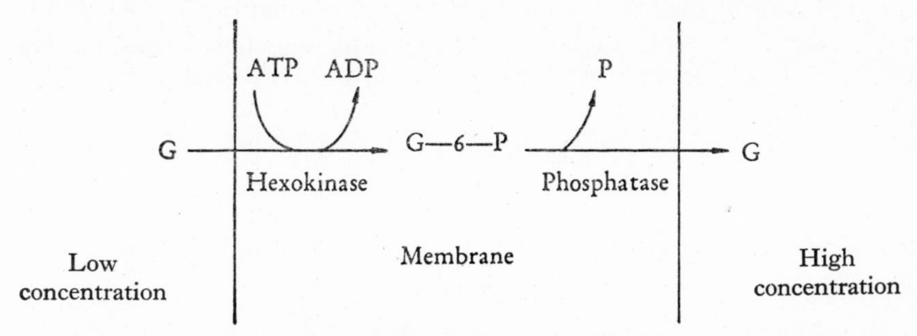

FIG. 29 (Cantarow and Schepartz)—Transfer of a glucose molecule against the concentration gradient at the price of an ATP pyrophosphate bond.

VIII. CHEMICAL EQUILIBRIUM AND THE STATIONARY STATE

Let us recall the definition of a reversible reaction : it is a reaction in which the reacting substances are not completely used up in forming the products of the reaction. If, for example, we mix equimolecular amounts of ethyl alcohol and acetic acid, water and an ester will be formed according to the equation

$$C_2H_5OH + CH_3COOH = CH_3COOC_2H_5 + H_2O$$

Whatever the duration of the reaction, at equilibrium a third of the ethyl alcohol and a third of the acid will remain unchanged, in the presence of the reaction products from the other two-thirds.

If, on the other hand, we mix equimolecular amounts of the ester and water, ethyl alcohol and acetic acid will be formed

$$CH_3COOC_2H_5 + H_2O = C_2H_5OH + CH_3COOH$$

But two-thirds of the reactants will remain unchanged in the presence of the products from the remaining third.

So, one can write

$$C_2H_5OH + CH_3COOH \rightleftarrows CH_3COOC_2H_5 + H_2O$$

The reaction is reversible. Whether the reaction begins from the left or the right it will reach equilibrium when there are twice as many ester molecules as there are alcohol molecules.

In a reversible reaction it is the difference in the reaction velocities in opposing directions which regulates the position of equilibrium. In effect, all reactions are reversible, but if the velocity from left to right is very great and the velocity from right to left very small, then the reaction may be considered as irreversible.

However, even though the reaction velocity is appreciable in either direction, one of the reaction products may be constantly removed, and in such a case a reversible reaction can go to completion in one direction. For example, if we react iron and water vapour in a closed vessel we shall have the reversible reaction :

$$3Fe + 4H_2O \rightleftarrows Fe_3O_4 + 4H_2$$

Now, if we pass the water vapour over the iron, the hydrogen will be swept away and the reaction will go to completion from left to right :

$$3Fe + 4H_2O \rightarrow Fe_3O_4 + 4H_2$$

If, on the other hand, we pass a stream of hydrogen over the heated iron oxide, it will be the reaction from right to left which will go to completion, the current of gas sweeping away the water vapour :

$$Fe_3O_4 + 4H_2 \rightarrow 3Fe + 4H_2O$$

The equilibrium of a reversible reaction is the resultant of velocities in the two directions. Temperature influences these velocities but it does not change them relative to each other, nor consequently the position of equilibrium. The presence of a catalyst will influence the velocities but likewise will not alter the point of equilibrium. It is the concentrations of the substances present which control the direction of a reversible reaction, as stated by the law of mass action.

In living organisms, it happens frequently that the products of a reversible reaction are used in another reaction, or that they are removed from the site of their formation. Inside the cell, a reversible reaction often goes to completion in one direction and becomes, in effect, an irreversible reaction.

A closed system can only do work at the cost of an increase in entropy. And irreversible reactions can only take place in one direction, that of an increase in entropy. The reactions will continue until equilibrium is established.

The situation is quite different in an *open system* or in an assembly of open systems, as is the case for a cell or an organism. In such an open system, the organism takes complex organic molecules from the environment, liberates free energy from these molecules, and rejects the products of the reaction. It can maintain its entropy constant and even decrease it so that its constituents become more ordered. It has been described as being nourished by negative entropy (Schrödinger). There is nothing here which contradicts the second law of thermodynamics, for in the total system made up of the organism and its surroundings the entropy increases. An organism is made up of one or more cells; each cell is itself an assembly of open systems which receive free energy and dispose of it.

As Prigogine (1947) has shown, open systems have some very remarkable properties.

(1) They tend towards a "stationary state" corresponding to a state of minimum entropy compatible with the conditions of the system.

(2) The entropy of the system can decrease when the "stationary state" is established.

(3) If one of the components of the system is modified, the system changes in an opposing direction, revealing a capacity for self-regulation.

It can be seen that the *stationary state* of "constrained disequilibrium", which is manifest in organisms, with its continual introduction and removal of materials, is quite different from the equilibrium of a reversible reaction.

Let us take, for example, the case of a monomolecular reversible reaction

$$A \underset{k'}{\overset{k}{\rightleftarrows}} B$$

According to the law of mass action, we may write :

$$\frac{(B)}{(A)} = \frac{k}{k'} = K \text{ (equilibrium constant)}$$

When equilibrium is reached, the rates of conversion of A into B, and B into A, are equal.

If B is constantly removed to a pool Z and if A is constantly replaced from a source of supply S, the flux will be defined as follows :

$$S \overset{k_s}{\longleftrightarrow} A \underset{k'}{\overset{k}{\rightleftarrows}} B \overset{k_z}{\longleftrightarrow} Z$$

k_s and k_z are the diffusion constants (or "permeabilities"). It can be seen that to define the stationary state we must consider not only the size of the source and the pool but also the equilibrium constant of the reaction itself. In order for the stationary state to be maintained, S and Z must remain constant regardless of subtractions or additions.

There are many cases in organisms where the equilibrium of a reversible reaction has been upset in one direction or the other. For example, in vertebrates when oxygen is transported, the reversible reaction

$$Hb + O_2 \rightleftarrows HbO_2$$

takes place from left to right when the blood passes through the lungs and from right to left when the blood reaches the tissues.

But this is not the case in the reactions of intermediary metabolism. When these are under consideration, one must always bear in mind the complex stationary states of open systems, in which the equilibrium is not limited to the consideration of only one reaction and is not controlled solely by the equilibrium constant of a reversible reaction.

REFERENCES

BLADERGROEN, W. (1955). *Einführung in die Energetik und Kinetik biologischer Vorgänge.* Wepf, Basel.

JOHNSON, M. J. (1949). Oxidation-reduction potentials. *Respiratory Enzymes,* edited by LARDY, H. A., Burgess, Minneapolis, revised edition, 58–70.

JOHNSON, M. J. (1949) Energy relations in metabolic reactions. *Respiratory Enzymes,* edited by LARDY, H. A, Burgess, Minneapolis, revised edition. 255–263.

PARDEE, A. P. (1954). Free energy and metabolism. *Chemical Pathways of Metabolism,* edited by GREENBERG, D. E., vol. I, Academic Press, New York, 1–25.

PRIGOGINE, I. (1955). *Introduction to Thermodynamics of Irreversible Processes.* Thomas, Springfield.

CHAPTER II

ENZYMES

I. DEFINITION

In order for a reaction to take place spontaneously, we have seen that it must have a negative ΔF. But this condition alone is not sufficient to say that the reaction will take place. The petrol in the tank of a car has a very negative ΔF for the oxidation reaction, but it remains stable in air. Similarly, food in a grocer's shop, in contact with air, is also stable, although this food is destined to provide much energy in the oxidations it will undergo, in the presence of oxygen, in the human body. In order to react, most molecules have to be activated. The act of bringing a lighted match to the surface of the petrol accomplishes the activation.

Conforming to the concept of activation introduced by Arrhenius, the energy content of molecules is not constant but is continually changing. Certain molecules, the activated molecules, have an energy higher than the other molecules, and only they are capable of entering into a reaction. In a solution of sucrose, for example, the number of activated molecules is extremely small but if the temperature is increased by 10° their number is increased two or three times. These activated molecules travel faster and are more labile.

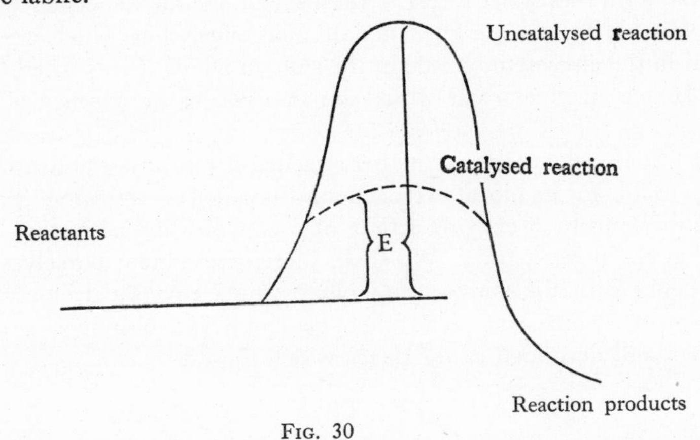

Fig. 30

When the molecules have absorbed a certain amount of energy (E in Fig. 30), reaction takes place between the reactants and the reaction products are formed. Nevertheless, the need for activation can be reduced, to varying degrees, by the presence of catalysts, which, in effect, lower the activation-energy barrier. In Nature, reactions do not take place at high temperatures, and most of them only occur because of the presence of the organic catalysts which we call enzymes.

As we saw in the preceding chapter, one of the characteristics of the biochemical machine is a constant opposition to the establishment of thermodynamic equilibrium.

A cell, even if after a given period we do not observe any change in its composition, is not in a state of thermodynamic equilibrium, but is in a stationary state of flux in which the velocities of synthesis and breakdown, for example, are equilibrated. Such an equilibrium is the result of the control of the velocities in question. The control of these velocities is the work of the very many specific catalysts which each cell contains.

II. ENZYMES AND ACTIVATORS

It was in 1926 that an enzyme, urease, was crystallized for the first time by Sumner. Since then, many other enzymes have been crystallized and the list is constantly increasing. All these purified enzymes are proteins. However, as long ago as 1897, Gabriel Bertrand introduced the name "coenzyme" or "coferment" for those metal ions whose presence was indispensable for the action of certain enzymes.

It soon became evident that certain enzymes were heteroproteins in nature, that is that they contained a *prosthetic group* firmly attached to the protein. For example the haem in catalase. Also there are a number of cofactors in the absence of which biocatalysis does not occur. At the present time the term *coenzymes* refers to these small organic molecules which are indispensable for the performance of biocatalysis but which are not included in the enzyme molecule in the state in which it is isolated from the cell. Hence enzymes exist which are inactive in the absence of the coenzyme.

In addition, when an ion, whether attached firmly or not to the protein, is indispensable for its biocatalytic action, it is called an *activator*. The study of the mechanism of enzyme action, of coenzymes and activators, is in full swing at the present time. We shall, therefore, content ourselves for the time being with the above terminology which covers extremely diverse mechanisms. Some examples of these general biochemical mechanisms will be taken and described in the pages which follow.

III. CLASSIFICATION OF ENZYMES

A. Hydrolases

These catalyse reactions of the type: $AB + H_2O \rightleftarrows AOH + HB$. These enzymes can be considered as catalysing the transfer of a transferable group with water playing the role of specific acceptor. They can be divided into several types according to the nature of the donor system and the transferable group. The general type of transfer reaction and the particular case where water is the acceptor can be represented by the following two schemes of reaction :

$$\begin{array}{ccc} R-X+HE & \rightleftharpoons & R-E+XH \\ & & \downarrow\uparrow \; YH \\ & & R-Y+HE \end{array} \qquad \begin{array}{ccc} R-X+HE & \rightleftharpoons & R-E+XH \\ & & \downarrow\uparrow \; H\ OH \\ & & R-OH+HE \end{array}$$

in which R—X is the substrate (donor system), R is the transferable group, Y is the acceptor system and E is the enzyme.

Hydrolases catalyse the transfer of transferable groups to water. If another acceptor is present, in sufficient quantities and in the presence of the specific enzyme for the activation and transfer of the group to this other acceptor, then this reaction will compete with the hydrolysis.

The donor system varies according to the various types of hydrolases and the transferable group may be attached by a peptide bond, oside bond, ester bond, amine linkage, amide bond or an amidine linkage.

In all living beings, as a rule, seven types of hydrolases are recognized.

(a) Peptidases $$R\overset{\overset{O}{\|}}{C}-NHR' + H_2O \rightleftharpoons R\overset{\overset{O}{\|}}{C}-OH + NH_2R$$

(b) Carbohydrases $$R^1-O-R^2+H_2O \rightleftharpoons R^1OH+R^2OH$$

(R^1 and R^2 are sugar residues or osides, they can be identical.)

(c) Esterases $$R^1-\overset{\overset{O}{\|}}{C}-OR^2 + H_2O \rightleftharpoons R^1\overset{\overset{O}{\|}}{C}-OH + R^2OH$$

(d) Phosphatases $$R-O-PO_3H_2 + H_2O \rightleftharpoons ROH + H_3PO_4$$

(e) Deaminases $$R-NH_2 + H_2O \rightleftharpoons ROH + NH_3$$

(f) Deamidases $$R-\overset{\overset{O}{\|}}{C}-NH_2 + H_2O \rightleftharpoons R-\overset{\overset{O}{\|}}{C}-OH + NH_3$$

(g) Deamidinases $$R-NH-\overset{\overset{NH}{\|}}{C}-NH_2 + H_2O \rightleftharpoons R-NH_2 + H_2NCONH_2$$

When the transferase systems (transphosphorylases, transglycosidases, transpeptidases, transmethylases, transacylases, etc.) which function inside the cell, cease to act and compete with the transfer to water, the hydrolases take over and cause a certain amount of hydrolysis of the cellular contents.

(*a*) *Peptidases*

All cells contain peptidases, and in many specialized cases they secrete enzymes of this type to the exterior; this is the case, for example, with many bacteria, and with certain cells of the digestive tract of animals, etc. There are many special aspects of this subject which will not be discussed here.

The peptidases are divided into endopeptidases and exopeptidases. The endopeptidases (formerly proteinases) are able to attack all the peptide bonds in a molecule, even those which are some distance from terminal groups, whilst the exopeptidases (formerly peptidases) can only hydrolyse peptide bonds at the ends of the chain. Among the exopeptidases, some remove terminal residues having a free carboxyl group (carboxypeptidases) whilst others remove those where the amino group is free (aminopeptidases).

Still little is known about the system of intracellular peptidases. Some studies have been made of the so-called cathepsin, which is the intracellular peptidase system of mammalian kidney and spleen. The studies of Bergmann and his collaborators have revealed that the system contains endopeptidases, carboxypeptidases and aminopeptidases.

(*b*) *Carbohydrases*

Like the peptidases, these enzymes are universally found in the biosphere. They are considered under two headings, *glycosidases* which hydrolyse di- and trisaccharides and glycosides, and polysaccharases which hydrolyse macromolecules such as starch or cellulose.

The glycosides possessing a free reducing group can exist in the α form or the β form. One can also characterize the reducing group involved in the glycoside linkage by referring to α-glycosides and to β-glycosides. Maltose, for example, is an α-glucoside, lactose a β-galactoside, and sucrose, at the same time, is both an α-glucoside and a β-fructoside.

There are a certain number of glycosidases which are specific for a given linkage regardless of the molecule which contains it: α-glucosidase (formerly maltase), β-glucosidase (formerly emulsin, cellobiase, gentiobiase), α-galactosidase, β-galactosidase, β-fructosidase (formerly invertase, saccharase, etc.), α-mannosidase. In addition, there are a number of glycosidases which are specific for a given compound (for example, trehalase which acts only on trehalose and not on other α-glucoside linkages).

The glycosidases are without action on polysaccharide macromolecules, although starch and glycogen, for example, consist of chains of glucose molecules joined together by α-glucoside linkages. The hydrolysis of starch only takes place in the presence of amylases. β-amylase attacks the long chains of amylose and hydrolyses it completely. With amylopectin (or with glycogen), β-amylase acts on the outer chains but its action is stopped at the point of branching. When acting on amylopectin, β-amylase hydrolyses it to maltose to the extent of 65% and the residue is attacked by α-amylase.

Whilst α-amylase appears to be very widely distributed in living beings, up to the present β-amylase has not been detected in animals.

A whole series of other polyases exists and they are more or less widely distributed in the biosphere : cellulases, dextranases, lichenases, inulinases, pectin-polygalacturonidases, mucopolysaccharases, lysozymes, hyaluronidases, etc.

(*c*) *Esterases*

These enzymes hydrolyse esters of organic acids and alcohols. They are widely distributed but, in general, their specificity is of a low order.

It is possible to divide them into the true esterases (catalysing the hydrolysis of all esters of monocarboxylic acids and monohydric alcohols) and the lipases (catalysing the hydrolysis of esters of fatty acids and glycerol). However it is not always easy to make this distinction because of the low specificity of these enzymes.

In certain regions of the biosphere are localized esterases possessing a more marked specificity: chlorophyllase, pectin-esterases, cholinesterases, etc.

Besides the esterases for esters of organic acids, there are esterases for the esters of inorganic acids. A widely distributed group is that of the sulphatases or esterases for esters of sulphuric acid.

(*d*) *Phosphatases*

Phosphatases are present throughout the biosphere. They can be divided into four groups:—

1. *Phosphomonoesterases*

$$R{-}O{-}\overset{\overset{\displaystyle O}{\|}}{\underset{\underset{\displaystyle OH}{|}}{P}}{-}OH + H_2O \rightleftarrows ROH + H_3PO_4$$

These are of low specificity as far as the alcohol radical R is concerned. In this category are included alkaline phosphatase, acid phosphatase, acetylphosphatase, hexosediphosphatase, etc.

2. *Phosphodiesterases*

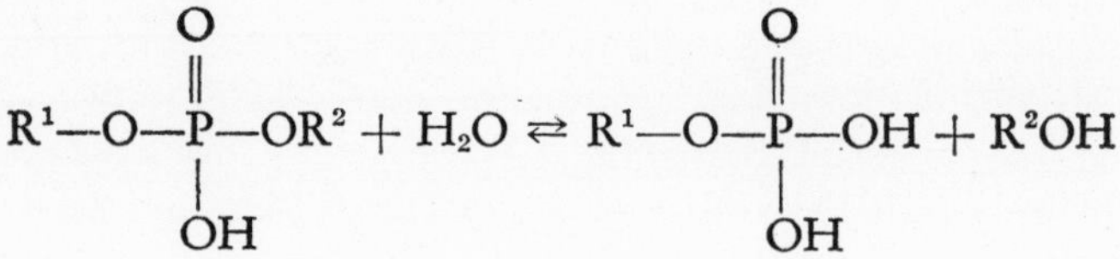

$$R^1{-}O{-}\underset{\underset{OH}{|}}{\overset{\overset{O}{\|}}{P}}{-}OR^2 + H_2O \rightleftharpoons R^1{-}O{-}\underset{\underset{OH}{|}}{\overset{\overset{O}{\|}}{P}}{-}OH + R^2OH$$

Likewise their specificity with respect to R^1 and R^2 is low. In this group are such universally distributed enzymes as ribonuclease and desoxyribonuclease.

3. *Pyrophosphatases*

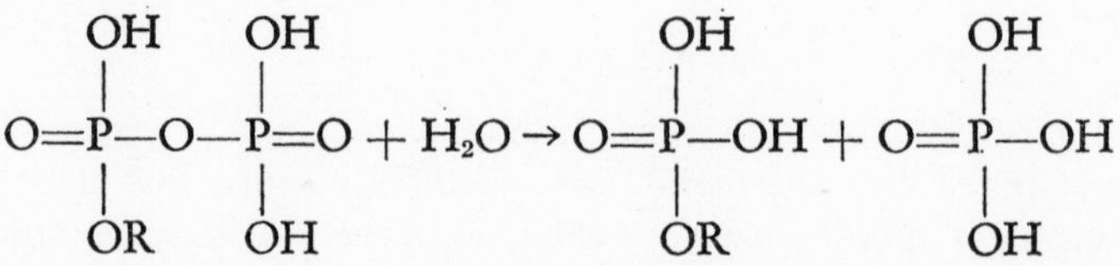

$$O{=}\underset{\underset{OR}{|}}{\overset{\overset{OH}{|}}{P}}{-}O{-}\underset{\underset{OH}{|}}{\overset{\overset{OH}{|}}{P}}{=}O + H_2O \rightarrow O{=}\underset{\underset{OR}{|}}{\overset{\overset{OH}{|}}{P}}{-}OH + O{=}\underset{\underset{OH}{|}}{\overset{\overset{OH}{|}}{P}}{-}OH$$

The adenosinetriphosphatases (ATPases), which catalyse the hydrolysis of ATP to ADP and phosphoric acid, fall in this category.

4. *Metaphosphatases*

$$(HPO_3)_n + nH_2O \rightarrow nH_3PO_4$$

(*e*) *Deaminases*

They catalyse the hydrolysis of the C—N bond of amines

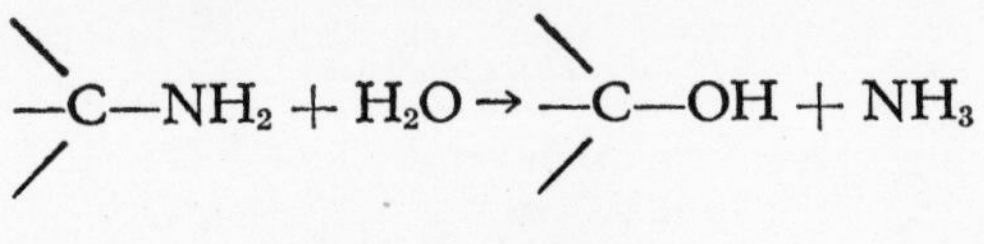

$$\diagdown\!\!-C{-}NH_2 + H_2O \rightarrow \diagdown\!\!-C{-}OH + NH_3$$

(*f*) *Deamidases*

They catalyse hydrolysis of the amide bond.

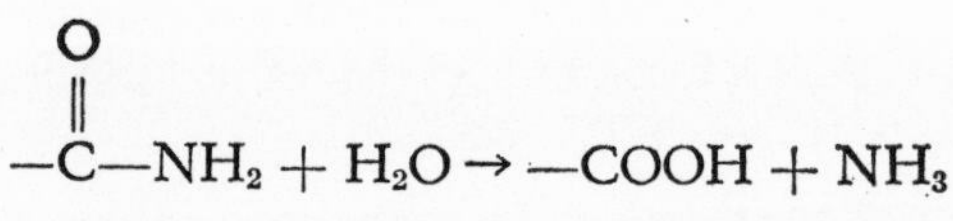

$$-\overset{\overset{O}{\|}}{C}{-}NH_2 + H_2O \rightarrow -COOH + NH_3$$

Examples are urease, asparaginase, and glutaminase. Glutaminase catalyses the hydrolysis of glutamine into glutamic acid and ammonia and asparaginase of asparagine into aspartic acid and ammonia.

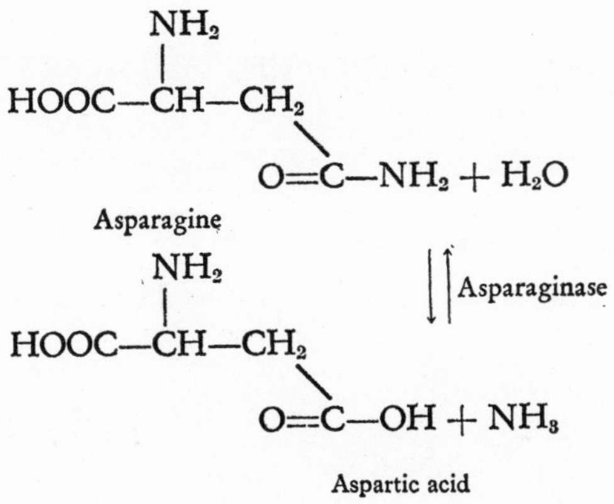

$$
\begin{array}{l}
\quad\quad\ NH_2 \\
\quad\quad\quad | \\
HOOC-CH-CH_2 \\
\quad\quad\quad\quad\quad\quad \diagdown \\
\quad\quad\quad\quad\quad\quad O=C-NH_2 + H_2O
\end{array}
$$

Asparagine

$$\rightleftharpoons \text{Asparaginase}$$

$$
\begin{array}{l}
\quad\quad\ NH_2 \\
\quad\quad\quad | \\
HOOC-CH-CH_2 \\
\quad\quad\quad\quad\quad\quad \diagdown \\
\quad\quad\quad\quad\quad\quad O=C-OH + NH_3
\end{array}
$$

Aspartic acid

$$
\begin{array}{l}
\quad\quad\ NH_2 \\
\quad\quad\quad | \\
HOOC-CH-CH_2-CH_2 + H_2O \\
\quad\quad\quad\quad\quad\quad\quad\quad\quad \diagdown \\
\quad\quad\quad\quad\quad\quad\quad\quad\quad O=C-NH_2
\end{array}
$$

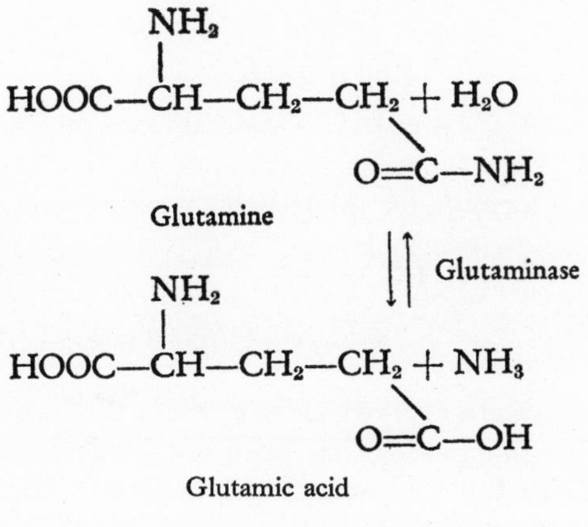

Glutamine

$$\rightleftharpoons \text{Glutaminase}$$

$$
\begin{array}{l}
\quad\quad\ NH_2 \\
\quad\quad\quad | \\
HOOC-CH-CH_2-CH_2 + NH_3 \\
\quad\quad\quad\quad\quad\quad\quad\quad\quad \diagdown \\
\quad\quad\quad\quad\quad\quad\quad\quad\quad O=C-OH
\end{array}
$$

Glutamic acid

(*g*) *Deamidinases*

These enzymes catalyse the hydrolysis of amidine bonds. The most well-known of them is arginase catalysing the hydrolysis of arginine to ornithine and urea. Its molecule contains manganese.

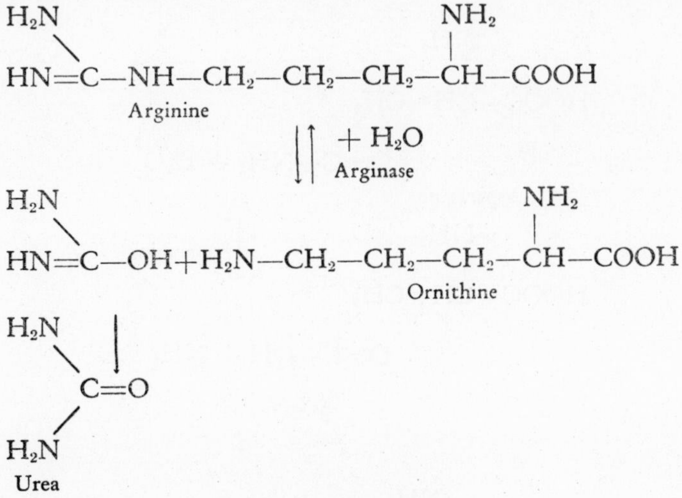

$$\underset{\text{Arginine}}{\overset{H_2N\diagdown}{HN{=}C}{-}NH{-}CH_2{-}CH_2{-}CH_2{-}\overset{NH_2}{\overset{|}{C}H}{-}COOH}$$

$$\rightleftarrows \; + H_2O \; \text{(Arginase)}$$

$$\overset{H_2N\diagdown}{HN{=}C}{-}OH + \underset{\text{Ornithine}}{H_2N{-}CH_2{-}CH_2{-}CH_2{-}\overset{NH_2}{\overset{|}{C}H}{-}COOH}$$

$$\downarrow$$

$$\underset{\text{Urea}}{(H_2N)_2C{=}O}$$

B. Phosphorylases

They catalyse the transfer of a transferable group, not to water, but to phosphoric acid. They are transglucosidases whose acceptor is phosphoric acid. The general formula for the transfer reaction is as follows :

$$(C_6H_{10}O_5)_n + H_3PO_4 \rightleftarrows \underset{\text{Glucose-1-phosphate}}{C_6H_{11}O_5{-}OPO_3H_2} + (C_6H_{10}O_5)_{n-1}$$

The phosphorylases are everywhere present in the biosphere. An enzyme of this type (phosphorylase-*a*) has been obtained crystalline from rabbit muscle. In the presence of an excess of orthophosphate the reaction occurs in the direction of phosphorolysis, whilst in the absence of orthophosphate or in the presence of an excess of glucose-1-phosphate, the synthesis of amylose takes place. The enzyme is also called glucose-1-phosphate → amylose-transglucosidase.

From various microbial sources have been isolated a *sucrose phosphorylase* (sucrose → orthophosphate transglucosidase) and a *maltose phosphorylase* (maltose → orthophosphate transglucosidase).

C. Transferring Enzymes (Transferases)

Assembled in this group are the transferring biocatalysts having acceptors other than water or phosphoric acid. They catalyse the transfer of a group from one compound to another, and, in certain cases, they also transfer the energy of the bond to which the group was attached. This point is particularly important in biochemical energetics.

$$\mathrm{D{-}X + E \rightleftharpoons D{-}X{-}E \rightleftharpoons D + E{-}X}$$
$$\mathrm{E{-}X + A \rightleftharpoons A{-}E{-}X \rightleftharpoons A{-}X + E}$$

As the equations show, when the transferred portion X combines with the enzyme E before passing to the acceptor A, the energy of the D—X bond is not dissipated but is also transferred with little energy loss. In such a case the system is a reversible one and there is only a small change in ΔF.

(*a*) *Transphosphorylases*
(*Transphosphatases, Phosphokinases*)

These important enzymes are numerous and universally present in the biosphere. The Lohmann enzyme or creatine-phosphokinase has been known for a long time. It catalyses the transfer of a phosphoric acid residue from adenosine triphosphate to creatine (Lohmann reaction).

$$\mathrm{ATP} + \underset{\text{Creatine}}{\mathrm{H_2N{-}\overset{\overset{\displaystyle NH}{\|}}{C}{-}\underset{\underset{\displaystyle CH_3}{|}}{N}{-}CH_2{-}COOH}} \rightleftharpoons$$

$$\mathrm{ADP} + \mathrm{HO{-}\overset{\overset{\displaystyle O}{\|}}{\underset{\underset{\displaystyle OH}{|}}{P}}{-}NH{-}\overset{\overset{\displaystyle NH}{\|}}{C}{-}\underset{\underset{\displaystyle CH_3}{|}}{N}{-}CH{-}COOH}$$

Hexokinase transfers a phosphate group from ATP to glucose with the formation of glucose-6-phosphate, and fructohexokinase performs the same transfer to fructose forming fructose-1-phosphate. The transphosphorylases can be divided into several types according to the magnitude of ΔF for the transfer reaction.

Two examples will illustrate this.

Let us take the case of hexokinase which transfers a phosphate residue from ATP to glucose with the formation of ADP and glucose-6-phosphate. The hydrolysis of the pyrophosphate linkage of ATP gives 12,000 calories and that of glucose-6-phosphate only yields 2,000–4,000 cal. During the course of the transfer there will be a ΔF of the order of 9000 cal. The position of equilibrium is such that there is almost complete conversion of glucose into its phosphate and consequently glucose-6-phosphate is not readily able to give up its phosphate to ADP. The situation is quite different when the transfer takes place with a small value of $-\Delta F$ as is the case in the Lohmann reaction. ATP and phosphocreatine are molecules containing an energy-rich bond and equilibrium between them will be established when their concentrations are of about the same order.

Among the transphosphorylase systems in which energy-rich bonds are involved and the $-\Delta F$ is small (so that the reaction is readily reversible) we may list the following :

Creatine phosphokinase	ATP+creatine ⇌ ADP+phosphocreatine
Arginine phosphokinase	ATP+arginine ⇌ ADP+phosphoarginine
Myokinase	ATP+AMP ⇌ 2 ADP
Phosphoglyceric phosphokinase	ATP + 3-phosphoglyceric acid ⇌ ADP + 1, 3-diphosphoglyceric acid

Conversely, the following systems whose $-\Delta F$ values are high will be practically irreversible :

Hexokinase	ATP+glucose→ADP+G—6—P
Fructohexokinase	ATP+fructose→ADP+F—1—P
Phosphohexokinase	ATP+F—6—P→ADP+F—1,6—PP
Galactohexokinase	ATP+galactose→ADP+Gal.—1—P
Glucose-1-phosphokinase	ATP+G—1—P→ADP+G—1,6—PP

(*b*) *Transaminases*

These enzymes were discovered in 1930 by D. M. Needham, they catalyse transfers of the following general type :

$$\underset{\displaystyle NH_2}{RCH}\text{—COOH} + \text{R'CO—COOH} \rightleftharpoons \text{RCO—COOH} + \text{R'}\underset{\displaystyle NH_2}{CH}\text{COOH}$$

An example is the glutamate-aspartate transaminase which catalyses the reaction

glutamate + oxaloacetate ⇌ α-ketoglutarate + aspartate, and also glutamate-alanine transaminase

glutamate + pyruvate ⇌ α-ketoglutarate + alanine.

There also exist transaminases which catalyse the transfer of an amino group from amino-purines to α-ketoglutaric acid. Pyridoxal phosphate is the coenzyme for transaminations between amino acids and keto-acids and also between amino-purines and keto-acids.

(c) *Transpeptidases*

The general reaction catalysed by transpeptidases is the following:

$$\mathrm{RCO{-}HN\overset{\overset{\displaystyle R'}{|}}{C}HCO{-}NHR'' + NH_2X \rightleftharpoons RCOHN\overset{\overset{\displaystyle R'}{|}}{C}HCO{-}NHX + NH_2R''}$$

Certain peptidases catalyse these transpeptidations e.g. papain and tryspin.

(d) *Transmethylases*

In general, in the biosphere, methyl groups can be transferred from a given donor to a given acceptor in the following way:

$$\mathrm{R{-}CH_3 + R'{-}H \rightleftharpoons RH + R'{-}CH_3}$$

An example of a catalyst for transmethylation is nicotine-methyl-transferase which catalyses the reaction:

active methionine + nicotinamide ⇆ N-methylnicotinamide

(e) *Transacylases*

These are enzymes catalysing the transfer of acyl residues. Certain enzymes catalyse the transfer of the acyl residue from its combination with CoA (cofactor for transacylations) to an acceptor.

Example: choline acetylase, catalyses the reaction

acteyl-CoA + choline ⇆ acetylcholine + CoA

(f) *Transadenylases and Transuridylases*

These are enzymes which catalyse the transfer from a given donor to a given acceptor of a purine or pyrimidine nucleotide residue. An example is that ATP → nicotinamide—mononucleotide—transadenylase, catalysing (in presence of Mg^{++}) the reaction:

ATP + nicotinamide mononucleotide ⇌ DPN + pyrophosphate

or UTP + glucose-1-phosphate ⇌ UDP-glucose + pyrophosphate

(g) *Transketolases (Glycolaldehyde-Transferases)*

They catalyse the transfer of a glycolaldehyde residue, for example in the reaction:

ribulose-5-phosphate + ribose-5-phosphate
⇌ 3-phosphoglyceraldehyde + sedoheptulose-7-phosphate

(*h*) *CoA Transferases*

These catalyse the transfer of CoA from an acyl-CoA to a series of fatty acids e.g. the microbial CoA transferase catalyses the reaction :

$$\text{acetyl-CoA} + \text{propionate} \rightleftharpoons \text{propionyl-CoA} + \text{acetate}$$

or the CoA transferase from animals catalyses the reaction :

$$\text{succinyl-CoA} + \text{acetoacetate} \rightleftharpoons \text{acetoacetyl-CoA} + \text{succinate}$$

(*i*) *Other Transferases*

Other groups of transferases, which have been little studied up to the present, are the trans-sulphurases, transglutamases, transaspartases, etc.

D. Oxido-reduction Enzymes

(Oxidoreductases, Electrontransferases)

These are transferases of a particular type, transferring electrons accompanied by protons (transhydrogenases) or electrons alone (trans-electronases) from a donor to an acceptor. If the acceptor is oxygen the transhydrogenase or transelectronase is called aerobic. If the acceptor is another type of molecule, they are called anaerobic. Here are some examples of these four types :

(*a*) Anaerobic transhydrogenases

$$\text{R}\genfrac{}{}{0pt}{}{\diagup \text{H}}{\diagdown \text{H}} + \text{R}' \rightleftharpoons \text{R} + \text{R}'\genfrac{}{}{0pt}{}{\diagup \text{H}}{\diagdown \text{H}}$$

e.g. DPNH $\rightarrow$ pyruvate transhydrogenase (lactic dehydrogenase)

DPNH $\rightarrow$ aldehyde transhydrogenase (alcohol dehydrogenases).

(*b*) Aerobic transhydrogenase

$$\text{R}\genfrac{}{}{0pt}{}{\diagup \text{H}}{\diagdown \text{H}} + O_2 \rightarrow \text{R} + H_2O_2$$

e.g. β-glucose $\rightarrow$ O_2-transhydrogenase or glucose–oxidase

Xanthine $\rightarrow$ O_2-transhydrogenase or xanthine–oxidase.

(*c*) Anaerobic transelectronases

$$R + R'^{+} \rightleftharpoons R^{+} + R'$$

e.g. DPNH → cytochrome-*c*–transelectronase or DPN-cytochrome–reductase.

(*d*) Aerobic transelectronases

$$R + O_2 \rightarrow R^{+} + O_2^{-}$$

e.g. Cytochrome oxidase or cytochrome-a_3.

(*a*) *Anaerobic Transhydrogenases*

1. *Enzymes Specific for the Pyridine Nucleotides*

The reaction which is catalysed is:

$$\text{DPN (or TPN)} + RH_2 \rightleftharpoons \text{DPNH (or TPNH)} + R$$

or more correctly

$$\text{DPN}^{+} \text{(or TPN}^{+}\text{)} + RH_2 \rightleftharpoons \text{DPNH (or TPNH)} + R + H^{+}$$

Here are a few examples of reactions catalysed by specific anaerobic transhydrogenases

$$+ \text{DPN}^{+} \rightleftharpoons \text{DPNH} +$$

α-glycerophosphate	phosphodihydroxyacetone
glycerol	glyceraldehyde
glucose	gluconic acid
lactic acid	pyruvic acid
ethanol	acetaldehyde

$$+ \text{TPN}^{+} \rightleftharpoons \text{TPNH} +$$

glucose-6-phosphate	6-phosphogluconic acid
2 SH-glutathione	glutathione-S-S-glutathione

2. *Enzymes of Still Undefined Specificity*

The nature of the specific acceptor is unknown for choline-dehydrogenase, thiamine-dehydrogenase, and succinic dehydrogenase which is a metalloflavoprotein containing iron.

(*b*) *Aerobic Transhydrogenases*

The transfer of hydrogen takes place, in the presence of these enzymes, to oxygen forming H_2O_2. The majority of these enzymes contain a flavin prosthetic group (FMN or FAD), but the presence of this grouping in every enzyme of this type has not been proved. In a number of cases, the aerobic transhydrogenases are metalloproteins containing a metal (Fe, Cu or Mo) in addition to the flavin nucleotide.

Here is a representative list of these enzymes :

1. (with FMN)

TPNH → O_2-transhydrogenase (see "yellow enzyme");
L-amino acids → O_2-transhydrogenease (L-amino acid oxidase).

2. (with FAD)

Aldehyde → O_2-transhydrogenase (aldehyde—oxidase);

Xanthine → O_2-transhydrogenase (xanthine—oxidase).

(*c*) *Anaerobic Transelectronases*

Some enzymes of this type have a flavin prosthetic group, others a haem prosthetic group.

In the first category are the metalloflavoproteins (Fe) such as DPN-cytochrome reductase and TPN-cytochrome reductase, enzymes which Hoffmann-Ostenhof suggests should be called DPNH → cytochrome-*c*–transelectronase and TPNH → cytochrome-*c*–transelectronase, respectively.

Among the anaerobic transelectronases containing haem derivatives are the cytochromes, described on page 119.

(*d*) *Aerobic Transelectronases*

Cytochrome oxidase or cytochrome-a_3 is an example of this type of enzyme (see p. 120). It is highly specific for the transport of electrons from cytochrome-*c* to oxygen. The phenolases (see p. 123) are also aerobic transelectronases, transporting electrons from copper to oxygen.

E. Hydroperoxidases

(See page 120).

F. Lyases and Synthetases

This name applies to enzymes catalysing reactions of the type

$$A + B \rightleftharpoons C$$

whilst the enzymes of the preceding categories (A, B, C, D, E) catalysed reactions of the type

$$A + B \rightleftharpoons C + D$$

Among the lyases and synthetases, some break or form a C—C bond, these are the carboxylases or carbosynthetases, whilst others split or form C—N or C—S bonds. Among the lyases we have the hydrases and dehydrases, enzymes which add or remove water.

Pyruvic carboxylase, whose role in alcoholic fermentation is an important one, contains thiamine pyrophosphate (TPP) as its prosthetic group and the presence of Mg^{++}, or in its absence, of Mn^{++}, is necessary for its action. This enzyme catalyses the reaction

$$CH_3COCOOH \rightarrow CH_3CHO + CO_2$$

It is found in vegetable tissues and in bacteria but not in animal tissues. Nevertheless, in animals and in certain micro-organisms, there is a system for the oxidative decarboxylation of pyruvic acid which requires a series of cofactors (CoA, DPN, TPP and thioctic acid); the initial reaction is as follows :

$$CH_3COCOOH + DPN^+ \rightarrow CH_3CHO + DPNH + CO_2$$

The amino acid decarboxylases are universally distributed. They catalyse the general reaction

$$RCH(NH_2)COOH \rightarrow RCH_2NH_2 + CO_2$$

Each of these enzymes is specific for a definite amino acid, their coenzyme is pyridoxal phosphate attached to the enzyme protein via its phosphate.

The ketonic acid decarboxylases fall into two groups, the α-ketodecarboxylases and the β-ketodecarboxylases. They catalyse respectively the following reactions:

$$RCOCOOH \rightarrow RCHO + CO_2$$

$$RCOCH_2COOH \rightarrow RCOCH_3 + CO_2$$

A further type of carboxylase are the triosephosphate-lyases which, without the intervention of water, decompose hexose phosphates into a molecule of triose phosphate and some other molecule.

Such, for example, is aldolase or FDP-triosephosphate-lyase. Universally present in the biosphere, it catalyses the reaction

F-1, 6-PP $\leftrightarrows$ 3-phosphoglyceraldehyde + phosphodihydroxyacetone

Enolase is an example of the dehydrase type of enzyme. It is universally distributed and catalyses the reaction

$$-\underset{OH}{\overset{H}{\underset{|}{\overset{|}{C}}}}-\underset{OH}{\overset{H}{\underset{|}{\overset{|}{C}}}}- \rightleftharpoons -\underset{OH}{\underset{|}{C}}=\overset{H}{\overset{|}{C}}- + H_2O$$

Aconitase is another hydrase, widely distributed, catalysing the reaction

$$\text{Citric acid} \underset{+H_2O}{\overset{-H_2O}{\rightleftharpoons}} \textit{cis}\text{-aconitic acid} \underset{-H_2O}{\overset{+H_2O}{\rightleftharpoons}} \text{L-isocitric acid}$$

G. Isomerases and Racemases

Racemases catalyse the conversion of an optically active substance into its racemate. An example is alanine racemase

D-alanine ⇌ L-alanine

glutamic racemase

D-glutamic acid ⇌ L-glutamic acid

and mutarotase

α-glucose ⇌ β-glucose

Isomerases catalyse molecular rearrangements, either by modifying the structure of part of the molecule, or by displacing a part of it. To the first class belong the following enzymes :

	Reaction catalysed
Galactowaldenase	Gal-1-P ⇌ G-1-P (cofactor : uridine-diphosphate-glucose)
Phosphoribose—isomerase	Ribose-5-P ⇌ ribulose -5-P
Triosephosphate—isomerase	Dihydroxyacetone-P ⇌ 3-phospho-D-glyceraldehyde

To the second class belong :

Phosphoribumutase	Ribose-1-P ⇌ ribose-5-P
Phosphoglucomutase	G-1-P ⇌ G-6-P (cofactor : G-1, 6-PP)
Phosphoglyceromutase	2-phospho-D-glycerate ⇌ 3-phospho-D-glycerate (2-phospoglyceric acid) (3-phosphoglyceric acid) (cofactor : 2, 3-diphosphoglyceric acid)

IV. KINETICS

The velocity of an enzymatic reaction can be measured by following the change in concentration (increase or decrease) of one of the substances involved in the catalysed reaction, either a reactant or a product of the reaction.

For example, consider the hydrolysis of the amide groups of urea or carbamide $CO(NH_2)_2$, a hydrolysis catalysed by a specific enzyme (the amidase named urease) :

$$CO(NH_2)_2 + H_2O \rightarrow CO_2 + 2NH_3$$

Having fixed the conditions (pH, temperature, urea concentration, urease concentration), we may remove samples of the solution, at definite intervals of time, inactivate the enzyme and determine, say, the ammonia.

Now if we plot these quantities of ammonia nitrogen as ordinates against time intervals as abscissae, we shall obtain the graph shown in Fig. 31. From the graph we can obtain the reaction velocity in moles/l./sec. It is the initial reaction velocity which is of interest, since as the reaction progresses the conditions change as a result of the disappearance of the substrate and the accumulation of the reaction products, etc.

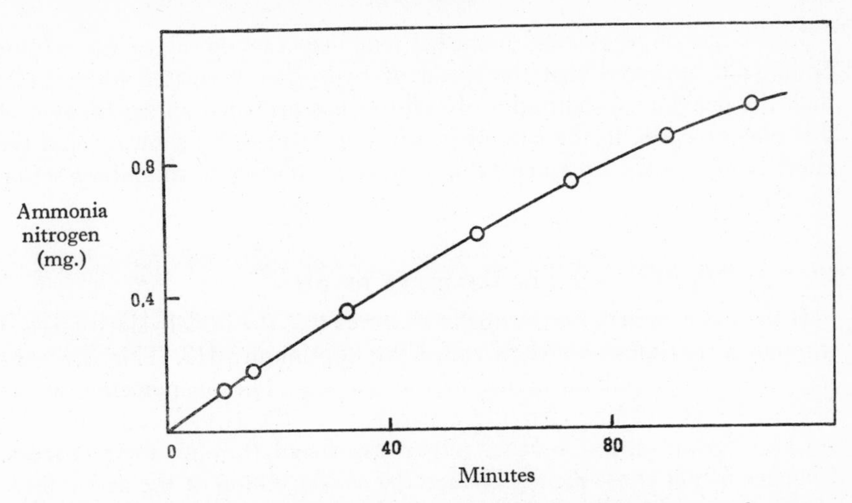

FIG. 31—Ammonia production during the hydrolysis of urea in the presence of urease.

A. INFLUENCE OF ENZYME CONCENTRATION

If we vary the concentration of the enzyme present at the beginning of the reaction and measure the initial reaction velocity for each different concentration, we shall find, in general, that the velocity increases linearly with the concentration of the enzyme : the reaction is therefore first order with respect to the enzyme.

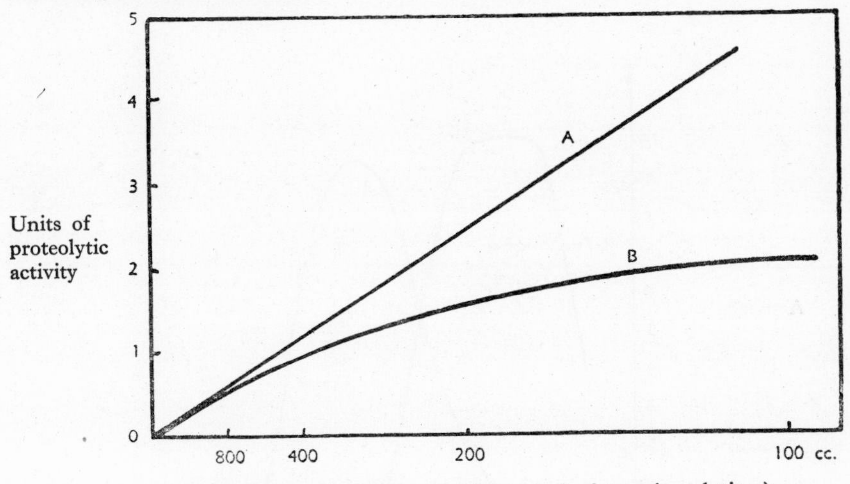

FIG. 32 (Northrop).—Influence of the enzyme concentration on the speed of hydrolysis. Curve A : pure trypsin, proportionality between hydrolysis and trypsin concentration. Curve B : ordinary impure enzyme; the speed of hydrolysis is not proportionately increased as the enzyme concentration is increased.

In the case of peptidases, doubt has long been cast on the validity of this finding: it appeared that the speed of hydrolysis increased less rapidly than the enzyme concentration. Northrop has provided an explanation of this phenomenon, in the case of pepsin and trypsin, by showing that the effect is due to the presence of impurities exercising an inhibitory action on the enzyme.

B. Influence of pH

If the pH is varied, one normally observes that the initial velocity passes through a maximum which is called the "optimum pH". This is a consequence of the protein nature of the enzyme. The phenomenon is explained by postulating that the active part of the enzyme consists of a —COO^- group and a —HN_3^+ group associated through their charges. Changes in pH consequently change the concentration of the active form of the enzyme in the solution.

$$NH_2 \sim COO^- \underset{OH^-}{\overset{H^+}{\rightleftharpoons}} NH_3^+ \sim COO^- \underset{OH^-}{\overset{H^+}{\rightleftharpoons}} NH_3^+ \sim COOH.$$

Inactive enzyme — Active enzyme — Inactive enzyme

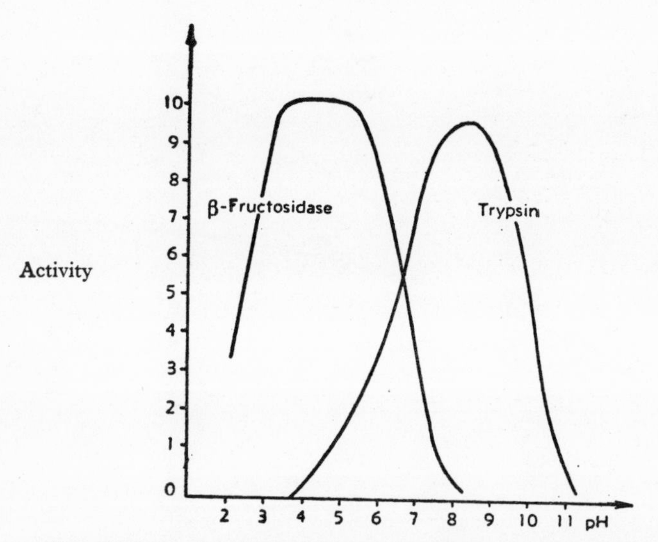

Fig. 33 (Michaelis and Davidson)—Activities of β-fructosidase (invertase) and trypsin at different pH values.

C. Influence of Substrate Concentration

When the substrate concentration is varied, in general it is found that the initial velocity changes with the concentration of substrate in a linear manner. In other words the reaction is first order with respect to the substrate.

However this is no longer the case when the substrate concentration is greater than a certain value: the initial velocity may then become independent of the substrate concentration. In order to explain this, it is postulated that the reaction takes place in two stages, a combination of the enzyme with the substrate ($E + S \rightleftharpoons X$), and a decomposition of the enzyme-substrate complex with regeneration of the enzyme ($X \rightleftharpoons P + E$).

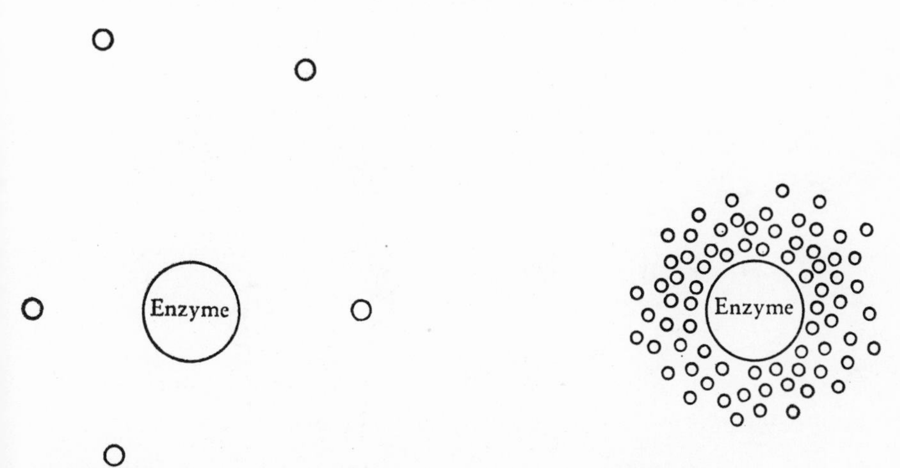

Fig. 34—Enzyme-substrate relations at a low, and at a high, concentration of substrate.

When the amount of substrate is small, a little of the enzyme combines with the substrate but many free enzyme molecules remain. The quantity of the enzyme-substrate complex formed in unit time is proportional to the concentration of the substrate, and the initial velocity, too, is proportional to this concentration. But if, relative to the enzyme, there is plenty of substrate, the enzyme will be present wholly in the form of the complex, such that the addition of further molecules of substrate does not alter the situation as far as the concentration of the enzyme-substrate complex is concerned (Fig. 34).

D. The Michaelis Constant

Let us represent by $[E]_0$ the total concentration of the enzyme and by $[E]$ the concentration of the free enzyme. $[S]$ will represent the concentration of the substrate and $[X]$ the concentration of the enzyme-substrate complex. When the enzyme-substrate reaction is at equilibrium:

$$\frac{[X]}{[E]\,[S]} = K \text{ (equilibrium constant for the enzyme-substrate reaction)} \quad (1)$$

Each molecule of the enzyme-substrate complex contains a molecule of enzyme and a molecule of substrate so

$$[E]_0 = [E] + [X] \quad (2)$$

Equation (1) can therefore be written:

$$\frac{[X]}{([E]_0 - [X])[S]} = K \quad (3)$$

whence

$$[X] = \frac{K[E]_0[S]}{1 + K[S]} \quad (4)$$

Now, it is the concentration of the complex $[X]$ which governs the velocity of the reaction

$$v = k_2[X] \quad (5)$$

The dissociation of the complex X is very far from the position of equilibrium and we may neglect the velocity of the reaction

$$S + E \rightarrow X$$

From (4) and (5),

$$v = \frac{k_2K[E]_0[S]}{1 + K[S]} \quad (6)$$

K (the equilibrium constant of the enzyme-substrate reaction) is often replaced by its reciprocal $1/K = K_m$, or the Michaelis constant.

If we replace K by $1/K_m$, equation (6) becomes

$$v = \frac{k_2/K_m[E]_0[S]}{1 + (1/K_m)[S]} \quad (7)$$

It can be shown that K_m, the Michaelis constant, which has the dimensions of concentration (moles/l.), is in fact the substrate concentration corresponding to a value of half the maximum velocity (Fig. 35). Knowledge of the Michaelis constant for a given enzymatic reaction, allows v to be calculated for any value of $[S]$, provided that k_2 is known.

If we compare $K = 1/K_m$ and $K = [X]/[E]\,[S]$, we see that K_m is the value of $[S]$ for which $[X] = [E]$, that is to say it is the value of $[S]$ at which half the enzyme is combined with the substrate, and at which consequently ($v = k_2[X]$), the reaction velocity is half the maximum velocity for that enzyme concentration (Fig. 35). K_m is measured, like S, in moles/l.

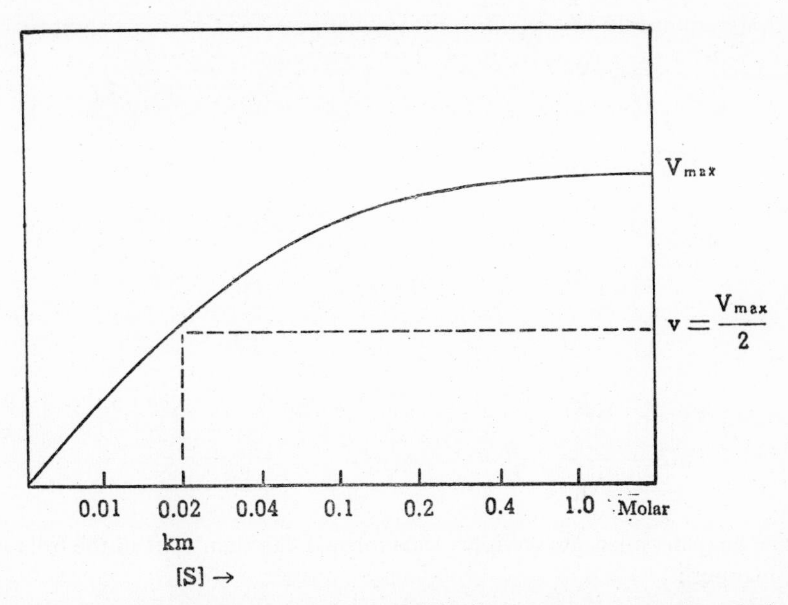

FIG. 35— Current method of measuring the Michaelis constant. v = reaction velocity in moles per min. V_{max} = maximum velocity (the reaction velocity increases with the concentration of substrate but not proportionately). When all the enzyme molecules have formed the enzyme-substrate complex, a further addition of substrate no longer increases the velocity. The maximum velocity has been reached. $[S]$ = molar concentration of the substrate (the abscissa scale is logarithmic). $K_m = 0{\cdot}02$ in this example.

V. THE MECHANISM OF ACTION OF ENZYMES AND COENZYMES

A. ENZYMES

At the present time, our views on the manner in which enzymes evade the necessity for molecular activation are very hypothetical.

Barnard and Laidlaw for example have attempted to explain the mode of action of hydrolases by a "bifunctional" effect. One can discuss catalysis with respect to amino and carboxyl groups without implying that these groups are necessarily the ones which are responsible for the catalytic action.

The enzyme molecule bears —NH_3^+ and —COO^- groups. The former may lose a proton and the latter can accept a proton. It can be postulated that when an ester is hydrolysed by an esterase, the —NH_3^+ grouping approaches the alcohol oxygen and donates a proton to it. Simultaneously, the —COO^- approaches the carbon of the carbonyl group. Also, it must be postulated that a water molecule remains sandwiched between the —COO^- and the C atom, and that the —COO^- tends to draw to itself a proton from the water molecule at the same time assisting the OH^- ion to approach the carbon of the carbonyl group. The picture is as follows :

```
      O                                   O⁻
      ‖                                   |
R—C—O—R'                          R—C——O⁺—R'
                                          |       |
H—O                                      HO⁺      |
   |                                      |       |
   H   H              ⇌                   H⁻      H⁻
       |                                  |       |
   O⁻  |                                  O       |
   |   |                                  |       |
O=C   N⁺                                O=C       N⁺
   |   |||                                |       |||
[ Enzyme ]                               [ Enzyme ]
```

The enzyme-substrate complex thus formed can then split in the following manner :

```
        O
        ‖
     R—C
        |
        OH   +   H—O—R'

        H
        |
        O
        |
     O=C     N
        |    |||
     [ Enzyme ]
```

This proposed mechanism is based upon the idea that a protein is a semi-conductor, in which, as in a metal, certain electrons are not strictly localized to definite points in the macromolecule, but are, to a certain degree, free to move around in the space occupied by the macromolecule. According to this conception, the electrons are poured into a "pool" covering the macromolecule and the tributaries of this pool are the hydrogen bonds between the polypeptide chains. In this context, an enzyme is a semi-conductor of greater efficiency than an ordinary non-enzymatic protein.

In the explanation of the hydrolytic action outlined above, the enzyme is considered as a conductor of electrons through which an electron flow takes place, so modifying the distribution of electrons that certain bonds are ruptured.

For the hydrolysis of a peptide, the picture will be as follows :

```
      O  H                          O⁻     H
      ‖  |                          |      |
   R—C—N—R'                     R—C———N⁺—R'
                                    |      |
   H—O                             HO⁺     |
      |                             |      |
      H  H              ⇌           H⁻     H⁻
         |                          |      |
      O⁻ |                          O      |
      |  |                          |      |
   O=C  N⁺                       O=C     N⁺
      |  |||                        |     |||
   [Enzyme]                       [Enzyme]
                                      ↓
                                   O
                                   ‖
                                R—C      +  R'NH₂
                                   |
                                   OH

                                   H
                                   |
                                   O
                                   |
                                O=C    N
                                   |   |||
                                 [Enzyme]
```

B. Coenzymes

When the enzyme requires a coenzyme, we know a little more about the mechanism, at least as far as the latter is concerned.

If, for example, we consider the lactic dehydrogenase system, we may postulate that the reaction begins by the fixation of lactic acid and the coenzyme DPN^+ on the enzyme protein molecule (apoenzyme).

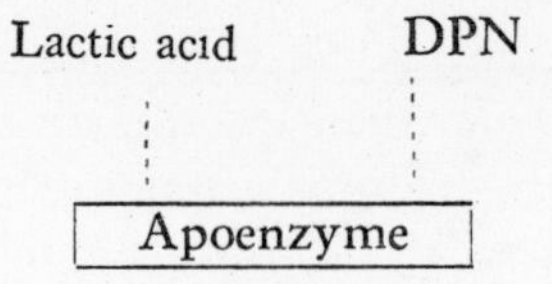

A proton is then lost by the lactic acid to the solution and, simultaneously, an electron passes from the lactic acid to the apoenzyme.

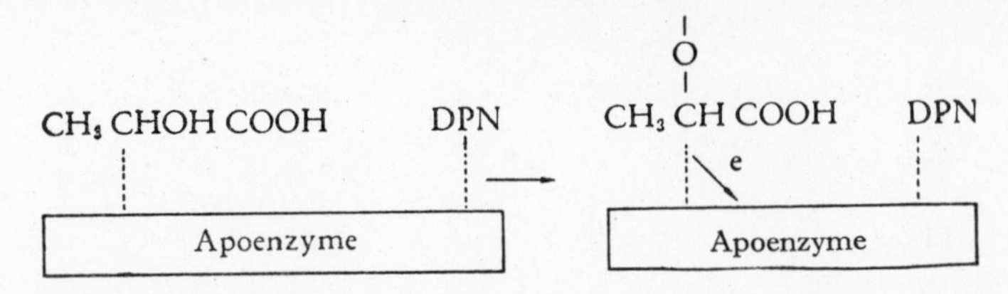

The electron travels along the apoenzyme until it reaches the coenzyme where it combines with a proton furnished by the solution and the DPN^+ is reduced to DPNH.

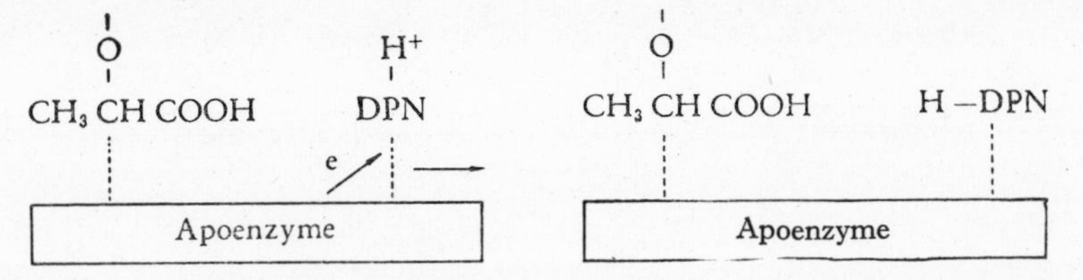

The role of pyridoxal phosphate as a coenzyme in the decarboxylation of amino acids can, according to Mendeles, Koppelman and Hanke (1954), be explained by the following scheme :

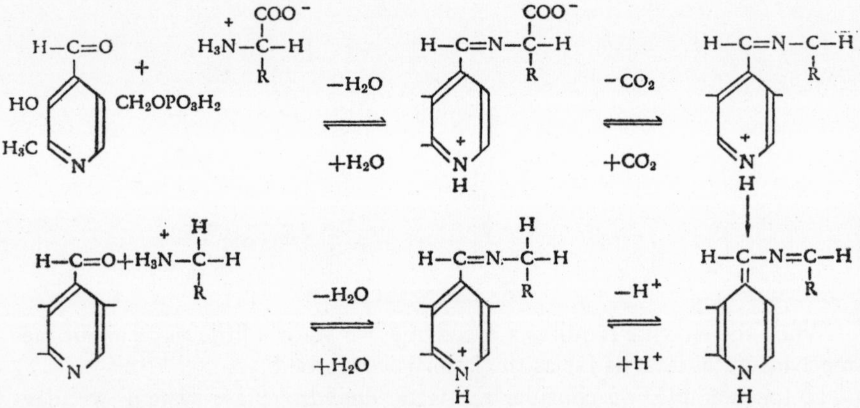

H–C=O + $H_3\overset{+}{N}$–C(COO⁻)(R)–H (HO, $CH_2OPO_3H_2$, H_3C, N) $\underset{+H_2O}{\overset{-H_2O}{\rightleftharpoons}}$ H–C=N–C(COO⁻)(R)–H ($\overset{+}{N}$H) $\underset{+CO_2}{\overset{-CO_2}{\rightleftharpoons}}$ H–C=N–C(R)–H ($\overset{+}{N}$H)

↓

H–C=O + $H_3\overset{+}{N}$–C(H)(R)–H (N) $\underset{+H_2O}{\overset{-H_2O}{\rightleftharpoons}}$ H–C=N–C(H)(R)–H ($\overset{+}{N}$H) $\underset{+H^+}{\overset{-H^+}{\rightleftharpoons}}$ H–C–N=C(R)–H (NH)

Another example in which the intervention of a coenzyme is explained, is the case of the conversion of G—1—P into G—6—P. Here, G—1, 6—PP plays the part of coenzyme. Unlike the case of DPN cited previously, this coenzyme does not function as a second substrate, but on the contrary it is constantly reformed from the substrate. In effect a cycle is operating in which G—6—P accumulates.

$$G{-}1,6{-}PP + \overset{*}{G}{-}1{-}P \rightleftharpoons \overset{*}{G}{-}1,6{-}PP + G{-}6{-}P$$

An exactly analogous mechanism is that in which 2, 3-diphosphoglyceric acid acts as the coenzyme for the phosphoglyceromutase system (transformation of 2-phosphoglyceric acid into 3-phosphoglyceric acid or the inverse) (Sutherland, Posternak and Cori, 1949) :

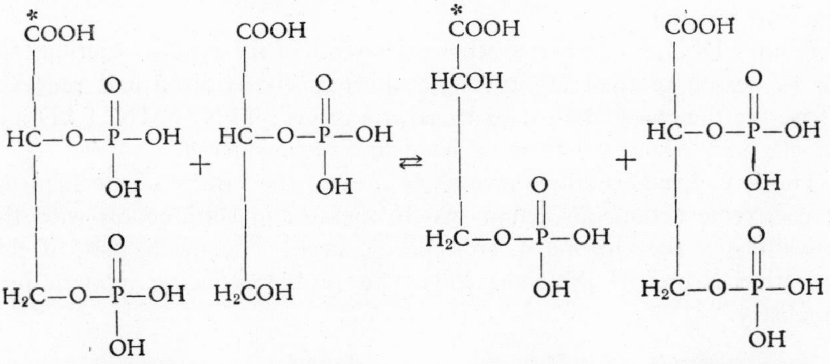

$$\begin{array}{ccccccc}
\overset{*}{C}OOH & & COOH & & \overset{*}{C}OOH & & COOH \\
| & & | & & | & & | \\
HC{-}O{-}\overset{O}{\overset{\|}{P}}{-}OH & & HC{-}O{-}\overset{O}{\overset{\|}{P}}{-}OH & & HCOH & & HC{-}O{-}\overset{O}{\overset{\|}{P}}{-}OH \\
\quad\;\; | \;OH & + & \quad\;\; | \;OH & \rightleftharpoons & | & + & \quad\;\; | \;OH \\
| & & | & & | & & | \\
H_2C{-}O{-}\overset{O}{\overset{\|}{P}}{-}OH & & H_2COH & & H_2C{-}O{-}\overset{O}{\overset{\|}{P}}{-}OH & & H_2C{-}O{-}\overset{O}{\overset{\|}{P}}{-}OH \\
\quad\;\; | \;OH & & & & \quad\;\; | \;OH & & \quad\;\; | \;OH
\end{array}$$

2, 3-diphospho-glyceric acid — **2-phospho-glyceric acid** — **3-phospho-glyceric acid** — **2, 3-diphospho-glyceric acid**

Another coenzyme whose action has been clearly elucidated is coenzyme A, the coenzyme for acetyl transfer. Its sulphydryl group is capable of being alternately acetylated and deacetylated in the same way as DPN can be alternately oxidized and reduced.

$$\underset{\text{Acyl}}{R{-}\overset{O}{\overset{\|}{C}}{-}OH} + HS{-}CoA \rightleftharpoons R{-}\overset{O}{\overset{\|}{C}} \sim S{-}CoA + H_2O$$

To illustrate the mechanism of CoA intervention, let us take for an example the acetylation of an amine, the energy being supplied by ATP.

Thermodynamically, we may have

$$ATP + CH_3{-}COOH \rightleftharpoons CH_3CO{\sim}P + ADP$$
$$CH_3CO{\sim}P + NH_2{-}R \rightarrow CH_3CO{-}NHR + P$$

Nevertheless, if we consider the two sets of reactions, A and B, below, we see that either of them is faster than that written above. Both introduce CoA, which acts as the catalyst.

A) $CH_3CO{\sim}P + CoA{-}SH \rightleftharpoons CoA{-}S{\sim}COCH_3 + P$
$CoA{-}S{\sim}COCH_3 + NH_2{-}R \rightarrow CH_3CO{-}NHR + (CoA{-}SH)$

B) $ATP + CoA{-}SH \rightleftharpoons CoA{-}S{\sim}PP + AMP$
$CoA{-}S{\sim}PP + CH_3COOH \rightleftharpoons CoA{-}S{\sim}COCH_3 + PP$
$CoA{-}S{\sim}COCH_3 + NH_2{-}R \rightarrow CH_3CO{-}NHR + (CoA{-}SH)$

We see that at the end of the reaction, the catalyst remains intact and ready to function again.

Besides DPN, a number of other coenzymes of the oxido-reduction type act by reason of their ability to be alternatively oxidized and reduced. These are the coenzymes of hydrogen transport : TPN, FMN, FAD and thioctic acid, whose structure we have already considered.

The few examples above give some idea of the variety of mechanisms of coenzyme action, an action which operates in conjunction with the activation by the enzyme macromolecule itself. The mechanism of this activation is one of the most important problems facing modern biochemistry.

REFERENCES

LAIDLER, K. J. (1954). *Introduction to the Chemistry of Enzymes*, McGraw Hill New York.

HOFFMANN-OSTENHOF, O. (1954). *Enzymologie*, Springer, Wien.

MEHLER, A. H. (1957). *Introduction to Enzymology*, Academic Press, New York.

DIXON, M. and WEBB, E. C. (1958). *Enzymes*, Longmans, Green and Co, London.

PART THREE

CHEMICAL REACTIONS IN THE BIOSPHERE

INTRODUCTION

THE biosphere is the seat of a continuous transformation of matter and energy. Despite influences tending constantly to convert the chemical elements into the highly oxidized state characteristic of inanimate matter, this activity maintains the living material and replaces it continuously throughout its more or less prolonged, but finite, life-span. The metabolism of the organisms which make up the biosphere shows certain general characteristics common to all organisms, besides those applying only to particular types or classes. The organism makes pyrophosphate bonds ready for the performance of various types of cellular work by means of a chemical machine whose essential character is everywhere the same. This machine can be fed by the chief types of chemical structure which are present to a high proportion in all types of protoplasm : sugars, fatty acids and amino acids. This applies also to those organisms which receive their energy from outside the biosphere and are called autotrophes (see Part Five). In the autotrophes, which can build up organic macromolecules from simple inorganic materials, and in the heterotrophes (organisms depending on a supply of protoplasm from another organism, which can be broken down), the supply of cellular nutrients (sugars, fatty acids and amino acids) in most cases requires a corresponding breakdown of macromolecules formed by the association of these nutrients. Here we have an important generalization which has already been mentioned by Herbert Spencer in his *Principles of Biology*. The macromolecules which form the plastic structure predominant in living beings should in fact have a certain stability, which will allow them to act as a reserve for nutritional purposes and which will assure the persistence of form, despite what we now know to be a *dynamic state* which, in the course of time, renews these molecules more or less quickly, completely or partially. On the other hand these polymers should be endowed with a certain instability permitting them to deliver up the whole of their monomer content to the turnover of cellular nutrients when protoplasm is acting as food. This, we know now, is not due to the instability of the macromolecules but to the presence of specific enzymes, the hydrolases, which can cleave peptide, oside and ester bonds. There are not very many different kinds of hydrolases, but they are found in extremely diverse locations and employed in a variety of different ways; in fact their study is of interest both to the biochemist and to the comparative physiologist. The final result of their action is the liberation of fatty acids, sugars and amino acids, which become available to the metabolism of the cell and form its actual nutrient.

The cell is the place where an important series of reactions occur which we shall term *priming reactions* since their purpose is the formation of the energy-rich linkages of ATP. These reactions are the most important mechanism for the provision of these energy-rich bonds. They are not what were formerly known as catabolic reactions, but they consist of a series of closely interrelated cycles which are more or less reversible. As the cellular nutrients are metabolized and consumed in these cycles, a certain number of energy-rich bonds are formed, some new molecules are synthesized and above all, the cell is provided with a series of fragments containing one, two or more carbon atoms. These fragments can serve as building blocks for the construction of many different molecules which can be incorporated into the structure and functioning of that particular organism.

CHAPTER I

DESTRUCTIVE AND NON-DESTRUCTIVE METHODS IN MODERN BIOCHEMISTRY

I. FROM THE WHOLE ORGANISM TO THE PURE ENZYME

MANY types of biochemical research are carried out on the whole organism, with a minimum of disturbance. This is the case, for example, when a given compound is added to the food and the excreta is investigated for this substance or its transformation products.

An example of important information obtained by this non-destructive procedure is the demonstration of nitrogen equilibrium in the adult animal, as in the classic experiments of Bischoff and Voit on the dog. If meat is given to a dog continuously over a period of several days, and the nitrogen excretion is measured over this time, it is found that no nitrogen is retained. The nitrogen excreted corresponds to the nitrogen ingested; the animal is said to be in nitrogen equilibrium.

The organism can also be subjected to experimental intervention such as, for example, the removal of an organ. The normal mammal converts the nitrogen of amino acids into urea, but this is no longer the case when the organism is deprived of the liver. The amino acids and ammonia accumulate in the blood. Alternatively, the urea formed when the liver is present is eliminated by the kidneys and it is the urea which would accumulate in the blood if the kidneys were removed.

A more destructive process is experimentation using isolated or perfused organs. Thus it is possible to introduce a substance to an organ by way of the perfusion fluid and to observe the changes it undergoes in the organ by studying the efferent fluid. For example, introduction of ammonia into the liquid perfusing the isolated liver of a dog results in the appearance of urea in the efferent liquid. Alternatively, the same experiment using isolated goose liver would show the appearance of uric acid. It is evident that an isolated perfused organ, whether perfused with "physiological saline" or with blood, is in fact a highly abnormal experimental material. It is abnormal when we consider the supply of oxygen to the cells, the supply of blood, the inervation of the material, etc. Even more destructive is experimentation using thin tissue slices. Such slices of tissue, provided that they have been prepared under suitable conditions, will survive for several hours, the cells appearing to lead a normal life. The pressure of oxygen must be sufficient to meet the oxygen requirements of the tissue. If the medium is buffered and the slice is sufficiently thin (0·3 mm approx.) this method is very useful. Thanks to the manometric method developed by Warburg, the use of tissue slices has given much important information.

The next stage in the order of gradually increasing destruction is the use of minces, breis and homogenates. Here, the cells are destroyed but the intra-cellular particles are intact. They may even be isolated by centrifugation, and mitochondria are often separated in this way. However, although all the above methods are useful and instructive, only the results obtained with purified enzymes have been capable of giving precise information about metabolic mechanisms. The rapid progress of biochemistry during the course of the last few years is primarily the result of the perfecting of methods for the isolation, purification and characterization of enzymes.

If the results so obtained are clear and precise, they are evidently also reached through the most extreme of destructive processes and the reconstitution of the complex phenomena of metabolism from such results might appear, and in fact does appear to certain intellects, a most far-fetched undertaking.

As enzymology was developing, biochemistry also was shaking off the shackles imposed upon it by chemists on the one hand, and physiologists on the other. As the particular nature of its own problems became apparent, biochemistry began to explore all the paths of Nature in search of their solution, breaking open the compartments into which an out-of-date classification of the sciences had tended to confine it. Having recourse to recent discoveries in physics and genetics, the biochemists took the certainties obtained from the use of purified enzymes, and with indications provided by the use of isotopes and mutant forms of micro-organisms they developed new non-destructive methods to go with the extremely destructive methods of enzymology. It is due to this combination of ingenuity and patience that numerous problems of biosynthesis, up till then obscure, have been solved.

II. BIOCHEMICAL INVESTIGATION AND THE USE OF ISOTOPES

By means of isotopes it is possible to mark a compound at one or more positions in the molecule and to follow the fate of these labelled atoms. With the introduction of isotopes of the most common elements in the biosphere (hydrogen, carbon, nitrogen, oxygen, phosphorous, sulphur), the method has proved most fruitful.

REFERENCES

NEILANDS, J. B. and STUMPF, P. K. (1955). *Outlines of Enzyme Chemistry*. Wiley, New York.

According to the present view, the nucleus of an atom is formed from protons of mass 1 and charge + 1 and neutrons of mass 1 and charge 0. The atomic number corresponds to the number of protons and all the atoms of a given element have the same number of protons in the nucleus. But the total number of protons and neutrons can vary. To designate the different *isotopes* of an element, its symbol is written preceded by a number corresponding to the atomic number (i.e. to the number of protons) and it is followed by an index corresponding to the number of nucleons (protons + neutrons).

The three isotopes of hydrogen, *protium*, *deuterium* and *tritium* are written as follows:

$$_1H^1 \qquad _1H^2 \qquad _1H^3$$

and the four most important isotopes of carbon thus :

$$_6C^{11} \qquad _6C^{12} \qquad _6C^{13} \qquad _6C^{14}$$

Since the atomic number is the same for the several isotopes of an element, it is often omitted, and only the number of nucleons is noted. Certain isotopes are stable and occur naturally and they may be concentrated from these natural sources. The most important as far as the biochemist is concerned, are $_1H^2$, $_6C^{13}$, $_7N^{15}$ and $_8O^{18}$.

It is also possible to prepare artificial isotopes by bombardment with protons, neutrons, α-particles, etc. These isotopes are radioactive and after varying lengths of time they undergo transmutation accompanied by the emission of electrons. The determination of stable isotopes is carried out with the mass spectrometer and radioactive isotopes are determined by measuring their degree of radioactivity.

If we consider a homogeneous population of radioactive atoms, a constant proportion of this population will decay in any given period of time.

An interesting characteristic of each isotope is its half life, a figure corresponding to the time required for exactly half of the total number of atoms to decay. It is equal to infinity for the stable isotopes. It is twelve years for tritium, 5900 years for $_6C^{14}$, but only fifteen hours for $_{11}Na^{24}$ and 20·5 minutes for $_6C^{11}$.

One of the most useful applications of isotopes is in the study of metabolic problems and the determination of a *precursor-product* sequence. Suppose that we wish to know whether A is converted to B inside the organism. We synthesize A; introducing atoms of an isotope, we administer it to the organism and then we isolate the compound B after some little time. We degrade this compound and determine the distribution of the isotopic atoms in the molecule. This procedure often casts useful light on the mechanism of the conversion.

Isotopes also enable us to measure the speed of synthesis or breakdown of a compound. In this way one can measure the *turnover* of a substance, that is the rate at which its molecules are replaced (although the concentration remains the same) when it is in a *steady state* resulting from an equilibrium between the rate of synthesis on the one hand, and the rate of breakdown or incorporation, on the other.

III. THE USE OF MUTANT STRAINS OF MICRO-ORGANISMS

The name auxotrophes is given to those mutant forms of a micro-organism which are dependent on the provision of a growth factor not required by the natural form. At the present time, a very large number of mutants are known which are characterized by the loss of a given enzyme, their metabolism is blocked at the stage of a definite chemical reaction. To define the particular reaction which is blocked, two sets of information are required : a knowledge of the substances which the mutant can use as growth factors, and knowledge of the substances which accumulate in the cell. Let us suppose that A and B are two different precursors of X. If we have a mutant which is an auxotrophe for X, which accumulates A, and which responds by growing when B is supplied, we can deduce that the block is situated after A and before B in the series of metabolic reactions.

Distinction between a Possible Precursor and an Obligatory Intermediate

To show that a given substance *can* serve as a precursor of a second substance is one thing; to show that it is in fact the normal intermediate in the organism is quite another. The study of mutants of micro-organisms has revealed the existence of auxotrophes for each of the naturally occurring amino acids. This illustrates very well the idea of an obligatory metabolic pathway, at least in these organisms.

Let us once more consider the case of A and B, precursors of X in a micro-organism. The wild strain of this micro-organism is able, as can be demonstrated by the use of isotopes or by means of the purified enzymes, to convert A and B into X. A single enzyme, extracted from the micro-organism and purified, converts A into B. A mutant auxotrophic for X does

REFERENCES

Calvin, M., Heidelberger, Ch., Reid, J. C., Tolbert, B. M., Yanknich, P. F. (1949). *Isotopic Carbon. Techniques in its measurement and chemical manipulation.* Wiley, New York.

Kamen, M. D. (1948). *Radioactive Tracers in Biology*. Academic Press, New York.

not contain this enzyme. In this way, by association of destructive and non-destructive methods, both of which are indispensable, it is possible to demonstrate with certainty that the metabolic sequence is A–B–X.

Nevertheless, it can be objected that a product accumulated by one mutant and utilized by another mutant could very possibly be the product of a side-reaction.

For example, consider the reaction scheme

$$\begin{array}{c} O \rightarrow \rightarrow A \rightarrow B \rightarrow \rightarrow X \\ \upharpoonleft\downharpoonright \\ A' \end{array}$$

It is possible to imagine, if the block is between A and B, that an extract of the wild strain of the micro-organism would covert A' into B whilst an extract of the blocked mutant would not. Is this a reason for placing A' in the direct metabolic sequence to X, that is for writing $A \rightarrow A' \rightarrow B \rightarrow X$? No, because the isolation of enzymes enables us to demonstrate that a single enzyme is capable of converting A into B and that, for the conversion of A' into B, two enzymes are necessary; in addition to the first, we require an enzyme catalysing the reaction: $A' \rightarrow A$. This is an illustration of the importance of studies on purified enzymes, alongside experiments using non-destructive methods.

REFERENCES

HARRIS, H. (1953). *An Introduction to Human Biochemical Genetics.* Univ. Press, Cambridge.

WAGNER, R. P. and MITCHELL, H. K. (1955). *Genetics and Metabolism.* Wiley, New York.

CHAPTER II

PRIMING REACTIONS

I. GLYCOLYSIS AND THE HEXOSEMONOPHOSPHATE SHUNT

THE name glycolysis is given to the sequence of enzymatic reactions (Embden–Meyerhof scheme) which bring about the fragmentation of carbohydrates by a pathway which does not involve the intervention of oxygen molecules. The enzymatic system for glycolysis is a universal one, at least in its main outlines, although there are numerous variations differing in certain details.

The most completely understood system is that of the alcoholic fermentation of glucose in the presence of yeast.

A. ALCOHOLIC FERMENTATION

The fermentation of grape juice (pH around 5·0) under the influence of yeasts growing on the surface of the grape (especially *Saccharomyces cerevisiae*) and transported from one to another by insects (in particular wasps), has been known since ancient times. The manufacture of beer and of bread are further well-known examples of alcoholic fermentation, that is the anaerobic breakdown of glucose with production of ethanol and CO_2. It was Theodor Schwann who first showed, in 1837, that the alcoholic fermentation of grape juice, at that time a phenomenon of some mystery, depended on the introduction of living cells into the sweet solution. He described yeast simultaneously with Cagniard–Latour. This great discovery at once encountered the open opposition of the chemists. For them, alcoholic fermentation was a simple chemical process, expressed by the equation

$$C_6H_{12}O_6 \rightarrow 2C_2H_5OH + 2CO_2$$

Liebig even went so far as to draw up with Wöhler, and to publish anonymously in *Annalen der Pharmacie*, a facetious article ridiculing Schwann's views and depicting yeast as a sort of infusoria eating sugar, excreting alcohol from the digestive tract and CO_2 from a bladder in the shape of a bottle of champagne. Twenty years later, in 1860, Pasteur confirmed the views of Schwann, and the "vitalist" theory of fermentation triumphed.

In 1897 Buchner, whilst preparing extracts of yeast for a therapeutic purpose, wished to assure their preservation by the addition of sugar and he made an important observation : the mixture frothed and became rich in alcohol. Alcoholic fermentation without cells had been discovered. Our present knowledge of this phenomenon derives from elaboration of the results of an experiment done by Harden and Young in 1906. Buchner had observed that if one added phosphate to yeast juice, the CO_2 production was increased—for him this was the result of the change in acidity.

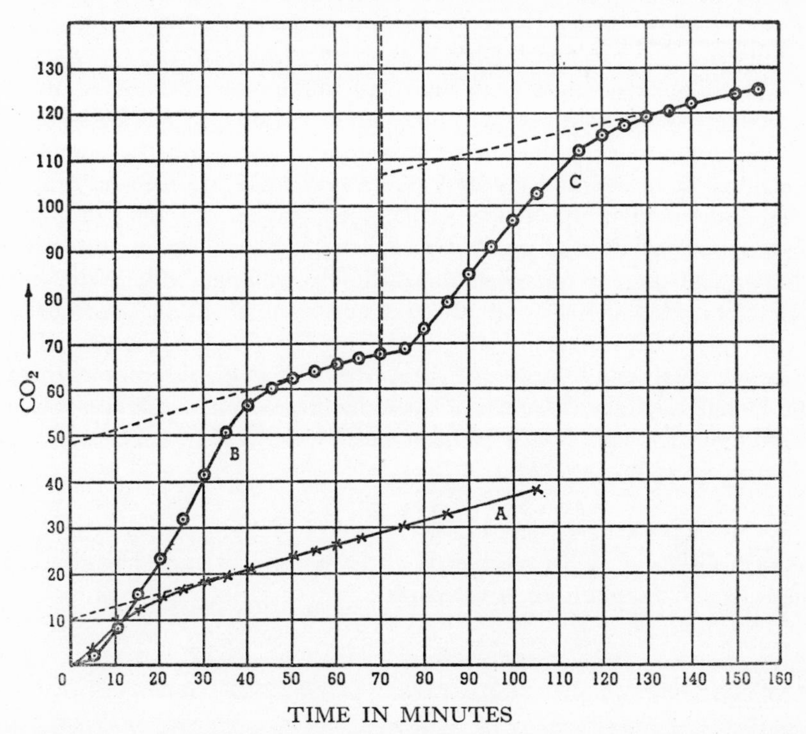

FIG. 36 (Harden and Young)—Production of CO_2 with time in yeast juice to which has been added : A. glucose; B. the same mixture (25 ml of yeast juice + 25 ml of water in which 5g of glucose is dissolved) plus 5 ml of a 0·3M mixture of primary and secondary phosphates; C. a further addition of the same quantity of phosphates after 70 min.

Harden and Young observed that after a temporary increase in CO_2 evolution, following the addition of phosphate, the effect died away, only to be renewed on a further addition of phosphate. Moreover, successive additions of phosphate led to a production of one mole of CO_2 for each mole of phosphate added and the increase in the production of alcohol corresponded mole for mole to the amount of CO_2 produced (Fig. 36).

When Harden and Young sought the phosphate which they had added, they found that it was not in its free form but was bound as phosphoric esters. They isolated fructofuranose —1,6—PP (Harden and Young ester) and later other esters have been isolated from the fermentation liquor: fructofuranose—6—P (Neuberg ester); glucose—6—P (Robinson ester) and glucose—1—P (Cori ester).

In 1905, a new fundamental discovery was announced simultaneously by Buchner and by Harden and Young. When a fermenting juice is dialysed, fermentation ceases in the dialysate (termed cozymase) and in the residue (termed apoenzyme). In the "cozymase" or "coenzyme" (the name given initially to the dialysate), we find substances of the nature of our "coenzymes", ATP, DPN, DPT.

The reducing action of yeast thus became the foremost topic of interest.

Neuberg carried out another important experiment by adding bisulphite to the fermenting mixture. A precipitation of the bisulphite complex of acetaldehyde occurs and glycerol accumulates (one mole per mole of the bisulphite compound). Neuberg concluded that fermentation takes place by a decarboxylation of pyruvic acid forming acetaldehyde, and that the glycerol contains the hydrogen which, in fermentation, reduces the acetaldehyde to alcohol. But what was the substance which on hydrogenation yielded glycerol? This could only be a triose. For a long time it was believed to be methylglyoxal, but we now know that it is an equilibrium mixture of phosphoglyceraldehyde and phosphodihydroxyacetone. We know today how these trioses are produced from glucose. Alcoholic fermentation takes place in the following stages:

1. In the presence of hexokinase, a molecule of ATP reacts with glucose to form G—6—P. This reaction is a transphosphorylation having a large negative ΔF. Equilibrium is as follows:

$$\underset{1\%}{\text{ATP} + \text{glucose}} \rightarrow \underset{99\%}{\text{ADP} + \text{G—6—P}}$$

Hence it is an almost irreversible reaction in which the energy of the ATP bond is lost almost completely.

2. In the presence of phosphoglucoisomerase, G—6—P is transformed rapidly into F—6—P and the equilibrium of this reversible reaction is:

$$\underset{70\%}{\text{G—6—P}} \rightleftharpoons \underset{30\%}{\text{F—6—P}}$$

3. Phosphofructokinase, in the presence of Mg^{++}, and very specifically, catalyses the transfer of the terminal group of ATP to F—6—P with formation F—1, 6—PP. Here also, as in 1, we have a transphosphorylase

system of high negative ΔF, such that the energy of the energy-rich bond of ATP is not conserved and the reaction is irreversible.

$$F—6—P + ATP \rightarrow F—1,6—PP + ADP$$

4. The formation of phosphotriose, the substrate for glycolysis, takes place by the splitting, in the presence of aldolase, of F—1,6—PP into a mixture of two triosephosphates. Equilibrium between the hexose-phosphate and the mixture of triosephosphates is established in the cell.

$$
F - 1,6 - PP \underset{aldolase}{\rightleftharpoons}
\begin{array}{l}
\text{Phosphodihydroxyacetone} \quad \left.\begin{array}{l} CH_2OPO(OH)_2 \\ | \\ CO \\ | \\ CH_2OH \end{array}\right\} 96\% \\
+ \qquad\qquad\qquad\qquad \upharpoonleft\downharpoonright \\
\text{3-phosphoglyceraldehyde} \quad \left.\begin{array}{l} CHO \\ | \\ CHOH \\ | \\ CH_2OPO(OH)_2 \end{array}\right\} 4\%
\end{array}
$$

89 % — 11 %

5. In the course of reactions 1 to 4, a molecule of glucose has been transformed into a mixture of F—1,6—PP and two triosephosphates. Now occurs the first anaerobic oxido-reduction (see p. 142) in which, in the presence of triosephosphate dehydrogenase and its coenzyme DPN, an internal oxido-reduction takes place forming 1,3-diphosphoglyceric acid, a molecule containing an energy-rich acylphosphate bond.

$$
\begin{array}{l} H \\ / \\ C{=}O \\ | \\ CHOH \\ | \\ CH_2OPO(OH)_2 \end{array}
+ DPN^+ + H_3PO_4 \rightleftharpoons
\begin{array}{l} O{\sim}PO(OH)_2 \\ / \\ C{=}O \\ | \\ CHOH \\ | \\ CH_2OPO(OH)_2 \end{array}
+ DPNH + H^+
$$

3-phosphoglyceraldehyde — 1,3-diphosphoglyceric acid

6. This reaction causes the F—1,6—PP to dissociate into triose phosphates, since it uses up one of the products of that reaction. Reaction 5 itself is pushed completely to the right (although it is a reversible reaction) by the fact that, in the presence of the very specific enzyme 3-phosphoglycerate phosphokinase, the energy-rich compound 1,3-diphosphoglyceric acid transfers its energy-rich bond to ADP to form ATP. The phosphokinase acts almost at equilibrium so that the energy-rich bond is transferred with little loss (1 acylphosphate bond → 1 pyrophosphate bond) (low $-\Delta F$).

7. After the first transfer of phosphate described in 6, 3-phosphoglyceric acid is left. In the presence of phosphoglyceromutase and 2,3-diphosphoglyceric acid as coenzyme (see p. 175) an isomerization to 2-phosphoglyceric acid occurs.

8. It is at the level of 2-phosphoglyceric acid that the second internal oxido-reduction appears. In the presence of enolase and Mg^{++}, a molecule of water is removed and a molecular rearrangement generates (see p. 143) an energy-rich bond.

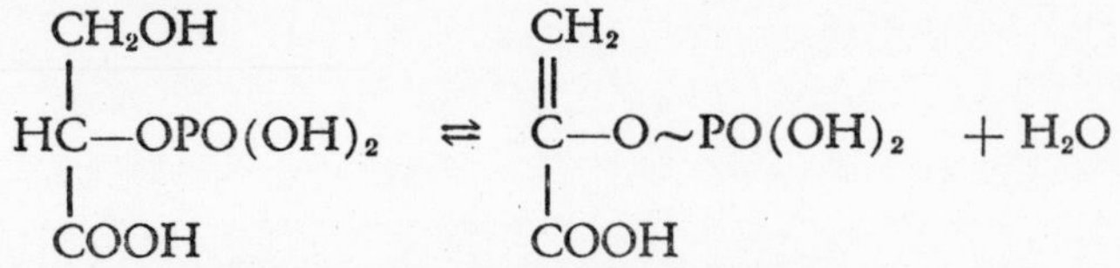

$$\underset{\text{2-phosphoglyceric acid}}{\begin{array}{c} CH_2OH \\ | \\ HC{-}OPO(OH)_2 \\ | \\ COOH \end{array}} \rightleftharpoons \underset{\text{phosphoenolpyruvic acid}}{\begin{array}{c} CH_2 \\ \| \\ C{-}O{\sim}PO(OH)_2 \\ | \\ COOH \end{array}} + H_2O$$

9. The phosphoenolpyruvic acid is the subject of the second transfer of phosphate, in the presence of pyruvic phosphokinase, a phosphokinase acting almost at equilibrium (low ΔF) the transfer is brought about with conservation of the energy-rich bond.

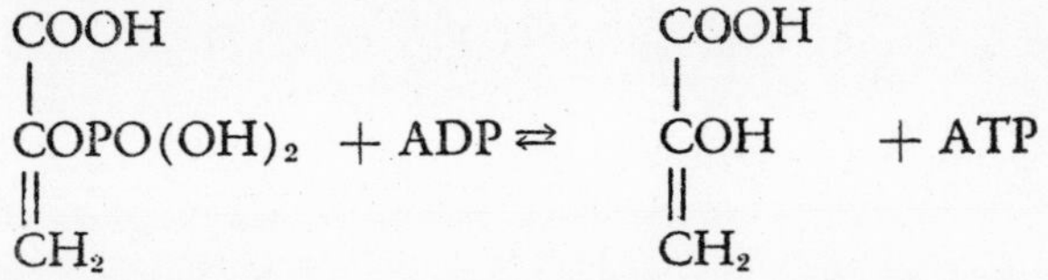

$$\underset{\text{phosphoenolpyruvic acid}}{\begin{array}{c} COOH \\ | \\ COPO(OH)_2 \\ \| \\ CH_2 \end{array}} + ADP \rightleftharpoons \underset{\text{enol-pyruvic acid}}{\begin{array}{c} COOH \\ | \\ COH \\ \| \\ CH_2 \end{array}} + ATP$$

$$\begin{array}{c} \text{enol-pyruvic acid} \\ \updownarrow \\ COOH \\ | \\ CO \\ | \\ CH_3 \\ \text{pyruvic acid} \end{array}$$

10. The pyruvic acid, in the presence of pyruvic carboxylase (the prosthetic group of which is DPT) and Mg^{++}, is decarboxylated to acetaldehyde.

$$CH_3{-}CO{-}COOH \xrightarrow[DPT]{Mg^{++}} CH_3{-}CHO + CO_2$$

11. When the 1,3-diphosphoglyceric acid is formed, in reaction 5, DPN^+ is reduced. The DPNH which results is first of all dehydrogenated by phosphodihydroxyacetone producing 3-phosphoglycerol, which is then hydrolysed by a phosphatase to form glycerol. This is the explanation of

the production, first noted by Pasteur, of small amounts of glycerol during alcoholic fermentation. But acetaldehyde is more strongly oxidizing than phosphodihydroxyacetone. As long as it is present it will take hydrogen from the DPNH to form ethanol.

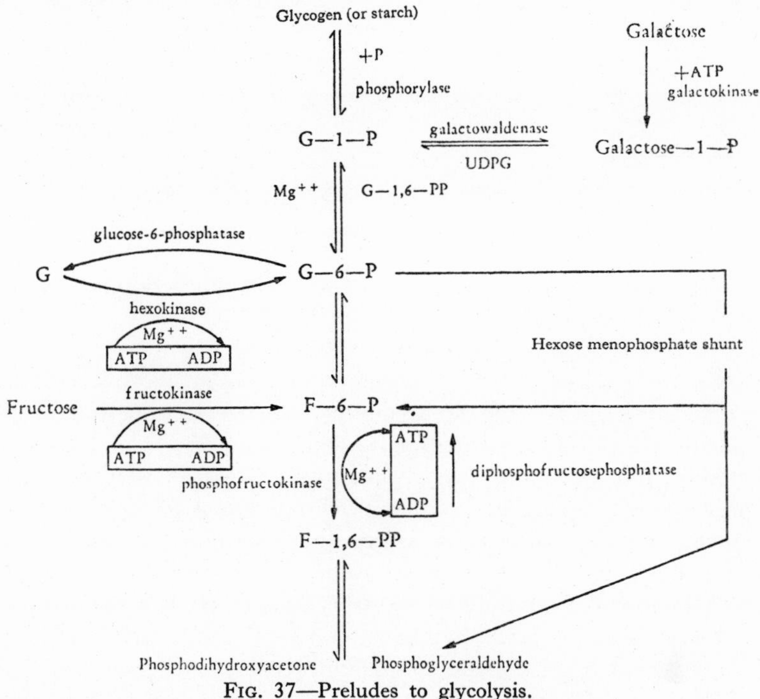

FIG. 37—Preludes to glycolysis.

B. Preludes to Glycolysis

Glycolysis is essentially the passage of F—1,6—PP to pyruvic acid by the intermediary of a splitting into two triosephosphates, two oxido-reductions and two transfers of phosphate groups. It is an anaerobic oxido-reduction of trioses, at substrate level, with formation of two energy-rich bonds per molecule of triose.

Glycolysis, defined as above, is very common in the biosphere. There are numerous variants of the beginning of the process. The entry into the pathway varies from one carbohydrate to another, as Fig. 37 sufficiently illustrates.

C. The Hexosemonophosphate Shunt (Pentose Cycle)

Although it is true that the Embden–Meyerhof scheme traces the most general form of the start of carbohydrate catabolism, there exists an alternative route, oxidative in nature, which with a fragment of the glycolysis chain constitutes a cycle resulting from the attachment of a shunt, one end on G—6—P and the other on F—6—P and the triosephosphates. The multi-enzyme system of the hexosemonophosphate shunt (HMS) is sometimes called the pentose cycle because it contains mechanisms for the formation of pentoses either by decarboxylation of hexoses or from phosphoglyceraldehyde. The cycle is quite widely found in the biosphere, but its relative importance compared to glycolysis is extremely variable. The different tissues of an organism differ in this respect. In mammals, for example, glycolysis is predominant in the muscles and the hexosemonophosphate shunt in the liver.

Knowledge of the different reactions which have been carried out *in vitro* with purified enzymes, reactions which are collected together in the scheme shown in Fig. 38, give experimental confirmation to the ideas summarized in this scheme. It does not exclude the existence of other, as yet unknown, pathways.

The cycle contains two oxidations, each coupled with TPN (and not DPN which in general is the coenzyme required in glycolysis). Glycolysis is inhibited by fluoride and iodoacetate or bromacetate, the first affecting enolase and the second triosephosphate-dehydrogenase.

In 1936, Lipmann found that an extract of yeast continued to respire in the presence of bromacetate, although fermentation is blocked by this substance. This contradicted the notion that respiration is necessarily an appendix attached to a preceding anaerobic glycolysis leading to pyruvate. The year before, Warburg (1935) had described, at the time he discovered TPN, the oxidative transformation of G—6—P into 6-phosphogluconic acid in yeast and erythrocytes, the dehydrogenase being named by him *Zwischenferment*. The study of these phenomena by Warburg and by Dickens showed that an oxidative decarboxylation with formation of a pentose phosphate was involved. From 1950 onwards, the researches of S. Cohen and Scott on the one hand, and of Horecker and Smyrniotis on the other, provided new information leading to the identification of the pentoses formed. Ribulose-5-phosphate is first formed in the oxidation followed by decarboxylation of the phosphogluconate brought about by purified preparations of the dehydrogenase. Then the ribulose-5-phosphate is converted by phosphopentose-isomerase into an equilibrium mixture of two pentose phosphates : ribose-P and xylulose-P.

The chain leading from the hexoses to the pentoses is theoretically reversible, but this reversal is probably only of biological importance under very special circumstances.

It is nonetheless true that in many cases a pentose phosphate can give a hexose. But it is not by a reversal of the hexosemonophosphate oxidative chain. The action in question is a non-oxidative action by transketolase and transaldolase on the pentose phosphates. The demonstration of this important metabolic pathway is due to Racker and to Horecker and their co-workers. If ribose-5-phosphate is present to act as an aldehyde acceptor, the xylulose-5-phosphate is rapidly converted by an enzyme in the yeast into triose phosphate.

By means of the cycle can be explained the formation of sedoheptulose-7-P (thus named because of its accumulation in the leaves of *Sedum* which lacks the enzyme system for its further transformation).

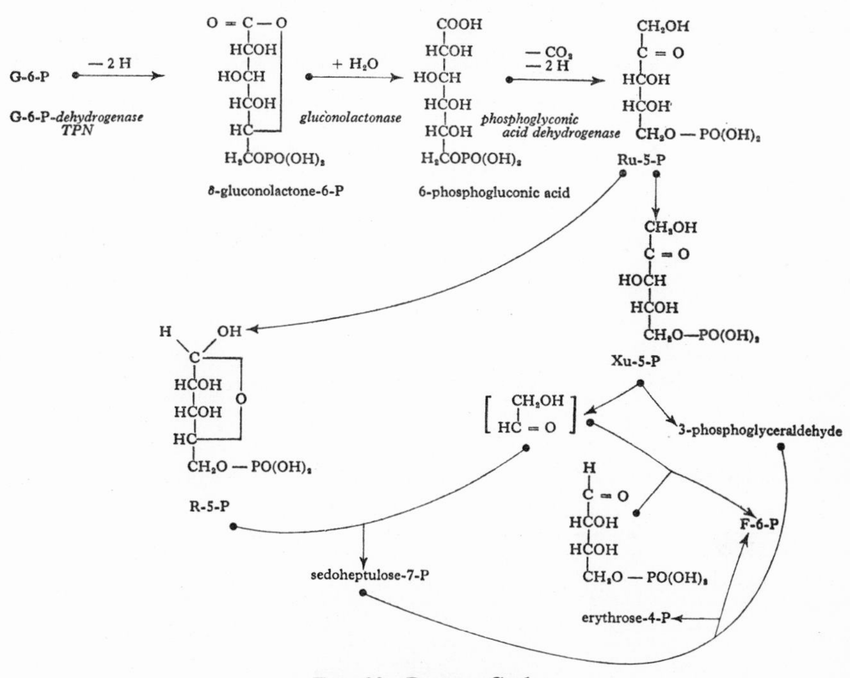

FIG. 38—Pentose Cycle
Xu = xylulose, the ketose corresponding to xylose.

The next step is the action of a transaldolase which transfers the dihydroxyacetone group of sedoheptulose to an acceptor aldehyde (3-phosphoglyceraldehyde) forming fructose-6-P and leaving a phosphotetrose, D-erythrose-4-P.

A further molecule of ribulose-5-P furnishes an "active glycolaldehyde" to the tetrose, forming a new molecule of F—6—P.

The overall reaction is the following:

$$3G—6—P + 3O_2 \rightarrow 2F—6—P + 1\ \text{Triose-P} + 3CO_2 + 3H_2O$$

Thus in the course of the complete cycle, one molecule of glucose is broken down to 3 molecules of CO_2, 3 molecules of water and a molecule of triose; a molecule of triose is oxidized completely.

D. The Terminal Stages of Glycolysis

The glycolysis process (Embden–Meyerhof pathway) leads, as we have said, to pyruvate. In the case of yeast fermenting glucose, the acetaldehyde resulting from the decarboxylation of pyruvate serves as an acceptor of electrons borne by the DPNH from the dehydrogenation of phosphoglyceraldehyde at the time of the first oxido-reduction. Ethanol is formed. However, the formation of acetaldehyde from pyruvic acid is not a general

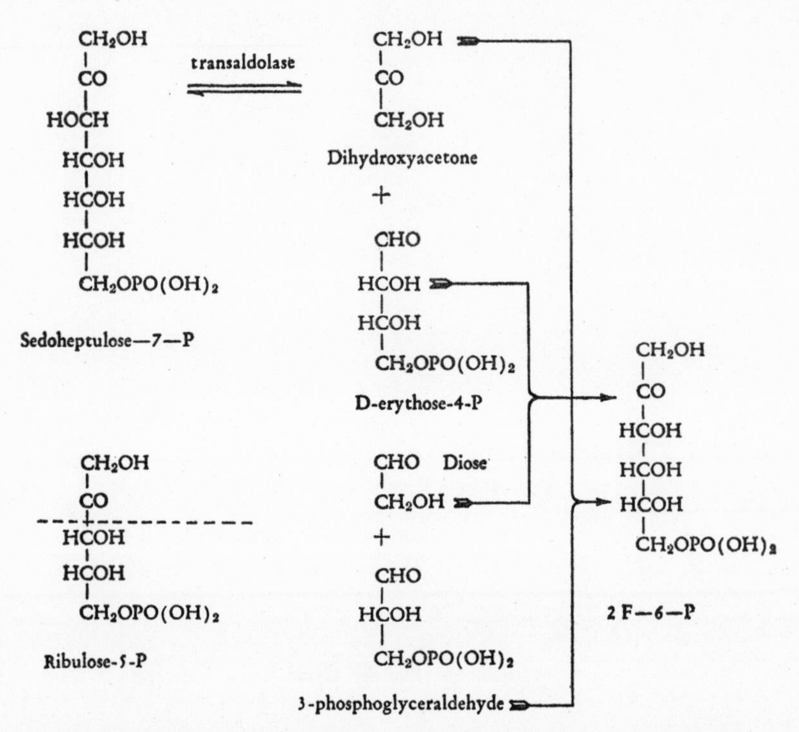

Fig. 39 (Dickens)—Formation of F—6—P in the hexosemonophosphate shunt.

phenomenon. It is a phenomenon peculiar to certain bacteria, yeasts and plants which because of a particular specialization contain carboxylase. The general phenomenon is the presence of a hydrogen acceptor more highly oxidizing than phosphodihydroxyacetone. This oxidizing substance is pyruvic acid in animals and in certain bacteria provided with lactic dehydrogenase. This enzyme in the presence of DPNH converts pyruvate to lactate, which is the product of anaerobic carbohydrate catabolism in animals and some bacteria. In addition, certain bacteria are specialized to accept the same hydrogen in various other ways, either by organic compounds such as oxalo-acetic acid, or by inorganic substances.

But the above are all variants operating during the anaerobic state. In the presence of oxygen, pyruvate undergoes the same fate in all the different organisms. It undergoes oxidative decarboxylation with production of *acetyl-CoA*

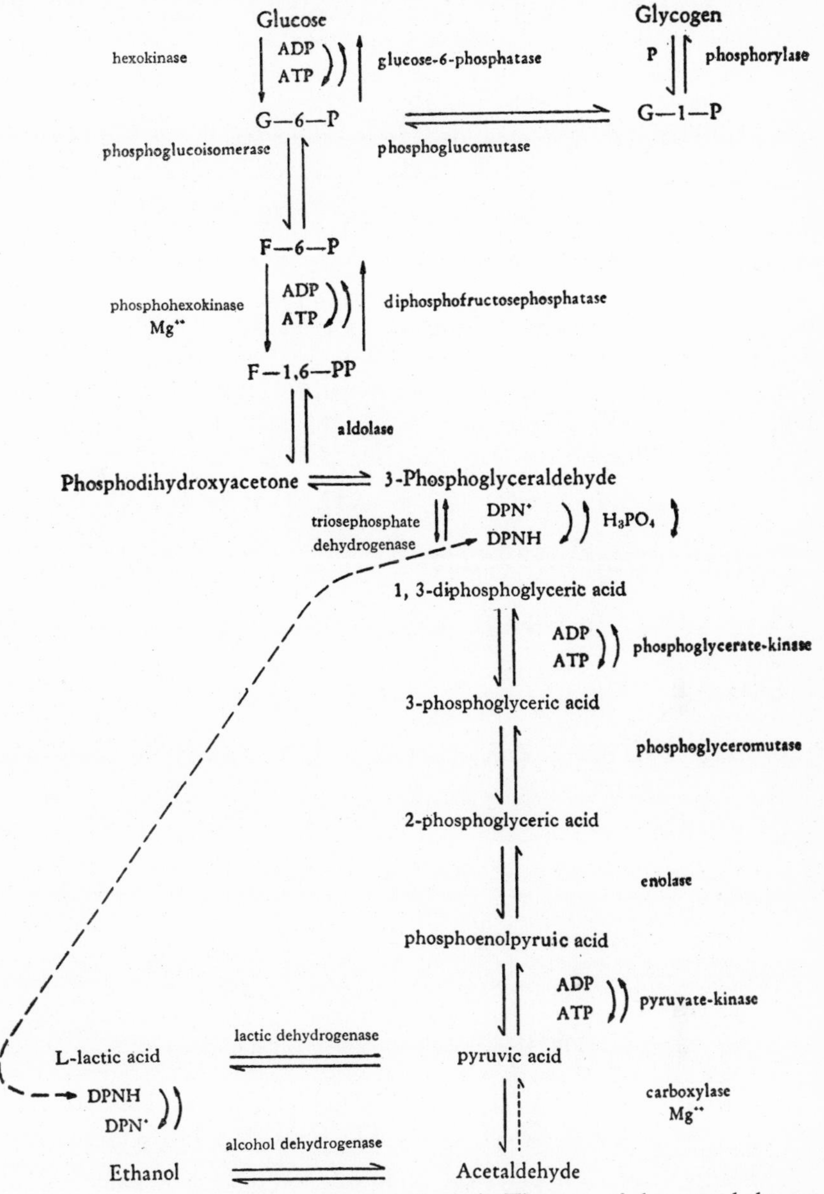

FIG. 40—Scheme to summarize reactions of glycolysis. The entry of glucose and glycogen is shown. For other entries see Fig. 37. Two terminations are shown : that of alcoholic fermentation and that of lactic fermentation.

Pyruvic decarboxylase is a complex enzyme system the coenzymes of which are lipoic (or thioctic) acid, thiamine pyrophosphate (TPP), coenzyme A and DPN.

Some workers maintain that a compound of thiamine pyrophosphate and lipoic acid is present, lipothiamide pyrophosphate. The oxidative decarboxylation of pyruvate actually occurs in three stages. In the first, pyruvate is condensed with lipothiamide pyrophosphate (LTPP) with loss of CO_2. The accompanying dehydrogenation results in the formation of a thioester link (energy-rich bond). Here the dehydrogenation is not at the start of the respiratory chain but leads to an energy-rich thioester bond. The LTPP which has been acetylated in this first step and contains the thioester bond reacts with the -SH group of coenzyme A an exchange of thioacyl takes place producing a molecule of acetyl-CoA (containing the energy rich thioester bond) and a molecule of LTPP in the sulphydryl form. In a third reaction, the sulphydryl form is converted to the disulphide form with loss of two hydrogen to DPN^+ with formation of $DPNH + H^+$. The DPNH on entering the respiratory chain gives the usual three ATP's.

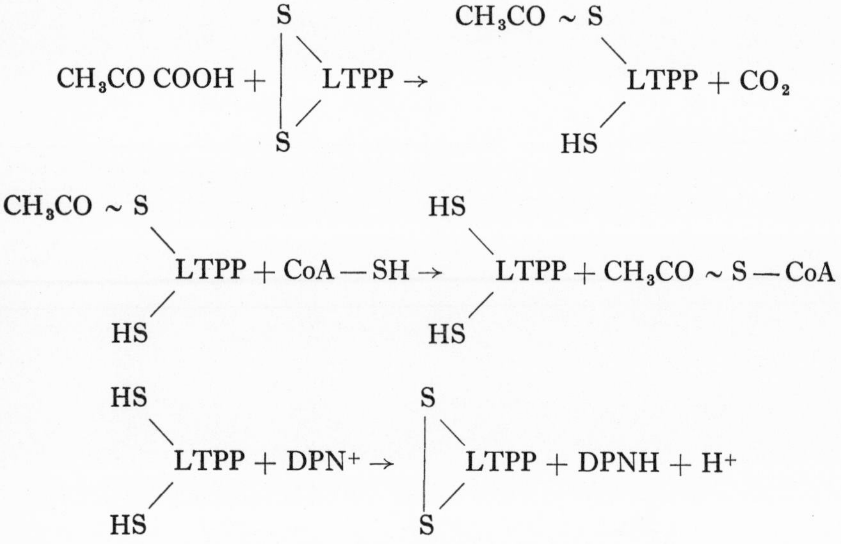

$$CH_3CO\,COOH + \begin{matrix} S \\ | \diagdown \\ | \quad LTPP \\ | \diagup \\ S \end{matrix} \rightarrow \begin{matrix} CH_3CO \sim S \\ \diagdown \\ LTPP \\ \diagup \\ HS \end{matrix} + CO_2$$

$$\begin{matrix} CH_3CO \sim S \\ \diagdown \\ LTPP \\ \diagup \\ HS \end{matrix} + CoA - SH \rightarrow \begin{matrix} HS \\ \diagdown \\ LTPP \\ \diagup \\ HS \end{matrix} + CH_3CO \sim S - CoA$$

$$\begin{matrix} HS \\ \diagdown \\ LTPP \\ \diagup \\ HS \end{matrix} + DPN^+ \rightarrow \begin{matrix} S \\ | \diagdown \\ | \quad LTPP \\ | \diagup \\ S \end{matrix} + DPNH + H^+$$

FIG. 41—Oxidative decarboxylation of pyruvate.

II. ANOTHER PATHWAY FOR THE PRODUCTION OF ACETYL-CoA: THE FATTY ACID CYCLE

The sulphur of CoA plays the same role for the introduction of fatty acids into the metabolic cycle as inorganic phosphate does for molecules of the sugars. The key to what has long been known as the Knoop

β-oxidation has been provided by the fatty acid cycle, the elucidation of which owes much to the researches of Lynen. This cycle is completely reversible and it has been reproduced *in vitro*, in both directions, using purified enzymes extracted from bacteria or animal tissues.

The cycle is made up of four parts.

1. Condensation of acetyl-CoA (active acetate) with a second molecule of acetyl-CoA to give acetoacetyl-CoA and free CoA.

$$CH_3—CO—S—CoA \quad —CH_2—CO—S—CoA$$

$$HS—CoA \quad —CH_2—CO—CH_2—CO—S—CoA$$

2. Reduction of the acetoacetyl-CoA to β-hydroxybutyryl-CoA

$$—CH_2—CO—CH_2—CO—S—CoA \underset{-2H}{\overset{+2H}{\rightleftharpoons}} —CH_2—\underset{OH}{\underset{|}{CH}}—CH_2—CO—S—CoA$$

3. Dehydration of the β-hydroxybutyryl-CoA to crotonyl-CoA.

$$—CH_2—\underset{OH}{\underset{|}{CH}}—CH_2—CO—S—CoA \underset{+H_2O}{\overset{-H_2O}{\rightleftharpoons}} —CH_2—CH{=}CH—CO—S—CoA$$

4. Reduction of crotonyl-CoA to butyryl-CoA

$$—CH_2—CH{=}CH—CO—S—CoA \underset{-2H}{\overset{+2H}{\rightleftharpoons}} —CH_2—CH_2—CH_2—CO—S—CoA$$

$$FADH_2 \rightleftharpoons FAD$$

We started with acetyl-CoA and we have lengthened the chain by 2 carbon atoms, at the price of one acetyl-CoA molecule and four hydrogen atoms. The breakdown of sugar can give us both of these. If we repeat the

REFERENCES

STUMPF, P. K. (1954). Glycolysis. *Chemical Pathways of Metabolism*, GREENBERG (Editor) vol. 1, Academic Press, New York, 67–108.

COHEN, S. (1954). Other pathways of carbohydrate metabolism, *Chemical Pathways of Metabolism*, GREENBERG (Editor) vol. 1. Academic Press, 173–233.

DICKENS, F. (1956). The hexosemonophosphate oxidative pathway of yeast and animal tissues, *Proceedings of the 3rd International Congress of Biochemistry, Brussels 1955*, Academic Press, New York, 170–179.

HORECKER, B. L. (1958). Le cycle des pentose et sa signification physiologique. *Bull. Soc. Chim. Biol.*, **40**, 555–578.

operation according to the general equations above, we again lengthen the chain by two carbon atoms. If, for example, we repeat the operation eight times, we shall obtain stearic acid according to the equation :

$$9CH_3—CO—S—CoA + 32H \rightleftharpoons$$
$$\rightleftharpoons C_{17}H_{35}—CO—S—CoA + 8HS—CoA + 8H_2O$$

Since the cycle is completely reversible, it also explains β-oxidation. Starting from a fatty acid, this acid will be activated by conversion to an acyl-CoA derivative, it will be the object of a dehydrogenation, of a hydration and a further dehydrogenation to give a β-ketoacyl-CoA. The thiolysis of this latter substance will give a molecule of acetyl-CoA and the acyl-CoA of the fatty acid containing two less carbon atoms.

The overall scheme is summarized in Fig. 42.

The different enzyme reactions intervening in the fatty acid cycle are as follows :

1. β-ketoreductase

$$CH_3—\underset{\displaystyle OH}{\underset{|}{CH}}—CH_2—CO—S—CoA + DPN \rightleftharpoons CH_3—\underset{\displaystyle O}{\underset{\|}{C}}—CH_2—CO—S—CoA + DPNH_2$$

2. Ethylene-reductase

$$CH_3—CH = CH—CO—S—CoA + FADH_2 \rightleftharpoons$$
$$CH_3—CH_2—CH_2—CO—S—CoA + FAD$$

3. β-ketothiolase

$$R—CH_2—CO—CH_2—CO—S—CoA + HS—enz. \rightleftharpoons$$
$$R—CH_2—CO—S—enz. + CH_3—CO—S—CoA$$
$$R—CH_2—CO—S—enz. + HS—CoA \rightleftharpoons R—CH_2—CO—S—CoA + HS—enz.$$

The end result being:

$$R—CH_2—CO—CH_2—CO—S—CoA + HS—CoA \rightleftharpoons$$
$$R—CH_2—CO—S—CoA— + CH_3—CO—S—CoA$$

Before entering the cycle, a fatty acid must be attached to CoA. This is the general mechanism; it can take several forms :

1. Reaction with CoA and ATP. This is the mechanism occurring in animal tissues. Three enzymes of differing specificity are known, reacting with—acetate and propionate, C_4 to C_{12} fatty acids, and acids containing longer chains.

2. Transfer of CoA. The transfer takes place from an acylated derivative (for example from acetyl-CoA for the C_1 to C_8 acids in *Clostridium kluyveri*). In the heart, and probably also in the kidney in vertebrates, such

a transfer takes place from succinyl-CoA to acetoacetate. Thus the acetoacetate formed in the liver is activated, brought to the tissues by the blood and oxidized by way of the tricarboxylic acid cycle.

III. THE TRICARBOXYLIC ACID CYCLE

Acetyl-CoA is the starting point of a series of transformations known under the name of the tricarboxylic acid cycle. Into this cycle, at various points, are introduced other products of the degradation of cellular nutrients, particularly of the different amino acids. This terminal cycle, common to the main structures forming the organism, is the chief source of the energy-rich bonds required for biosynthesis.

Our knowledge of this cycle began with some experiments carried out by Szent-Györgyi on a mince of pigeon breast muscle. This mince respires vigorously without producing lactic acid. The respiration, at first intense, diminishes with time. Parallel with the fall in respiratory activity, the concentration of succinate in the muscle-mince decreases, but the addition of small amounts of succinate (or of fumarate) brings about an increase in the respiration. Since the respiratory quotient is equal to 1, we can conclude that carbohydrate is being broken down. The conclusion therefore is that the oxidation of carbohydrates is catalysed by succinate and fumarate; succinic dehydrogenase must also play an important part because malonate blocks the stimulant effect of succinate.

Szent-Györgyi having also observed the depressant effect of malonate (an inhibitor of succinic dehydrogenase) on the respiration of the muscle mince, he saw that the malonate must hinder the restoration by the succinate of the respiratory system which had become completely oxidized.

He therefore proposed the following scheme to explain respiration :

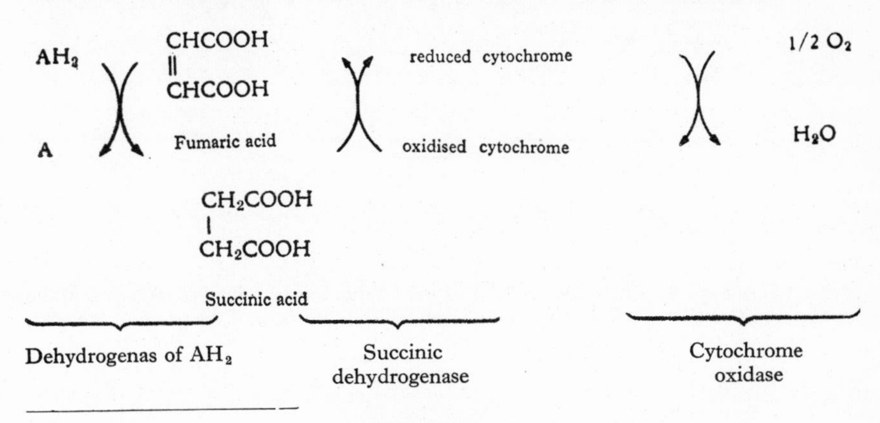

REFERENCES

LYNEN, F. (1954). Acetylcoenzyme A and the "fatty acid cycle". *Harvey Lectures*, **48**, 210–244.

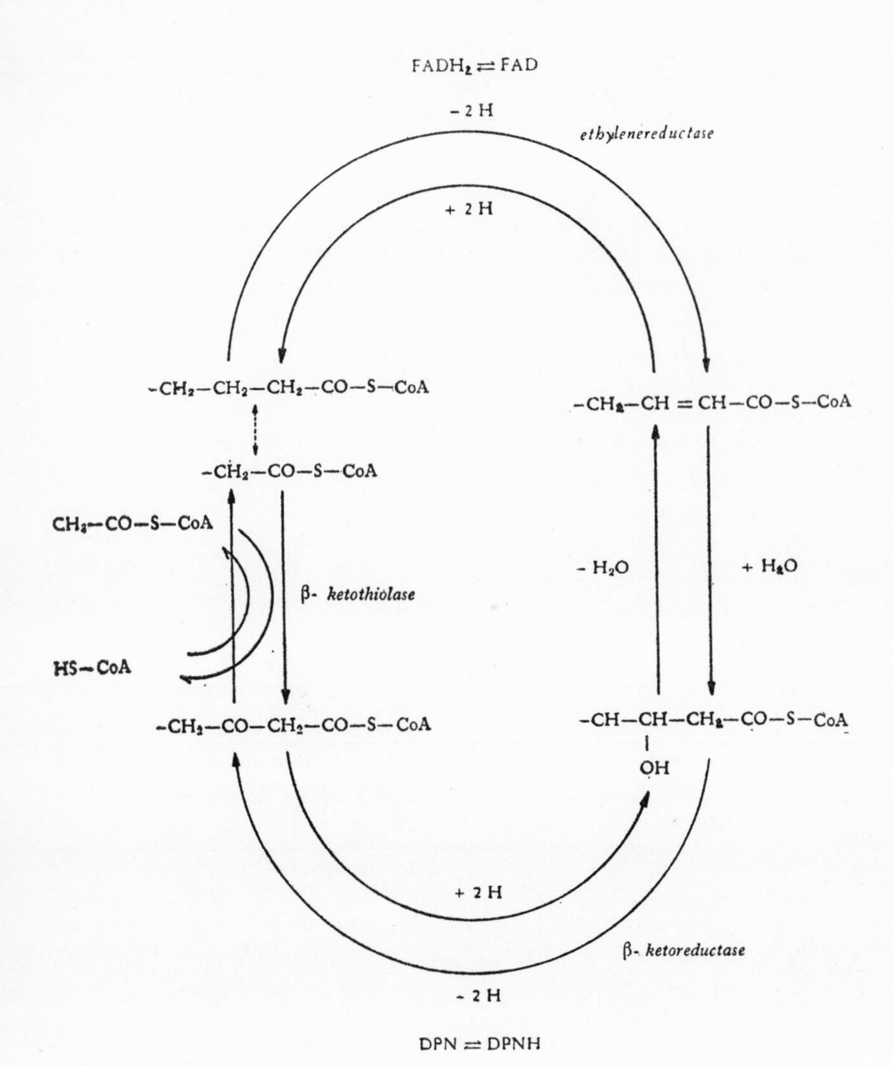

FIG. 42 (after Lynen)—The enzymatic cycle for the fatty acids. (This process can also be considered as a spiral of fatty acids, a C_2 fragment being lost or gained at each turn in the form of $CH_3CO—S—CoA$. In Fig. 42, the change from one turn of the spiral to the next, with addition or subtraction of a C_2 fragment, is indicated by the dotted arrow.)

When he found that malate and oxaloacetate had the same action as succinate and fumarate, and that their intervention is abolished by malonate, Szent-Györgyi introduced the oxaloacetate-malate system into his scheme, which became :

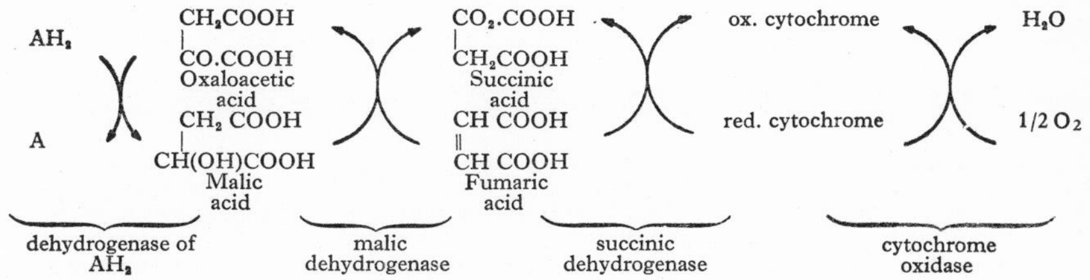

AH_2 / A — dehydrogenase of AH_2

CH_2COOH | $CO.COOH$ Oxaloacetic acid
CH_2 COOH | CH(OH)COOH Malic acid — malic dehydrogenase

$CO_2.COOH$ | CH_2COOH Succinic acid
CH COOH || CH COOH Fumaric acid — succinic dehydrogenase

ox. cytochrome / red. cytochrome — H_2O / 1/2 O_2 — cytochrome oxidase

When it was demonstrated that the succinic-fumaric system has no coenzyme whilst the oxaloacetic-malic system requires the mediation of DPN, the idea of the coupling of the two systems was recognized as impossible and it was abandoned.

But it was known that fumarase catalyses the malate-fumarate transformation, and that malic dehydrogenase catalyses the oxaloacetate-malate conversion. From which facts sprung a new formulation of the cycle of the dicarboxylic acids.

In the new scheme, the system catalysed by fumarase and malic dehydrogenase is a supply system inserted laterally into the first scheme of Szent-Györgyi :

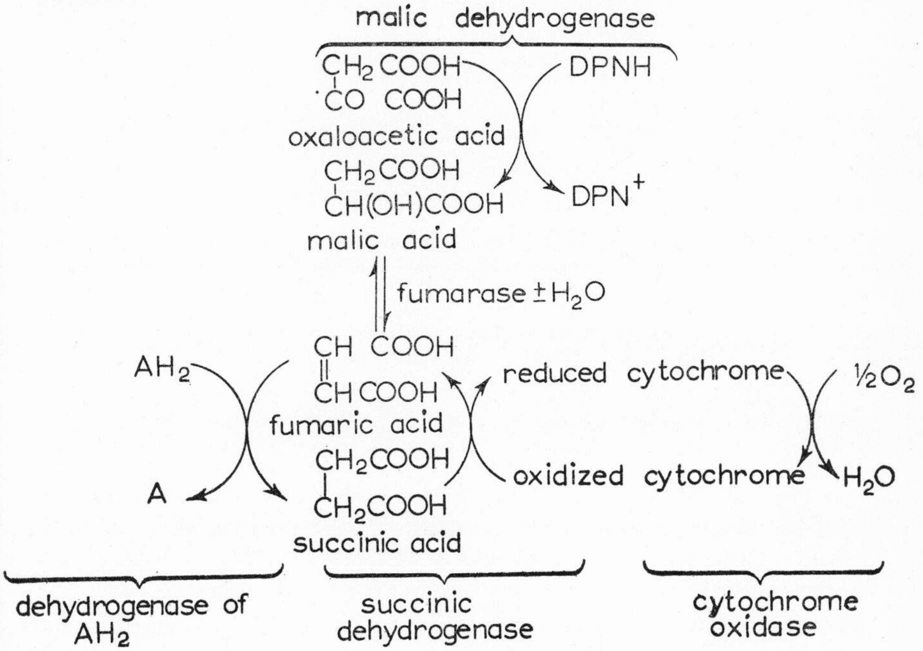

malic dehydrogenase

CH_2 COOH | CO COOH oxaloacetic acid — DPNH
CH_2COOH | CH(OH)COOH malic acid — DPN^+

fumarase $\pm H_2O$

AH_2 → A — dehydrogenase of AH_2

CH COOH || CH COOH fumaric acid
CH_2COOH | CH_2COOH succinic acid — succinic dehydrogenase

reduced cytochrome / oxidized cytochrome — ½O_2 / H_2O — cytochrome oxidase

This particular form of the system of dicarboxylic acids had to be abandoned when Krebs showed that α-ketoglutarate and citrate, in addition to succinate, fumarate, malate and oxaloacetate, also re-establish the respiration of a muscle pulp. The case of α-ketoglutaric acid, in the scheme of Szent-Györgyi, did not present an insurmountable difficulty since the oxidative decarboxylation of α-ketoglutarate yields succinic acid.

$$\begin{array}{c} COOH \\ | \\ CH_2 \\ | \\ CH_2 \\ | \\ CO \\ | \\ COOH \end{array} \xrightarrow[-2\,H]{+H_2O} \begin{array}{c} COOH \\ | \\ CH_2 \\ | \\ CH_2 \\ | \\ COOH \end{array} + CO_2$$

α-ketoglutaric acid — succinic acid

Apparently the entry of citric acid into the scheme can be explained by the conversion of citrate into α-ketoglutarate under the action of a citric dehydrogenase. But an examination of the formulas of citric acid and α-ketoglutaric acid shows that citric dehydrogenase cannot convert the first into the second in one step.

$$\begin{array}{c} COOH \\ | \\ CH_2 \\ | \\ C(OH)COOH \\ | \\ CH_2 \\ | \\ COOH \end{array} \qquad \begin{array}{c} COOH \\ | \\ CH_2 \\ | \\ CH_2 \\ | \\ CO \\ | \\ COOH \end{array}$$

citric acid — α-ketoglutaric acid

It was then that the very important discovery of aconitase (Martius and Knoop) was announced and it was demonstrated that the so-called citric dehydrogenase was in fact a mixture of aconitase, isocitric dehydrogenase, and oxalosuccinic decarboxylase. This multi-enzyme system explained the passage of citrate to succinate.

$$\underset{\text{citric acid}}{\begin{matrix}COOH\\ |\\ CH_2\\ |\\ C(OH)COOH\\ |\\ CH_2\\ |\\ COOH\end{matrix}} \underset{\text{aconitase}}{\overset{\pm H_2O}{\rightleftharpoons}} \underset{\textit{cis}\text{—aconitic acid}}{\begin{matrix}COOH\\ |\\ CH_2\\ |\\ CHCOOH\\ \|\\ CH\\ |\\ COOH\end{matrix}} \underset{\textit{aconitase}}{\overset{\pm H_2O}{\rightleftharpoons}} \underset{\text{isocitric acid}}{\begin{matrix}COOH\\ |\\ CH_2\\ |\\ CHCOOH\\ |\\ CHOH\\ |\\ COOH\end{matrix}} \underset{\text{isocitric dehydrogenase}}{\rightleftharpoons} \underset{\text{oxalosuccinic acid}}{\begin{matrix}COOH\\ |\\ CH_2\\ |\\ CHCOOH\\ |\\ CO\\ |\\ COOH\end{matrix}} \rightleftharpoons$$

$$\underset{\text{oxalosuccinic decarboxylase}}{\overset{\pm CO_2}{\rightleftharpoons}} \underset{\alpha\text{-ketoglutaric acid}}{\begin{matrix}COOH\\ |\\ CH_2\\ |\\ CH_2\\ |\\ CO\\ |\\ COOH\end{matrix}} \xrightarrow[\text{oxidative decarboxylation}]{-CO_2 \; + 1/2\,O_2} \underset{\text{succinic acid}}{\begin{matrix}COOH\\ |\\ CH_2\\ |\\ CH_2\\ |\\ COOH\end{matrix}}$$

Following on these fundamental discoveries, Krebs formulated the cycle in Fig. 43.

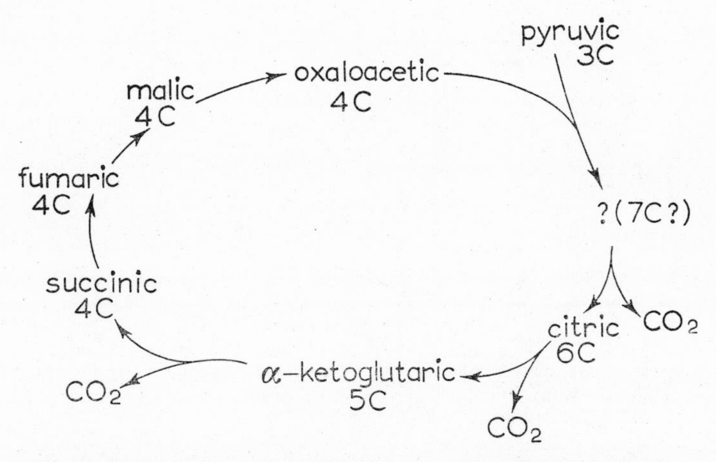

FIG. 43 (Krebs)—First formulation of the tricarboxylic acid cycle.

The discovery of the mechanism for the oxidative decarboxylation of pyruvate with formation of acetyl-CoA permitted the filling in of the missing parts of the cycle.

The cycle (Fig. 44) begins with acetyl-CoA derived from the fatty acid cycle or from the decarboxylation of pyruvate. The entry into the cycle

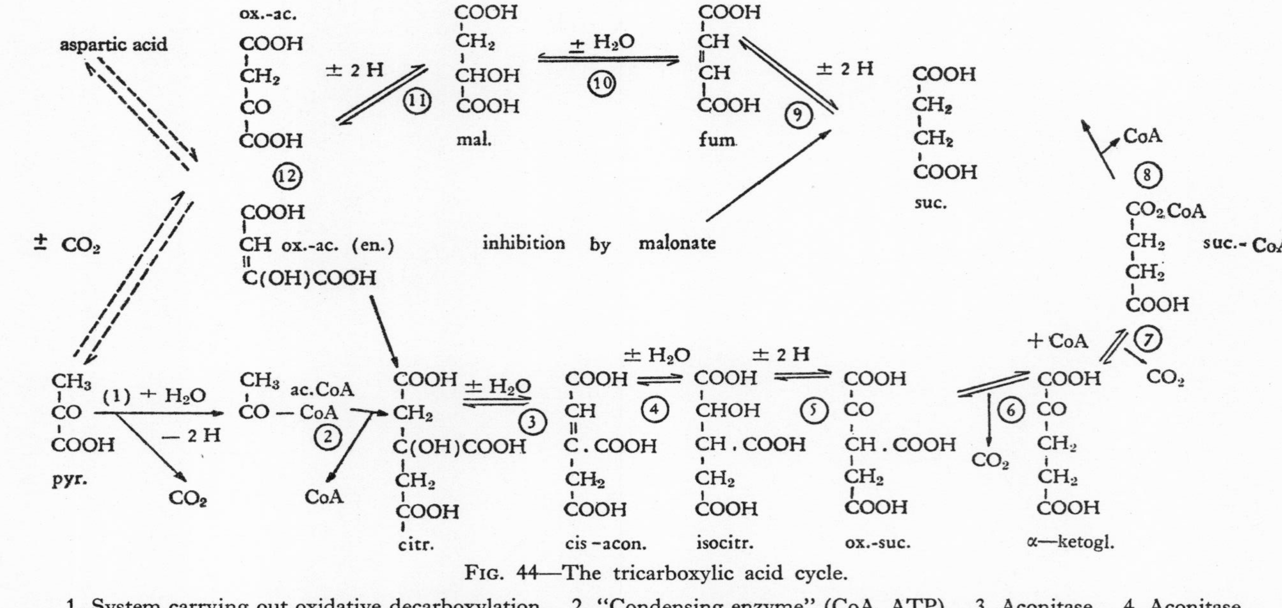

FIG. 44—The tricarboxylic acid cycle.

1. System carrying out oxidative decarboxylation. 2. "Condensing enzyme" (CoA, ATP). 3. Aconitase. 4. Aconitase. 5. Isocitric dehydrogenase (TPN). 6. Oxalosuccinic decarboxylase (Mn^{++}). 7. Oxidative decarboxylation (CoA, DPN, DPT, thioctic acid). 8. Formation of a phosphorylated derivative of CoA (H_3PO_4). 9. Succinic dehydrogenase. 10. Fumarase. 11. Malic dehydrogenase (DPN). 12. Spontaneous isomerization.

of acetyl-CoA is governed by the condensation enzyme discovered by Ochoa. In the presence of this enzyme, acetyl-CoA reacts with a molecule of oxaloacetate to form citric acid with the liberation of a molecule of CoA. (If the concentration of oxaloacetic acid is low, as is the case in starvation, diabetes, etc., two molecules of acetyl-CoA may combine to give aceto-acetyl-CoA which, losing CoA, will give acetoacetate and eventually acetone or other ketonic bodies). In this operation an energy-rich bond of

$$CH_3—CO—S—CoA + \begin{matrix} CH_2COOH \\ | \\ COCOOH \end{matrix} + H_2O$$

oxaloacetic acid

$$= \begin{matrix} CH_2COOH \\ | \\ HOCCOOH \\ | \\ CH_2COOH \end{matrix} + HS—CoA$$

citric acid

ATP is consumed. However this loss is compensated by the recovery of an energy-rich thioester bond in acetyl-CoA. The condensation reaction has a large $-\Delta F$ and is practically irreversible. Reactions 3 and 4 are catalysed by aconitase. A molecule of water is removed in reaction 3 with the formation of a double bond, and during reaction 4 the chain is again saturated with the OH at another position. Reactions 3 and 4 are reversible. Reaction 5 is a reversible oxidation utilizing TPN as the coenzyme for the dehydrogenase (isocitric dehydrogenase). Reaction 6 is a non-oxidative decarboxylation producing α-ketoglutaric acid. The equilibrium lies far to the right and is practically irreversible. It is however reversible under certain conditions. Reaction 7 is an oxidative decarboxylation having several characteristics in common with the decarboxylation of pyruvic acid. It can be depicted as commencing with a decarboxylation accompanied by a dehydrogenation, yielding a succinyl derivative of LTPP containing an energy-rich thioester linkage. This latter, in a second reaction, exchanges its thioester bond with CoA to give succinyl-CoA and disulphydryl-LTPP. In a third reaction, the latter gives up two H atoms to DPN^+ giving the disulphide form, DPNH and H^+. The DPNH on entering the respiratory chain gives three ATP energy-rich bonds.

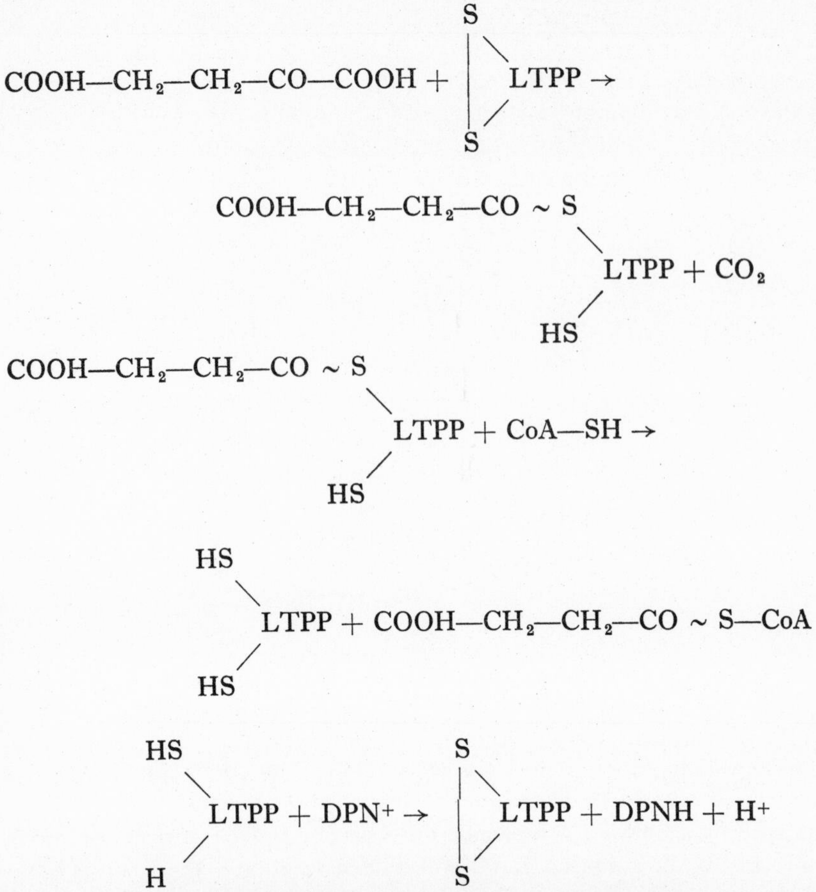

$$COOH{-}CH_2{-}CH_2{-}CO{-}COOH + \begin{array}{c} S \\ | \diagdown \\ | \quad LTPP \rightarrow \\ | \diagup \\ S \end{array}$$

$$\begin{array}{l} COOH{-}CH_2{-}CH_2{-}CO \sim S \\ \qquad\qquad\qquad\qquad \diagdown \\ \qquad\qquad\qquad\qquad\quad LTPP + CO_2 \\ \qquad\qquad\qquad\qquad \diagup \\ \qquad\qquad\qquad\quad HS \end{array}$$

$$\begin{array}{l} COOH{-}CH_2{-}CH_2{-}CO \sim S \\ \qquad\qquad\qquad\qquad \diagdown \\ \qquad\qquad\qquad\qquad\quad LTPP + CoA{-}SH \rightarrow \\ \qquad\qquad\qquad\qquad \diagup \\ \qquad\qquad\qquad\quad HS \end{array}$$

$$\begin{array}{l} HS \\ \quad \diagdown \\ \qquad LTPP + COOH{-}CH_2{-}CH_2{-}CO \sim S{-}CoA \\ \quad \diagup \\ HS \end{array}$$

$$\begin{array}{l} HS \\ \quad \diagdown \\ \qquad LTPP + DPN^+ \rightarrow \\ \quad \diagup \\ H \end{array} \begin{array}{c} S \\ | \diagdown \\ | \quad LTPP + DPNH + H^+ \\ | \diagup \\ S \end{array}$$

FIG. 45—Oxidative decarboxylation of α-ketoglutarate.

Succinyl-CoA, in the presence of ADP and inorganic phosphate, undergoes an internal oxido-reduction at substrate level with the formation of succinic acid, CoA and a molecule of ATP whose energy-rich bond arises from the transfer of the energy of the thioester bond (reaction 8). Thus the route from α-ketoglutarate to succinate yields four molecules of ATP. The reaction α-ketoglutarate-succinyl-CoA reaction is reversible, but the pathway from α-ketoglutarate to succinate is not. Reaction 9, the reversible passage of succinate to fumarate in the presence of succinic dehydrogenase, involves the disposal of the resulting hydrogen by a respiratory chain differing from those to be described presently in which DPN^+ and TPN^+ are the initial receptors. In the case of the removal of two atoms of hydrogen from succinic acid in the presence of succinic dehydrogenase, the electron acceptor is cytochrome-*b* followed by cytochrome-*c*, cytochrome-*a*, cytochrome-a_3 and oxygen. This shortened respiratory chain gives only two molecules of ATP. Reaction 10 is a reversible hydration of fumarate to malate in the presence of fumarase. Although, in the liver, malate may give rise to pyruvate, this is not the case in most tissues. The malate is dehydrogenated in the presence of malic dehydrogenase and DPN^+ forming oxaloacetate and DPNH. This reaction is reversible. The oxaloacetic acid formed can, in its enolic form, react with acetyl-CoA to give citric acid and traverse the cycle once more.

IV. RESPIRATORY CHAINS

This name is applied to the series of carriers along which pass the protons and electrons liberated in the course of a dehydrogenation in the tricarboxylic acid cycle or other aerobic dehydrogenation before they reach oxygen and unite with it to form water. As we have seen, it is along the respiratory chain that by a series of phosphorylations coupled to it by a still unknown mechanism (see p. 144) the main quota of energy-rich bonds is formed and placed at the disposition of the cells.

In the course of the successive dehydrogenations of the cycle, the greater part of the protons and electrons liberated pass to the same series of carriers. The first acceptor of the series being most often DPN^+, DPNH appears as the principal "fuel" in cells.

The successive transfers are the following :

Substrate + DPN^+ → oxidized substrate + DPNH + H^+ (ΔF variable)

DPNH + H^+ + Flavopr. → DNN^+ red Flavopr. (ΔF = — 10 kcal)

red. Flavopr. + Ferricytochr. *c* → Flavopr. + Ferrocytochr. *c* (ΔF = — 16 kcal)

Ferrocytochr. *c* + O_2 → Ferricytochr. *c* (ΔF = — 25 kcal)

The last reaction can be split up into the following stages :

Ferrocytochr. *c* + Ferricytochr. *a* → Ferricytochr. *c* + Ferrocytochr. *a*

Ferrocytochr. *a* + Ferrocytochr. a_3 → Ferricytochr. *a* + Ferrocytochr. a_3

Ferrocytochr. a_3 + O → Ferricytochr. a_3 + O

REFERENCES

KREBS, H. A. (1954). The tricarboxylic acid cycle. *Chemical Pathways of Metabolism*, GREENBERG, D. M. (Editor) vol. I, Academic Press, New York 109–171.

OCHOA, S. (1954) Enzymic mechanisms in the citric acid cycle. *Advance. Enzymol.*, **15**, 183–270.

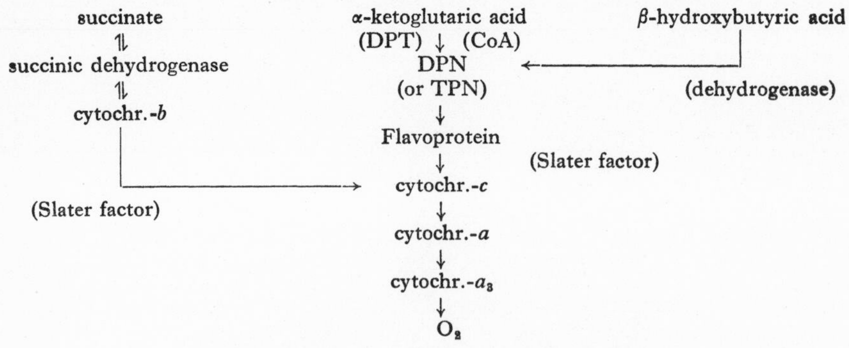

FIG. 46 (Slater)—Forms of the respiratory chain.

Although DPN is the first hydrogen acceptor in the dehydrogenation for example, of β-hydroxybutyric acid, TPN is the primary acceptor in other cases, and where succinic acid is concerned, the primary acceptor is cytochrome-*b*.

In addition, dehydrogenations exist, such as that of α-ketoglutaric acid, where thioctic acid acts as an intermediate between the donor and DPN.

All these paths converge at the level of cytochrome-*c*.

The scheme in Fig. 46 summarizes the form of the respiratory chain.

In Slater's scheme, α-ketoglutarate and β-hydroxybutyrate are taken as examples of hydrogen donors typical of the class to which each belongs. The substances shown in parentheses are those which intervene at the stages indicated, but it cannot be stated whether they give or receive protons or electrons. This is especially the case for the Slater factor, coming between cytochrome-*b* and cytochrome-*c* or between flavoprotein and cytochrome-*c*.

In the course of the transfers just described, a series of energy-rich bonds is formed by phosphorylations associated with the respiratory chain. In the scheme reproduced above, a single phosphorylation has been so far identified and this is situated at the level of the reaction between α-keto-glutarate and thioctic acid. However the sum of experimental observations

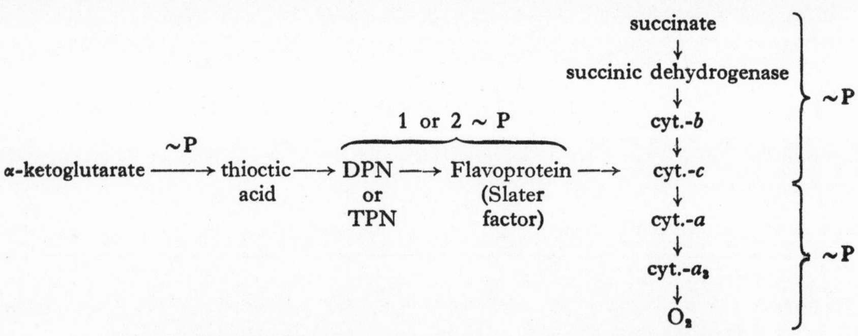

FIG. 47 (Slater)—Phosphorylations tied to the respiratory chain.

indicates that phosphorylations with formation of energy-rich bonds take place in conjunction with the following links of the respiratory chain: (1) between succinate and cytochrome-*c*; (2) between cytochrome-*c* and oxygen; (3) between DPN and cytochrome-*c*; at this point two phosphorylations appear to occur.

This is summarized in Slater's scheme reproduced in Fig. 47.

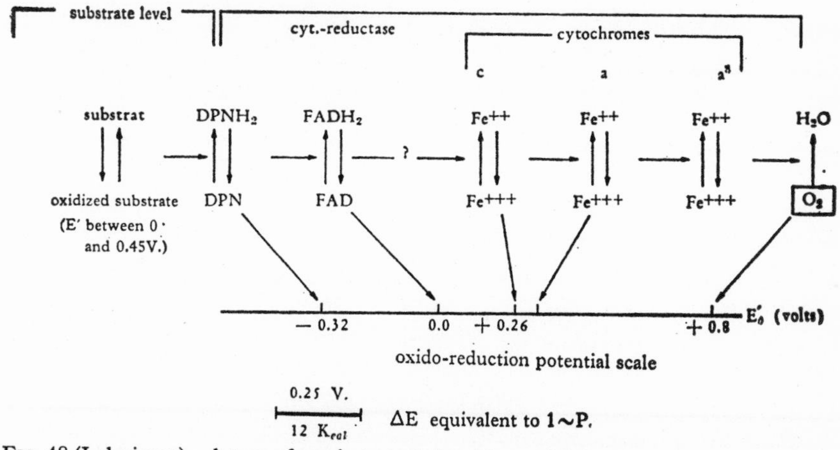

FIG. 48 (Lehninger)—A type of respiratory chain with a scale of oxido-reduction potentials

The sequence of the intermediates, in the case of the chain where α-ketoglutaric acid is the model substrate (in Fig. 46) is represented with the corresponding oxidation-reduction potentials in Fig. 48.

V. MECHANISMS FOR THE BREAKDOWN OF AMINO ACIDS

A. GENERAL MECHANISMS

(*a*) *Decarboxylation of Amino Acids*

In the presence of decarboxylases amino acids give CO_2 and an amine according to the general reaction:

$$NH_2\text{—}\underset{|}{\overset{R}{C}}H\text{—}COOH \rightarrow NH_2\text{—}\overset{R}{\underset{|}{C}}H_2 + CO_2$$

this is referred to as "decarboxylation".

REFERENCES

LEHNINGER, A. L. (1955). Oxidative phosphorylation. *Harvey Lectures*, **49**, 176–215.
SLATER, E. C. (1956). Respiratory chain phosphorylation. *Proceedings of the 3rd International Congress of Biochemistry, Brussels 1955*. Academic Press, New York, 264–277.

The carboxylases have for their coenzyme pyridoxal phosphate which acts according to the mechanism described on p. 174. A whole series of decarboxylases exists, each being specific for the L-form of a given amino acid. Certain of them have been isolated from animal tissues such as liver and kidney, but the majority have been isolated from micro-organisms in which the enzymes appear if their specific substrate is present in the culture medium. In micro-organisms therefore these decarboxylases are adaptive enzymes. The amines produced by the decarboxylation of amino acids (Table XIII) often possess pharmacological activity; this is the case for histamine, the product of the decarboxylation of histidine.

TABLE XIII

Amines resulting from the decarboxylation of various amino acids.

Amino acid	*Amine*	*Amino acid*	*Amine*
L–lysine	cadaverine	L–phénylalanine	phényléthylamine
L–arginine	agmatine	L–glutamic acid	γ–aminobutryic acid
L–histidine	histamine	L–aspartic acid	{ L–alanine β–alanine
L–ornithine	putrescine	L–tryptophan	β-indolethylamine
L–tyrosine	tyramine	L-cysteic acid	taurine

(*b*) *Deaminations*

1. *Oxidative deamination*

Many cells, and in particular those of mammalian tissues can deaminate amino acids to form the corresponding ketonic acids in the presence of the specific enzyme and oxygen, according to the general reaction :

$$NH_2\text{—}\underset{|}{\overset{R}{C}}H\text{—}COOH + \frac{1}{2}O_2 \rightarrow O\text{=}\overset{R}{\overset{|}{C}}\text{—}COOH + NH_3$$

The enzymes catalysing this reaction are the L-amino acid oxidases and the D-amino acid oxidases. The role of the latter in metabolism has not yet been elucidated, for the naturally occurring amino acids are generally of the L-series.

The D-amino acid oxidase of sheep kidney has been purified; it is a flavoprotein containing FAD. It is of low specificity and catalyses the oxidative deamination of all the amino acids of the D-series with the exception of glutamic acid. It does not act on amino acids of the L-series, or on glycine.

The L-amino acid oxidases isolated from various animal cells and micro-organisms are also flavoproteins, containing FMN, but they likewise are not very specific; they act on a number of amino acids, but not on all. Glycine is deaminated neither by D-amino acid oxidases nor by L-amino acid oxidases. Its oxidative deamination is accomplished in the presence of a specific enzyme, glycine-oxidase, in the following manner :

$$NH_2CH_2COOH + \tfrac{1}{2}O_2 \rightarrow NH_3 + \underset{\text{glyoxylic acid}}{CHO\text{—}COOH}$$

In the presence of the same enzyme, methylglycine or sarcosine is degraded as follows:

$$CH_3NHCH_2COOH + \tfrac{1}{2}O_2 \rightarrow \underset{\text{methylamine}}{CH_3NH_2} + \underset{\text{glyoxylic acid}}{CHO\text{—}COOH}$$

Another specific enzyme of oxidative deamination is glutamic acid dehydrogenase. This is an anaerobic dehydrogenase:

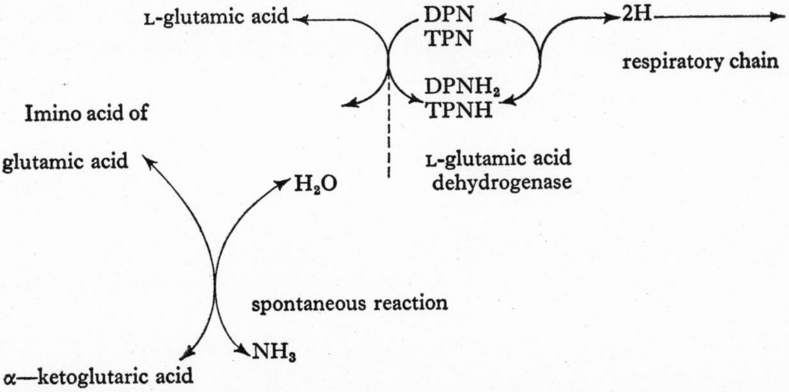

L-glutamic acid
DPN
TPN
2H
respiratory chain
Imino acid of
glutamic acid
DPNH$_2$
TPNH
L-glutamic acid
dehydrogenase
H_2O
spontaneous reaction
NH_3
α—ketoglutaric acid

FAD can utilize molecular oxygen as an electron acceptor and hydrogen peroxide is formed. The oxidative deamination of an amino acid in the presence of an amino acid oxidase containing FAD can be written as follows:

$$NH_2\text{—}\overset{\overset{\displaystyle R}{|}}{C}H\text{—}COOH + FAD \rightarrow NH{=}\overset{\overset{\displaystyle R}{|}}{C}\text{—}COOH + FADH_2$$

$$NH{=}\overset{\overset{\displaystyle R}{|}}{C}\text{—}COOH + H_2O \rightarrow O{=}\overset{\overset{\displaystyle R}{|}}{C}\text{—}COOH + NH_3$$

$$FADH_2 + O_2 \rightarrow FAD + H_2O_2$$

$$H_2O_2 \xrightarrow{\textit{catalase}} H_2O + \frac{1}{2}O_2$$

$$NH_2\text{—}\overset{\overset{\displaystyle R}{|}}{C}H\text{—}COOH + \frac{1}{2}O_2 \rightarrow O{=}\overset{\overset{\displaystyle R}{|}}{C}\text{—}COOH + NH_3$$

In the absence of catalase, the hydrogen peroxide oxidizes the ketonic acid with formation of the aliphatic acid having one carbon atom less and the overall reaction becomes

$$NH_2{-}\underset{\displaystyle |}{\overset{\displaystyle R}{CH}}{-}COOH + O_2 \rightarrow \overset{\displaystyle R}{\underset{}{|}}COOH + CO_2 + NH_3$$

2. *Non-oxidative deaminations*

Enzymes also exist, in the case of serine, threonine and homoserine, which can catalyse a non-oxidative deamination commencing with a dehydration of the substrate.

In the case of serine for example, the mechanism is as follows :

$$\underset{\text{serine}}{HOCH_2\underset{|}{C}HCOOH \atop \quad NH_2} \xrightarrow[\text{serine dehydrase}]{-H_2O} \underset{\alpha\text{—aminoacrylic acid}}{CH_2{=}\underset{|}{C}COOH \atop NH_2} \rightleftarrows \underset{\alpha\text{—iminopropionic acid}}{CH_3\underset{\|}{C}{-}COOH \atop NH}$$

$$\underset{\alpha\text{—iminopropionic acid}}{CH_3\underset{\|}{C}COOH \atop NH} \xrightarrow[\text{hydrolysis}]{H_2O} CH_3COCOOH + NH_3$$

(*c*) *Deamidations*

The deamidation of glutamine and asparagine have already been considered with the enzymes catalysing the reaction (p. 156).

(*d*) *Decarboxylation of the Ketonic Acids formed by Deamination of Amino Acids*

These reactions are brought about by four types of decarboxylases.

1. *α-ketodecarboxylases*

The α-ketonic acids are decarboxylated in the presence of these enzymes with formation of the aldehyde having one carbon atom less and liberation of CO_2. The coenzyme is DPT. The carboxylase is formed by the union of the coenzyme and the specific protein. This protein appears to be present only in plants and micro-organisms, whilst DPT is present in animal tissues also. The decarboxylation of pyruvic acid to form acetaldehyde during alcoholic fermentation is due to an α-ketodecarboxylase.

2. *Oxidative α-ketodecarboxylases*

One example has already been described at the point of entry of pyruvic acid into the tricarboxylic acid cycle.

3. *β-ketodecarboxylases*

An example of this type of decarboxylation is the action of oxaloacetic decarboxylase which is present in animal tissues and in many micro-organisms.

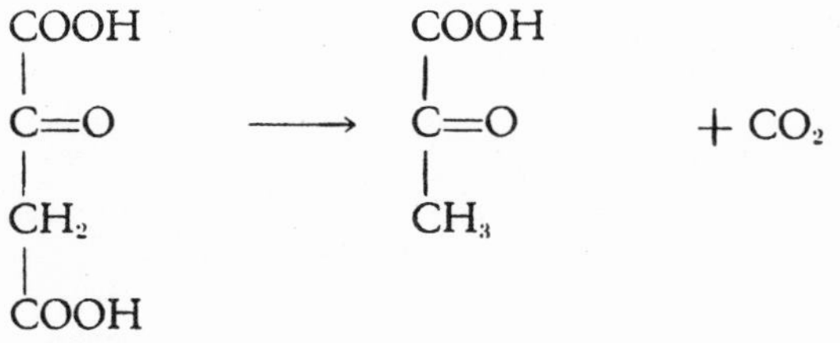

$$\begin{array}{l} COOH \\ | \\ C{=}O \\ | \\ CH_2 \\ | \\ COOH \end{array} \longrightarrow \begin{array}{l} COOH \\ | \\ C{=}O \\ | \\ CH_3 \end{array} + CO_2$$

4. *Oxidative β-decarboxylases*

The oxidation of a β-hydroxyacid with decarboxylation of the β-ketonic acid formed has already been described above in the case of the passage of isocitric acid into oxalosuccinic acid and then to α-ketoglutaric acid during the tricarboxylic acid cycle.

Another enzyme of the same type has been discovered by Ochoa in animal tissues : it is known as "malic enzyme" and catalyses the oxidation of malic acid to pyruvic acid and CO_2.

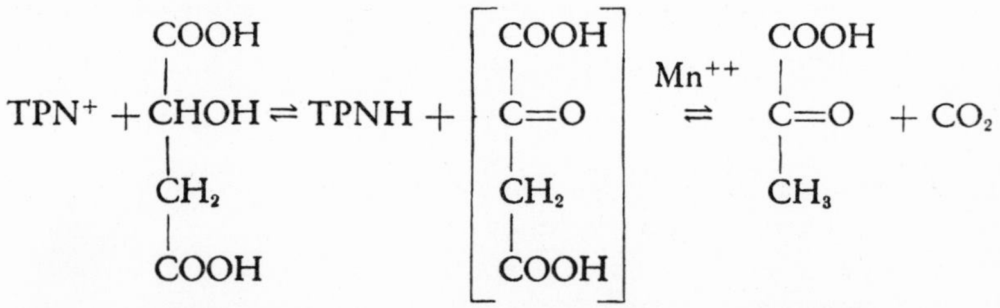

$$TPN^+ + \begin{array}{l} COOH \\ | \\ CHOH \\ | \\ CH_2 \\ | \\ COOH \end{array} \rightleftharpoons TPNH + \left[\begin{array}{l} COOH \\ | \\ C{=}O \\ | \\ CH_2 \\ | \\ COOH \end{array}\right] \overset{Mn^{++}}{\rightleftharpoons} \begin{array}{l} COOH \\ | \\ C{=}O \\ | \\ CH_3 \end{array} + CO_2$$

malic acid — oxaloacetic acid — pyruvic acid

The equilibrium constant favours the reaction occurring from left to right but the reverse reaction occurs if the TPN formed is continuously removed. The oxaloacetic acid is shown in brackets because it does not appear in the free form during the reaction. Under the action of the enzyme it is decarboxylated straight away; the enzyme must not be confused with malic dehydrogenase which requires DPN as its coenzyme.

(*e*) *Transaminations*

All the naturally occurring amino acids can *in vivo* participate in *transamination reactions* catalysed by *transaminases*. The reactions are universal in the biosphere in which they play an important role. They form important metabolic links between aspartate, glutamate and alanine on the one hand, and their corresponding α-keto acids in the tricarboxylic acid cycle on the other. The most active and the most widely distributed transaminase is the glutamic–oxaloacetic enzyme:

L-glutamic acid + oxaloacetic acid ⇌
α-ketoglutaric acid + aspartic acid

The following reaction is also very common:

amino acid + α-ketoglutaric acid ⇌
α-ketonic acid + glutamic acid

The participation of oxaloacetic acid in transaminations appears to be limited to the glutamic–oxaloacetic system. Another common system is the glutamic–pyruvic one:

L-glutamic acid + pyruvic acid ⇌
α-ketoglutaric acid + L-alanine

It has long been thought from our knowledge of these two systems that one of the members of the pair of substrates for a transaminase must be a dicarboxylic acid. Since then, leucine-pyruvate, phenylalanine-pyruvate and ornithine–pyruvate transaminations have been demonstrated. However it is not possible to exclude the presence of a trace of glutamate, thus:

pyruvic acid + glutamic acid ⇌ alanine + α-ketoglutatic acid
amino acid + α-ketoglutaric acid ⇌ α-ketonic acid + glutamic acid

Numerous transaminases exist. Their specificity appears to be narrow in some cases and very much wider in others.

Each transaminase consists of a specific apoenzyme and a coenzyme which is pyridoxal phosphate.

It was long believed that glutamine and asparagine did not take part in transamination reactions except after hydrolysis. In fact enzymatic systems have been demonstrated which catalyse transminations from glutamine and asparagine to many ketonic acids. Glutamine is an even better donor than glutamate but the specificity of glutamine transaminase for the α-ketonic acid is low.

(*f*) *Transdeaminations*

One of the mechanisms which has been proposed to account for the oxidative deamination of amino acids invokes a transamination followed by a deamination. This mechanism appears to be capable of explaining the rapid and reversible deaminations whose character is not in accordance with the properties and action of the L-amino acid oxidases. A transamination to α-ketoglutaric acid would remove the amino group from an amino acid and the glutamic acid formed would be deaminated by the specific L-glutaminase. In addition this mechanism accounts for the rapid synthesis of amino acids from ammonia and α-keto acids.

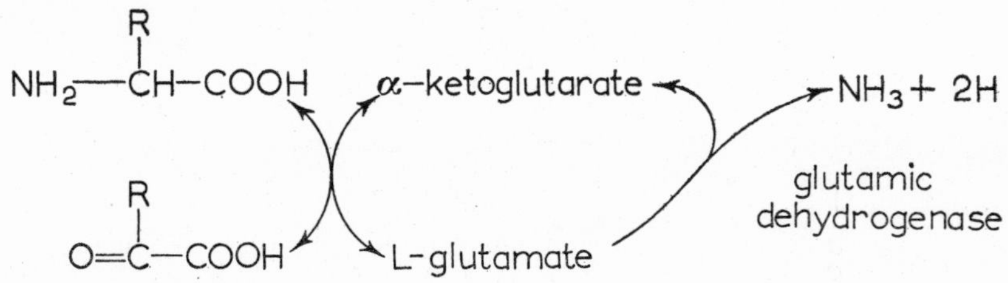

$$\begin{array}{ccccc} NH_2-\overset{\displaystyle R}{\overset{|}{C}}H-COOH & & \alpha\text{-ketoglutarate} & \leftarrow\!\!\!\rightarrow & NH_3 + 2H \\ & \times & & & \text{glutamic dehydrogenase} \\ O=\overset{\displaystyle R}{\overset{|}{C}}-COOH & & \text{L-glutamate} & & \end{array}$$

B. The Complete Degradation of various Amino Acids

(a) Glutamic Acid

As we have just seen, L-glutamic acid is not deaminated by the action of the L-amino acid oxidase of animal tissues and bacteria. But, in the presence of a specific enzyme, glutamic dehydrogenase, it undergoes oxidative deamination in the presence of either DPN or TPN. This reversible reaction gives α-iminoglutaric acid.

$$\begin{array}{c} COOH \\ | \\ CH_2 \\ | \\ CH_2 \\ | \\ NH_2-CH-COOH \\ \text{L—glutamic acid} \end{array} + DPN^+ \rightleftarrows \begin{array}{c} COOH \\ | \\ CH_2 \\ | \\ CH_2 \\ | \\ NH=C-COOH \\ \alpha\text{—iminoglutaric acid} \end{array} + DPNH + H^+$$

The α-iminoglutaric acid is hydrolysed spontaneously to α-ketoglutaric acid and ammonia. The α-ketoglutaric acid can enter the tricarboxylic acid cycle.

(b) Aspartic Acid

Aspartic acid, by transamination, gives oxaloacetic acid which then also enters the tricarboxylic acid cycle.

(c) Histidine

Histidine, besides its connection with the metabolism of pentoses, nucleotides and certain other amino acids, follows a path leading to glutamic acid. In certain bacteria, the enzyme system forms one mole of glutamic acid, one mole of formic acid, and two moles of ammonia from one mole of histidine, whilst in other bacteria one mole of glutamic acid, one mole of formamide and one mole of ammonia are produced. The separate steps of this degradation have been worked out from a study of a number of systems and are shown in Fig. 49 (still hypothetical steps are between brackets).

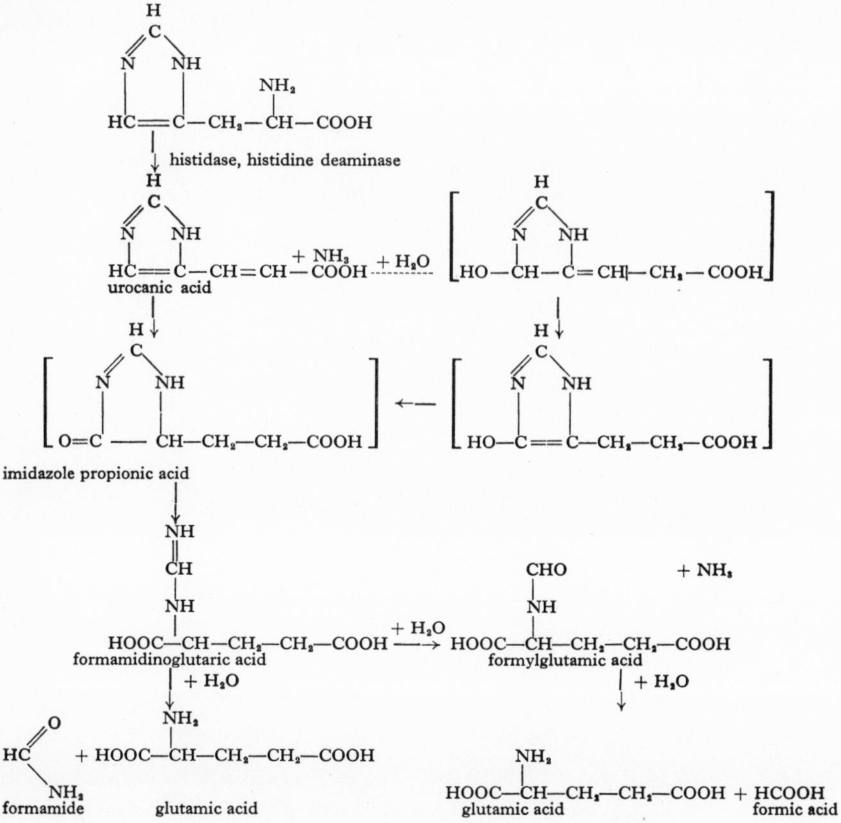

H
C
N NH
NH_2
HC=C—CH_2—CH—COOH
histidase, histidine deaminase
H
C
N NH
HC=C—CH=CH—COOH + NH_3 + H_2O
urocanic acid
[HO—CH—C=CH—CH_2—COOH]
H
C
N NH
[O=C — CH—CH_2—CH_2—COOH] ← [HO—C=C—CH_2—CH_2—COOH]
imidazole propionic acid
NH
CH
NH
HOOC—CH—CH_2—CH_2—COOH + H_2O → HOOC—CH—CH_2—CH_2—COOH (CHO, NH) + NH_3
formamidinoglutaric acid → formylglutamic acid
+ H_2O + H_2O
HC(=O)—NH_2 + HOOC—CH(NH_2)—CH_2—CH_2—COOH
formamide glutamic acid
HOOC—CH(NH_2)—CH_2—CH_2—COOH + HCOOH
glutamic acid formic acid

FIG. 49 (after Tabor)—Degradation of histidine.

The glutamic acid can enter the tricarboxylic acid cycle through α-keto-glutaric acid, so histidine is thus degraded to CO_2 and water.

(d) *Leucine, Isoleucine, Valine*

The degradation of leucine, isoleucine and valine operates by oxidative deamination and then decarboxylation of the corresponding keto-acids.

Leucine is first transformed into α-ketoisocaproic acid. This latter combines with CoA and is oxidized to senecioyl-CoA, this is followed by a hydration with formation of β-hydroxyisovaleryl-CoA. Then, in the course of a reaction requiring ATP, CO_2 is attached to the end of the chain and the β–hydroxy–β–methylglutaryl–CoA formed is split into acetoacetic acid

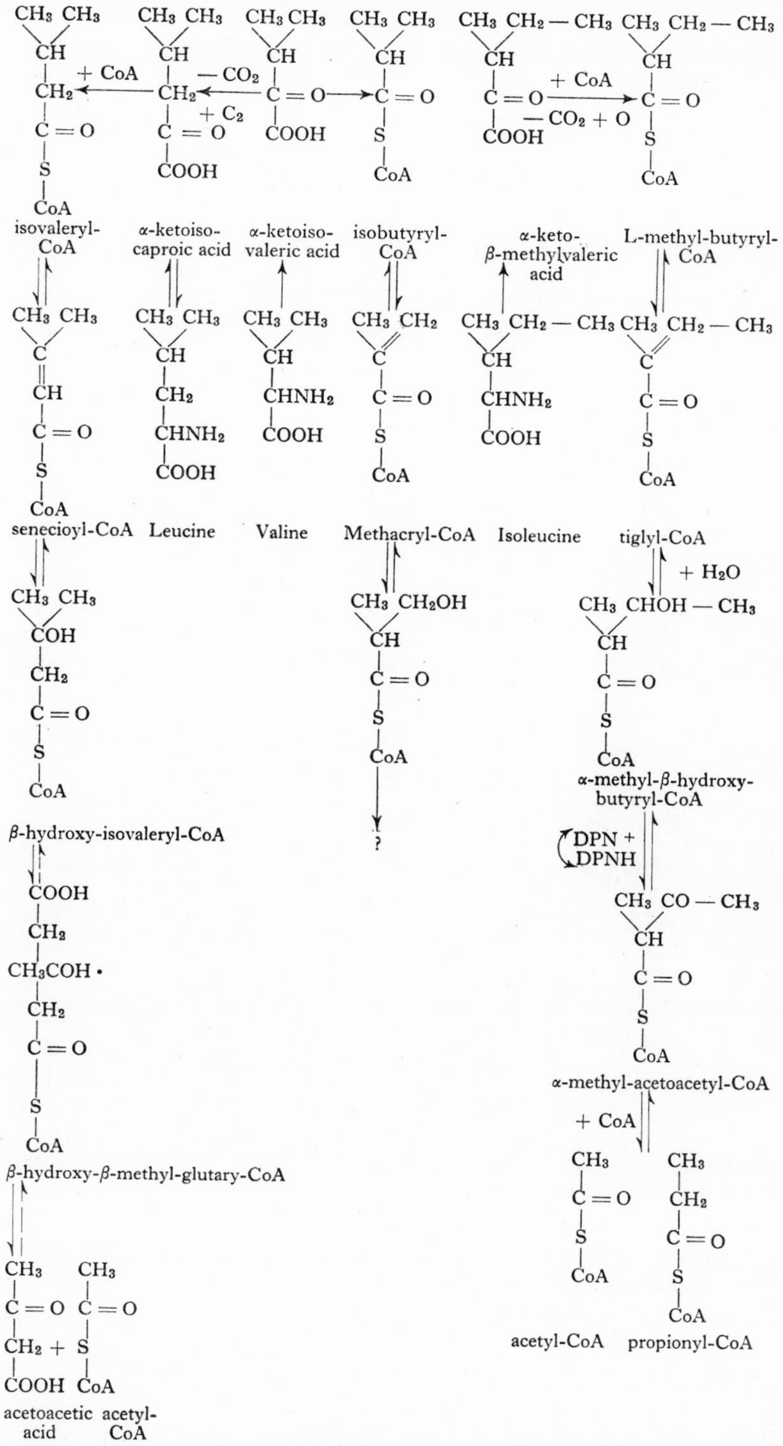

Leucine pathway

Leucine: $(CH_3)_2CH{-}CH_2{-}CHNH_2{-}COOH$

⇌ α-ketoisocaproic acid: $(CH_3)_2CH{-}CH_2{-}C{=}O{-}COOH$

$-CO_2$ / $+C_2$ ⇄ $+ CoA$

isovaleryl-CoA: $(CH_3)_2CH{-}CH_2{-}C{=}O{-}S{-}CoA$

⇌ senecioyl-CoA: $(CH_3)_2C{=}CH{-}C{=}O{-}S{-}CoA$

⇌ β-hydroxy-isovaleryl-CoA: $(CH_3)_2COH{-}CH_2{-}C{=}O{-}S{-}CoA$

⇌ β-hydroxy-β-methyl-glutary-CoA: $COOH{-}CH_2{-}CH_3COH\cdot{-}CH_2{-}C{=}O{-}S{-}CoA$

⇌ acetoacetic acid + acetyl-CoA: $CH_3{-}C{=}O{-}CH_2{-}COOH$ + $CH_3{-}C{=}O{-}S{-}CoA$

Valine pathway

Valine: $(CH_3)_2CH{-}CHNH_2{-}COOH$

→ α-ketoisovaleric acid: $(CH_3)_2CH{-}C{=}O{-}COOH$

→ isobutyryl-CoA: $(CH_3)_2CH{-}C{=}O{-}S{-}CoA$

⇌ Methacryl-CoA: $CH_3(CH_2{=})C{-}C{=}O{-}S{-}CoA$

⇌ $CH_3(CH_2OH)CH{-}C{=}O{-}S{-}CoA$

→ ?

Isoleucine pathway

Isoleucine: $CH_3(CH_2{-}CH_3)CH{-}CHNH_2{-}COOH$

→ α-keto-β-methylvaleric acid: $CH_3(CH_2{-}CH_3)CH{-}C{=}O{-}COOH$

$+ CoA$, $-CO_2 + O$ →

L-methyl-butyryl-CoA: $CH_3(CH_2{-}CH_3)CH{-}C{=}O{-}S{-}CoA$

⇌ tiglyl-CoA: $CH_3(CH_2{-}CH_3)C{=}{-}C{=}O{-}S{-}CoA$

⇌ $+ H_2O$

α-methyl-β-hydroxy-butyryl-CoA: $CH_3(CHOH{-}CH_3)CH{-}C{=}O{-}S{-}CoA$

⇌ (DPN + → DPNH)

α-methyl-acetoacetyl-CoA: $CH_3(CO{-}CH_3)CH{-}C{=}O{-}S{-}CoA$

⇌ $+ CoA$

acetyl-CoA + propionyl-CoA: $CH_3{-}C{=}O{-}S{-}CoA$ + $CH_3{-}CH_2{-}C{=}O{-}S{-}CoA$

FIG. 50 (after Coon)—Degradation of leucine, valine and isoleucine.

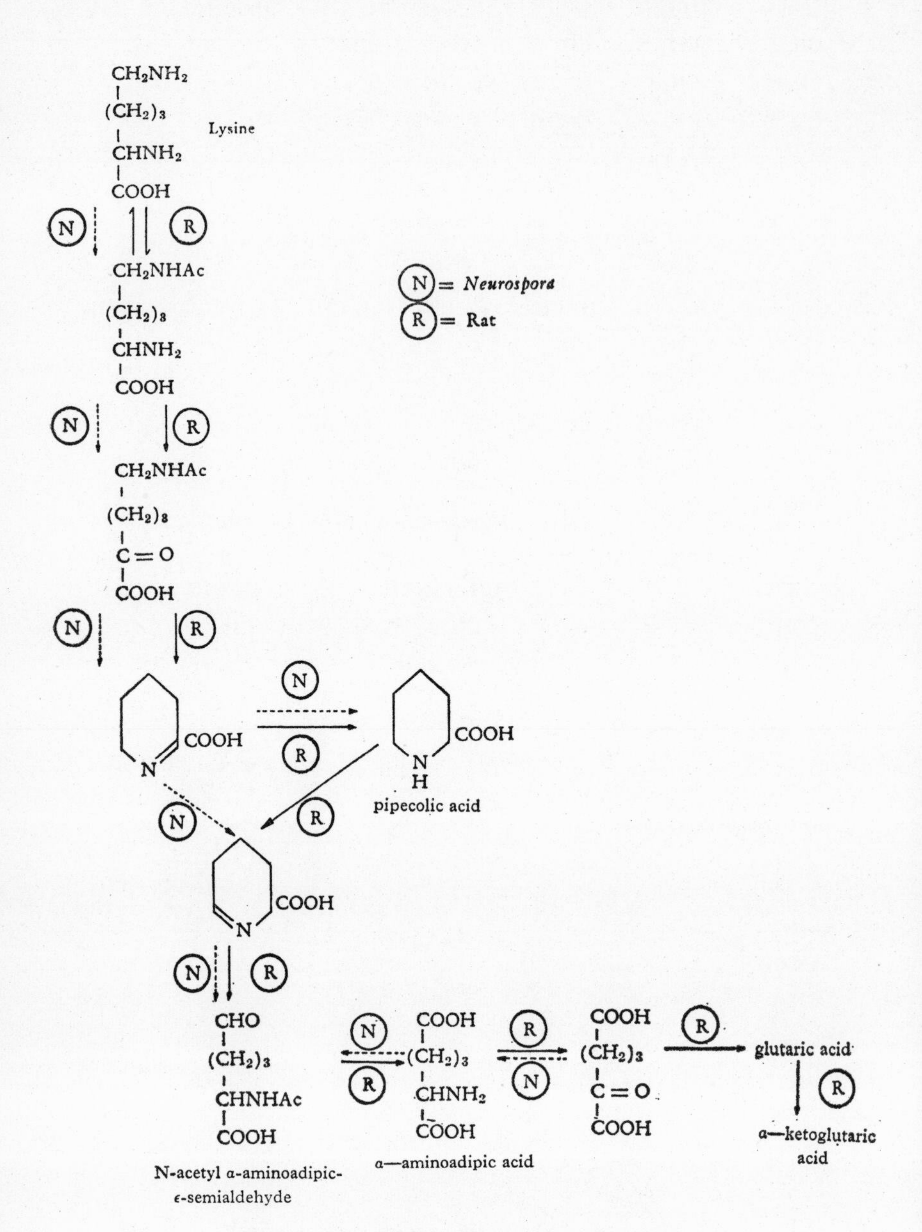

Fig. 51 (after Work)—Degradation of lysine.

and acetyl-CoA. Isoleucine undergoes a similar fate, the fixation of CO_2 being replaced by a dehydrogenation. Finally, acetyl-CoA and propionyl-CoA (Fig. 50) are obtained.

The path of valine joins that of leucine at the level of α-ketoisocaproic acid.

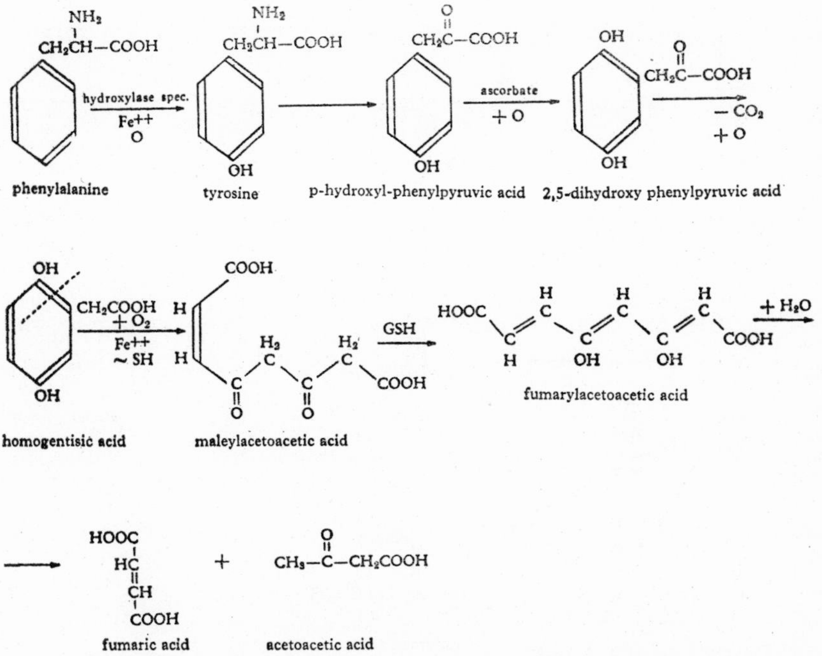

phenylalanine —(hydroxylase spec., Fe^{++}, O)→ tyrosine → p-hydroxyl-phenylpyruvic acid —(ascorbate, +O)→ 2,5-dihydroxy phenylpyruvic acid —(− CO_2, +O)→

homogentisic acid —(+ O_2, Fe^{++}, ~SH)→ maleylacetoacetic acid —(GSH)→ fumarylacetoacetic acid —(+ H_2O)→

fumaric acid + acetoacetic acid

FIG. 52 (after Knox)—Degradation of phenylalanine and tyrosine.

(e) *Lysine*

Lysine does not participate in the general deamination reactions of the amino acids. It is degraded by way of pipecolic acid both in animal tissues and in plants. The steps leading from lysine to α-ketoglutaric acid shown in Fig. 51, have been demonstrated both in the rat and in the mould *Neurospora*.

As the scheme shows, the various steps of lysine catabolism are not all reversible and though they have all been demonstrated to occur in the rat this is not the case for *Neurospora*.

(f) *Phenylalanine and Tyrosine*

Phenylalanine and tyrosine are degraded as far as fumaric acid and acetoacetic acid as shown in Fig. 52.

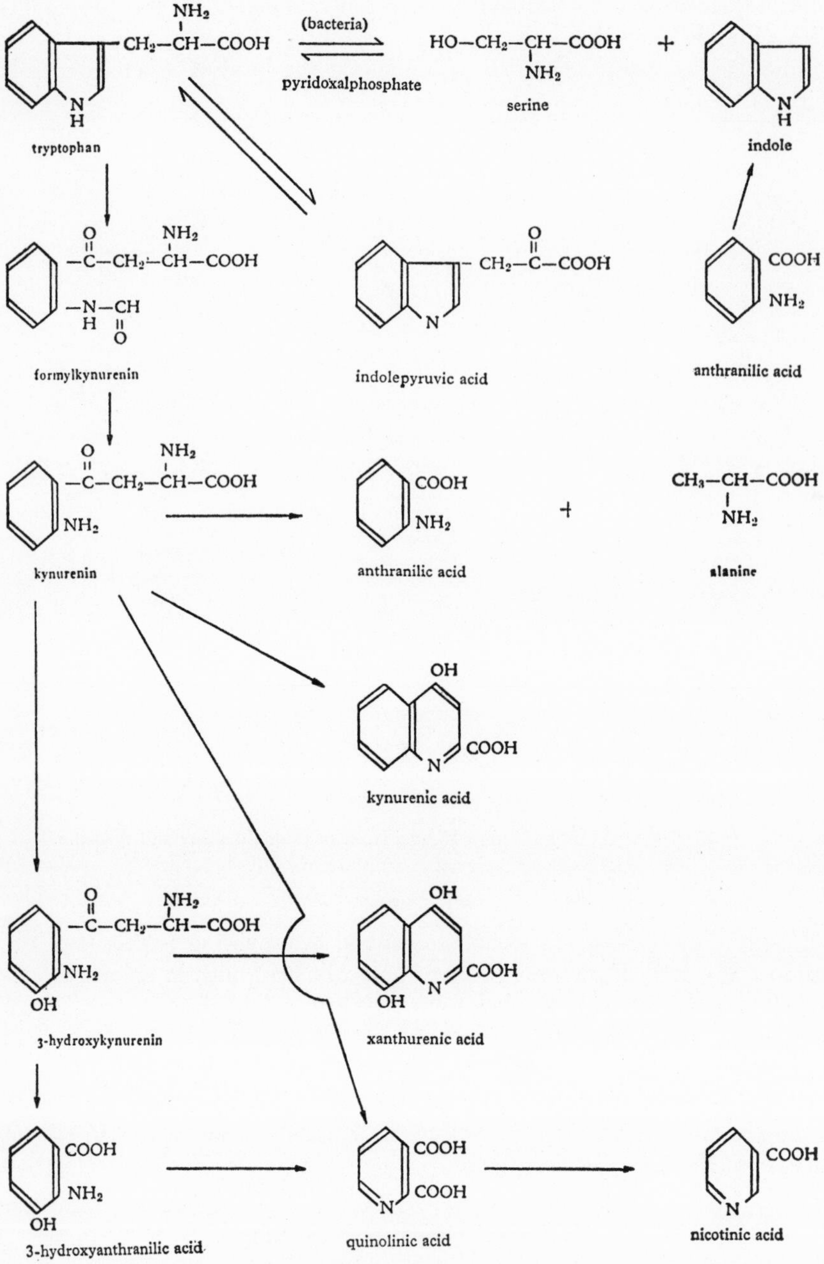

tryptophan — $CH_2-CH(NH_2)-COOH$ ⇌ (bacteria) pyridoxalphosphate ⇌ $HO-CH_2-CH(NH_2)-COOH$ (serine) + indole

formylkynurenin — $-C(=O)-CH_2-CH(NH_2)-COOH$, $-NH-CH=O$

indolepyruvic acid — $CH_2-C(=O)-COOH$

anthranilic acid — COOH, NH_2

kynurenin — $-C(=O)-CH_2-CH(NH_2)-COOH$, NH_2 → anthranilic acid (COOH, NH_2) + alanine ($CH_3-CH(NH_2)-COOH$)

kynurenic acid — OH, COOH, N

3-hydroxykynurenin — $-C(=O)-CH_2-CH(NH_2)-COOH$, NH_2, OH

xanthurenic acid — OH, COOH, N, OH

3-hydroxyanthranilic acid — COOH, NH_2, OH → quinolinic acid (COOH, COOH, N) → nicotinic acid (COOH, N)

FIG. 53—Degradation of tryptophan.

(*g*) *Tryptophan*

The ketonic acid corresponding to tryptophan is α-keto-β-indolyl-pyruvic acid, which can be obtained by transamination. The metabolism of this substance is unknown but it is not the main metabolic pathway for tryptophan which follows a series of different paths, as shown in Fig. 53. The most notable of these is the one leading to nicotinic acid.

The main pathway of tryptophan breakdown is still unknown.

(*h*) *Glycine and Serine*

Glycine can follow any one of a number of paths and during metabolism it may be transformed into a variety of substances: formate, acetate, ethanolamine, serine, aspartic acid, fatty acids, purines, pyrimidines, ribose or protoporphyrin. Its complete degradation, like that of serine or ethanolamine into which it is readily transformed, may be brought about by conversion to pyruvic acid from whence it can enter the glycolysis chain or the tricarboxylic acid cycle.

$$
\begin{array}{lclclclclc}
CH_2OH & & CH_2OH & & CH_2 & & CH_3 & & CH_3 & \\
| & & | & & \| & & | & & | & \\
CH_2NH_2 & & CHNH_2 & -H_2O & C{-}NH_2 & & C{=}NH & +H_2O & CO & +NH_3 \\
 & \leftarrow & | & \rightarrow & | & \rightarrow & | & \rightarrow & | & \\
+CO_2 & & COOH & & COOH & & COOH & & COOH & \\
 & & \text{serine} & & & & & & \text{pyruvic acid} &
\end{array}
$$

But this is not the only entry of glycine into the priming reactions. Glycine can be converted into CO_2 and water by means of the Shemin cycle, where the catalyst is not oxaloacetate as in the Krebs cycle, but succinate, whose active form, succinyl-CoA, condenses with the glycine. The Shemin cycle can therefore be worked into that of Krebs to form a shunt (Fig. 54).

The succinyl-CoA condenses with glycine, at the α-carbon atom, to form α-amino-β-ketoadipic acid which is then decarboxylated to δ-amino-levulinic acid. The latter is deaminated to ketoglutaraldehyde which is oxidized to ketoglutaric acid. This compound enters the tricarboxylic acid cycle or is decarboxylated to succinic acid. In one revolution of the cycle one molecule of glycine is completely oxidized to CO_2 and water.

(*i*) *Proline*

Proline is first oxidized to glutamic acid whose metabolic path it then follows. Hydroxyproline gives rise to β-hydroxyglutamate-semialdehyde.

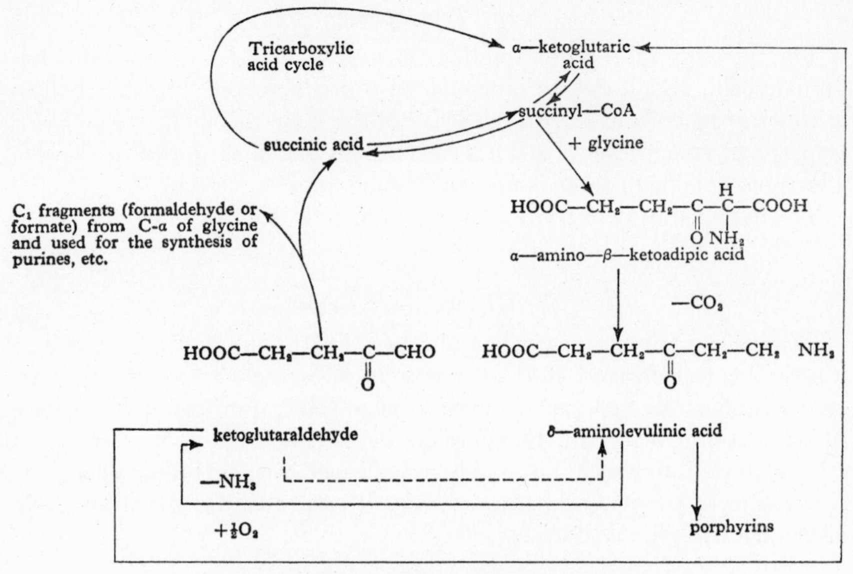

FIG. 54 (Shemin)—The succinate-glycine cycle.

(j) *Cystine and Cysteine*

Among various other metabolic fates these two acids can yield pyruvic acid.

$$HOOC{-}\underset{\displaystyle NH_2}{\underset{|}{HC}}{-}H_2C{-}S{-}S{-}CH_2{-}\underset{\displaystyle NH_2}{\underset{|}{CH}}{-}COOH \quad \text{cystine}$$

$$H_2 \downarrow \qquad \uparrow O_2$$

$$HS{-}CH_2{-}\underset{\displaystyle NH_2}{\underset{|}{CH}}{-}COOH \xrightarrow[\textit{desulphydrase}]{} H_2S + NH_3 + CH_3{-}\underset{\displaystyle O}{\underset{\|}{C}}{-}COOH$$

cysteine pyruvic acid

Quantitatively the most important path is the following :

$$\begin{array}{c} SH \\ | \\ CH_2 \\ | \\ CHNH_2 \\ | \\ COOH \end{array} \longrightarrow \begin{array}{c} SO_2H \\ | \\ CH_2 \\ | \\ CHNH_2 \\ | \\ COOH \end{array}$$

cysteine cysteine-sulphinic acid

Cysteine-sulphinic acid, by transamination, can yield β-sulphinyl-pyruvic acid which is decomposed into pyruvic acid and SO_3^{--} which oxidizes to SO_4^{--}. The cysteine-sulphinic acid can also be oxidized to cysteic acid, or decarboxylated to form taurine.

(*k*) *Alanine*

It is deaminated to pyruvic acid which enters the cycles of priming reactions.

C. The General Scheme

The overall plan in Fig. 55 shows the general pathways for the complete oxidation of the amino acids. This does not necessarily mean that the amino acids always follow these paths. There may exist, and do exist, particularly in animals, numerous interrelations between the metabolic paths of the amino acids. Figure 55 shows the most important ways in which the carbon chains of the amino acids can be oxidized completely.

VI. INTERRELATIONS BETWEEN PRIMING REACTIONS

These are represented as shown in Fig. 56. Certain aspects, such as the relation between pyruvate and oxaloacetate, or malate, will be explained later.

Figure 56 shows the interrelations between glycolysis and the hexosemonophosphate shunt at the level of G—6—P and F—6—P, between glycolysis, the fatty acid cycle and the tricarboxylic acid cycle at the level of acetyl-CoA, between the tricarboxylic acid cycle and the succinate-glycine cycle at the level of succinyl-CoA.

Figure 56 also shows the points of entry of the various amino acids into the series of priming reactions.

VII. ENERGETICS OF THE PRIMING REACTIONS

A. Glycolysis

In Fig. 57 are shown the values of $-\Delta F_0$ in kilocalories per mole for the conversion of glucose into alcohol or into lactic acid and for the conversion of glycogen into lactic acid. A part of this free energy is lost as heat but the remainder is retained in reserve in the form of ATP energy-rich bonds. A balance-sheet can be drawn up for the free energy and for the phosphate bonds and from it we can determine the efficiency of the process. In the course of the phosphorylation of glucose and of the phosphorylation of F—6—P, in each case a mole of ATP has been used up. On the other hand,

REFERENCES

MEISTER, A. (1955), Transamination, *Advanc. Enzymol.* **16**, 185–246.

MCELROY, W. D. and BENTLEY GLASS H. (Editors), 1955. *A Symposium on Amino Acid Metabolism.* Johns Hopkins Press, Baltimore.

FROMAGEOT, C. (1955), The metabolism of sulfur and its relations to general metabolism. *Harvey Lectures* **49**, 1–36.

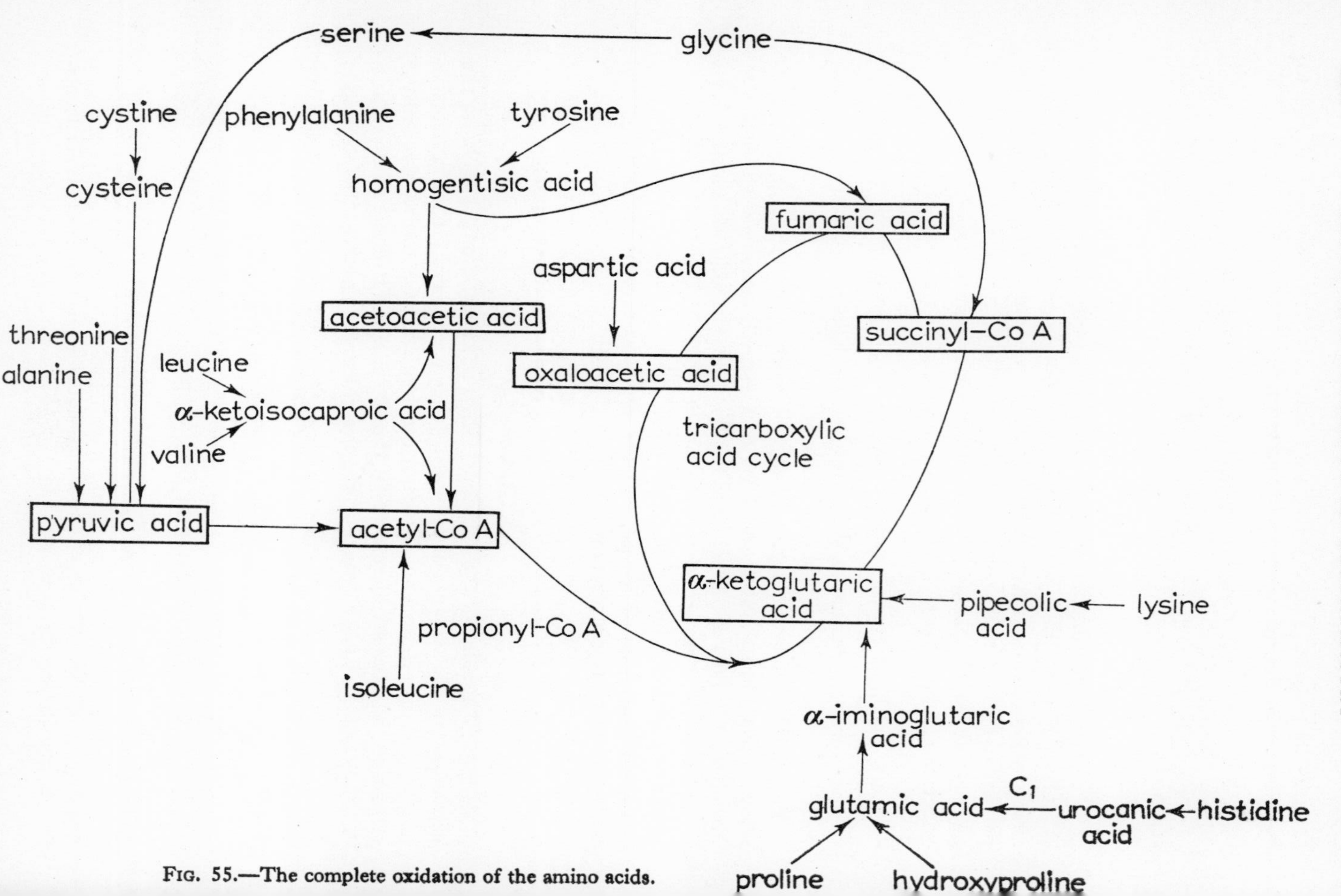

FIG. 55.—The complete oxidation of the amino acids.

for each mole of triose which has undergone oxido-reduction two moles of ATP have been formed, making four moles per mole of glucose. The net gain is therefore two moles of ATP per mole of glucose.

The free energy liberated when a mole of glucose is converted into two moles of lactate is 49,700 calories. Two energy-rich bonds of ATP have been recovered representing 24,000 calories, so the overall yield is one of 47%.

In the case of glycogen the formation of G—1—P in the presence of phosphorylase and inorganic phosphate takes place without the intervention of ATP (see Fig. 38). Consequently, only one molecule of ATP is used up in the phosphorylations at the beginning of the chain. Hence, the net gain per mole of glycogen monomer is three moles of ATP.

Since the free energy liberated in the course of the passage of the monomer to lactic acid is 56,700 calories and 36,000 calories is regained, the yield is 63%.

B. The Tricarboxylic Acid Cycle

The changes in free energy which accompany the various stages of the cycle are shown in Fig. 56.

When we estimate the energy yield it must be noted that the molecules of pyruvic acid which enter the cycle by way of acetyl-CoA come from the glycolysis chain, but that the DPNH formed during the oxidation of phosphoglyceraldehyde has not been taken into account. Since each dehydrogenation involving DPN or TPN yields three moles of ATP per mole of substrate, when glucose has provided two moles of pyruvate, 8 moles of ATP have been formed at the same time. In the tricarboxylic acid cycle we have a series of dehydrogenations where the primary acceptor is DPN. They are the malate-oxaloacetate and α-ketoglutarate-succinyl-CoA reactions. Succinyl-CoA when it decomposes gives a further mole of ATP. The succinate-fumarate reaction does not require the mediation of DPN and only two energy-rich bonds are formed. Thus during one complete turn of the cycle, that is for all the various stages from citrate to oxaloacetate, twelve energy-rich bonds of ATP are obtained:

isocitrate → oxalosuccinate	3
α-ketoglutarate → succinate	4
succinate → fumarate	2
malate → oxaloacetate	3
	12

When pyruvate is condensed with oxaloacetate to form citrate, three moles of ATP are formed per mole of pyruvate, or six per mole of glucose.

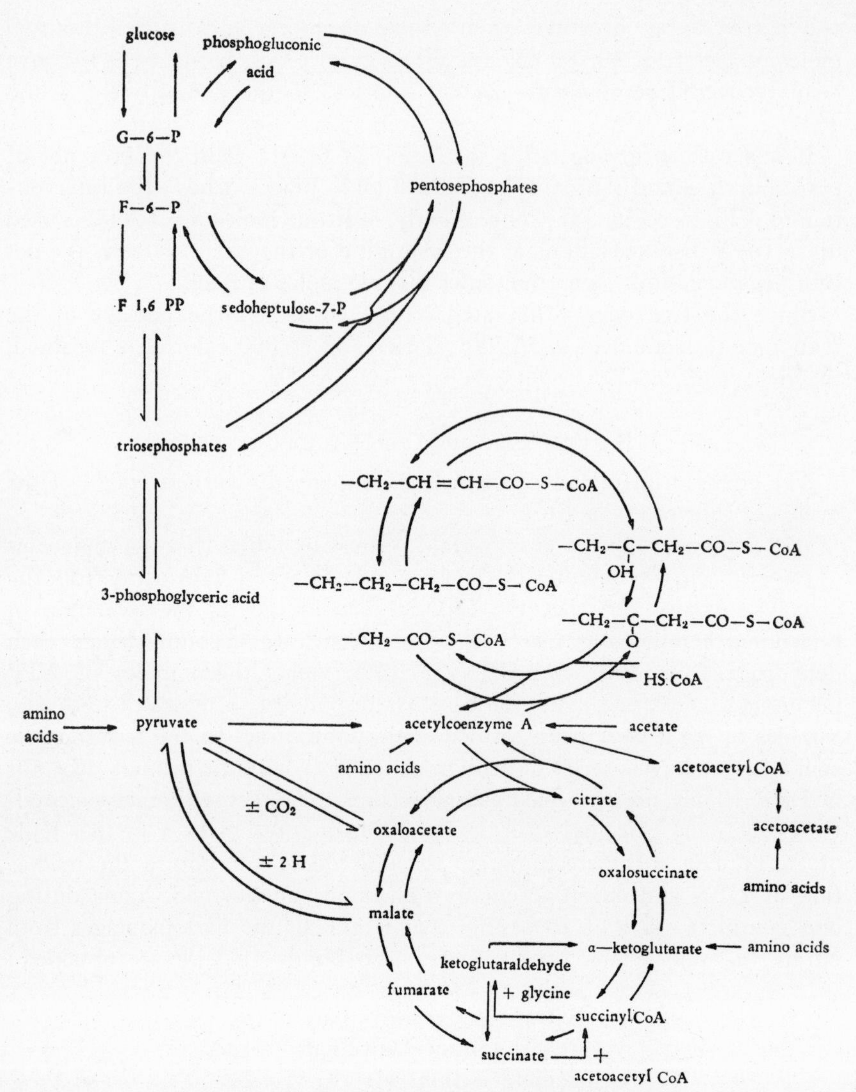

FIG. 56—Interrelation of the various priming reactions.

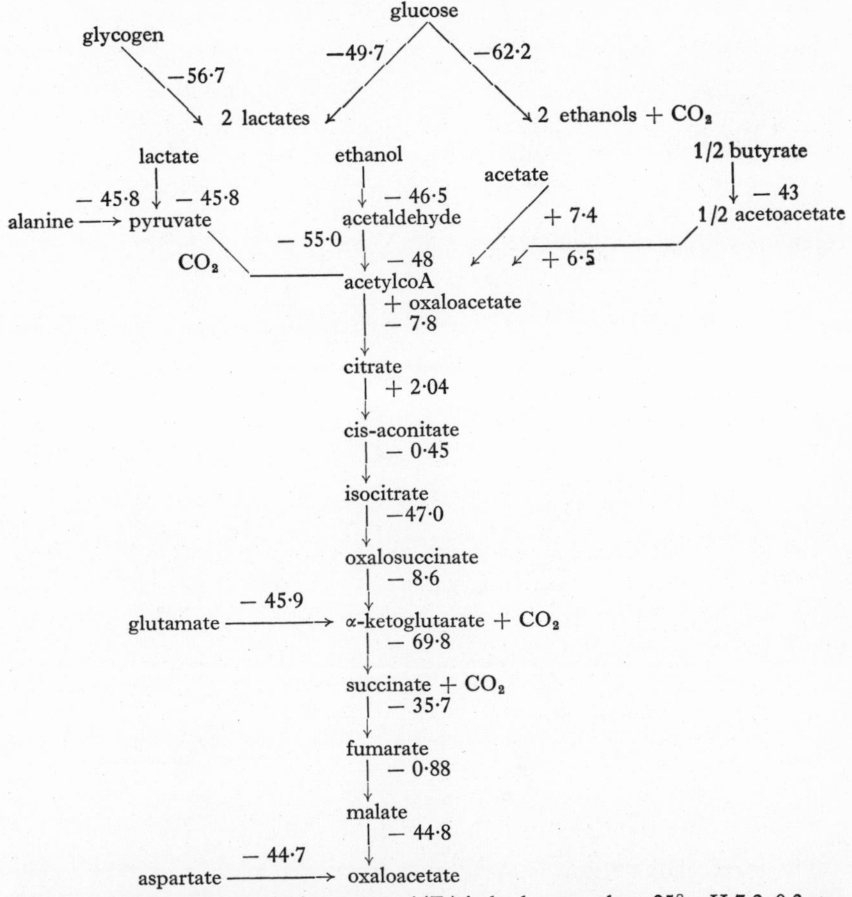

FIG. 57 (Krebs)—Changes in free energy (ΔF_0) in kcal. per mole at 25°, pH 7·2, 0·2 atm. O_2, 0·05 atm. CO_2. and the other reactants having a concentration of 0·01M. The free energy changes include changes due to associated reactions notably reactions with molecular oxygen acting as an acceptor for hydrogen removed at various stages.

Consequently, in the overall reaction for the oxidation of glucose, the moles of ATP formed from ADP add up as follows :

glucose → 2 pyruvate + 2 H_2O	8
2 pyruvate + 2 oxaloacetate + O_2 → 2 citrate + 2 CO_2	6
2 citrate + 4 O_2 → 2 oxaloacetate + 4 H_2O + 4 CO_2	24
Total	38

The overall reaction can thus be written

$$C_6H_{12}O_6 + 6O_2 + 38ADP + 38P \rightarrow 6H_2O + 6CO_2 + 38ATP$$

If glycogen is the starting point, we may add 1 ATP, giving a total of 39 ATP.

C. The Fatty Acid Cycle

Here, the calculation of the energy yield is less certain. It is believed that 5 energy-rich bonds are formed as each acetyl group is split off. Now each of the latter as it traverses the tricarboxylic acid cycle will give twelve energy-rich bonds (one complete turn of the cycle).

One mole of palmitic acid gives eight acetyls, so that the production of ATP during the passage of a mole of palmitic acid through the priming reactions will be as follows :

palmitic acid + $7O_2 \rightarrow$ 8 acetyls	$7 \times 5 = 35$
8 acetyls + 16 $O_2 \rightarrow 16H_2O + 16CO_2$	$8 \times 12 = 96$
Total	131

The overall reaction can be written :

$$C_{16}H_{32}O_2\ 23O_2 + 131ADP + 131P \rightarrow 16H_2O + 16CO_2 + 131ATP$$

D. Degradation of Amino Acids

Let us take the example of alanine, the heat of combustion of which is 392,000 cal per mole: on deamination it will yield a mole of pyruvate. The latter will be oxidized by the respiratory mechanism yielding energy-rich bonds calculated as follows :

pyruvate + oxaloacetate + O $\rightarrow$ citrate+CO_2	3
citrate + 23 $O_2 \rightarrow$ oxaloacetate + 2 H_2O + 2 CO_2	12
	15

E. Remarks on the Preceding Calculations

These calculations must be accepted with caution. In fact they imply values which may in some cases only be approached rather than attained. For example the P/O ratio in the course of oxidative phosphorylations. Moreover they assume a perfect *coupling* between phosphorylations and oxido-reductions. In practice numerous factors bring about the *uncoupling* of these two processes, examples are dinitrophenol and thyroxine. There are good reasons to believe that even in a given species the efficiency of coupling varies from one individual to another.

Furthermore, the values used in the above calculations have been obtained from measurements made *in vitro* on systems of the purified substances. This is not the situation in the cell. Most important is the fact that it contains an enzyme, adenosine triphosphatase, which hydrolyses ATP into ADP and inorganic phosphate, and it is not impossible that *in vivo* part of the ATP formed is lost through the action of this enzyme, also this enzyme is involved in a specific way in the transformation of ATP bond energy into work.

CHAPTER III

BIOSYNTHESES

I. THE MATERIALS FOR BIOSYNTHESES

THE priming reactions described in the preceding chapter are the principal sources of the coin which pays for the performance of cellular work : the pyrophosphate bond of ATP. This coin also pays for the energy required in biosyntheses, with the exception of assimilation phenomena whose mechanism will be studied later (see Part Six). But the priming reactions do not furnish only ATP, they also provide a series of construction materials for these biosyntheses. For example two-carbon fragments in the form of "active acetate" or acetyl-CoA are obtained during the priming reactions from glucose, fatty acids, acetoacetic acid and amino acids.

There are also one-carbon atom materials, together with CO_2 which is liberated at numerous points in the priming system. But the most important material of this type is that referred to as "formate" (C_1) that is CHO- or active formyl, into which can be converted not only formic acid, formaldehyde and methanol, but also the α-carbon of glycine, the α-carbon of glycollic acid, and α- and β-carbons of serine, the α-carbon of threonine, the C—2 of histidine, the C—2 of tryptophan, the α-C and the C—6 (or C—2) of phenylalanine and tyrosine, etc. Acetone can be split into an acetyl fragment and a formyl fragment.

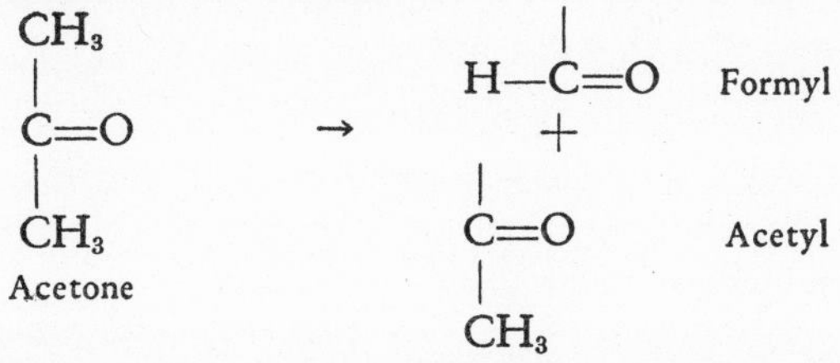

$$\underset{\text{Acetone}}{CH_3-C(=O)-CH_3} \rightarrow \underset{\text{Formyl}}{H-\overset{|}{C}=O} + \underset{\text{Acetyl}}{-C(=O)-CH_3}$$

In certain bacteria (but not in mammals), pyruvic acid can undergo fission into acetyl phosphate and formic acid (phosphoroclastic reaction), providing C_1 units.

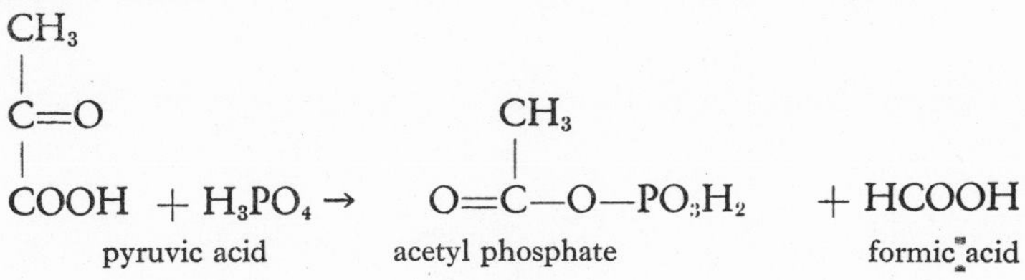

$$\underset{\text{pyruvic acid}}{CH_3-C(=O)-COOH} + H_3PO_4 \rightarrow \underset{\text{acetyl phosphate}}{O=C(CH_3)-O-PO_3H_2} + \underset{\text{formic acid}}{HCOOH}$$

One-carbon materials also exist which are not in the oxidized form as in CO_2 and C_1, but are in the reduced form of labile methyl groups (CH_3-). These labile methyl groups can give C_1 units and they originate from C_1 units.

By oxidation it is possible to pass from C_1 to CO_2, but the reverse reaction is impossible, at least in mammals.

Glycine is another material which is used. These molecules of glycine come from the proteins of the diet, from the degradation of serine or threonine, or are provided by synthesis from pyruvic acid.

In addition, biosyntheses draw materials of a more complex structure from different points in the priming reactions, and in particular from the tricarboxylic acid cycle.

II. BIOSYNTHESIS

A. Biosynthesis of Simple Chemical Structures

(*a*) *The Utilization of* CO_2 *to Form* —C—C— *Bonds* (*excepting Assimilation by Autotrophes*)

This is essentially the opposite of the reversible decarboxylations (p. 212) of ketonic acids. We shall therefore consider β-carboxylation, the inverse of the decarboxylation catalysed by a β-ketodecarboxylase, and α-carboxylation, the inverse of the decarboxylation catalysed by an α-ketodecarboxylase (see pp. 212 and 213).

1. *β-carboxylation*

This process for the fixation of CO_2 is very important. Two examples are, fixation by pyruvic acid to form oxaloacetic acid, and fixation of CO_2 by α-ketoglutaric acid. The former is the mechanism for the synthesis of dicarboxylic acids and the latter for the synthesis of tricarboxylic acids.

(*a*) *Fixation of* CO_2 *by α-ketoglutaric acid.*—The conversion of isocitric acid into α-ketoglutaric acid and CO_2 in the tricarboxylic acid cycle has been shown by Ochoa to take place in two stages :

$$\text{isocitric acid} + \text{TPN}^+ \underset{\text{Mn}^{++}}{\rightleftharpoons} \text{oxalosuccinic acid} + \text{TPNH} \quad (1)$$

$$\text{oxalosuccinic acid} \rightleftharpoons \alpha\text{-ketoglutaric acid} + CO_2 \quad (2)$$

The sum of (1) and (2) is

$$\text{isocitric acid} + \text{TPN}^+ \overset{\text{Mn}^{++}}{\rightleftharpoons} \alpha\text{-ketoglutaric acid} + CO_2 + \text{TPNH} \quad (3)$$

Reaction (3) can be caused by proceeding from right to left by coupling the system to an oxido-reduction system capable of reducing TPN, for example the glucose-6-phosphate dehydrogenase system, and we obtain

$$\text{G—6—P} + \text{TPN}^+ \rightleftharpoons \text{6-phosphogluconic acid} + \text{TPNH} \quad (4)$$

$$\alpha\text{-ketoglutaric acid} + CO_2 + \text{TPNH} \rightleftharpoons \text{isocitric acid} + \text{TPN}^+ \quad (5)$$

The sum of (4) and (5) gives

$$\text{G—6—P} + \alpha\text{-ketoglutaric acid} + CO_2 \rightleftharpoons \text{6-phosphogluconic acid} + \text{isocitric acid} \quad (6)$$

If aconitase is added, the equilibrium is shifted still more in favour of CO_2 fixation since 90% of the isocitric acid is continuously removed. Since the enzyme systems here described are universally distributed in cells, both in animals and in plants and in micro-organisms, this means of fixation is an important one.

(*b*) *Fixation of* CO_2 *by pyruvic acid.*—The entry of pyruvic acid into the tricarboxylic acid cycle by way of acetyl-CoA, then by formation of citric acid, depends upon there being a sufficiently high concentration of oxaloacetic acid. This concentration is maintained by the fixation of CO_2 by pyruvate with formation of oxaloacetate.

From the moment that the C_4 acids are used up, CO_2 becomes essential for the continuation of respiration by means of the cycle.

The discovery of the fixation of CO_2 by heterotrophes was first made in the propionic acid bacteria (Wood and Werkmann). In these bacteria when fermenting glycerol the CO_2 is utilized for the formation of succinic acid. Elsden has shown that for *E. coli* the rate of formation of succinate in the presence of pyruvate depends upon the CO_2 pressure.

The CO_2 is incorporated into succinate according to the following reactions :

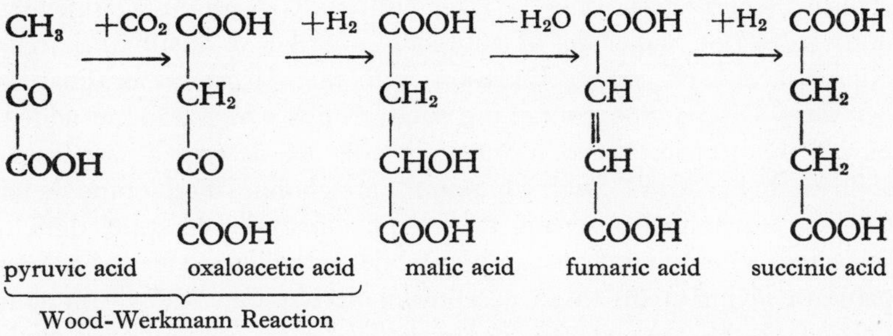

$$\begin{array}{ccccccccc} CH_3 & & COOH & & COOH & & COOH & & COOH \\ | & \xrightarrow{+CO_2} & | & \xrightarrow{+H_2} & | & \xrightarrow{-H_2O} & | & \xrightarrow{+H_2} & | \\ CO & & CH_2 & & CH_2 & & CH & & CH_2 \\ | & & | & & | & & \| & & | \\ COOH & & CO & & CHOH & & CH & & CH_2 \\ & & | & & | & & | & & | \\ & & COOH & & COOH & & COOH & & COOH \\ \text{pyruvic acid} & & \text{oxaloacetic acid} & & \text{malic acid} & & \text{fumaric acid} & & \text{succinic acid} \end{array}$$

(pyruvic acid → oxaloacetic acid: Wood-Werkmann Reaction)

By use of labelled carbon it has been shown that CO_2 fixed by pyruvate contributes to carbohydrate synthesis in heterotrophes. For example, the liver glycogen of animals contains carbon atoms derived from CO_2, (those which occupy the 3 and 4 positions in the hexose molecule).

This proves that glycolysis is partially reversible, a CO_2 molecule being introduced into a triosephosphate and passing through 3-phosphoglyceric acid to glycogen.

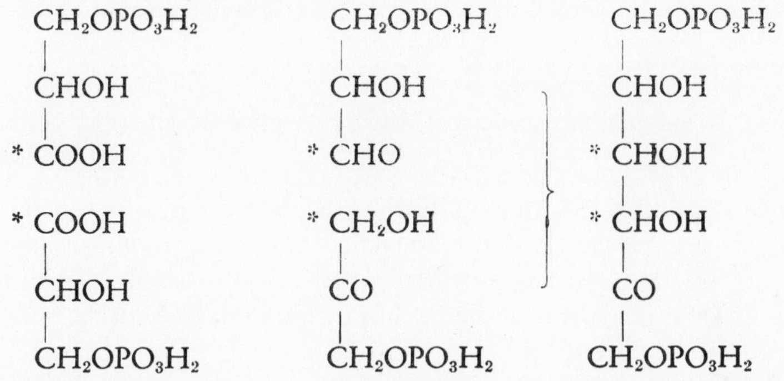

3-phosphoglyceric acid	Triosephosphate	Fructose-1, 6-PP
$CH_2OPO_3H_2$	$CH_2OPO_3H_2$	$CH_2OPO_3H_2$
CHOH	CHOH	CHOH
* COOH	* CHO	* CHOH
* COOH	* CH_2OH	* CHOH
CHOH	CO	CO
$CH_2OPO_3H_2$	$CH_2OPO_3H_2$	$CH_2OPO_3H_2$

2. *α-carboxylation*

This takes place by a reversal of the oxidative decarboxylation catalysed by an α-ketodecarboxylase. α-Carboxylation (giving pyruvic acid or α-ketoglutaric acid, for example), contrary to β-carboxylation, requires the intervention of ATP, the general reaction being

$$R—COO^- + CO_2 + 2H^+ + 2e + ATP \rightleftharpoons R—CO—COOH + P + ADP$$

The reversibility of the oxidative decarboxylation catalysed by an α-ketodecarboxylase can be considered as possible, but not as established.

(*b*) *Transmethylation*

This is the term describing the transfer of a $—CH_3$ group (a labile methyl group) from one molecule to another. In order to distinguish methyl groups attached by transmethylation from methyl groups originating in other ways, compounds containing such groups which can be added or removed in the presence of transmethylases are described as possessing "labile methyl groups". Such compounds are choline, methionine, betaine, sarcosine, adrenaline, anserine, methyl-nicotinamide, creatine, dimethyl-glycine, etc. A compound containing a labile methyl group is not necessarily capable of giving it up to an acceptor molecule. But, those compounds which can do this are given the name *methyl donors*. Examples are choline, betaine and methionine.

It would be wrong to believe that methyl donors, after activation by

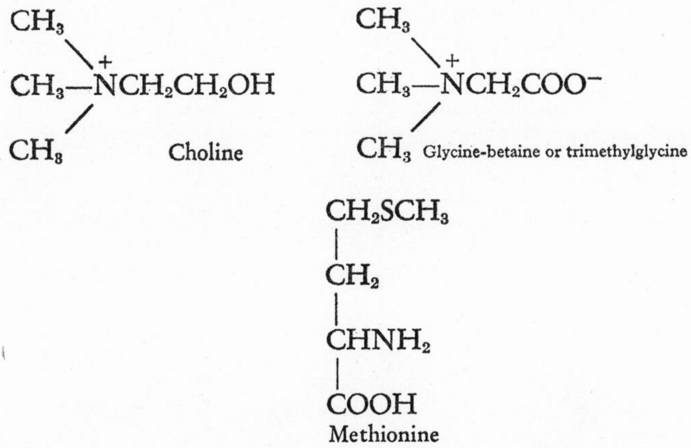

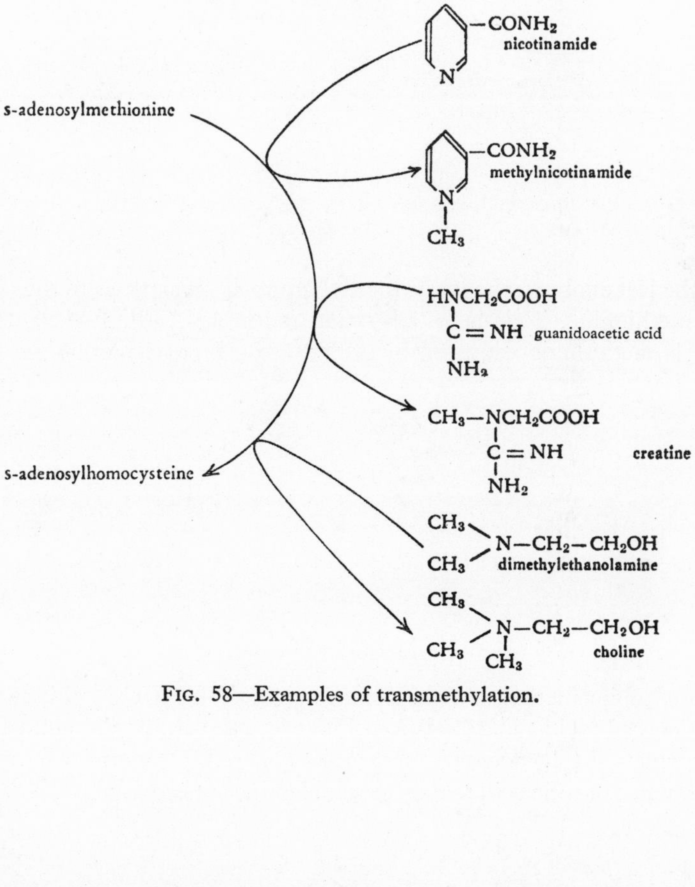

$$CH_3-\overset{+}{N}(CH_3)_2CH_2CH_2OH$$

Choline

$$CH_3-\overset{+}{N}(CH_3)_2CH_2COO^-$$

Glycine-betaine or trimethylglycine

$$CH_2SCH_3-CH_2-CHNH_2-COOH$$

Methionine

FIG. 58—Examples of transmethylation.

transmethylases, form a common pool of methyl groups. On the contrary each donor lies on a definite metabolic pathway :

choline → betaine → methionine → acceptor

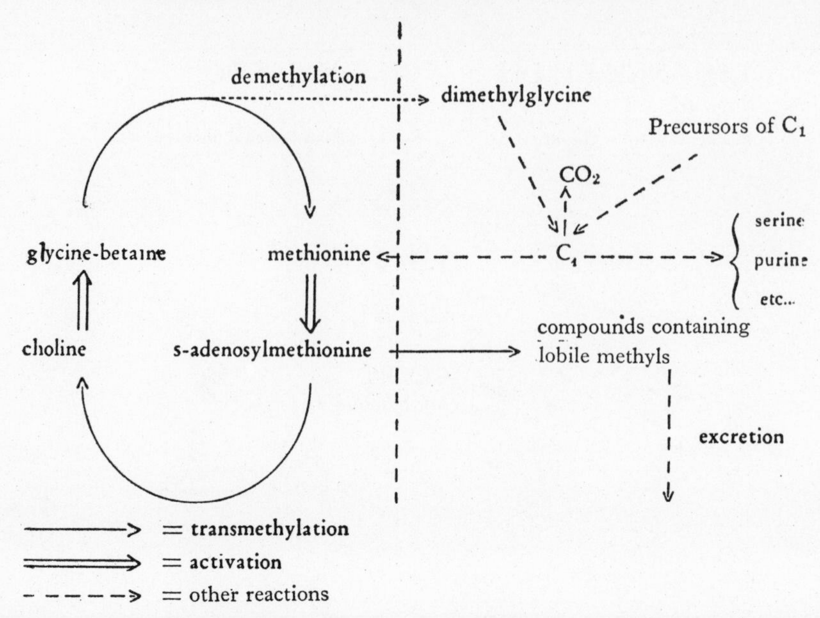

FIG. 59 (Verly)—The methyl-group cycle. At each cycle, two out of three methyl groups are lost, since the dimethylglycine formed by demethylation of betaine is not a methyl donor.

In the last analysis, the labile methyl group always passes to the acceptor from methionine. This is an operation requiring ATP. In fact, the true donor is methionine activated by ATP, or S-adenosyl-methionine.

```
N——CNH2
||    ||
NH2  C—N
|     |   \\
|     |    CH
|     |   /                                +
N===C—N—CH—CHOH—CHOH—CH—CH2—S—CH2—CH2—CH—COOH
         |_______ O _______|      |          |
                                 CH3        NH2
```

S-adenosylmethionine

These labile methyl groups cannot originate from CO_2 although their oxidation can yield this substance. The precursors of labile methyl groups are "formates" (C_1) and as in other cases where C_1 fragments are required the presence of folic acid and cyanocobalamine is necessary.

(*c*) *Passage from Free Acetate to Active Acetate*

We have seen how, in the priming reactions, active acetate or acetyl-CoA is produced starting from various types of nutrient. Acetyl-CoA can also be produced by activation of free acetate and this operation presents certain curious features. In yeast and animal tissues the acetate is activated by ATP and a special type of splitting of the molecule occurs, resulting in the formation of AMP and pyrophosphate.

$$\begin{array}{l} \mathrm{ATP} + \mathrm{CoA{-}SH} \rightleftarrows \mathrm{CoA{-}S{\sim}PP} + \mathrm{AMP} \\ \mathrm{CH_3{-}COOH} + \mathrm{CoA{-}S{\sim}PP} \rightleftarrows \mathrm{CoA{-}S{\sim}COCH_3} + \mathrm{PP} \\ \hline \mathrm{ATP} + \mathrm{CoA{-}SH} + \mathrm{CH_3COOH} \rightleftarrows \mathrm{CoA{-}S{\sim}COCH_3} + \mathrm{AMP} + \mathrm{PP} \end{array}$$

(*d*) *Condensation of C_2 Fragments to Form Acetoacetate*

This is a modified Claisen condensation between two molecules of acetyl-CoA resulting in the appearance of acetoacetyl-CoA and separation of CoA. The reaction is reversible and the enzyme catalysing the condensation also catalyses the reverse thiolysis. If a specific deacylase is present, the acetoacetate is liberated and the equilibrium is distributed until the acetyl-CoA is completely transformed into acetoacetate.

$$\mathrm{CH_3{-}\overset{\overset{\displaystyle O}{\|}}{C}{-}S{-}CoA} + \mathrm{CH_3{-}\overset{\overset{\displaystyle O}{\|}}{C}{-}S{-}CoA}$$

$$\text{condensation} \downarrow \qquad \uparrow \text{thiolysis}$$

$$\left[\ \mathrm{CH_3{-}\underset{\underset{\displaystyle S{-}CoA}{|}}{\overset{\overset{\displaystyle OH}{|}}{C}}{-}CH_2{-}\overset{\overset{\displaystyle O}{\|}}{C}{-}S{-}CoA}\ \right]$$

$$\downarrow\uparrow$$

$$\mathrm{CH_3{-}\overset{\overset{\displaystyle O}{\|}}{C}{-}CH_2{-}\overset{\overset{\displaystyle O}{\|}}{C}{-}S{-}CoA} + \mathrm{HS{-}CoA}$$

$$\text{hydrolysis} \downarrow \qquad + \mathrm{H_2O}$$

$$\mathrm{CH_3{-}CO{-}CH_2{-}COOH} + \mathrm{HS{-}CoA}$$

(*e*) *Biosynthesis of Isoprene and Carotenoids*

Their biosynthesis is from C_2 fragments by the intermediary of aceto-acetyl-CoA. In isoprene, two carbon atoms are derived from the carboxy- of acetate and three from its methyl, as shown below.

The carotenoids synthesized by plants also derive from acetyl-CoA.

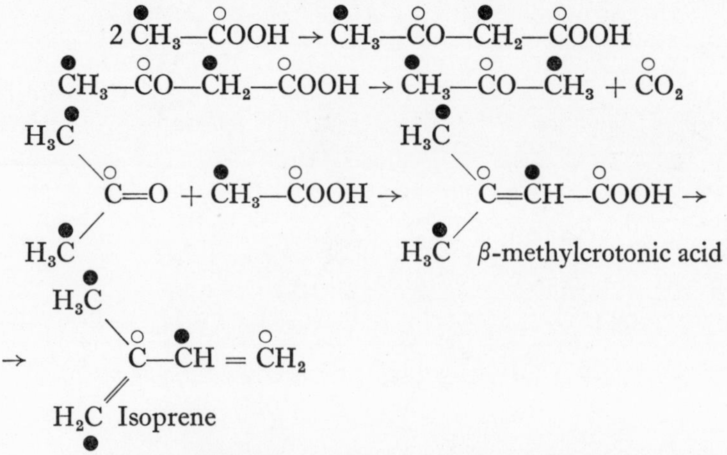

$$2\,\overset{\bullet}{C}H_3\text{—}\overset{\circ}{C}OOH \rightarrow \overset{\bullet}{C}H_3\text{—}\overset{\circ}{C}O\text{—}\overset{\bullet}{C}H_2\text{—}\overset{\circ}{C}OOH$$

$$\overset{\bullet}{C}H_3\text{—}\overset{\circ}{C}O\text{—}\overset{\bullet}{C}H_2\text{—}\overset{\circ}{C}OOH \rightarrow \overset{\bullet}{C}H_3\text{—}\overset{\circ}{C}O\text{—}\overset{\bullet}{C}H_3 + \overset{\circ}{C}O_2$$

$$\begin{matrix}H_3\overset{\bullet}{C}\\ \quad\diagdown\\ \quad\overset{\circ}{C}=O\\ \quad\diagup\\ H_3\overset{\bullet}{C}\end{matrix} + \overset{\bullet}{C}H_3\text{—}\overset{\circ}{C}OOH \rightarrow \begin{matrix}H_3\overset{\bullet}{C}\\ \quad\diagdown\\ \quad\overset{\circ}{C}=\overset{\bullet}{C}H\text{—}\overset{\circ}{C}OOH\\ \quad\diagup\\ H_3\overset{\bullet}{C}\end{matrix} \rightarrow$$

β-methylcrotonic acid

$$\rightarrow \begin{matrix}H_3\overset{\bullet}{C}\\ \quad\diagdown\\ \quad\overset{\circ}{C}\text{—}\overset{\bullet}{C}H = \overset{\circ}{C}H_2\\ \quad /\!\!/\\ H_2\underset{\bullet}{C}\end{matrix}$$

Isoprene

FIG. 60 (Fukushima and Rosenfeld)—The synthesis of isoprene
○ = carboxyl carbon ● = methyl carbon

(*f*) *Biosynthesis of the Steroid Ring System*

The use of isotopes and mutant strains has demonstrated that acetate is the essential starting material for the synthesis of the principal plant sterol, ergosterol. Studies of cholesterol synthesis in animals have also provided evidence of the importance of acetate. Neither formate nor labile methyl groups (of methionine for example) can take part in the reaction, as has been shown by the use of labelled carbon. It is most unlikely that cholesterol obtains any of its carbons from a source other than the acetate molecule. As shown in Fig. 61, by means of a series of chemical degradations it has been possible to demonstrate the origin of most of the atoms in the skeleton either in the methyl or in the carboxyl of acetic acid.

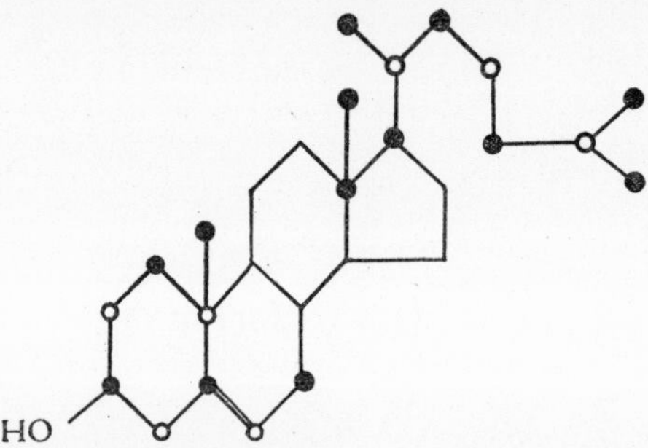

FIG. 61 (Fukushima and Rosenfeld)—Origin of the carbon atoms of cholesterol.
● = derived from the methyl of acetate.
○ = derived from the carboxyl group.

The bile acids, the sex hormones, the hormones of the adrenal cortex, in animals, can all be obtained by modifying cholesterol and also directly from acetate. In the case of the corticosteroids, experiment has shown that they are formed from cholesterol molecules brought to the gland in the plasma. The formation of cholesterol from acetate takes place through the intermediate stage of acetoacetate, as has been shown in numerous experiments.

An examination of the distribution in the cholesterol molecule of the carbons from methyl and those from the carboxyl of acetate, does not immediately suggest the mode of synthesis. But it does limit the possibilities.

The addition of a further acetic acid residue to the keto-group of acetoacetic acid, followed by a decarboxylation, yields a C_5 branched chain (three carbons arising from methyl groups and two from the carboxyl of acetate).

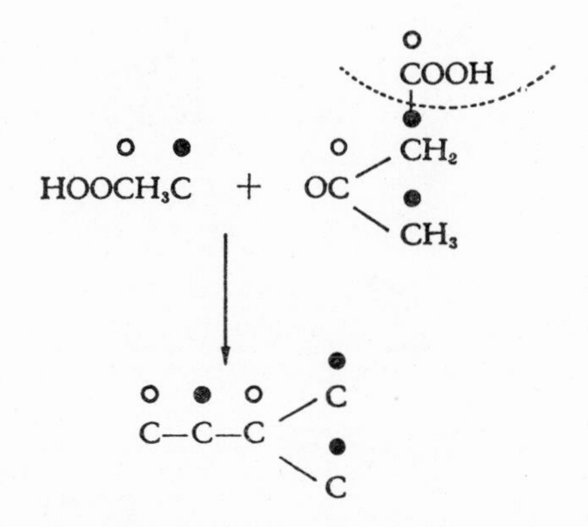

It can be seen that this hypothetical C_5 compound can be superimposed, with respect to the origin of the carbon atoms, on the terminal part of the side chain of the cholesterol molecule (Fig. 61). If we now consider the distribution in the ring, we see that the latter can also be conceived of as a polymer of the same C_5 chain. It has however been objected that this makes isovaleric acid appear to be a possible precursor of cholesterol. In reality, this happens only by way of acetoacetate. Isovaleric acid (and also leucine) gives an isopropyl residue which combines with CO_2 to form acetoacetate.

What is the nature of the substance with the C_5 chain? Let us recall the synthesis of isoprene, the starting point for carotenoids and terpenes, from acetate; we see that this synthesis leads to the C_5 arrangement we are seeking. Arguments have been advanced previously to implicate the isoprenoid, squalene, in the biosynthesis of steroids. Squalene is not limited solely to the tissues of the selachians. Traces have been found everywhere in animal tissues where it has been sought. When we consider that isoprene units, as we have already indicated, are derived from acetate, we may represent squalene as in Fig. 62 and compare it with Fig. 61.

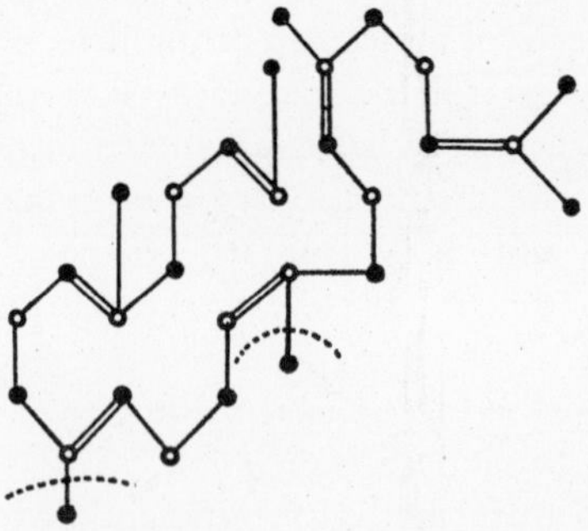

FIG. 62 (Bloch)—Likely distribution of carbon isotopes in squalene.

This hypothesis has been tested using labelled squalene and the results have been favourable. However the ultimate mechanism of sterol formation from squalene still remains undiscovered. The scheme shown in Fig. 63 has been proposed but part of this is still conjecture.

(g) *Biosynthesis of Porphyrins*

These substances are synthesized from δ-amino-levulinic acid formed in the Shemin cycle (p. 222). Two molecules of the acid are condensed to porphobilinogen, which is the precursor ring of the porphyrins.

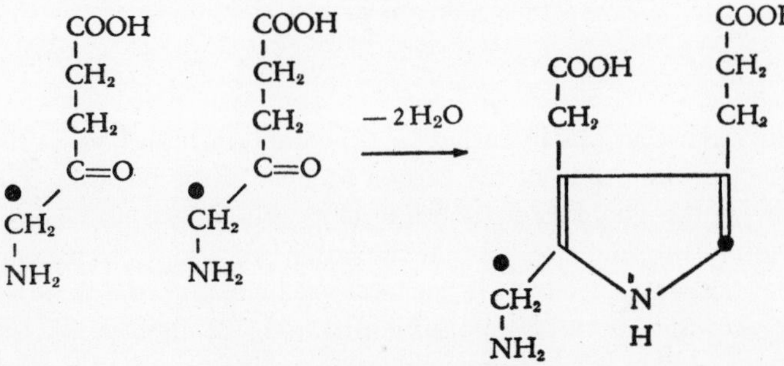

COOH–CH₂–CH₂–C=O–●CH₂–NH₂ + COOH–CH₂–CH₂–C=O–●CH₂–NH₂ $\xrightarrow{-2H_2O}$ porphobilinogen (pyrrole ring with COOH–CH₂, COOH–CH₂–CH₂, ●CH₂–NH₂ and N–H)

● = originally C_α of glycine.

Several suggestions have been made as to the mode of conversion of the precursor to the different porphyrins. In order to account for the distribution of the α-carbon of glycine and the δ-carbon of amino-levulinic acid in the porphyrins of series I and II, Shemin has proposed the following: the condensation of three molecules of porphobilinogen forms a tripyrrylmethane which is then split into a dipyrrylmethane and a monopyrrole. The structure of the dipyrrylmethane will differ depending on the place where scission has occurred. Fission at A or at B will produce the types of dipyrrylmethane indicated by the letters A and B (Fig. 64).

The condensation of 2 molecules of dipyrrylmethane A will give a porphyrin I and that of a molecule of A and a molecule of B will give a porphyrin of series III (in this case with the loss of one carbon in the form of formaldehyde) (Fig. 64).

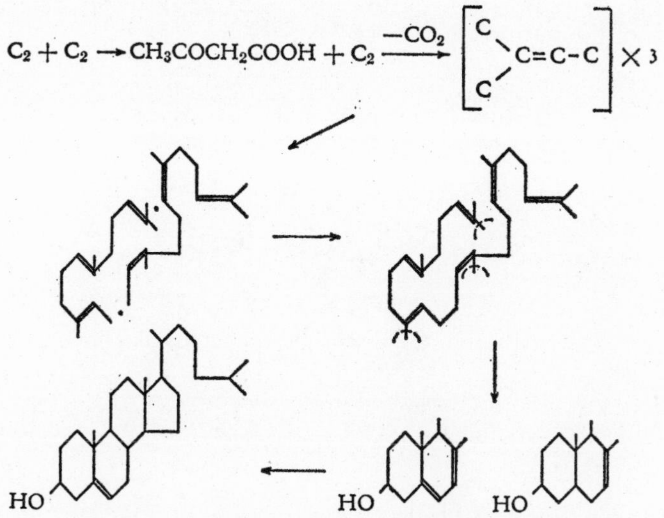

$$C_2 + C_2 \rightarrow CH_3COCH_2COOH + C_2 \xrightarrow{-CO_2} \left[\begin{matrix} C \\ \\ C \end{matrix} \!\!>\! C{=}C{-}C \right] \times 3$$

HO HO HO

FIG. 63 (Bloch)—Proposed scheme for the synthesis of cholesterol.

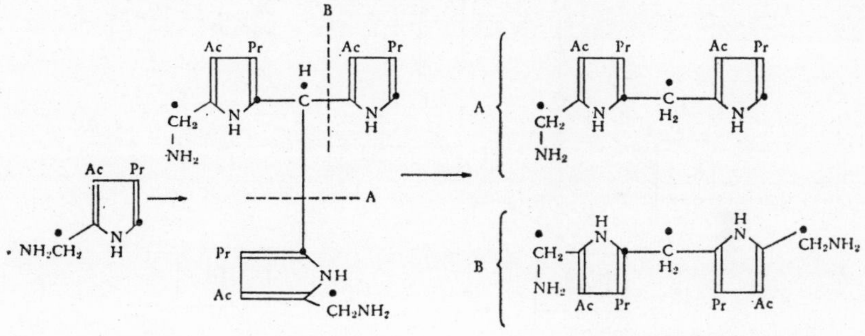

Ac = chain of acetic acid

Pr = chain of propionic acid

FIG. 64 (Shemin)—• = C_α of glycine and C_δ of amino-levulinic acid.

(*h*) *Biosynthesis of the Purine Ring*

The use of radioactive isotopes has allowed the various carbon and nitrogen atoms in the purine ring to be identified with regard to their origin. The purine ring cannot be formed in the living organism from pyrimidines and as the diagram shows all the contributing fragments are small units.

The biosynthesis of the purine ring takes place in the course of the synthesis of the purine nucleotides. (p. 255).

4-aminoimidazole-5-carboxamide

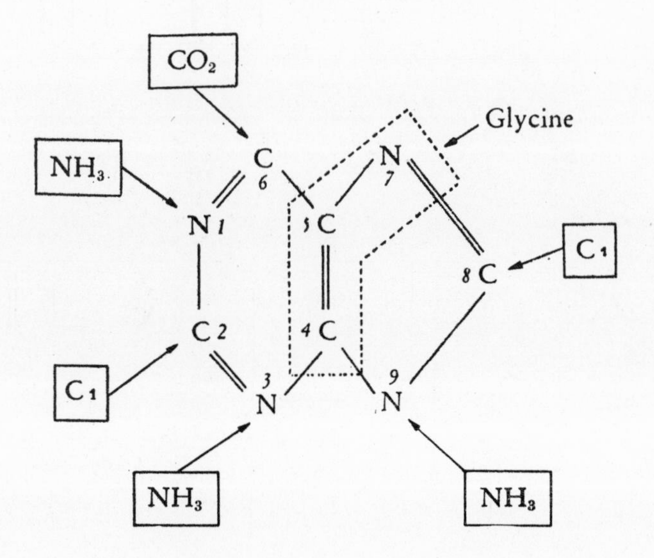

(*i*) *Biosynthesis of Fatty Acids*

The mechanism has been described together with the "fatty acid cycle" (p. 196).

(*j*) *Biosynthesis of Sugars*

The major process for the synthesis of sugars in Nature is the autotrophic synthesis which we shall be studying later (Part Six).

However, the synthesis of sugar molecules can, in general, be brought about in the cell by a reversal of the priming reactions. In this way, in certain types of cell, a fatty acid may give acetyl-CoA which does not enter the tricarboxylic acid cycle but instead follows the reversed glycolysis chain whose non-reversible stages are replaced by synthetic reactions the enzymes for which are shown in Fig. 40.

Amino acids also can give molecules of hexoses and this "glucogenic" property is particularly evident with those amino acids which enter the cycle of priming reactions at the level of α-ketoglutaric acid and pyruvic acid. Amino acids which enter at the level of acetoacetate can also, generally, follow the same path, but they tend to bring about an accumulation of acetoacetic acid and other "ketone bodies". They are therefore termed "ketogenic".

As for the biosynthesis of the pentoses, we have already shown that this can take place during the operation of the hexosemonophosphate shunt (p. 193) and we shall return to other aspects of this biosynthesis when we consider the formation of pentose phosphates (p. 253).

(*k*) *Biosynthesis of Pyrimidines*

The origin of the carbon and nitrogen atoms contributing to the structure of the pyrimidine ring is shown in Fig. 65. The biosynthesis of the pyrimidine ring takes place in the course of pyrimidine nucleotide biosynthesis (p. 255).

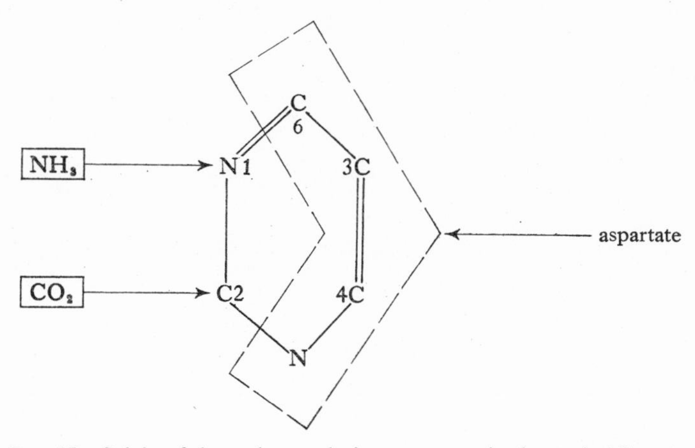

FIG. 65—Origin of the carbon and nitrogen atoms in the pyrimidine ring.

(*l*) *Biosynthesis of Short Chain Amino Acids*

Alanine is formed by transamination of pyruvate, and this latter substance is the starting material for the synthesis of other short chain amino acids: glycine, serine, cysteine and cystine. According to Shemin, serine is converted into glycine by way of formylglycine.

$$\underset{\text{Serine}}{NH_2\text{—}\overset{\displaystyle CH_2OH}{\overset{|}{C}H}\text{—}COOH} \xrightarrow{-2\,H} \underset{\text{Formylglycine}}{NH_2\text{—}\overset{\displaystyle CHO}{\overset{|}{C}H}\text{—}COOH} \xrightarrow{+H_2O} HCOOH + \underset{\text{Glycine}}{NH_2CH_2COOH}$$

The serine is synthesized from "formate" and glycine. If the formate is tagged with C^{14} and the carboxyl of the glycine with C^{13}, doubly-labelled serine is obtained:

$$HC^{14}OOH + NH_2CH_2C^{13}OOH \rightarrow NH_2\text{—}\overset{\displaystyle C^{14}H_2OH}{\overset{|}{C}H}\text{—}C^{13}OOH$$

The formation of serine from glycine and "formate" implies the participation of folic acid and pyridoxal, and this has been demonstrated by several experiments with bacteria. A number of observations has shown that the serine is derived from the glycolysis pathway and finally yields glycine. The glycine can be formed not only from serine but also from threonine with formation of acetate.

The carbon skeleton of cystine is also derived from serine, both in mammals and in micro-organisms, as has been demonstrated by experiments carried out with isotopes. Cysteine is actually an intermediate. The sulphur of cysteine and cystine is derived from sulphates in micro-organisms and from methionine in mammals.

Cysteine is readily transformed into cystine in the cell, according to the equation

$$2\begin{array}{c}COOH\\|\\HCNH_2\\|\\CH_2SH\end{array} \underset{+2\,H}{\overset{-2\,H}{\rightleftharpoons}} \begin{array}{ccc}COOH & & COOH\\| & & |\\HCNH_2 & & HCNH_2\\| & & |\\CH_2\text{—}S & \text{—} & S\text{—}CH_2\end{array}$$

Cysteine Cystine

The oxidation of cysteine to cystine is catalysed by cytochrome-*c* and cytochrome-oxidase, whilst the reduction of cystine is accomplished by a number of reducing agents : H_2S, glutathione, SH-enzymes, etc.

The conversion of serine into cysteine is brought about by condensation of the serine with homocysteine, formed by the demethylation of methionine, or more exactly of S-adenosylmethionine, in the course of transmethylation reactions.

$$CH_3—S—CH_2—CH_2—CHNH_2—COOH \rightarrow HS\,CH_2—CH_2—CHNH_2—COOH$$

methionine → homocysteine

homocysteine + serine ($HOCH_2—CH\,NH_2—COOH$) → cystathionine:

$$S \begin{cases} CH_2—CH_2—CHNH_2—COOH \\ CH_2—CHNH_2—COOH \end{cases}$$

cystathionine → cysteine + homoserine

$$HS\,CH_2—CHNH_2—COOH \qquad HOCH_2—CH_2—CH\,NH_2—COOH$$

cysteine — homoserine

(*m*) *Biosynthesis of Glutamic Acid*

The chief source of glutamic acid is α-ketoglutaric acid produced in the Krebs cycle. This acid can itself only arise in the oxidative decarboxylation of isocitric acid, for the decarboxylation of α-ketoglutarate to give succinate is irreversible. This is the sole pathway for the formation of glutamic acid from carbohydrate.

In certain micro-organisms like *Escherichia coli*, it is the only source, whilst in other organisms other substances can contribute to the formation of glutamic acid. These substances are proline, arginine, histidine, glycine and succinic acid, by way of δ-aminolevulinic acid.

The amino group is derived from ammonia fixed to α-ketoglutaric acid by glutamic dehydrogenase, or from the amino group of another amino acid, transferred by transamination.

(*n*) *From Glutamate to Glutamine, Proline, Hydroxyproline and Arginine*

Here, we have a biosynthetic pathway which, starting from α-ketoglutaric acid in the Krebs cycle, divides at the level of glutamic acid into three branches, one leading to glutamine, a second to proline and hydroxyproline, and the third to ornithine, citrulline and arginine.

1. *Glutamine*

Starting from glutamic acid and ammonia, in the presence of ATP, glutamine is formed in a reaction whose mechanism is unknown.

2. *Proline, hydroxyproline*

The biosynthesis of proline has been elucidated with the aid of strains of *E. coli* which are specifically auxotrophic for proline. These strains fall into two groups: those which accumulate glutamic γ-semialdehyde and those in which this substance can replace glutamic acid as a growth factor. The reduction of glutamic acid to the semialdehyde is no doubt not so simple as is indicated by the arrow in the scheme set out below. The cyclization of proline would not require enzymic aid since γ and δ-amino-aldehydes cyclize rapidly in neutral aqueous solution.

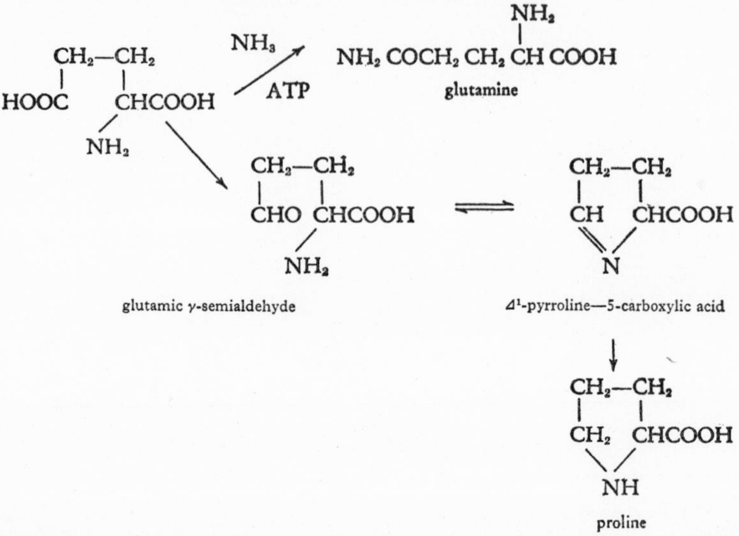

$CH_2—CH_2$ / HOOC CHCOOH / NH_2 —(NH_3, ATP)→ $NH_2COCH_2CH_2CH(NH_2)COOH$ glutamine

→ $CH_2—CH_2$ / CHO CHCOOH / NH_2 glutamic γ-semialdehyde ⇌ $CH_2—CH_2$ / CH CHCOOH / N Δ^1-pyrroline—5-carboxylic acid

↓

$CH_2—CH_2$ / CH_2 CHCOOH / NH proline

Hydroxyproline is notably present in the connective tissue of animals. In the latter, the use of isotopes has enabled it to be demonstrated that it results from a modification of proline, which apparently is already present since labelled hydroxyproline is not readily incorporated into the tissues.

3. *Ornithine, citrulline, arginine*

The formation of arginine from ornithine, *via* citrulline, has long been known. In fact, the "ornithine cycle" of Krebs and Henseleit was one of the first biosynthetic pathways ever proposed.

The sequence ornithine-citrulline-arginine, first shown to occur in mammalian liver, has been found in many other organisms (*Neurospora, Penicillium, E. coli*, lactobacilli, animal tissues, etc.).

The glutamate-ornithine relationship has been confirmed by the use of isotopes and by the discovery of a *Penicillium* mutant responding to either substance.

The use of mutants of *E. coli* has enabled Vogel to identify the three acetylated compounds shown in the scheme.

Study of the pathway from ornithine to citrulline, using mutants of *Neurospora*, has shown that there are two stages. The first requires ATP; CO_2 and NH_3 are fixed to form an as yet unidentified compound, which is then transformed into citrulline.

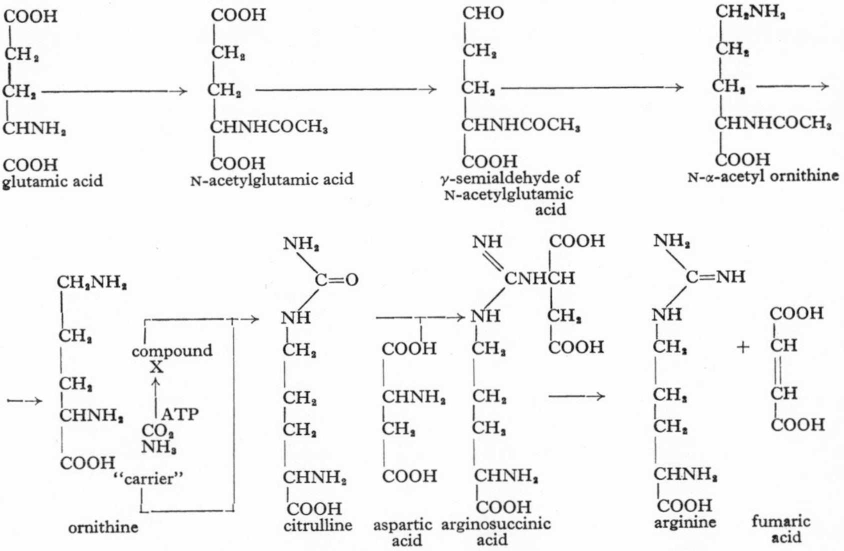

COOH—CH_2—CH_2—$CHNH_2$—COOH (glutamic acid) → COOH—CH_2—CH_2—$CHNHCOCH_3$—COOH (N-acetylglutamic acid) → CHO—CH_2—CH_2—$CHNHCOCH_3$—COOH (γ-semialdehyde of N-acetylglutamic acid) → CH_2NH_2—CH_2—CH_2—$CHNHCOCH_3$—COOH (N-α-acetyl ornithine) →

→ CH_2NH_2—CH_2—CH_2—$CHNH_2$—COOH (ornithine) → [ATP, CO_2, NH_3, "carrier" → compound X] → NH_2—C(=O)—NH—CH_2—CH_2—CH_2—$CHNH_2$—COOH (citrulline) + COOH—$CHNH_2$—CH_2—COOH (aspartic acid) → NH=C(NH—CH_2—CH_2—CH_2—$CHNH_2$—COOH)—NHCH(COOH)—CH_2—COOH (arginosuccinic acid) → NH_2—C(=NH)—NH—CH_2—CH_2—CH_2—$CHNH_2$—COOH (arginine) + COOH—CH=CH—COOH (fumaric acid)

FIG. 66 (Davis)—Biosynthesis of arginine from glutamic acid.

The path from citrulline to arginine is made up of several stages. Citrulline is condensed with aspartate to form argino-succinate. A specific enzyme cleaves the argino-succinate to arginine and fumaric acid.

(*o*) *Biosynthesis of* C_4 *Amino Acids* (*Aspartic Acid, Methionine and Threonine*)

These molecules are derived from aspartic acid, itself formed from members of the Krebs cycle. In plants and micro-organisms fumaric acid is combined with ammonia in the presence of aspartase, whilst in mammals which do not possess aspartase, aspartic acid is formed by reductive deamination of oxaloacetate in a reaction of unknown mechanism.

Chemical genetic experiments on *Neurospora* have shown that threonine and methionine have a common precursor. In fact, a mutant requiring both amino acids at once can satisfy this double requirement when L-homoserine is supplied. On the other hand a mutant whose only block is in the synthesis of methionine accumulates threonine and L-homoserine in ts mycelium. The idea of a single precursor has been confirmed with

E. coli and with yeast in isotopic experiments, and in enzymic experiments. The synthesis of methionine is the reverse of the synthesis of cysteine described previously (p. 243), *via* homocysteine and with cystathionine as

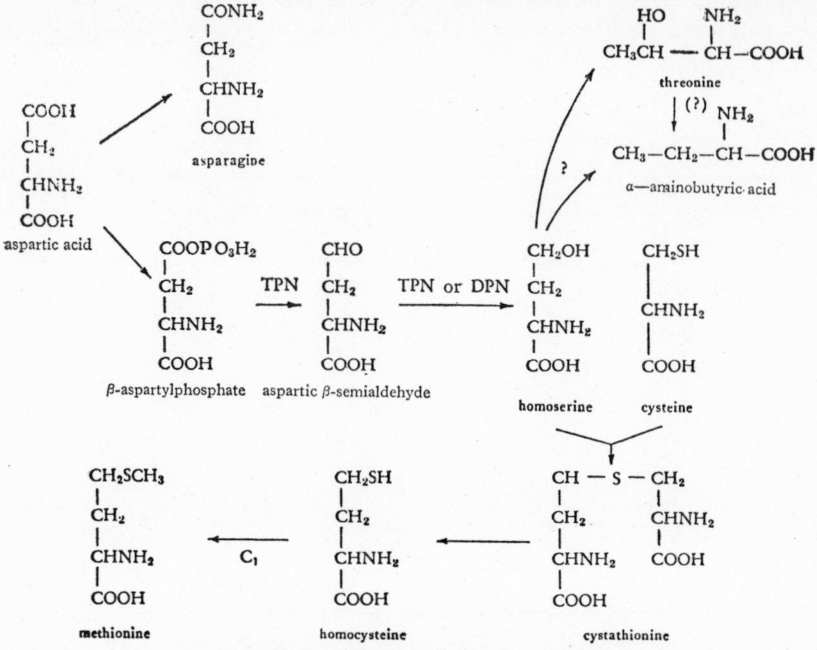

$CONH_2-CH_2-CHNH_2-COOH$ asparagine

$CH_3CH(OH)-CH(NH_2)-COOH$ threonine

(?)

$CH_3-CH_2-CH(NH_2)-COOH$ α—aminobutyric acid

$COOH-CH_2-CHNH_2-COOH$ aspartic acid

$COOPO_3H_2-CH_2-CHNH_2-COOH$ β-aspartylphosphate → TPN → $CHO-CH_2-CHNH_2-COOH$ aspartic β-semialdehyde → TPN or DPN → $CH_2OH-CH_2-CHNH_2-COOH$ homoserine

$CH_2SH-CHNH_2-COOH$ cysteine

$CH-S-CH_2$; CH_2-CHNH_2-COOH; $CHNH_2-COOH$ cystathionine → $CH_2SH-CH_2-CHNH_2-COOH$ homocysteine → C_1 → $CH_2SCH_3-CH_2-CHNH_2-COOH$ methionine

FIG. 67 (Davis)—Biosynthesis of C_4 amino acids.

an intermediate (Fig. 67). (In micro-organisms cystathionine can be split on either side of the sulphur atom. By contrast, in mammals it can only be cleaved between the sulphur atom and the seryl residue. Hence mammals cannot synthesize homocysteine.)

(*p*) *Biosynthesis of Isoleucine, Valine and Leucine*

The starting point of our knowledge of the mechanism of the biosynthesis of these substances is the discovery of a *Neurospora* mutant requiring both isoleucine and valine. This mutant accumulates the corresponding dihydroxy-derivatives — dihydroxy-methylvaleric and dihydroxy-isovaleric acids. Furthermore, a mutant of *E. coli* accumulates the corresponding ketonic acids, α-ketomethylvaleric and α-ketoisovaleric acids. The mutants accumulating the ketonic acids respond only to isoleucine and valine whilst the accumulators of dihydroxy-acids respond not only to the amino acids but also the the corresponding keto-acids. In an auxotrophe for isoleucine alone, dihydroxy-methylvaleric acid and dihydroxy-isovaleric acid are active, whilst in an auxotrophe for valine alone, dihydroxy-isovaleric acid and α-ketoisovaleric acid are active.

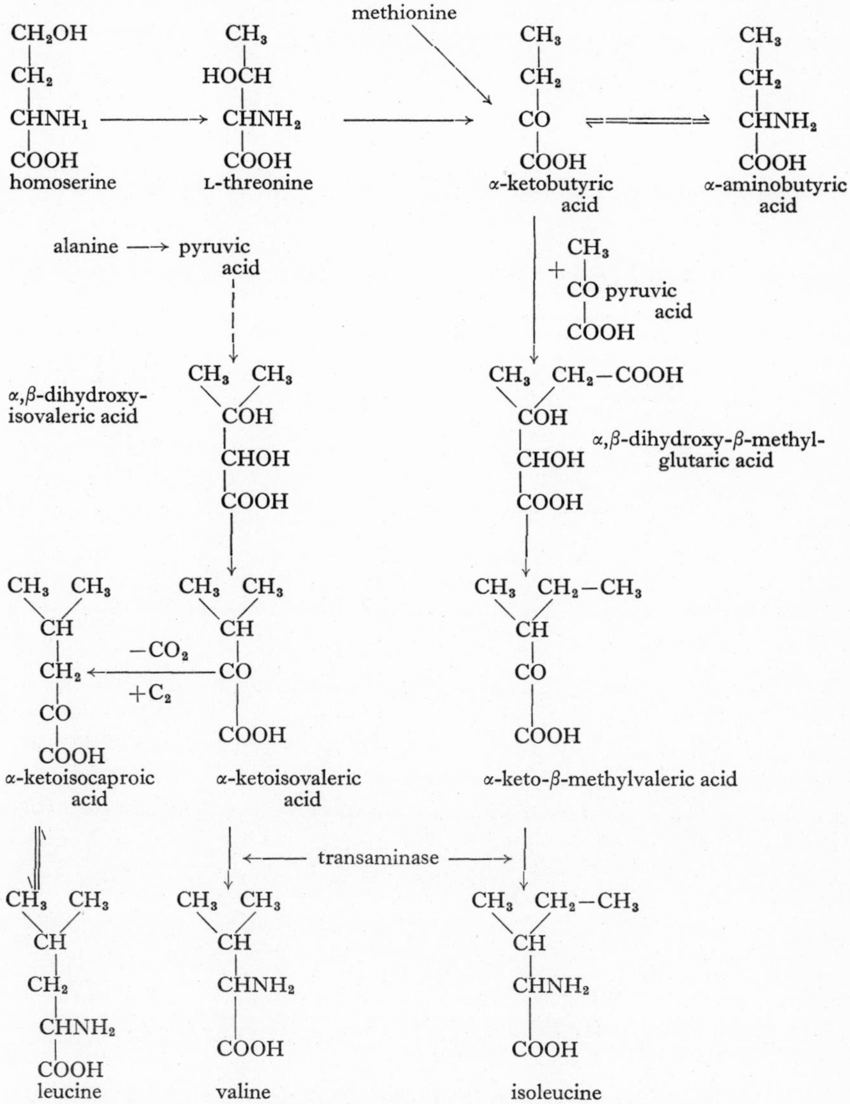

methionine

$CH_2OH-CH_2-CHNH_2-COOH$ (homoserine) ⟶ $CH_3-HOCH-CHNH_2-COOH$ (L-threonine) ⟶ $CH_3-CH_2-CO-COOH$ (α-ketobutyric acid) ⇌ $CH_3-CH_2-CHNH_2-COOH$ (α-aminobutyric acid)

alanine ⟶ pyruvic acid

+ $CH_3-CO-COOH$ pyruvic acid

α,β-dihydroxy-isovaleric acid: $(CH_3)(CH_3)COH-CHOH-COOH$

α,β-dihydroxy-β-methyl-glutaric acid: $(CH_3)(CH_2-COOH)COH-CHOH-COOH$

$(CH_3)(CH_3)CH-CH_2-CO-COOH$ α-ketoisocaproic acid ⟵ ($-CO_2$, $+C_2$) $(CH_3)(CH_3)CH-CO-COOH$ α-ketoisovaleric acid

$(CH_3)(CH_2-CH_3)CH-CO-COOH$ α-keto-β-methylvaleric acid

⟵ transaminase ⟶

$(CH_3)(CH_3)CH-CH_2-CHNH_2-COOH$ leucine

$(CH_3)(CH_3)CH-CHNH_2-COOH$ valine

$(CH_3)(CH_2-CH_3)CH-CHNH_2-COOH$ isoleucine

FIG. 68—Biosynthesis of leucine, isoleucine and valine.

In addition, the synthesis of isoleucine and valine is blocked by the absence of a single transaminase.

The sum total of facts indicates that α-ketoisovaleric acid yields leucine by decarboxylation and condensation with a C_2 fragment.

For the case of isoleucine and valine, the mode of biosynthesis is indicated in Fig. 68.

(*q*) *Biosynthesis of Amino Acids Derived from Benzene (Tyrosine, Phenylalanine, Tryptophan)*

The existence of mutants of *E. coli* and *Aerobacter aerogenes* requiring for their growth the three amino acids containing the benzene ring, has greatly aided the elucidation of the biosynthesis of these compounds. These mutants require not only a mixture of the three benzenoid amino acids, but also for the most part they require *p*-aminobenzoate, *p*-hydroxybenzoate or a sixth factor, still unidentified. A large number of observations have been made on mutants requiring the benzenoid amino acids — determination of the substances accumulating in each case, study of competition between compounds, etc. Further, at the enzyme level, comparative studies have been carried out on vegetable tissues and micro-organisms, which synthesize the benzene ring and on animal tissues which do not. The cofactors of each enzyme, etc., have also been studied. All these investigations lead to the conclusion that the intermediates in the synthesis of the benzene ring are 5-dehydroquinic acid, 5-dehydroshikimic acid and shikimic acid. What is the precursor of 5-dehydroquinic acid? On this point, so far, the mutants have told us nothing. But a certain amount of information has been provided by the use of isotopes and from enzyme studies. This work shows that the transformation of glucose into the benzene ring of tyrosine or phenylalanine does not operate through the Krebs cycle. With the aid of labelled glucose, using a mutant accumulating shikimic acid, it has been possible to show that the carboxyl of this acid is derived from C-3 and C-4 of glucose, the C-1 from C-2 and C-5 of glucose and C-2 of shikimic acid from C-1 and C-6 of glucose. Hence the C-1—C-2—carboxyl portion of shikimic acid comes from a degradation product of glucose, the four other carbon atoms being of a more complex origin. Sedoheptulose-1, 7-diphosphate is an excellent precursor of shikimic acid and there are good reasons to favour the theory which puts sedoheptulose as an intermediate in the synthesis of the benzenoid amino acids.

The terminal stage of the synthesis has had some light cast upon it by the results of enzyme studies. It has been shown that prephenic acid is an intermediate in the path from phenylalanine to tyrosine. Moreover, phenylpyruvic acid also lies along the pathway of phenylalanine synthesis.

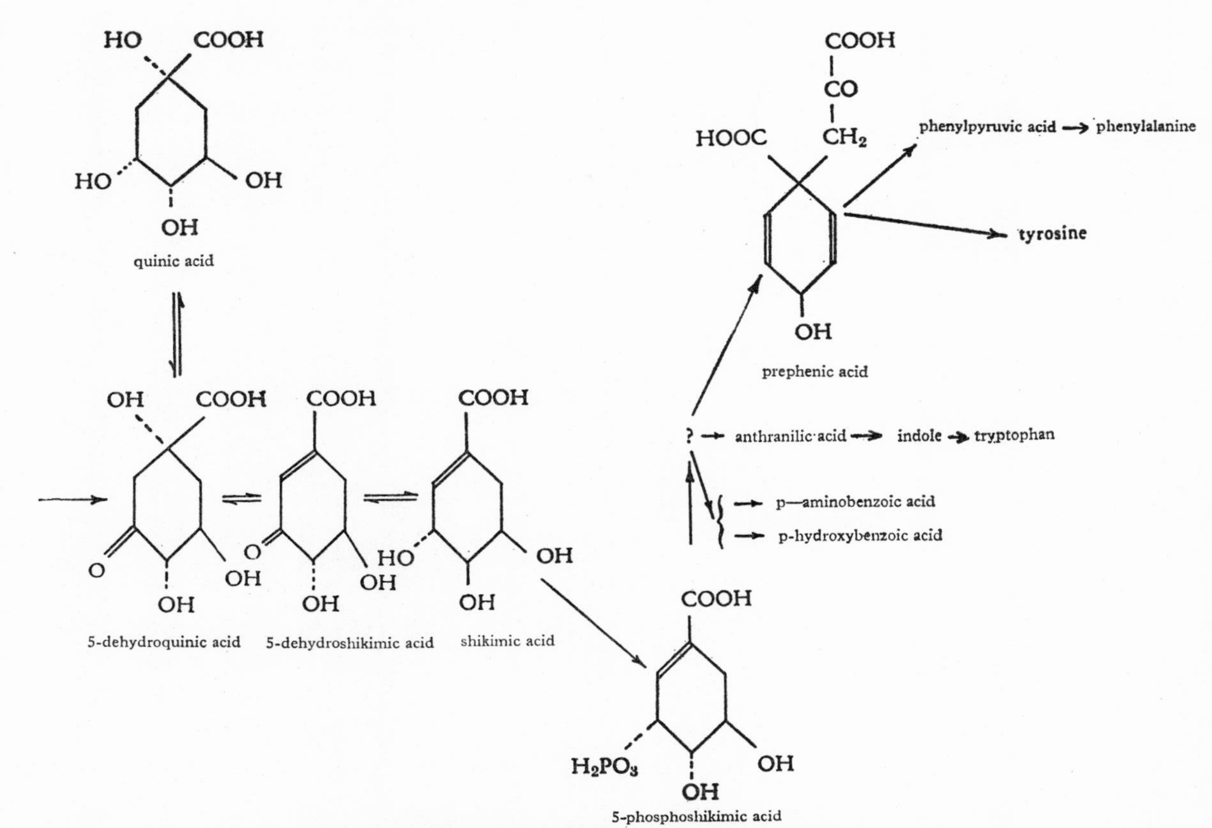

FIG. 69 (Davis)—Biosynthesis of the aromatic amino acids.

When we come to tryptophan, which lies after shikimic acid, anthranilic acid and indole are found to be intermediates in the synthesis. The condensation of indole with serine to give tryptophan is brought about by the action of a specific enzyme, indole-ligase or tryptophan desmolase, whose coenzyme is pyridoxal phosphate (this enzyme is not to be confused with tryptophanase which splits tryptophan into indole and *pyruvic acid*).

In addition to the pathway just outlined, tryptophan can result from the transamination of indole-pyruvic acid, but it seems unlikely that this reaction makes any important contribution to the biosynthesis. A tryptophan–kynurenine–anthranilate–indole–tryptophan cycle has also been proposed i.e. the reverse of the catabolic pathway described in Fig. 58. However this sequence of reactions is only traversed if an excess of tryptophan is present and its function appears to be purely degradative.

(*r*) *Biosynthesis of Histidine and the Imidazole Ring*

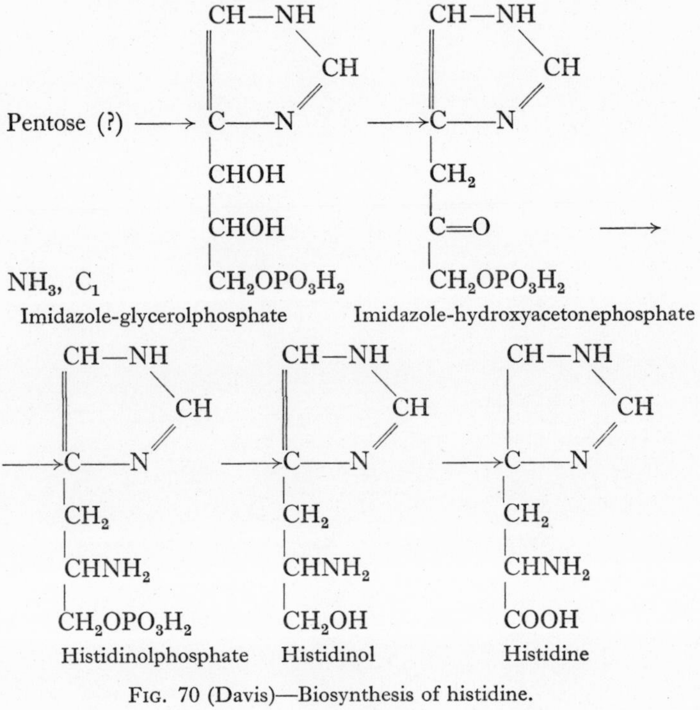

CH—NH CH—NH
CH CH
Pentose (?) ⟶ C—N ⟶ C—N
CHOH CH_2
CHOH C=O ⟶
NH_3, C_1 $CH_2OPO_3H_2$ $CH_2OPO_3H_2$
Imidazole-glycerolphosphate Imidazole-hydroxyacetonephosphate

CH—NH CH—NH CH—NH
CH CH CH
⟶ C—N ⟶ C—N ⟶ C—N
CH_2 CH_2 CH_2
$CHNH_2$ $CHNH_2$ $CHNH_2$
$CH_2OPO_3H_2$ CH_2OH COOH
Histidinolphosphate Histidinol Histidine

FIG. 70 (Davis)—Biosynthesis of histidine.

Mutants of *E. coli* which are auxotrophic for histidine accumulate L-histidinol, the corresponding aminoalcohol. Mutants of *Neurospora* have been discovered since, which accumulate not only histidinol but also imidazole-glycerol, imidazole-hydroxy-acetone and their derivatives phosphorylated in the terminal position of the side chain. It is these phosphorylated derivatives and free histidinol that are intermediates in the synthesis whose terminal operation, the conversion of histidinol to histidine, is catalysed by a DPN-containing enzyme which has been isolated from *E. coli.* When we come to the imidazole ring itself, experiments with sotopes have shown that C-2 is derived from "formate".

(*s*) *Biosynthesis of Lysine*

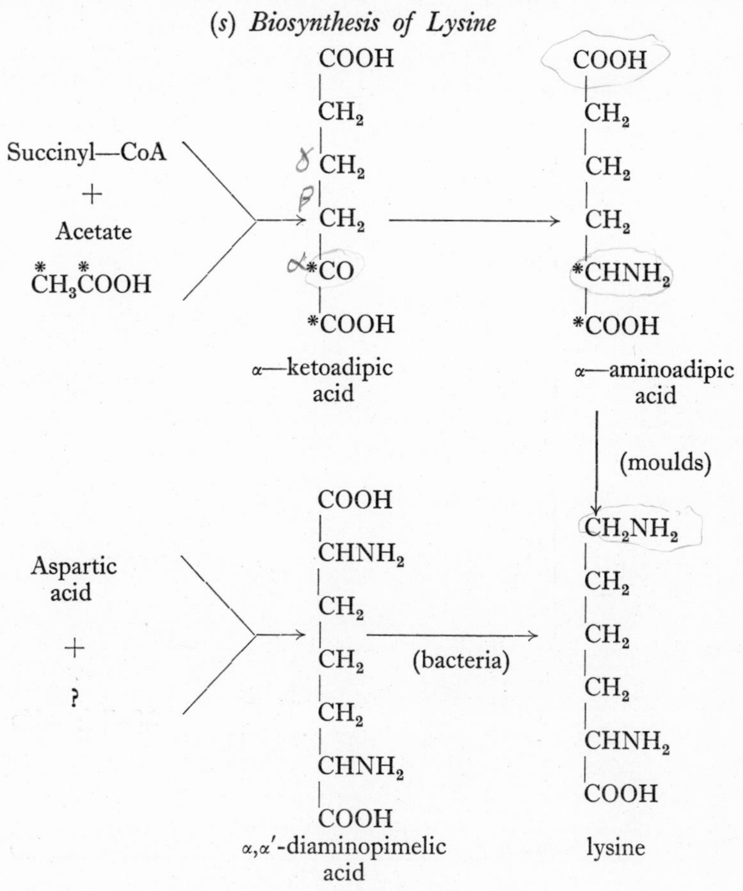

FIG. 71 (Davis)—Biosynthesis of lysine.

The biosynthesis of lysine forms an exception to the general run of biosynthetic processes we have so far considered and which we have been able to assume, at least in general outline, to be the same in all cells. Here the comparative biochemist has found a field of study at the level of a biosynthetic mechanism. The biosynthesis of lysine, in fact, differs in moulds and in bacteria. In the former, the starting materials are acetate and succinyl-CoA formed during the Krebs cycle. The intermediate stages are α-ketoadipic acid and α-aminoadipic acid (which have been found in the degradative pathway of lysine in the rat). In bacteria, one of the starting materials is aspartic acid and α,α′-diaminopimelic acid is an intermediate.

B. Biosynthesis of Compounds Containing Ester, Oside or Peptide Bonds

(a) *Biosynthesis of Complex Lipids*

This subject has been extensively studied in the case of the lecithins (phosphatidylcholines) and it has been shown that, in the presence of certain enzymes of different specificity, the same mechanism is responsible for the synthesis of cephalins (phosphatidylethanolamines). As with the formation of glycerides, the starting point is a phosphatidic acid. The

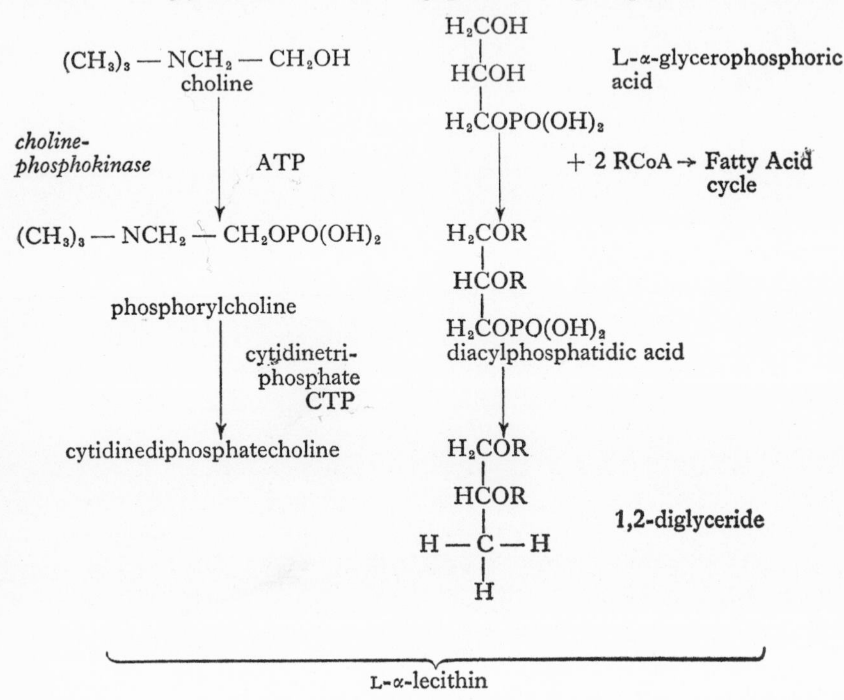

Fig. 72—Biosynthesis of a lecithin.

knowledge that we possess today about the biosynthesis of complex lipids stems from observations made on the incorporation of ^{32}P and ^{14}C-labelled phosphorylcholine into the lecithin fraction of isolated liver mitochondria. This incorporation is activated by CoA and ATP, and inhibited by metal ions, in particular by Ca^{++}. The incorporation requires a nucleotide as a cofactor, cytidine-triphosphate. The enzyme is phosphorylcytidyl-transferase and catalyses the combination of cytidine triphosphate with phosphorylcholine to form cytidine-diphosphate-choline which is the activated form of phosphorylcholine. A molecule of cytidine monophosphate is released in this reaction, and in the presence of ATP is reconverted to cytidine triphosphate. The phosphorylcholine itself is formed by a direct phosphorylation of choline by ATP in the presence of the specific enzyme choline-phosphokinase. But what is the acceptor of the activated phosphorylcholine? The acceptor is a 1, 2-diglyceride, thus explaining why natural lecithins are all of the α-type.

The 1, 2-diglyceride arises by a dephosphorylation of a diacyl-phosphatidic acid (a glycerophosphatide without the base) in the presence of a specific phosphatase. The phosphatidic acids which are intermediates in the biosynthesis of lecithins are the result of a combination, in the presence of ATP and a specific enzyme, of α-glycerophosphoric acid with two molecules of fatty acid activated by CoA. These compounds of aliphatic acids and CoA are provided by the fatty acid cycle functioning in the direction of biosynthesis. The enzyme catalysing acyl transfer has a special specificity for the acyl-CoA derivatives of the C_{16} and C_{18} acids.
Example:

palmityl-CoA + α-glycerophosphate
→ monopalmitylphosphatidic acid + CoA

palmityl-CoA monopalmitylphosphatic acid
→ dipalmitylphosphatidic acid + CoA

(*b*) *Biosynthesis of Glycerides*

It has long been recognized that the biosynthesis of glycerides occurs via the intermediate formation of complex lipids.

The 1, 2-diglycerides acting as intermediates in lecithin biosynthesis can also give triglycerides by the operation of an enzyme system present in liver.

The following reaction has been observed *in vitro* in the presence of an enzyme present in liver:

1, 2-diglyceride + palmityl-S-CoA → triglyceride + CoA-SH

This establishes an intimate relationship between the biosynthesis of complex lipids and that of ternary lipids, in the first case, the reaction being between a 1, 2-diglyceride and cytidinediphosphatecholine and in the second case between the 1, 2-diglyceride and a coenzyme A activated fatty acid.

(*c*) *Biosynthesis of Pentose Phosphates*

As we have seen, D-ribose-5-phosphate is formed from G—6—P in the hexosemonophosphate shunt.

Another mode of formation is the condensation of C_2 and C_3 fragments to form phosphoric esters of the pentoses and desoxypentoses, particularly of desoxyribose.

This reaction

$$\text{glyceraldehyde-3-P} + \text{acetaldehyde} \rightleftharpoons \text{desoxyribose-5-P}$$

is a reversible aldol condensation, catalysed by desoxyribose-phosphate aldolase. This enzyme has been prepared from *E. coli* and numerous animal tissues; the desoxyribose-5-P formed in the reaction is incorporated into nucleosides.

As far as the metabolism of the pentose phosphates is concerned, the principal reactions are those of transaldolization and transketolization.

A transketolase has been isolated from plant tissues and from animal tissues, it catalyses the following reaction :

$$\text{ribulose-5-P} + \text{ribose-5-P} \rightleftharpoons \text{sedoheptulose -7-P} + \text{glyceraldehyde-3-P}$$

The enzyme is of low specificity and it also acts on ribulose-5-P, sedoheptulose-7-P, L-erythrulose, hydroxypyruvate and fructose-6-P. A rupture of the ketol bond occurs and the "active glycolaldehyde" formed is condensed with an acceptor aldehyde. When the acceptor is glyceraldehyde 3-P, ribulose-5-P is formed.

(*d*) *Biosynthesis of Oside Linkages*

Although, theoretically, the enzymes catalysing the hydrolysis of oside linkages should be capable of catalysing the reverse reaction of synthesis, this is not considered to occur in practice.

In the case of sucrose, for example, the action of invertase causes the reaction to go almost to completion from left to right. One of the substances participating in the reaction, water, being present in overwhelming concentration, the hydrolysis of sucrose is in practice irreversible.

The synthesis of the osides operates, in fact, through their phosphorylated derivatives.

In plants, sucrose results from the condensation and the simultaneous dephosphorylation of a molecule of phosphorylated glucose and a molecule of phosphorylated fructose, in the presence of sucrose phosphorylase. A system exists, and has been isolated from various bacteria, which, in the presence of G—1—P and D-fructose, condenses these two molecules to form sucrose with the elimination of phosphoric acid. This sucrose phosphorylase can combine glucose with, say, an aldose such as L-arabinose with formation of a 1–3 oside linkage. Its specificity for the second half of the molecule is hence seen to be of a low order. On the other hand, the sucrose phosphorylase can utilize other sources than G—1—P as a donor of glucose for the formation of sucrose. It is therefore also a *transglucosidase* capable of transferring glucose derived from various donors, to a diversity of acceptors.

(*e*) *Biosynthesis of Purine Nucleotides*

The biosynthesis of these nucleotides, and consequently, of the purine ring, begins with the formation of 5′-phosphoribosyl-1′-pyrophosphate (phosphoribosylpyrophosphate, PRPP) which is the activated pentose required in purine biosynthesis. Figure 73 shows the various ways in which PRPP can be formed.

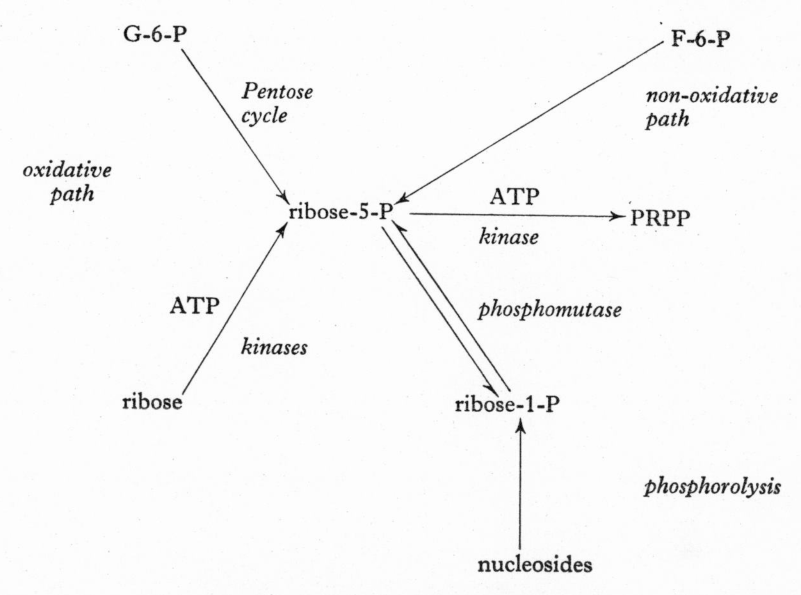

FIG. 73—Pathways of PRPP formation.

Starting with PRPP, in the presence of glutamine, 5′-phophoribosylamine is formed. Addition of glycine and then of formate to the molecule leads to formylglycinaminoribotide. The addition of CO_2 and the amino group of aspartate gives the ribotide of aminoimidazolecarboxamide, then an addition of a C_1 fragment followed by closing of the ring gives inosinic acid from which can be derived xanthosine-5′-phosphate by oxidation and guanosine-5′-phosphate by oxidation and amination (Fig. 58).

(*f*) *Biosynthesis of Pyrimidine Nucleotides*

The carbon in the 1-position and the nitrogen in the 2-position of the pyrimidine ring are derived from NH_3 and CO_2 which react in the presence of ATP to form carbamyl phosphate.

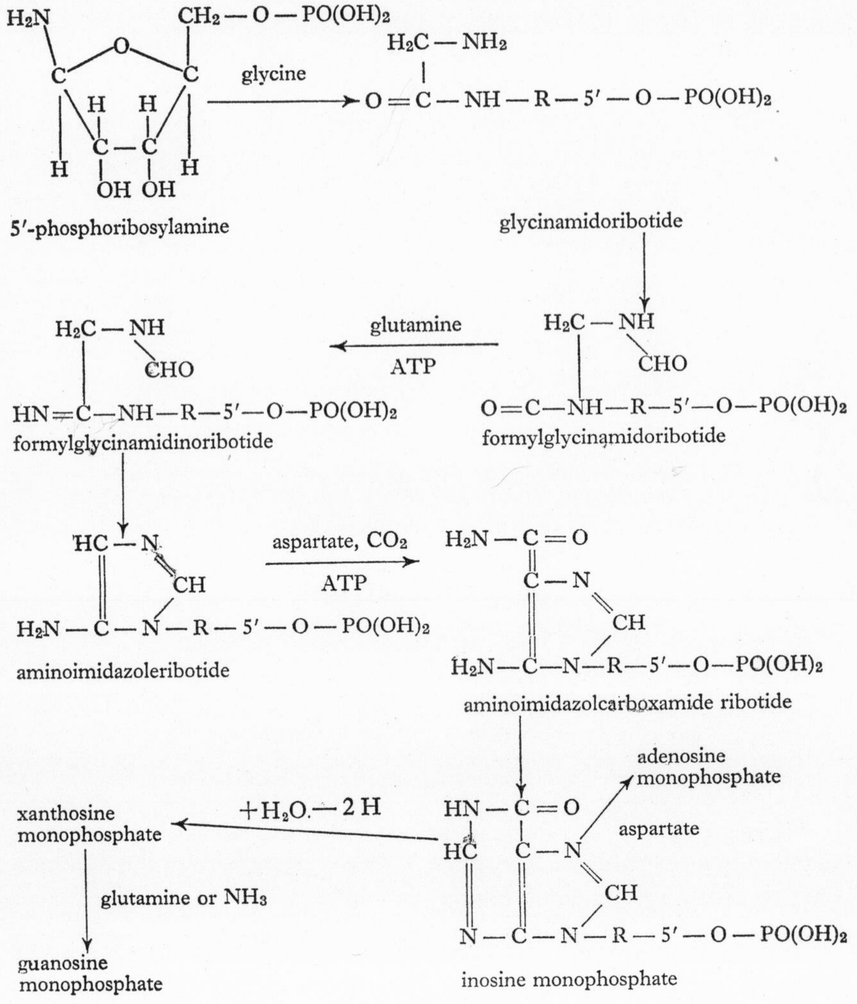

H_2N $CH_2—O—PO(OH)_2$

O

C C

H H

C—C

H H

OH OH

5′-phosphoribosylamine

glycine →

$H_2C—NH_2$

|

$O=C—NH—R—5'—O—PO(OH)_2$

glycinamidoribotide

↓

$H_2C—NH$

CHO

$O=C—NH—R—5'—O—PO(OH)_2$

formylglycinamidoribotide

glutamine

← ATP

$H_2C—NH$

CHO

$HN=C—NH—R—5'—O—PO(OH)_2$

formylglycinamidinoribotide

↓

HC—N

CH

$H_2N—C—N—R—5'—O—PO(OH)_2$

aminoimidazoleribotide

aspartate, CO_2

→ ATP

$H_2N—C=O$

C—N

CH

$H_2N—C—N—R—5'—O—PO(OH)_2$

aminoimidazolcarboxamide ribotide

↓

adenosine monophosphate

aspartate

HN—C=O

HC C—N

CH

$N—C—N—R—5'—O—PO(OH)_2$

inosine monophosphate

$+H_2O—2\,H$ →

xanthosine monophosphate

↓ glutamine or NH_3

guanosine monophosphate

Fig. 74.

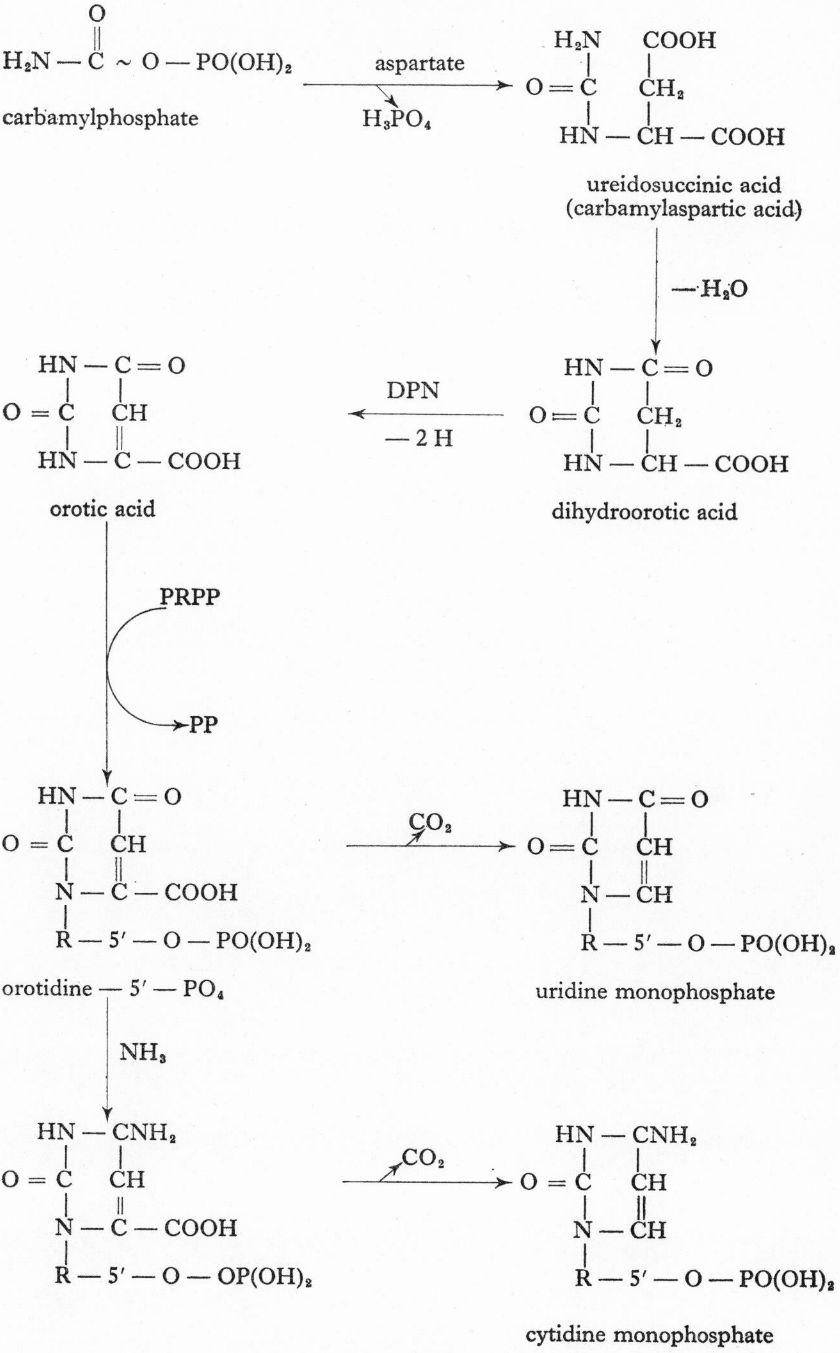

$$H_2N-\overset{O}{\overset{\|}{C}}\sim O-PO(OH)_2 \xrightarrow[H_3PO_4]{\text{aspartate}} \begin{array}{c} H_2N \quad COOH \\ | \qquad\ | \\ O=C \quad CH_2 \\ | \qquad\ | \\ HN-CH-COOH \end{array}$$

carbamylphosphate

ureidosuccinic acid
(carbamylaspartic acid)

$$\downarrow -H_2O$$

$$\begin{array}{c} HN-C=O \\ | \qquad | \\ O=C \quad CH \\ | \qquad \| \\ HN-C-COOH \end{array} \xleftarrow[-2H]{DPN} \begin{array}{c} HN-C=O \\ | \qquad | \\ O=C \quad CH_2 \\ | \qquad | \\ HN-CH-COOH \end{array}$$

orotic acid

dihydroorotic acid

$$\downarrow PRPP \rightarrow PP$$

$$\begin{array}{c} HN-C=O \\ | \qquad | \\ O=C \quad CH \\ | \qquad \| \\ N-C-COOH \\ | \\ R-5'-O-PO(OH)_2 \end{array} \xrightarrow{CO_2} \begin{array}{c} HN-C=O \\ | \qquad | \\ O=C \quad CH \\ | \qquad \| \\ N-CH \\ | \\ R-5'-O-PO(OH)_2 \end{array}$$

orotidine — 5′ — PO_4

uridine monophosphate

$$\downarrow NH_3$$

$$\begin{array}{c} HN-CNH_2 \\ | \qquad | \\ O=C \quad CH \\ | \qquad \| \\ N-C-COOH \\ | \\ R-5'-O-OP(OH)_2 \end{array} \xrightarrow{CO_2} \begin{array}{c} HN-CNH_2 \\ | \qquad | \\ O=C \quad CH \\ | \qquad \| \\ N-CH \\ | \\ R-5'-O-PO(OH)_2 \end{array}$$

cytidine monophosphate

Fig. 75.

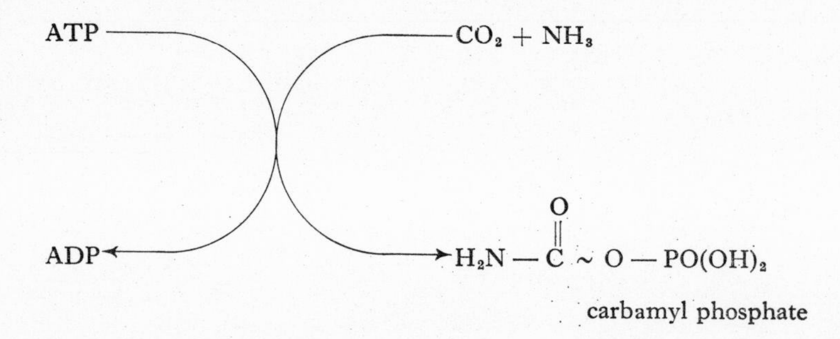

The carbamyl phosphate is condensed with a molecule of aspartate giving ureidosuccinic acid, from which orotic acid is formed by cyclization and oxidation. In the presence of PRPP and a pyrophosphorylase this acid forms a ribotide and decarboxylation yields uridine monophosphate. The decarboxylation of the product of amination of orotidine phosphate gives cytidine monophosphate (Fig. 75). It can be seen that the pentose intermediate in pyrimidine nucleotide biosynthesis is PRPP, the same as for purine nucleotide biosynthesis.

(*g*) *Biosynthesis of Nucleoside Diphosphates and Triphosphates*

This biosynthesis operates through the purine and pyrimidine mononucleotides as follows:

nucleoside-P + *nucleoside-PPP* ⇌ nucleoside-PP + *nucleoside-PP*

2 nucleoside-PP ⇌ nucleoside-P + nucleoside-PPP

2 *nucleoside-PP* ⇌ *nucleoside-P* + *nucleoside-PPP*

(nucleoside and *nucleoside* designating nucleosides differing in the nature of the base).

(*h*) *Biosynthesis of Dinucleotides*

1. *DPN and TPN*

Nicotinamide can be formed by animal cells from tryptophan but is usually present in the diet. Starting from ribose-1-phosphate and niacin (nicotinamide), DPN is probably synthesized as shown in Fig. 76. TPN results from the phosphorylation of DPN in the presence of a specific phosphokinase. TPN can be converted to DPN by a phosphatase.

2. *FAD*

Figure 77 depicts the formation of FMN, in the presence of a phosphokinase, from ATP and riboflavin, the latter a substance which is not synthesized by the cells of the body and consequently must be obtained from the diet. FMN is converted to FAD by stages analogous to those governing the biosynthesis of DPN.

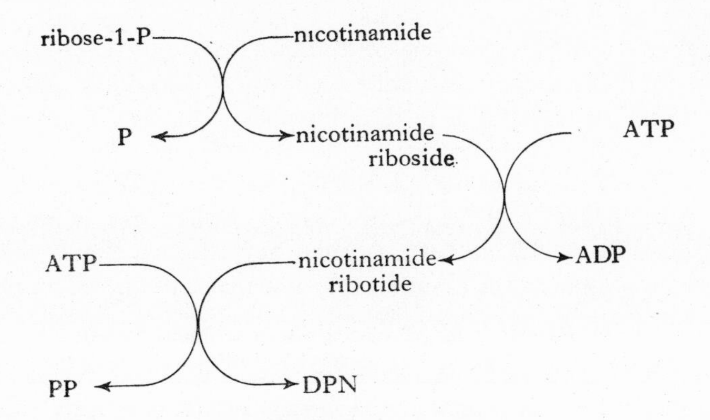

FIG. 76—Biosynthesis of DPN.

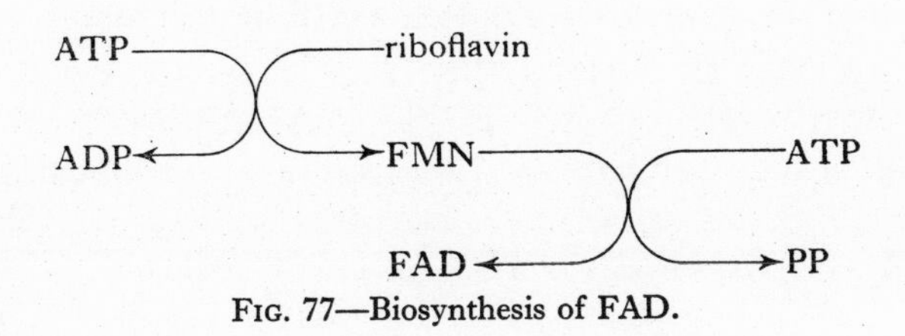

FIG. 77—Biosynthesis of FAD.

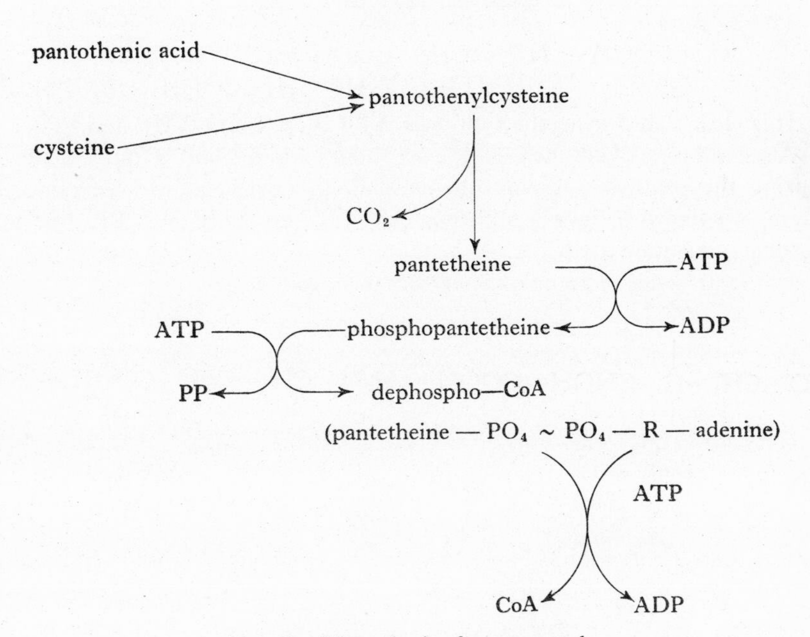

FIG. 78—Biosynthesis of coenzyme. A

3. *Coezyme A*

Pantothenic acid is not synthesized by the body and therefore must be obtained from the diet. It is condensed with a molecule of cysteine and the resulting pseudopeptide is decarboxylated to form a compound of pantothenic acid and thioethanolamine, pantetheine. The latter, in the presence of ATP and a phosphokinase, becomes phosphopantatheine, which, in the presence of ATP and a pyrophosphorylase, is converted to dephospho-CoA, which, in turn, is phosphorylated on the 3′ position of ribose in the presence of ATP and a phosphokinase to form CoA (Fig. 78).

(*i*) *Biosynthesis of Peptide and Amide Bonds*

In animals hippuric acid is formed from benzoic acid and glycine which are joined together by a secondary amide linkage similar to a peptide link. The reaction has been well studied, ATP is required as an energy-donor and the benzoic acid must be activated by being first combined with coenzyme A.

The stages of the synthesis are as follows: (**E** = enzyme)

(1) $\mathbf{E} + \text{ATP} \rightleftharpoons \mathbf{E}\text{—AMP} + \text{PP}$

(2) $\mathbf{E}\text{—AMP} + \text{HS—CoA} \rightleftharpoons \mathbf{E}\text{—S—CoA—AMP}$

(3) $\mathbf{E}\text{—J—CoA} + \text{HOOC—}C_6H_5 \rightleftharpoons \text{CoA—S—OC—}C_6H_5 + \mathbf{E} + H_2O$

(4) $\text{CoA—S—OC—}C_6H_5 + H_2N\text{—}CH_2\text{—COOH} \rightleftharpoons C_6H_5\text{—CONH—}CH_2\text{—COOH} + \text{CoA—SH}$

(1+2+3+4)

$$C_6H_5COOH + H_2N\text{—}CH_2\text{—COOH} + \text{ATP} \rightleftharpoons C_6H_5\text{—CONH—}CH_2\text{—COOH} + \text{AMP} + \text{PP}$$

It is clear that during the synthesis ATP is split into AMP and PP.

A second type of synthesis of the secondary amide bond is found to occur during the synthesis of pantothenic acid, a constituent of coenzyme A. Here, we likewise have a splitting of ATP into AMP and PP, but not through activation by CoA.

In the presence of an enzyme extract of *E. coli* we get

$$\underset{\text{pantoic acid}}{HO\text{—}CH_2\text{—}\overset{CH_3}{\underset{CH_3}{\overset{|}{\underset{|}{C}}}}\text{—CHOH—COOH}} + \underset{\beta\text{-alanine}}{H_2N\text{—}CH_2\text{—}CH_2\text{—COOH}} + \textbf{ATP}$$

$$\rightarrow \underset{\text{pantothenic acid}}{HO\text{—}CH_2\text{—}\overset{CH_3}{\underset{CH_3}{\overset{|}{\underset{|}{C}}}}\text{—CHOH—CONH—}CH_2\text{—}CH_2\text{—COOH}} + \text{AMP} + \textbf{PP}$$

In the biosynthesis of glutamine from glutamate and ammonia it is the γ-carboxyl of glutamic acid which is activated, and the cleavage of ATP to provide the 2500–4000 calories for formation of the amide bond takes place so that ADP and P are formed rather than AMP and PP. Glutamic acid can also form amide bonds with hydroxylamine, hydrazine or methylamine.

The enzyme system responsible for the synthesis catalyses the following series of reactions (**E** = enzyme):

$$(1) \qquad \mathbf{E} + \mathrm{ATP} + \mathrm{Glu} \rightleftharpoons \mathbf{E}\begin{smallmatrix}\diagup \mathrm{ATP} \\ \diagdown \mathrm{Glu}\end{smallmatrix}$$

$$(2) \qquad \mathbf{E}\begin{smallmatrix}\diagup \mathrm{ATP} \\ \diagdown \mathrm{Glu}\end{smallmatrix} + NH_3 \underset{Mn^{++}}{\overset{Mg^{++}}{\rightleftharpoons}} \mathrm{Glu{-}NH_2} + \mathrm{ADP} + \mathrm{P} + \mathbf{E}$$

According to Bloch and co-workers, the enzymatic synthesis of glutathione, requires only ATP

$$\mathbf{E} + \mathrm{ATP} \rightleftharpoons \mathbf{E}\mathrm{{-}P} + \mathrm{ADP}$$

$$\mathbf{E}\mathrm{{-}P} + \mathrm{Glu} \rightleftharpoons \mathbf{E}\mathrm{{-}Glu} + \mathrm{P}$$

$$\mathbf{E}\mathrm{{-}Glu} + \mathrm{Cys} \rightleftharpoons \mathbf{E} + \mathrm{Glu{-}Cys}$$

$$\mathbf{E}\mathrm{{-}P} + \mathrm{Glu{-}Cys} \rightleftharpoons \mathbf{E}\mathrm{{-}Glu{-}Cys} + \mathrm{P}$$

$$\mathbf{E}\mathrm{{-}Glu{-}Cys} + \mathrm{Gly} \rightleftharpoons \mathrm{Glu{-}Cys{-}Gly} + \mathbf{E}$$

In these four cases of formation of amide or peptide bonds, it is the carboxyl group which is activated at the expense of one or the other of the pyrophosphate linkages of ATP. The syntheses differ from each other in the form of the activated carboxyl: bound to CoA, bound directly to the enzyme or to the phosphorylated enzyme. But in no case has the activated carboxyl itself been phosphorylated.

C. Biosynthesis of Macromolecules

(a) *Polysaccharides*

1. *Synthesis of Glycogen*

As already stated, glycogen is a branched polymer made up of D-glucose units. Four enzymes are necessary for the degradation of glycogen to glucose, and for the synthesis of glycogen from glucose. Two of these enzymes can act equally well in either direction, but the other two are characteristic of the particular direction in which the reaction is taking place; this is shown in Fig. 79.

The first stage of the synthesis is phosphorylation by ATP, hexokinase being the catalyst. It is here that a major expenditure of energy occurs; a pyrophosphate bond (12,000 calories) forms a glucose-6-phosphate bond (3000 cal) and by means of this reaction, which in practice is irreversible, the glucose molecule is activated and prepared for a variety of metabolic sequels. In the case we are considering, under the influence of phosphoglucomutase an equilibrium is established between G—6—P and G—1—P, in fact this equilibrium is part of the *steady state* in the cell and varies from one cell to another as the *steady state* varies.

In the third stage, two enzymes act simultaneously, phosphorylase and the branching enzyme. The glucose portion of a molecule of glucose-1-phosphate is added to the terminal glucose residue of a chain, with loss of phosphate. The phosphate on C_1 is exchanged for a glucoside linkage with the fourth carbon atom of the terminal glucose residue, with little change in free energy. In this synthesis the two substrates therefore are glycogen

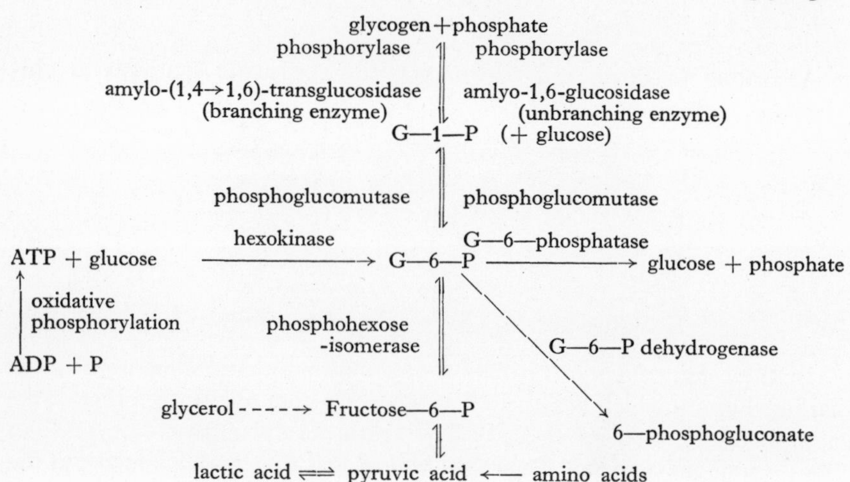

FIG. 79 (G. Cori)—Synthesis and degradation of glycogen in the liver.

and glucose-1-phosphate. It is the ratio of the concentrations of inorganic phosphate and glucose-1-phosphate which determines the direction of the reaction. Since, at pH 7·0, the equilibrium ratio for the reversible reaction is 3·2, the synthesis of glycogen will occur if there is more than one molecule of glucose-1-phosphate for every three molecules of inorganic phosphate. Hence factors tending to lower the concentration of inorganic phosphate will tend to favour synthesis taking place. When, in the branched structure of the glycogen macromolecule, a side-chain has been formed containing eight glucose units, then a new enzyme comes into play: this is the branching enzyme. It is a transglucosidase, amylo-1, 4 → 1,6-transglucosidase, which converts a 1–4 linkage into a 1–6 linkage thus producing a fork in the chain.

We see that whereas the *concentration* of glycogen in a cell can be influenced by the requisite enzymes, by hormones and by other possible regulators, the *structure* of the glycogen molecule depends on the relation between the respective activities of phosphorylase, the branching enzyme and the unbranching enzyme.

2. *Synthesis of amylopectin*

The so-called "Q-enzyme" is a transglucosidase which converts one in every twenty 1–4 linkages of amylose into 1–6 linkages to form a branched chain. The enzyme only acts when at least forty-two glucose residues have been united to form amylose. The formation reaction is the following:

$$\alpha\text{-D-glucose-1-phosphate} \rightleftharpoons \text{amylose} \rightarrow \text{amylopectin}$$

Like the branching enzyme, the "Q-enzyme" acts like a transglucosidase capable of forming 1–6 bonds.

3. *Synthesis of β linkages of polysaccharides*

Fitting and Doudoroff (1952) have described an enzyme which in the course of the synthesis of a glycoside linkage causes inversion of the type of bond.

$$\alpha\text{-D-glucosyl-D-glucose} + \text{P} \rightleftharpoons \beta\text{-D-glucose-1-P} + \text{D-glucose}$$

This demonstrates the possibility of the formation of complex polysaccharides containing β-linkages by the action of enzymes causing transglucosidation.

(*b*) *Proteins*

By analogy with what is observed when amide bonds are synthesized in peptides or amides, Borsook has suggested that during the synthesis of proteins from free amino acids, it is the carboxyl of one of the amino acids which is activated by utilization of a pyrophosphate linkage, the amino group of the other amino acid not needing to be activated before formation of the peptide bond. There are many arguments in favour of the idea that proteins are synthesized from free amino acids. The activated amino acids are transported on to a "template" where they arrange themselves in a definite order. The peptide linkages are established for the price of the energy of the pyrophosphate bonds and the molecule thus formed is detached from the template.

This mechanism implies the activation, in the presence of ATP, of the free carboxyl group of the amino acids which go to form the new protein molecule. This idea is supported by a large number of experimental observations. The activation of the carboxyl group is brought about by specific enzyme for a particular amino acid, which first attaches it to AMP. The resulting amino acid-AMP-anhydride is then joined to a short soluble piece of an RNA chain, the whole taking place on a complementary sequence of an RNA template.

1. *The intracellular pool of amino acids*

The existence of an intracellular pool of amino acids not combined as protein, either free or in the form of amides, etc., is now generally admitted. In vertebrate tissues, the amounts of these non-protein amino acids, acting as a source for protein synthesis, are small. On the other hand they are much greater in the tissues of such animals as the marine crustaceans, and in plant cells, in yeast cells, or in the cells of certain Gram-positive bacteria.

The factors regulating the total amount and composition (which in animals appears to be specific for each tissue of a particular species or, for a given tissue, specific for each species) of the intracellular pool of amino acids, are of special interest. The composition of the pool of non-protein amino acids differs from the overall composition of the proteins in the cell which contain it, and this has been demonstrated in widely different cases, for example in animal cells and in infusoria.

A particularly detailed study of the pool of non-protein amino acids in yeast was carried out in Spiegelmann's laboratory and has given some highly interesting results. It is possible to modify the composition and the amount of the intracellular pool by various changes in the culture medium. If the medium contains no nitrogen and contains glucose, the intracellular pool in the yeast decreases in amount and this decrease affects all the constituents. If the cells are then placed in a medium containing both glucose and nitrogen the pool is replenished, but in a manner which differs according to the nature of the source of nitrogen. If the nitrogen is provided by a casein hydrolysate the pool replenishes all its constituents. If ammonium chloride is the source the restoration is much slower and certain amino acids such as methionine, threonine, proline, lysine and histidine, only return to their former concentration after some considerable time. On the other hand, irradiation with ultraviolet light increases the amount of the pool in the yeast cell, and a considerable number of observations seem to indicate that in yeast cells there is an internal mechanism for replenishment of the pool which depends upon the degradation of a labile protein compound.

In *Staphylococcus aureus*, which has been studied from this aspect by Gale, the synthesis of a large number of amino acids is not possible and they must be obtained from outside the cell. If the medium is rich in amino acids, they accumulate in the cell during the period of growth and the intracellular pool is increased. However, if protein synthesis is rapid and normal, the amino acids do not accumulate.

2. *The template*

A large number of experimental facts and a series of indirect experiments have led Brachet and Caspersson, independently of each other, to the conclusion that nucleic acids are involved in protein synthesis. The concentration of RNA in the cell is approximately proportional to the growth of *Bac. lactic aerogenes*, thus leading Caldwell to consider RNA as being the template itself. Jeener has shown for his part that during experimental modifications of the volumes of the nucleus and the cytoplasm of *Thermobacterium acidophilus* protein synthesis was quantitatively related to the level of RNA. Finally, direct experiments have shown that in various cells or fragments of cells, treatment with ribonuclease suppresses protein synthesis.

HbA.........Val—His—Leu—Thr—Pro—*Glu*—Glu—Lys
HbS.........Val—His—Leu—Thr—Pro—*Val*—Glu—Lys
HbC.........Val—His—Leu—Thr—Pro—*Lys*—Glu—Lys
HbG.........Val—His—Leu—Thr—Pro—Glu—*Gly*—Lys

Fig. 80. (Perutz). Sequence of amino acid residues in a small segment of one of the polypeptide chain of haemoglobin.

These are the facts which point to RNA being the template on which the synthesis of proteins takes place. Another confirmation has been brought by experiments showing that the isolated nucleic acid of tobacco mosaic virus can introduce the disease into a leaf cell as well as the whole nucleoprotein of the virus.

3. *The synthetic process*

It is now a well established fact that the system of activation of the different amino acids in the presence of the specific enzyme for each of them, is the same in all cases of protein synthesis, and that the characteristic structure of the protein synthetized is due to the structure of the RNA template. This template is located in the cytoplasm. It is probably synthetized in the nucleus where the coded message for the synthesis of a particular protein is transferred from a section (or gene) of a long DNA macromolecule to a corresponding section of RNA. Each amino acid is brought to the template by a specific carrier. Crick has suggested that this carrier is a short length of RNA chain with a specific sequence of bases coding for the particular amino acid. It has been shown that each specific enzyme catalyzing the activation of a particular amino acid in the presence of ATP, with the formation of an amino acid-AMP-anhydride, also catalyzes the fixation of this compound on a short, soluble piece of RNA chain. This carrier brings the amino acid on to the complementary sequence of the template. By this mechanism, the long code represented by numerous genes on a DNA chain, copied on RNA chains, controls the biosynthesis of a number of proteins, among which are numerous enzymes controlling the specific metabolism of the cell.

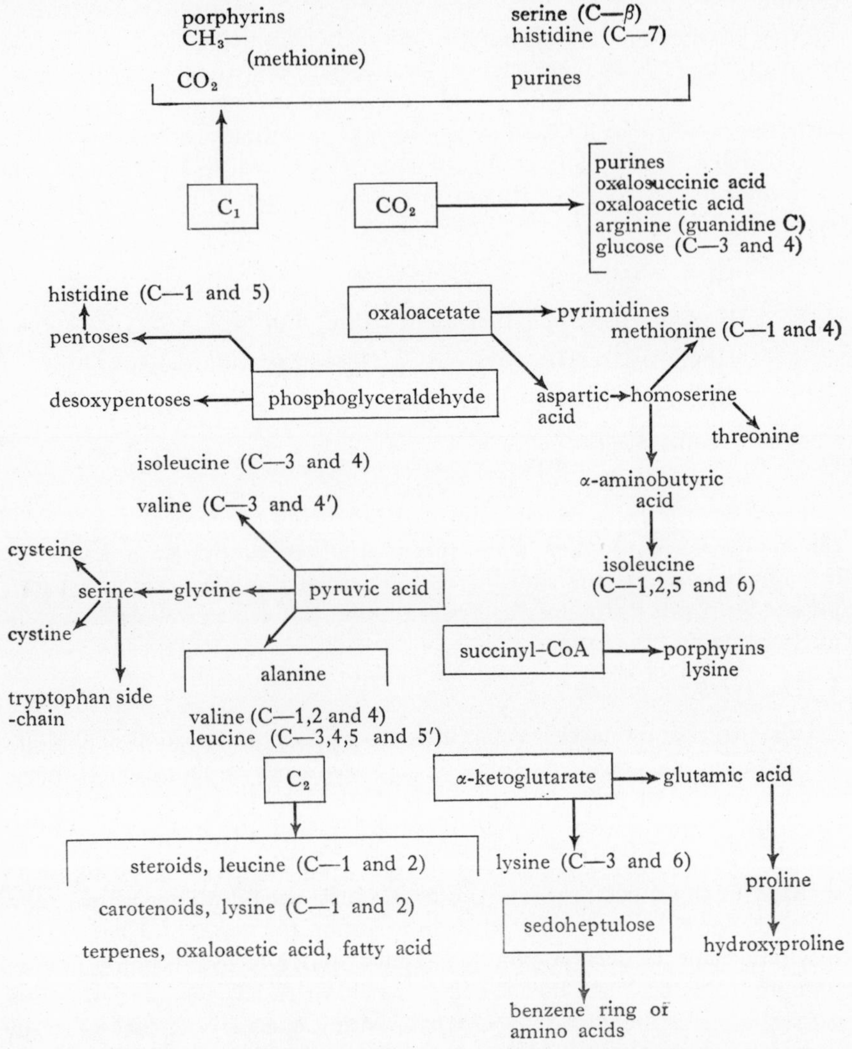

FIG. 81—Utilization of various key-materials for biosynthesis.

4. *The transmission of the code*

We have seen that the macromolecule of DNA is a double helix in the form of a spiral staircase in which the links between the different nucleic acids form the banisters and the purine and pyrimidine bases form the steps. As we have seen, each step is formed by one of the two combinations adenine-thymine (or thymine-adenine) and guanine-cytosine (or cytosine-guanine). This means that a particular sequence of bases on one of the banisters is paired to one definite complementary sequence on the other.

Now if the chains separate in a medium containing free nucleotides of deoxyribose and one of the bases (adenine, guanine, thymine or cytosine),

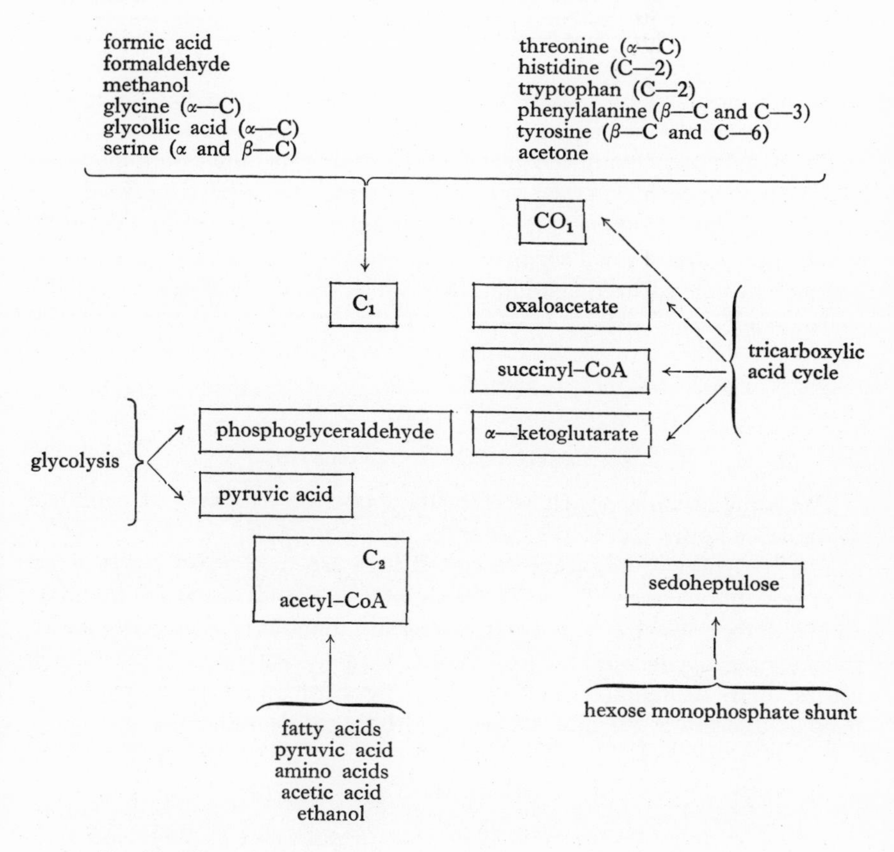

Fig. 82. The chief sources of the key-materials required for biosyntheses.

each of the two chains of the parent double helix will become a template for a complementary chain, the result being the formation of two daughter double helices, carrying an exact copy of the code. How the sequence on bases in one of the chains, copied on a RNA chain, is read in terms of amino acid succession, remains to be explained. Crick, Griffith and Orgel have devised a code in which the names of the twenty amino acids are read in terms of twenty triplets of bases, but this ingenious suggestion has not yet been experimentally confirmed.

We have said that we know at present a number of mutants of micro-organisms, characterized by the lack of a definite enzyme. Other mutants are characterized by the addition of a new enzyme. In each case we are dealing with changes in structure of protein molecules resulting in the loss or in the acquisition of the enzymatic activity.

This leads to the notion that, in certain cases at least, a mutation is primarily a change in the structure of a protein molecule, i.e. an aspect of the molecular evolution (heteromorphic evolution, p. 336) of proteins. Abnormal haemoglobins show that the alteration of a single residue may deeply change the properties of a protein macromolecule. In this case, a single mistake in copying the genetic code during its duplication may lead to a permanent change in the properties of haemoglobin. Each half molecule of haemoglobin is formed by about 300 amino acid residues. Figure 80 shows, in a definite small segment of this unit, the sequence of amino acid residues in normal haemoglobin (HbA), in sickle cell haemoglobin (HbS), in haemoglobin C disease (HbC) and in haemoglobin G disease (HbG). Figure 80 makes it quite clear that, in each of these diseases, only one residue, printed in italics, is altered.

D. Biosynthetic Interrelations

The same remarks which were made about the pathways of complete degradation apply also to the pathways of biosynthesis.

The biosynthetic pathways described here are the longest paths it has been possible to trace. These paths are not always traversed from end to end and they can be entered at numerous junctions. The existence of transferring enzymes and the reversibility of many sections of the metabolic routes, both degradative and synthetic, establish multiple interrelations between the routes for biosynthesis and those for degradations.

REFERENCES

Anfinsen, C. B. (1959) *The Molecular Basis of Evolution*, John Wiley and Sons, New York.

Bloch, K. (1954). Biological synthesis of cholesterol. *Harvey Lectures*, **48**, 68–88.

Davis, B. D. (1955). Intermediates in amino acid biosynthesis. *Advanc. Enzymol.*, **16**, 247–312.

Greenberg, D. M. (1954). *Chemical Pathways of Metabolism*, 2 vol. Academic Press, New York.

McElroy, W. D., and Bentley Glass, H. (Editors), (1955). *A Symposium on Amino Acid Metabolism*, Johns Hopkins Press, Baltimore.

Ochoa, S. J. B., (1952). Enzymatic mechanisms of carbon dioxide fixation. *The Enzymes*, Sumner, J. B., and Myrbäck, K. (Editors), vol. II, part 2. Academic Press, New York.

Perutz, M. F. (1959). The molecular basis of life. *Research*, **12**, 326-334.

PART FOUR

TOPOBIOCHEMISTRY AND CELLULAR REGULATION

CHAPTER I

CELLULAR TOPOCHEMISTRY

IT would be a grave mistake to believe, as is often stated, that the cellular theory of life, as proposed by Theodor Schwann, was of a purely morphological character. Schwann not only affirmed that "Everything which lives is made up of cells", but he also pointed out that the individual life of each cell "has its origin in forces which are inherent in each molecule". For his teacher Johannes Muller, the phenomena of life were the result of an idea acting on each tissue producing in it a "vital energy". On the other hand, Theodor Schwann stated that living phenomena are the product of forces which are essentially the same as those present in inorganic nature, forces acting blindly and compulsorily like physical forces. The forces which bring about the formation of organisms, Schwann added, do not act in non-living nature because the combinations of molecules which give rise to them do not occur there. But, he added, it does not follow that it is necessary to distinguish them from ordinary physical or chemical forces. In his work *Mikroskopische Untersuchungen*, Schwann proposed the classification of tissues which is still to be found, without major alterations, in text books of histology. But he was forced to watch in despair the development along purely morphological lines of the microscopic anatomy which he had founded. The never-ending controversies among the histologists and cytologists over their artifacts of coloration and fixation were of no interest to him. To Schwann, the pressing problem was the study, by physical and chemical methods, of metabolism (using the word he had created) of units smaller than the cell itself. But, he had arrived too soon, in a world too immature and only capable of producing great numbers of publications illustrated by beautiful colour pictures of tissues. This enormous mass of literature has left us little else than the idea of the presence in the cell of a nucleus containing a nucleolus, and a cytoplasm in which one can distinguish the presence of mitochondria and other inclusions. Classical histology, as the fruit of a hundred years of tissue-slicing, fixing and staining, has provided us with a great number of pictures of cells, pleasantly coloured with Janus green or gentian violet. Unfortunately they bear no relation to the complex phenomena described, in an abbreviated and simplified form, in the preceding pages. One might as well try to explain a watch to a Martian by drawing him a small circle, even though it have the agreeable brightness of gold.

It was necessary to wait until 1940 when Albert Claude had the idea of dissecting the cell into its constituents by means of a centrifugal field applied to a suspension of macerated cells under defined conditions. This mode of penetration into the unexplored world inside the cell gave access to previously recognized organelles and led to the identification of others, as was the case with the microsomes. The parallel use of the electron microscope gave further valuable help in this field. Once more the march of scientific progress continued. Schwann would not have formulated the cellular theory if he had not had the benefit of a microscope incorporating improvements introduced by Amici. Similarly, without the ultracentrifuge and the electron microscope, Claude, and many workers after him, would not have been able to penetrate inside the cell.

From a biochemical point of view, a cell can be divided into a nucleus and a cytoplasm containing mitochondria and other inclusions. Even with the ordinary microscope, and better still with the phase-contrast microscope, it is possible to distinguish granular or fibrillar inclusions in the cytoplasm. In cells which respire, mitochondria are found, and in certain cells there are other specialized structures buried in an apparently structureless cytoplasm.

A. Cytoplasm

(a) *The Fundamental Material*

The cytoplasm has been the subject of numerous theories. The most recent have been thought out with a view to explaining the physical properties of cytoplasm in terms of its structure. The most comprehensive is the theory of bonds, proposed by Frey-Wyssling.

During the first quarter of this century, ideas about the structure of protoplasm were dominated by a fallacious conception which sought to interpret the properties of protoplasm according to whether the material was in the sol or the gel state, where these terms have the same significance as in colloidal chemistry. Today, a large number of facts make us consider that the cellular elements are formed from macromolecules and not from small molecules associated together by physical forces to form micelles analogous to those found in soaps.

The cell is made up of a number of organelles bathed in a cellular juice. The cytoplasm contains protein filaments which make up a labile framework whose structure is due to bridges between the fibres and whose lability is due to the fact that the bridges are easily broken. The filaments themselves vary between 80 and 200 Å in thickness.

If we consider the number of different amino acids present in proteins, we can understand what a variety of side-chains is possible in a polypeptide chain.

The complex macromolecule represented by the network of protein fibres in the cytoplasm is maintained intact by a series of junctions between polypeptide chains (see p. 99). Certain of these linkages are homopolar in nature, for example the disulphide bonds. Others are joined by heteropolar bonds, or salt linkages. In addition there are cohesive bonds between non-polar groups (for example attraction between CH_3 groups) and polar groups (for example attraction between groups of a dipole nature).

These various linkages are shown in Fig. 83.

According to the theory of Frey-Wyssling, the four types of bond occurring between the peptide chains can explain the behaviour of cytoplasm.

1. *Cohesive bonds between non-polar groups (binding by Van der Waals forces)*

These are the same forces as are responsible for the cohesion of a crystal of a paraffin. The attraction between non-polar hydrocarbon groupings, feeble as it is, cannot be accounted for by an electric field for such a field is practically non-existent. (In substances containing lipophilic groups it is difficult to explain the attraction of these groups since their electric field of force is negligible when compared with that between polar molecules.) The cohesion between methyl groups, for example, is very small and temperature-sensitive. The change in viscosity of cytoplasm with temperature must be attributed to the presence of these bonds.

2. *Cohesive bonds between polar groups*

These are bonds due to residual or secondary valencies and are caused by dipole interaction. They are semi-chemical in character and they are commonly called hydrogen bonds (Pauling) (see p. 99). When a polar group carrying a peripheral hydrogen atom (—OH, —NH_2, etc.) is present, it can be attracted electrostatically by the negative charges located on the polar groups of neighbouring molecules thus uniting them through a hydrogen atom. If the polar groups of the two adjacent molecules cannot approach each other sufficiently, the electric field between them will attract water molecules. In this case the bridge is made up of attracted water molecules and the linkage is sensitive to any swelling of the cell, an action depending on the presence of inorganic ions. Small ions like Li^+ or Na^+ have a hydration shell thicker than that surrounding larger ions like K^+ or Cs^+. As the size of an ion increases with its atomic weight the hydration shell decreases correspondingly. Hence it can be seen that the introduction of various ions can modify the hydration of such structures as cytoplasm.

3. *Heteropolar valencies (salt linkages)*

If the positive and negative ends of two side-chains are in proximity they can enter into a salt linkage, their charges neutralizing each other and the degree of hydration decreasing. To break such linkages it is necessary to change the pH.

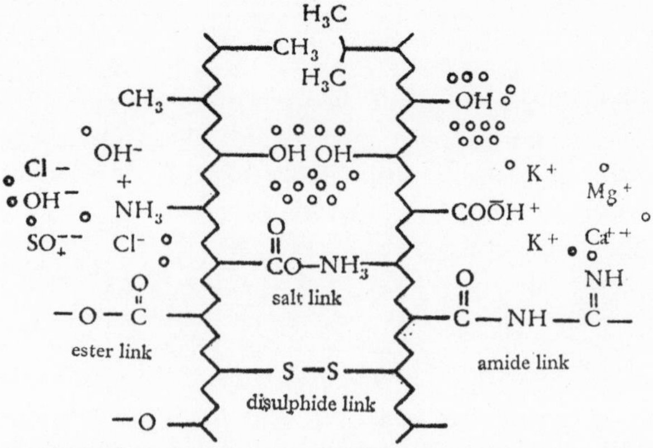

FIG. 83 (Frey-Wyssling)—Types of link between neighbouring polypeptide chains. O = a water molecule.

4. *Homopolar valencies*

These can be formed in a variety of ways: by elimination of water (formation of ester, glucoside or peptide linkages), by removal of hydrogen (formation of disulphide bridges, methylene bridge, etc.), they are influenced by the oxido-reduction potential of the system.

The theory of Frey-Wyssling postulates the existence of monomolecular polypeptide filaments which must be about 20 Å thick. However the electron microscope has revealed the presence in the cytoplasm of an *endoplasmic reticulum* made up of trabeculae 30 to 40 mμ in length, hollow tubes joining together vesicles 100 to 300 mμ in diameter. Attached to this system there are basophilic particles. In addition the cytoplasm contains fibres either singly or in bundles, which make up the contractile material of the cell and by means of a slow but continuous motion maintain the various organelles suspended in the cellular fluid.

Molecules such as the phosphatides can react with the protein side-chains regardless of whether they are lipophilic or hydrophilic in nature, as shown in Fig. 84.

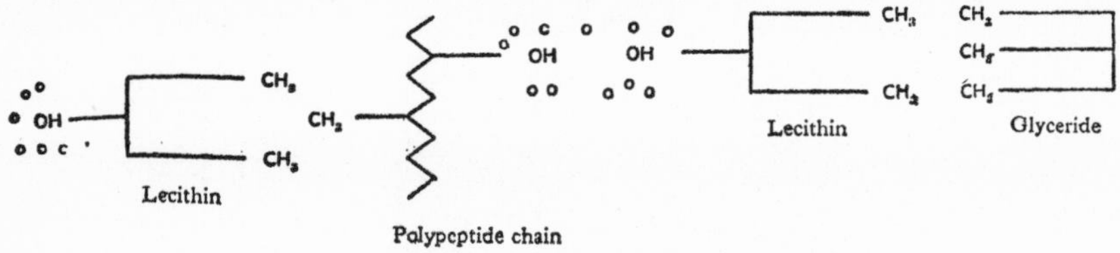

FIG. 84 (Frey-Wyssling)—O = a water molecule.

As for glycerides, which do not possess a hydrophilic group, they can only attach themselves to lipophilic side-chains and then, as shown in Fig. 88, only by the interposition of a phosphatide or similar molecule. The sterols have a polar structure analogous to that of the phosphatides. But the phosphatides are more reactive for their hydrophilic end bears an ionized phosphate group (negatively charged) and a positive ammonium group. By contrast the sterols can only form esters.

From the point of view of enzymology, cytoplasm is a not highly organized multi-enzyme system containing notably all the enzymes of the glycolysis system and which consequently is qualified for the formation of ATP energy-rich bonds. In addition to the conversion of sugars into pyruvic acid, cytoplasm can saponify lipides and split proteins into amino acids. In a cell living anaerobically, 80–90% of the glycolysis occurs in the cytoplasm.

(*b*) *The Outer Region of the Cell*

In all cells it is possible to distinguish an inner region and an outer region. In certain cases, such as the amoeba, the region of clear ectoplasm is plainly differentiated from the granular endoplasm.

The ectoplasm is itself surrounded by a thin layer of polysaccharide and lipide-containing material called the plasmalemma. This portion is elastic and contractile. The difference between the endoplasm and ectoplasm is a result of differences in the shapes of the constituent macromolecules.

We may represent the cellular "membrane", from the interior to the exterior, as formed, firstly, of a highly hydrated protein structure consisting of leaflets parallel to the surface, this explains its contractility and elasticity. Beyond this membrane are situated one or two layers of complex lipides, followed by a layer containing polysaccharides.

The presence of enzymes in the outer region of the cell has been demonstrated, chiefly with the aid of indirect methods. Thus, a portion of substrate can be introduced to see if the requisite enzyme is present; this has been done for certain esterases, phosphatases, etc.

(*c*) *Microsomes*

There is always present in cytoplasm an important basophilic material which forms the endoplasmic reticulum of vesicules and canaliculi. At least part of this material appears to consist of the particles which we call microsomes. The discovery of microsomes (50–150 mμ in diameter) is due to Claude, who isolated them from a mush of cells by prolonged centrifugation at 20,000 rev/min. The microsomes contain a large part of the nitrogen of the cell and a comparatively (more than the mitochondria) large fraction of the phospholipides and RNA. It was at one time considered that the microsomes consisted of mitochondrial fragments, but this view is no longer tenable for it has been shown that they are the exclusive carriers of certain enzymes like glucose-6-phosphatase and they are without the typical enzyme of the mitochondria, cytochrome-oxidase. As already stated, it is believed that protein synthesis takes place under the influence of ribonucleoproteins. The microsomes, amongst the other cellular organites, are the most abundantly provided with these substances, and this is why Brachet considers that the microsome, rich in RNA and incorporating amino acids very rapidly, is the probable site of protein synthesis.

The enzymatic composition of microsomes is still obscure. Nevertheless we know that they contain important amounts of cytochrome-reductases. They must therefore presumably play some part somewhere in the stage of electron transfer between DPNH or TPNH and cytochrome-*c*.

In addition, according to Brachet, they contain a number of hydrolases : phosphatases, amylases, cathepsin, and ribonuclease. Several experiments also indicate the presence in microsomes of the enzyme system responsible for the incorporation of alanine into proteins.

B. Mitochondria

We may say, and rightly, that the mitochondria is the engine which drives the cell. For although the energy-rich bonds of ATP are formed in the cytoplasm during glycolysis, the major production results from oxidative phosphorylations which take place in the mitochondria. We may also liken them to the central bank for the cell for it is from here that the currency in which the cell deals, is issued.

The mitochondria are cylindrical particles 1–4 μ in length and 0·3–0·7 μ thick. They are bounded by a double membrane of protein in the middle of which there is a double layer of complex lipides. In mitochondria from mammalian liver and kidney, each protein layer is 45 Å thick and the distance between the two protein layers is 70 Å, so that the membrane surrounding the mitochondria is 160 Å thick. This membrane is prolonged into the interior of the mitochondria by ridges penetrating into the substratum which appears to consist mainly of soluble proteins.

The general features of mitochondria have been found in all the cells of the different and varied organisms in which they have been studied : mammals, birds, batrachians, molluscs, annelids, protozoa, yeasts, plants, etc.

In mitochondria from rat liver the greater part (56%) of the organic phosphorous is in the form of complex lipides and 20% is present in RNA, the only nucleic acid they contain. A quarter of the total nitrogen of the liver cell is in the mitochondria and about 15% of the RNA of the cell is found there.

Cytochrome oxidase or cytochrome a_3, appears to occur only in the mitochondria. However, this is not the case for the cytochrome-reductases (DPN and TPN specific) which, as stated above, are also found in the microsomes. Succinic dehydrogenase, fumarase, and the oxido-reduction systems for α-ketoglutarate and oxaloacetate are also found only in the mitochondria, which contain in addition the enzymes of the fatty acid cycle.

Their enzymatic equipment shows that the mitochondria are the exclusive sites of aerobic oxidation and oxidative phosphorylation.

In addition to these heavy mitochondria, the exclusive carriers of cytochrome oxidase, de Duve distinguishes "light mitochondria" or "lysosomes", which contain alkaline phosphatase, ribonuclease, desoxyribonuclease, "cathepsin" (i.e. the complete assembly of intracellular peptidases), and most of the β-glucuronidase. In these intact particles, these hydrolases do not have access to their substrates when the latter are situated in the medium around the particles.

C. The Nucleus

The cellular nucleus, during interphase, consists principally of a nuclear sap or caryolymph, a nucleolus and certain chromatin filaments or *chromonemata* which condense into chromosomes during mitosis.

In the nucleus we find a whole series of compounds. The nuclear sap contains proteins not belonging to the histone or protamine families. In addition, we find in the nucleus either protamines or histones, depending on the cell, and also lipides (around 10%).

The nucleus contains practically all the DNA in the cell. For a given species, the amount of DNA per nucleus of diploid cells in interphase is constant. Although DNA in each case is a complex mixture of different nucleotides, its composition is the same for all the different cells of the organism, for they are all derived from the same fertilized egg. It differs from one species to another. Two insect viruses parasitic on the same organism, for example, will have different structures of their DNA. A cell of *E. coli* and its bacteriophage have DNA of differing structures.

The fact that a spermatozoid contains only half the amount of DNA present in normal cells clearly identifies DNA with the chromatin filaments which also contain protamines and histones.

However, the nucleus also always contains some RNA located in the nucleolus (which does not contain DNA) and in the chromatin filaments. The ratio RNA/DNA varies from one species to another and, in the same species, from one organ to another. Unlike DNA whose composition is characteristic of all the cells of a species, the composition of RNA varies in the same cell from one point to another. Thus the RNA of the nucleus, the microsomes, and the mitochondria are all of different composition. Physiological conditions can also modify the composition of the various types of RNA in an organism, although they have no influence on the composition of the DNA.

The nucleus contains a number of other phosphorylated derivatives and inorganic elements such a K, Ca and Mg.

When mitosis occurs, the chromatin filaments combine into chromosomes which divide longitudinally and then distribute themselves between the two halves of the cell. This process is aided by the *aster*, a structure formed at the beginning of mitosis and surrounding the centrosome. It has been isolated from sea urchin eggs and shown to be protein in nature.

The nucleus is lacking in a number of important enzymes for cellular oxidation such as cytochrome oxidase, succinic dehydrogenase, uricase, D-amino acid oxidase, etc., and so respiration does not occur. However, it does contain a glycolytic system, although of low activity. In the nucleus is concentrated a system of enzymes for the synthesis of nucleic acids and nucleotides. It is found that radioactive phosphorus is always incorporated more rapidly into the RNA of the nucleus than into the RNA of the cytoplasm. So, there is little doubt that the nucleus contains enzyme systems for the synthesis of the two types of nucleic acid.

D. Conclusions

It is true that the study of the distribution of enzymes in the cell has only just begun, nevertheless they have brought to our notice several important facts concerning cellular metabolism. From these studies we see that the cytoplasm is the principal region for the performance of anaerobic degradations which provide the mitochondrial machine with fatty acids, amino acids, and pyruvic acid. Since most of the glycolysis occurs in it, the cytoplasm is manufacturing energy-rich bonds by an anaerobic pathway. In addition the cytoplasm, or more particularly the microsomes, appears to be the home of protein synthesis.

In the mitochondria is localized the respiratory part of the priming reactions, the fatty acid cycle and the tricarboxylic acid cycle, the chief providers of the ATP required for cellular work. However it appears that the transfer of electrons from DPNH or TPNH to cytochrome-*c* can also take place apart from the mitochondria.

With its enzymes for the synthesis of nucleosides and nucleoproteins, the nucleus appears to be the repository of the specific DNA structure and the apparatus for its transmission. It also has a part to play in the control of the synthesis of the cytoplasmic nucleotides and of protein synthesis in the cytoplasm. Whether the latter is controlled through the synthesis of the microsomes or otherwise, the part played by the nucleus has been demonstrated on numerous occasions although the mechanism still remains to be discovered.

REFERENCES

Allfrey, V. G., Mirsky, A. E. and Stern, H. (1955). The chemistry of the cell nucleus. *Advanc. Enzymol.*, **16**, 411–500.

CLAUDE, ALBERT (1947–48). Studies on cells : morphology, chemical constitution, and distribution of biochemical functions. *Harvey Lectures*, 1950, **43**, 121–164.

DOUNCE, A. L. (1950). Cytochemical fundations of enzyme chemistry. *The Enzymes. Chemistry and Mechanism of Action.* SUMNER, J. B. and MYRBÄCK, K. (Editors) vol. I, Part 1. Academic Press, New York. 187–266.

DE DUVE, CHR. and BERTHET, S. (1954). The use of differential centrifugation in the study of tissue enzymes. *Internat. Rev. Cytol.*, **3**, 225–275.

HOOGEBOOM, G. H. and KUFF, E. L. (1955). Relation between cell structure and cell chemistry. *Fed. Proc.*, **14**, 633–638.

CHAPTER II

CELLULAR REGULATION

THE complexity of the priming reactions and the reactions which follow, and their interrelations, lead us to ask how the direction of the molecules along the various metabolic paths is controlled. Not only do the directions of these metabolic reactions, all of which are proceeding at the same time, have to be controlled, but also the velocities of these reactions must be regulated. For example, how is it that in a cell liberally provided with substrates and oxygen, respiration during a given period is no greater than the production of utilizable energy? These are a few of the questions we have to answer when considering the ways in which the metabolism of the cell is regulated.

I. FACTORS WHICH DETERMINE THE VELOCITY AND THE PATH OF ENZYMATIC REACTION CHAINS

By "reaction chain" the biochemist means a process made up of a series of chemical reactions joined together in a straight or in a branching manner. The idea that in a chain of reactions it is the slowest reaction which determines the overall speed of reaction has often appeared to be self-evident. Hinshelwood illustrates this concept by comparison with the transmission of telegraph messages. The speed of transmission depends upon a certain number of factors—the dexterity of the operator, the speed of the current along the wires, and the rapidity with which the telegraph boy delivers the message. It is undoubtedly, says Hinshelwood, the last factor which is the dominating one. This is no doubt true, but a series of biochemical reactions differs from the sending of a telegram. As pointed out by Burton, the agility of the telegraph boy does not normally depend on the number of telegrams waiting at the post office, whilst the velocity of biochemical reactions is influenced by the concentrations of the reactants, according to the law of mass action.

The stationary state for a biochemical reaction chain may perhaps be better compared, Burton points out, to that of the current in a stream. If an obstacle is placed across the stream, there will be a temporary decrease in the amount of water reaching the river mouth, but as soon as the water level has reached the top of the dam, a new steady state will establish itself and in the last analysis the amount of water arriving at the mouth of the stream will depend upon only one factor, the amount of rain falling at the source, which surely cannot be considered as the slowest process present. A series of different factors can influence the resultant of a number of reactions catalysed by a system of enzymes, both their velocity and the direction at alternative pathways and intersections will be affected.

A. Enzyme Concentration

In a chain of biochemical reactions, the concentration of an enzyme affects the velocity of the metabolic reaction it catalyses. The relative importance of two divergent paths at a fork in the metabolic chain can therefore be influenced by the concentrations of the participating enzymes. However, it is difficult to know with certainty what is the *active* concentration of a given enzyme and there are only a very few measurements of this type.

B. Kinetic Characteristics

The velocity of an enzyme reaction is defined as the change in substrate concentration per minute. The velocity of the reaction depends not only on the concentration of the enzyme, but also on the *turnover number*.

$$v = W \,.\, C_E$$

v = velocity of the reaction (in moles of substrate/l. per min).	W = turnover number (in moles of substrate/min per mole of enzyme).	C_E = enzyme concentration (moles/l.)

Under conditions where the enzyme is saturated with substrate, the *turnover number* is defined as the number of substrate molecules acted upon per minute by one mole of enzyme.

The *turnover number* and the enzyme concentration (see A, above) are therefore to be considered separately as regulating factors rather than their product which is the reaction velocity. However, conditions where the enzyme is saturated with substrate are rarely realized in cells and under actual conditions the Michaelis constant K_m is more useful since it enables us to calculate the reaction velocity for each substrate concentration.

C. Relation Between Thermodynamic Equilibrium and the Stationary State

In the case of a reversible reaction situated in the middle of a chain of reactions, when the stationary state is set up the establishment of equilibrium is only possible if the velocities of the reactions situated on either side of the reversible reaction are sufficiently low. If they are faster than the reaction in the middle, equilibrium will not be attained (see p. 148). There are cases where thermodynamic equilibrium is attained and where the concentrations of certain products (which, under these conditions, depend on equilibrium constants) decide the subsequent course of metabolism. Such a case are the stages of glycolysis between phosphoglyceraldehyde and 3-phosphoglyceric acid in the course of which an energy-rich bond is formed (p. 189). 1,3-Diphosphoglyceric acid undergoes a spontaneous hydrolysis into 3-phosphoglyceric acid and inorganic phosphate. The equilibrium constant for the enzymic conversion of phosphoglyceraldehyde into 1,3-diphosphoglyceric acid is such that only a small amount of this acid is present at equilibrium. For the step from 1,3-diphosphoglyceric acid to 3-phosphoglyceric acid, with the formation of ATP, the equilibrium constant favours the formation of a relatively large amount of the latter. When the two reactions are combined, a stationary state is set up in which the concentration of 1,3-diphosphoglyceric acid is very small. In this way the slow spontaneous hydrolysis of the latter is kept to a point where it is insignificant.

D. The Concentration of Coenzymes

An example of the importance of this in the regulation of metabolic processes is provided by the antagonistic effect of K^+ and Na^+ ions on the second transfer of phosphate during fermentation.

E. Temperature

Since temperature does not affect all enzymes in the same manner its influence is such as to cause changes in biochemical reactions.

F. Permeability of the Outer Region of the Cytoplasm

This acts as a regulator of metabolism by controlling the passage of substrates or metabolites. An example of the first mode of control is the fact that yeast ferments glucose but does not ferment F-1,6-PP, to which the surface of the cell is impermeable.

The second type of effect is illustrated by the ready permeability of the outer region of the yeast cell to ethyl alcohol. But for this ready permeability, the accumulation of alcohol inside the cell would soon cause alcoholic fermentation to cease.

G. Topobiochemistry

The cellular topobiochemistry of enzymes, as it has been described in the preceding chapter, offers numerous possibilities for intracellular regulation of reactions; yet the study of this subject has hardly begun. During alcoholic fermentation, for example, ATP is formed in the cytoplasm and transferred to cellular particles containing ATP-ase, from whence the molecules return to the cytoplasm to replenish the stock of adenine nucleotides acting as phosphate acceptors (AMP, ADP). The diffusion of ATP away from the cytoplasm and the diffusion of AMP and ADP towards the cytoplasm evidently form one of the regulating processes in glycolysis.

During mitochondrial respiration, on the other hand, the *turnover* of phosphate in the adenine nucleotides is more rapid than the diffusion of ATP to the outside of the mitochondria or of phosphate acceptors to the inside.

But the concentrations of AMP, ADP and ATP remain constant in the stationary state in mitochondria during active oxidative phosphorylation. So apparently there is a control of oxidative phosphorylation by means of a regulation of the entry of nucleotide phosphate acceptors. According to Siekevitz and Potter, this entry is under the control of an enzyme situated in the outer region of the mitochondria, this enzyme, adenylic kinase, catalyses the establishment of equilibrium between AMP, ADP and ATP.

H. Stationary States

The intervention of the various factors responsible for intracellular regulation leads to the persistence over an extended period of concentrations of the various substances which compose the cell. The stationary states themselves also serve to regulate the orientation of a reaction chain where alternative pathways are possible.

II. THE PASTEUR EFFECT

From the results of experiment it has been possible to deduce that the control of cellular oxidation depends upon two factors: the concentration of inorganic phosphate and the concentration of phosphate acceptors. An example of the regulatory influence of these concentrations is the so-called Pasteur Effect. First observed by Pasteur, as indicated by the name, this phenomenon consists of the fact that when a cell is using oxygen glycolysis proceeds less rapidly than in the absence of oxygen. Although glycolysis is not a process in which oxygen actually plays a part, yet it is partially inhibited by the presence of oxygen. In a cell lacking oxygen a much greater number of sugar molecules undergo glycolysis than in the presence of oxygen. Yet, in the second case, the amount of useful energy, obtained in the form of energy-rich bonds, is much greater. From a fundamental point of view the Pasteur Effect is of great interest, but it is its mechanism, as an example of intracellular regulation, which interests us here.

The Pasteur Effect can be described by saying that "aerobic glycolysis" is weaker than "anaerobic glycolysis". Also, in cells during growth and in cancer cells, aerobic glycolysis is greater than in resting cells, hence the statement of Warburg; "No growth without glycolysis". The explanation of the Pasteur Effect has been provided by Lynen who has shown that the intensity of glycolysis depends on the concentration of inorganic phosphate available at the stage of the dehydrogenation of phosphoglyceraldehyde with production of 1,3-diphosphoglyceric acid.

When the oxidative phosphorylations of respiration take place, the resulting consumption of inorganic phosphate brings about a decrease in the intensity of glycolysis, and inversely. The Pasteur Effect is therefore an example of an autoregulation of all the complex phenomena of the priming reactions. Another factor in the regulation of the intensity of respiratory metabolism is operative in the mitochondria, and this is the supply to the interior of the mitochondria of phosphate acceptors such as AMP and ADP.

To the autoregulatory processes of this type can be added the action of specialized regulators such as the hormones which have been developed by organisms in the course of biochemical evolution.

III. THE GENETIC CONTROL OF THE RELATIVE RATES OF ENZYMATIC REACTIONS

Although it is true that the cells of various organisms all possess metabolic systems having the general features described in part three of this book, each species has certain specific peculiarities in the macromolecules of which it is formed, the enzymes included.

Heredity transmits to the descendants of an organism the specific type of control of the relative rates of the diverse enzymic reactions which take place in each of its cells. It has now been well established that an alteration in a given gene can bring about definite biochemical changes manifested by the disappearance of one constituent in the organism, or the appearance of a new one, or by an increase or a decrease in the amount of a compound or of a group of compounds. New stationary states are set up resulting from changes in the speed of this or that metabolic process. For example, in a given organism consider the concentration of a substance A. In the stationary state in the organism, the concentration of A remains approximately constant as a result of an equilibrium between the production process and its transformation. If the rate of production decreases, even slightly, and if the rate of transformation does not alter, then substance A will disappear.

Although the biochemical phenotype, like phenotypes in general, is a product of the interaction of the internal *milieu* of the cell, and its genotype, the means by which the latter influences the system of macromolecules in the cell and in particular the enzymes still remains a mystery.

REFERENCES

HOLZER (1953). Über Fermentketten und ihre Bedeutung für die Regulation des Kohlenhydratstoffwechsels in lebenden Zellen. *Biologie und Wirkung der Fermente*. 4. Colloquium der Ges. für physiol. Chem., Springer, Berlin-Göttingen-Heidelberg. 89–112.

LARDY, H. A. (1952). The role of phosphate in metabolic control mechanisms. *The Biology of Phosphorus*, WOLTERINK, L. F. (Editor) Michigan State College Press, 131–147.

POTTER, VAN R. (1949). The control of metabolism. *Respiratory Enzymes*, LARDY, H. A. (Editor) Burgess, Minneapolis, revised ed., 264–272.

PART FIVE

BIOCHEMICAL DIVERSITY

CHAPTER I

SOME ASPECTS OF BIOCHEMICAL DIVERSITY

THE chemical processes described in Part Three of this book give an approximate and overall view of the metabolism and biosynthetic mechanisms in cells. However, numerous variations on these themes are possible and a few examples follow.

I. TERPENES

We have described (p. 235) the biosynthesis of isoprene from acetyl-CoA as it usually occurs in cells. In the essential oils of plants we find a large number of compounds which demonstrate the large number of possible compounds which can be formed in a similar manner, starting from acetyl-CoA. They are compounds made up of isopentane units. They contain 5, 10, 15, 20 or more carbon atoms and are called respectively, hemiterpenes, mono-, sesqui-, di- or polyterpenes. From the material which is not distillable in steam, by solvent extraction it is possible to obtain a series of other substances containing 20, 30, 40 carbon atoms or more and belonging to the groups of diterpenes (i.e. the resins), the triterpenes (i.e. the saponins), the tetraterpenes (i.e. the carotenoids) or to the polyterpenes (i.e. rubber). Moreover a whole series of organic compounds synthesized by plants are related to isopentane since they contain such units in their structure. Among these isoprenoids are the irones. There are many monoterpenes in plants and in general, but not always, one can consider their formula as being based on two isopentane units joined in head to tail union. The sesquiterpenes can be considered as formed from three isoprene units in head to tail union. The cyclic monoterpenes and sesquiterpenes can be considered as resulting from the rolling up of the same chains.

Certain of the diterpenes can be considered as containing four *iso*pentane units in head to tail union. This is the case of phytol and vitamin A. Others have an irregular arrangement.

Among the tetraterpenes, those related to lycopene and called carotenoids have been described previously). Plants are able to synthesize carotenoid molecules whilst animals are only able to modify them, for example by oxidation. Astaxanthin a carotenoid usually found in crustaceans, is one such oxidation product.

In mammals, birds, and certain amphibians, the ingestion of carotenoids in the food results in an absorption of carotene in the intestine, the extent of

U

absorption depending on the greater or lesser activity of the intestinal carotenase which converts carotene to vitamin A and as a result the reserve fats become more or less saturated with carotene. Man and other Primates absorb carotenoids in general, as does the frog also; other animals exercise a selective adsorption. For example, the horse and the cow selectively absorb carotenoids and store them without alteration, whilst birds and fish show a preference for xanthophylls. However birds and fish modify one of the ingested xanthophylls, lutein, by oxidation, and the products of the oxidation are deposited in the feathers in the case of birds, and in the skin in the case of fish.

The carotenoid structure appears to be connected in a general way with the function of photoreception. The most primitive type of photoreception, lacking the presence of any differentiated photoreceptors, is the type called dermatoptic, which is found in primitive types of organisms up to the amphibians and also in plants. The maximum sensitivity of this dermatoptic function is in the ultra-violet part of the spectrum around 365mμ, and it is the receptor in photokinetic processes involving tropisms towards light. Now, in a number of cases, photoreceptors have evolved secondarily and developed new kinds of receptor molecules adapted to the light from the sun and the sky. All these substances belong to the carotenoid group. In plants, phototropic bending depends on the properties of carotenoids such as xanthophyll in *Avena*, or β-carotene in the sporangiophores of *Phycomyces*. The orientation of an animal depends on visual photoreception and requires the presence of other carotenoids showing the same kind of adaptation to sunlight and having an absorption maximum at around 500mμ. This development is due to the ability, mentioned above, to change some of the plant carotenoids into vitamin A. There are two types of vitamin A : vitamin A_1 and vitamin A_2.

Let us first consider the system in the eye of land vertebrates such as mammals or birds. The pigment of their retina is rhodospin, a rose-coloured carotenoid-protein complex. In aqueous solution its absorption spectrum consists of a single broad band with a maximum at 500mμ. In light it is bleached to orange and yellow pigments and in the process the carotenoid retinene I is liberated. The latter substance has never been found anywhere except in the retina. Its spectrum in chloroform consists of a single band with a maximum at about 387mμ. In the retina the mxture of retinene I and protein reverts to rhodopsin and in addition retinene I is converted to vitamin A_1, which, in the intact eye, also reunites with protein to form rhodopsin. This system is not only present in the eyes of mammals and birds but also in the eyes of Invertebrates such as the squid, *Loligo*, and the crayfish *Cambarus*.

If we consider the system in the eye of a marine fish we find the rhodopsin system as in birds and mammals and Invertebrates, but this is not the system to be found in the eyes of freshwater fish which contain another system, the porphyropsin system. Porphyropsin, like rhodopsin, is a carotenoid-protein complex and is purple in colour. Its spectrum resembles that of rhodopsin, but with a maximum at 522mμ. On exposure to light a substance having properties similar to rhodopsin is liberated; it is called retinene II. In chloroform it has an absorption maximum at 405mμ. In the retina it is converted simultaneously to porphyropsin and to vitamin A_2.

II. PORPHYRINS

We have described the biosynthesis (p. 238) of porphyrins from δ-aminolevulinic acid *via* porphobilinogen. On to this basic process are superimposed a considerable number of variations. By insertion of iron into the protoporphyrin nucleus we obtain what Granick has called the "iron branch" of the biosynthetic chain (p. 111), and a number of other variants have been described in these pages. Protoporphyrin is also the starting point for the biosynthesis of chlorophyll (the "magnesium branch" of Granick) as well as for the biosynthesis of haem.

A cell capable of photosynthesis (see p. 354) contains at least one chlorophyll and at least one yellow pigment. In addition it often contains a phycobilin. The chief pigment in photosynthesis, both in algae and in the higher plants, is chlorophyll *a*. In the photosynthetic bacteria, on the other hand, we find a different chlorophyll, bacteriochlorophyll (p. 122). Thus whilst in green plants the chloroplasts contain chlorophyll *a* and chlorophyll *b*, the algae are much more variable and we find in them a number of combinations : $a + b$, $a + c$, $a + d$, $a + e$. In addition we sometimes find a phycobilin. The phycobilins are soluble in water and are proteins combined with a chromophore belonging to the class of bile pigments. The phycoerythrins are predominant in the red algae and the phycocyanins in the blue-green algae.

The chromophore of the phycoerythrins, phycoerythrobilin, is identical with mesobilierythrin the formula of which is

M E M P P M M E
N N
HO H CH_2 H CH N CH N OH

(M = methyl group E = ethyl group P = propyl group)

The chromophore of the phycocyanins is mesobiliviolin

M E M P P M M E
C N C N
HO N H H CH N H_2 H OH

Various phycoerythrins are found in algae which differ in the structure of the protein moiety. 2-Phycoerythrin is the most common and is found in the

Rhodophyceae whilst c-phycoerythrin is present in the Myxophyceae. Among the phycocyanins, r-phycocyanin is present in the Rhodophyceae and c-phycocyanin in the Myxophyceae. The phycobilins serve to absorb light and transmit energy to other systems, notably the chlorophyll system.

Plants are able to continue the synthesis of porphyrins along the "iron branch" and along the "magnesium branch" whilst in animals the latter is lacking. However, animals have particularly developed the "iron branch" as far as the biosynthesis of the compound of haem and globin, haemoglobin, is concerned. The biosynthesis of haemoglobin is sometimes observed in plants, for example in the root nodules of Legumes. In animals, the presence of haemoglobin in tissues other than blood has often been demonstrated. For example, it has been shown to occur in the nervous system of certain worms e.g. in the Annelid *Aphrodita* and in a number of the Nemertea : *Polia*, *Meckelia* and *Borlatia*.

In Insects haemoglobin is found in the Diptera and the Hemiptera. In *Gastrophilus intestinalis* which, during its larval period, is a parasite in the stomach of the horse, the young larva is a uniform red due to the coloration, by haemoglobin, of the fatty bodies, of the parietal muscles and of the hypodermis. As the larva grows further the haemoglobin becomes localized in special cells, the tracheal cells, forming a red mass localized in the posterior third of the body.

In certain of the Hemiptera such as *Buenoa margaritacea* and *Anisops producta*, the haemoglobin is similarly localized in masses made up of tracheal cells. In addition in another Hemiptera, *Macrocrixa geoffroyi*, haemoglobin is present in the accessory glands of the male genital system.

Vertebrate muscle contains a haemoglobin known as myoglobin and the respiratory pigment has also been demonstrated in the pharyngeal muscles of a number of gastropod molluscs (*Paludina*, *Littorina*, *Limnaea*, *Patella*, *Chiton*, *Aplysia*) and also in the body wall of *Ascaris lumbricoides*.

The presence of haemoglobin in the blood is a general characteristic of Vertebrates: it is always contained in blood cells, either nucleated or non-nucleated. Nevertheless, some fishes adapted to cold waters have been shown to have no haemoglobin and no erythrocytes in their blood whatsoever.

The distribution of haemoglobin in the blood of Invertebrates, where it may be present either in cells or dissolved in the blood, defies all systematization.

Among the Echinoderms, corpuscles containing haemoglobin have been demonstrated in one, sometimes in two, and occasionally in all three of the body fluids of the Ophiuroidea and in several of the Holothuroidea. Corpuscles have never been found in the Asteroidea, the Echinoidea, nor in those Holothuroidea that possess a test.

The presence of a haemoglobin in the blood or coelomic fluid of annelid worms has long been known. In the Polychetes there is generally a circulatory system and a red blood containing dissolved haemoglobin

(*Arenicola*, *Eunice*, *Cirrhatulus*, *Nephthys*, *Nereis*, *Nais*, *Ophelia*, *Marphysa*, etc.). In the Phyllodocidae, Syllidae and Chaetopteridae, the blood is colourless. No case is known of an Annelid having a blood containing an intracellular oxygen-carrier. Where there is haemoglobin in the coelomic fluid of an Annelid, the oxygen-carrier is always contained in a blood corpuscle. This is the case for a number of Polychetes not possessing a circulatory system, e.g. the Capitellidae, Glyceridae and Terebellidae *Polycirrus hematodes*. In other Terebellidae such as *Travisia forbesii* or *Terebella lapidaria*, there is also dissolved haemoglobin in the coelomic corpuscles. Among the Oligochaeta, we generally find colourless blood in the circulatory system of the Enchytraeides (though some of them, such as *Pachydrilus lineatus*, have haemoglobin in their blood). In many others of the Oligochaeta it contains dissolved haemoglobin: in *Lumbricus*, *Tubifex*, *Limnodrilus*, *Lumbriculus*, etc. When we come to the Hirudinea, we find dissolved haemoglobin in the blood of the Gnathobdellides (*Hirudo*, *Aulastoma*, *Nephelis*, etc.) and colourless blood in the Rhynchobdellides (*Pontobdella muricata*, *Branchiobdella astaci*, etc.).

In the nemertian or the turbellarian worms, we sometimes find haemoglobin-containing corpuscles in the blood (*Derostoma*, *Syndesmis*, *Drepanophorus*, *Polia*).

The Echiurioidea are sometimes considered as aberrant worms. They are not segmented and only possess a few chaetae arranged differently from that in the Annelids and their body consists of two parts, a retractile preoral lobe and the body proper. In the coelomic cavity of many Echiurioidea nucleated corpuscles containing haemoglobin are found. Moreover the coelomic fluid of the Echiurioidea is the only fluid in their *milieu interieur* for they are devoid of a circulatory system.

Among the molluscs, we find haemoglobin-containing corpuscles in the blood of numerous Lammellibranchs (belonging to the genera *Pectunculus*, *Glycimeris*, *Cutellus*, *Arca*, *Gastrana*, *Tellina*, *Solen*, *Poromya*, *Capsa*, *Astarte*, etc.) and in the coelomic fluid of certain Amphineura, the Neomenians. In a Gastropod, *Planorbis*, the blood contains dissolved haemoglobin.

Only very exceptionally do we find haemoglobin in the Arthropods. Among the Crustacea, many species of small size are without an oxygen carrier whilst others have haemocyanin in the blood. It is only in the group of the Entomostracea (*Apus*, *Branchipus*, *Artemia*, *Daphnia*, *Chirocephalus*, *Lernanthropus*, *Clavella*, *Congericola*) that we find bloods containing dissolved haemoglobin. When we come to the insects, who, in order to bring oxygen to the cells, have had recourse to a direct transfer from the air *via* the tracheae, we find that their blood is without an oxygen carrier, with the remarkable exception of the blood of the larvae of certain of the Chironomides. The similarity to haemoglobin of the red pigment dissolved in the blood of the larva of the Diptera *Chironomus*, was demonstrated by Rollet in 1861.

The term haemoglobin applied to certain molecules implies that they have a number of common characteristics and among them :

(*a*) that they are derived from protohaem; the prosthetic groups of different haemoglobins when combined with a given basic nitrogen compound, in general give rise to the same haemochromogen.

(*b*) that of being heteroprotein in nature, the protohaem being united to a holoprotein to which the name globin has been given;

(*c*) that of giving a characteristic spectrum, two-banded in the oxygenated state and one-banded in the reduced state.

(*d*) that of complexing reversibly with molecular oxygen instead of being oxidized by it to a ferrihaemoglobin. (As previously stated (p. 117) this property is due to the globin forming a paramagnetic complex with the ferroporphyrin, whilst the other haemochromogens are diamagnetic).

(*e*) that of combining with carbon monoxide to give carboxyhaemoglobin, whose visible spectrum has two bands in positions different from those of the corresponding oxyhaemoglobin;

(*f*) that of being, when oxygenated and in pure solution, transformed more or less slowly into methaemoglobin, containing trivalent iron and no longer capable of being oxygenated, the solution of this compound giving an absorption band in the visible region differing from that given by reduced haemoglobin.

The relationship implied by use of the term haemoglobin applied to haem-proteins which can be oxygenated and contain the base protohaem, does not preclude them possessing differences which is revealed when a comparison is made.

Besides the fact that haemoglobin crystals differ from one animal species to another, the amino acid composition of different haemoglobins show clear-cut differences as the examples in Table XIV indicate.

TABLE XIV

(Roche and Jean; Roche and Mourgue)

Mean amino acid composition of various haemoglobins

Haemoglobin of	Tryptophane %	Tyrosine %	Cystine %	Arginine %	Histidine %	Lysine %	Leucine %	Valline %	Alanine %
Lumbricus	4·41	3·47	1·41	10·07	4·68	1·73	—	—	—
Arenicola	1·64	2·52	4·08	10·04	4·03	1·85	9.688	6·69	—
Horse	2·38	3·38	0·74	3·57	8·13	8·31	19·15	9·92	8.93

The haemoglobin of Vertebrates is clearly different from other haemoglobins in containing less arginine and cystine and more histidine, lysine and leucine.

The positions of the α and β bands in the spectrum of the oxyhaemoglobins are also different: in the Annelids the two bands are shifted towards the violet end of the spectrum relative to the positions in the Vertebrates. Conversely, in the Holothuria the two bands are shifted towards the red end.

The isoelectric points of the various haemoglobins also show differences (see Table XV).

TABLE XV

Isoelectric points of haemoglobins

(see Florkin, 1948)

Planorbis	4·77
Thyone briareus	5·80
Nereis virens	5·10
Arenicols marina	4·76
Aphrodite aculeata	5·70
Glycera convoluta	5·60
Haemopis sanguisuga	5·01
Lumbricus terrestris	5·28
Chironomus plumosus	5·40
Gastrophilus intestinalis	6·20
Man	6·78
Horse	6·78
Pigeon	7·23

As can be seen from the Table, vertebrate haemoglobin has an isoelectric point around neutrality and differing from that of other types of haemoglobin whose isoelectric points are more acid.

The diversity in the molecular weights of a series of haemoglobins is illustrated by Table XVI.

TABLE XVI

The molecular weights of haemoglobins

(see Wyman, 1948)

	Based on sedimentation constant S_{20}	Based on equilibrium studies in ultracentrifuge
Haemoglobins		
Thyone		23,600
Arenicola		3,000,000
Notomastus		36,400
Lumbricus	3,150,000	2,950,000
Planorbis corneus	1,630,000	1,540,000
Arca	17,100	19,100
Myxine		23,100
Chironomus		31,500
Man	63,000	
Horse	68,000	68,000
Cytochrome-*c*	15,600	13,000
Myoglobin (horse)	16,900	17,500

The behaviour of the various haemoglobins in the course of oxygenation gives us a further means of characterizing them. This is done by plotting a graph showing the degree of oxygenation as a function of the partial pressure of oxygen and is commonly known as the dissociation curve of oxyhaemoglobin. If we represent by T the portion of the haemoglobin molecule corresponding to a group capable of being oxygenated, i.e. an iron atom, then the equilibrium will be represented by

$$TO_2 \rightleftarrows T + O_2 \tag{1}$$

and

$$\frac{[TO_2]}{[T_2]\cdot[O_2]} = K, \tag{2}$$

K being the equilibrium constant for the oxygenation. Since the concentration of oxygen in the solution, $[O_2]$, is proportional to the partial pressure of oxygen in accordance with Henry's Law, we can replace it in equation (2) by the partial pressure p.

If we represent the concentration of oxygenated haemoglobin by $[HbO_2]$ and that of the non-oxygenated haemoglobin by $[Hb]$, the equation becomes

$$\frac{[HbO_2]}{[Hb]} = Kp \tag{3}$$

$$\log \frac{[HbO_2]}{[Hb]} = \log p + \log K \tag{4}$$

The logarithmic form is particularly useful since if we plot the values of $\log [HbO_2]/[Hb]$ as ordinates and the values of $\log p$ as abscissae, then since K is a constant, we shall obtain a straight line inclined at 45° and cutting the ordinate axis at the value of $\log K$. In the usual form where the percentage saturation is plotted on the y axis against partial pressures on the x axis, one obtains a hyperbola. This is the case for the muscle haemoglobin of mammals and the larval haemoglobin of *Gastrophilus*. In the most general case the dissociation curve is not a hyperbola but a sigmoid-shaped curve whose form can be empirically expressed by the well-known equation :

$$\frac{[HbO_2]}{[Hb]} = Kp^n$$

in which the exponent represents, although rather vaguely, the degree of interdependance or difference of the various groups which are oxygenated. In fact, in solutions of the muscle haemoglobin of Vertebrates and the haemoglobin of *Gastrophilus* there is only one type of oxygen-binding group. Myoglobin contains only one iron atom, and the larval haemoglobin contains two atoms which are identical in character. In haemoglobins giving a sigmoid curve, either the oxygen-binding groups in the same molecule have different oxygenation constants or the oxygenation of one modifies the constants of its neighbours. In general, the dissociation curves of Vertebrate haemoglobins have a sigmoid form but the degree of flattening varies from one class to another (Fig. 86).

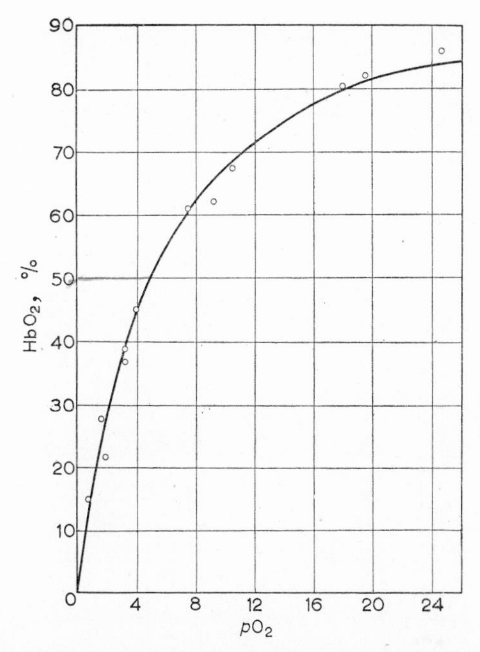

FIG. 85 (Keilin and Wang)—Dissociation curve of a concentrated solution (1×10^{-3} g.-mols haematin per litre) of a *Gastrophilus* haemoglobin. Temperature 39°C.

One can obtain an idea of the affinity of a particular haemoglobin for oxygen by noting the position of its dissociation curve at the p_{50} value, i.e. the partial pressure of oxygen corresponding to 50% oxygenation.

However it is necessary to compare values of p_{50} obtained under comparable conditions. Changes in temperature and pH displace the dissociation curve. The combination of molecular oxygen with a carrier being an exothermic process, an increase in temperature will lower the affinity, and a decrease in temperature will increase it. Figure 87 illustrates the shift in the dissociation curve of the oxyhaemoglobin of the ray *Raia ocellata* with temperature.

The influence which changes in the partial pressure of carbon dioxide (p_{CO_2}) have on the affinity of oxygen for haemoglobin is known as the

"Bohr effect". This influence of changes in the p_{CO_2} is due to changes in the pH causing changes in the dissociation of the amphoteric haemoglobin and thus altering the properties of the oxygen-binding groups. When the p_{CO_2} of an alkaline solution of haemoglobin is increased, the pH approaches

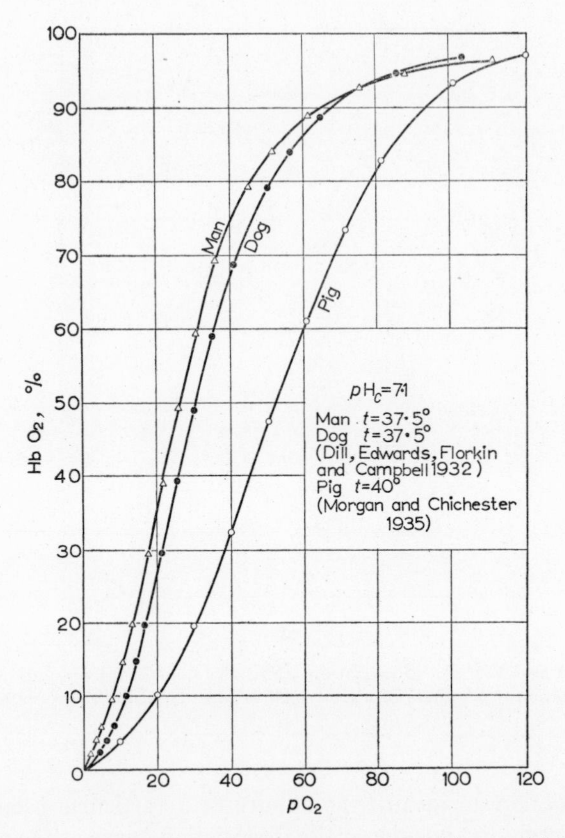

FIG. 86 (Morgan and Chichester)—Dissociation curves of haemoglobins of man, dog and pig.

the isoelectric point of the carrier and the dissociation of its acidic groups diminishes. The affinity of haemoglobin for oxygen diminishes likewise and the p_{50} value increases since the dissociation curve is displaced to the right. Figure 88 illustrates this phenomenon for horse haemoglobin. Since the influence and extent of the Bohr effect is very variable, to compare the oxygen affinities of different haemoglobins it is necessary to compare

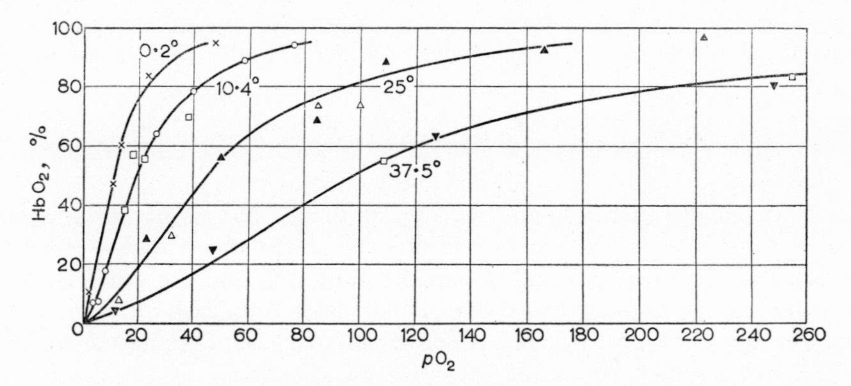

FIG. 87 (Dill, Edwards and Florkin)—Dissociation curves of haemoglobin of *Raia ocellata* at different temperatures.

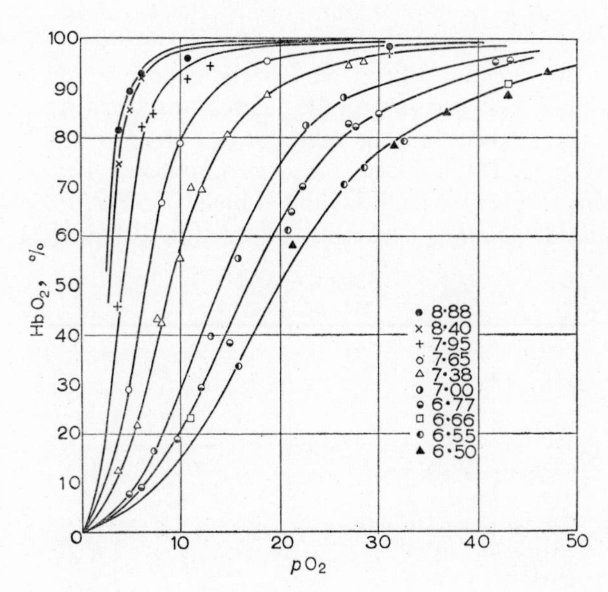

FIG. 88 (Ferry and Green)—Influence of changes in pH on the dissociation curve of horse haemoglobin.

dissociation curves obtained under similar conditions of pH and temperature. These conditions have not yet been satisfactorily fulfilled, since a change in the p_{CO_2} alters the pH of the blood and the pH of a solution of haemoglobin in different ways, and the dissociation curve in each case is displaced in a particular manner depending on the pH. The alteration in affinity with temperature also differs, for solutions of haemoglobin, according to the conditions and the nature of the haemoglobin. Whilst awaiting more precise results it is still possible to arrive at some interesting conclusions using the results published in the literature.

Of the known haemoglobins the one with the greatest affinity for oxygen is certainly that in the perienteric fluid of *Ascaris lumbricoides*. *Ascaris* possesses two haemoglobins, one in the body wall and the other in the perienteric fluid. These two haemoglobins differ from each other in their absorption spectra, which are both different from that of pig haemoglobin. The haemoglobins of *Ascaris* have a great affinity for oxygen: sodium hydrosulphite only reduces them very slowly and exposure to vacuum at 20° does not reduce them completely.

The haemoglobin of *Gastrophilus* larva has a lower affinity for oxygen. At 39° the p_{50} of a concentrated solution containing 1×10^{-3}g atoms of iron per litre has a value of 4·9mm; whilst the p_{50} of a dilute solution containing $0{\cdot}84 \times 10^{-4}$g atoms of iron per litre is 0·02mm Hg. The further complication we encounter here, namely the change in affinity with the degree of dilution, also occurs with the different mammalian haemoglobins.

Fox has compared the various values of p_{50}, at 10° and 17°, and in the absence of CO_2, for the undiluted bloods of *Chironomus* larva, of *Arenicola* and *Planorbis*, and for the slightly diluted bloods of *Tubifex*, *Daphnia* and *Ceriodaphnia*. He obtained the results collected in Table XVII.

TABLE XVII

(H. M. Fox)

	p_{50}	
	10°	17°
Chironomus riparius	0·5	0·6
Tubifex sp.	0·5	0·6
Ceriodaphnia laticaudata	—	0·8
Arenicola marina	1·5	1·8
Planorbis corneus	1·5	1·9
Daphnia magna	2·0	3·1

In this list, the haemoglobins of the *Chironomus* and of *Tubifex* have the highest affinity and that of *Daphnia* the lowest. We may compare the values in the second column with the p_{50} value of 27mm for human blood with a normal haemoglobin concentration and at 20° and pH 7·4. It is clear that the haemoglobin of Invertebrates has a distinctly higher affinity for oxygen than human haemoglobin.

The various haemoglobins also differ with respect to the change in their affinity for oxygen with pH (Bohr effect). Some haemoglobins do not show a Bohr effect; e.g. the haemoglobins of *Urechis*, of *Chironomus* larva and vertebrate myoglobin. The haemoglobins of Invertebrates other than those quoted above show only a very feeble effect (*Ceriodaphnia laticaudata*, *Thalassema neptuni*, *Arenicola marina*, *Planorbis corneus*, *Daphnia magna*). It is present in a more or less marked degree in the various classes of Vertebrates.

The haemoglobins also differ from each other in other ways. If for each haemoglobin we measure in ångström units the *span* separating the position in the absorption spectra of the α band of oxyhaemoglobin from the α band of carboxyhaemoglobin, we find clear-cut differences.

In addition, the auto-oxidation of haemoglobin to methaemoglobin is very slow for vertebrate haemoglobin and more rapid with that of *Gastrophilus*, mammalian myoglobin, and the haemoglobin found in the roots of legumes.

III. PROTEIN MACROMOLECULES

We have emphasized the specific character of macromolecules. Even in the arsenal of enzymes common to all cells we find indications of this specificity. The glucose dehydrogenase of vertebrate liver for example, is not inhibited by toluene, whilst that of *E. coli* is inhibited. Yeast alcohol dehydrogenase is completely inhibited by 0·001M iodoacetate, whilst even at a concentration of 0·01M, animal alcohol dehydrogenase remains unaffected. Glutamic acid dehydrogenase of yeast requires TPN as a coenzyme whilst the same enzyme from plants needs DPN.

When examining the various characteristics of the haemoglobins we noted a number of differences arising from the different properties of the protein moiety.

Another aspect of diversity in macromolecules is provided by the production, in animals, of protein molecules circulating in the blood in response to the injection of various substances. These antibodies are specific for the injection antigens (proteins, polysaccharides, etc.) and react with them to produce a precipitate, or agglutination if the antigen is attached to a cell surface. The antibodies circulating in the blood are usually present in the serum γ-globulin fraction.

The antibody properties of these molecules is due to the special characteristics of a given part of the macromolecule and numerous facts indicate that antibodies of various specificities are very similar to normal globulin except at one very small part of the macromolecule. For example, it is possible to split the macromolecule of an antibody with a protease and the antibody activity will remain localized in one of the hydrolysis products.

Substances capable of stimulating the production of antibody are called *complete antigens* and are generally protein in nature. However, a much smaller molecule attached to the antigen molecule may be the site for the specificity of action of the antibody so formed. This small molecule is known as a haptene. An example of this type is the antigenic activity of ovalbumin coupled to an azobenzoate ion. The antibodies formed will be of several types, certain of them reacting with the protein part of the molecule of antigen and others with its haptene, the azobenzoate ion. The antiserum prepared from a rabbit would precipitate the ovalbumin combined with the azobenzoate, but not ovalbumin alone. On the other hand, the antibody will combine with the free haptene but without giving rise to a precipitate. But the molecules of antibody which are combined with the free haptene will no longer combine with the antigen carrying the haptene and this competition between antigen and haptene for the site on the antibody molecule which is specific for the haptene will result in a decrease in the amount of precipitate formed by the combination of the antibody and the antigen.

The combination of the antigen with the antibody arises from the complementary character of their structures, the two corresponding regions of their molecules fitting each other in such a way that they are bound together without the intervention of strong chemical bonds. The complementary character of antigen and antibody is interpreted as due to the antibody being formed by the folding of its protein chain against the antigen acting as a template. According to Pauling the folding takes place so that hydrogen bonds may be formed and that charge interactions can be effective between the groups on the antigen and on the antibody.

Specific antiserums permit various antigens to be distinguished from each other and consequently also the various types of organisms which these antigens characterize.

Another aspect of diversity in marcomolecules shows itself by the insertion of the same enzyme unit into different systems.

The various systems containing the phenolase complex in animals and plants (heterotypical aspects of the same enzyme) are described in an excellent review by H. S. Mason (1955) and it will suffice to quote the conclusion of this review :

"At the phylogenetic level of the plants, it appears to catalyze the formation of intermediates in biosynthetic systems which produce the flower pigments and related flavonoids, the lacs and lacquers, the simple and polymeric tannins and their esters, the phenolic alkaloids, the quinones, tropolones and simple plant melanins, and the lignins. At higher phylogenetic levels the phenolase complex catalyzes intermediate phases in the pigmentation of the teguments, feathers, scales, hair and eyes of the chordates. A vital role for an enzyme of the phenolase type occurs during the biosynthesis of adrenaline and noradrenaline, but this remains to be clarified.

"Each of the numerous heterotypic expressions of the phenolase complex is produced by a unique biochemical sequence which is characterized by (1) a phenolase specificity becoming narrower with rise in the phylogenetic scale, (2) a characteristic chemical position in a metabolic network, and (3) a specific physical localization within cell and organ. These variables give ample play to the 'chance combination of genes which results in the development of short reaction chains utilizing substances whose synthesis had been previously acquired' (Horowitz, 1945), and to the states and composition of the environment which determine the extent to which the inherited phenolase complex can carry out its primary reaction. In this manner, the chemical structure of an enzyme and its substrate can be expressed as one of a number of biological characters."

REFERENCES

FLORKIN, M. (1948). La biologie des hématinoprotéides oxygénables. *Experientia*, **4**, 176–191.

GOODWIN, T. W. (1952). *The Comparative Biochemistry of the Carotenoids*, London, Chapman & Hall.

GRANICK, S. (1954). Metabolism of heme and chlorophyll. *Chemical Pathways of Metabolism*, edited by GREENBERG, D. M., vol. II, New York, Academic Press, 287–342.

HAAGEN-SMITH, A. J. (1953). The biogenesis of terpenes. *Ann. Rev. Plant Physiol.*, **4**, 305–324.

MASON, H. S. (1955). Comparative biochemistry of the phenolase complex. *Advanc. Enzymol.*, **16**, 105–184.

PAPPENHEIMER, A. M. (Editor) (1953), *The Nature and Significance of the Antibody Response*, Columbia University Press, New York.

WYMAN, J., Jnr. (1948). Heme proteins. *Advanc. Protein Chem.*, **4**, 407–531.

CHAPTER II

THE INHERITANCE OF BIOCHEMICAL CHARACTERISTICS

I. CONTROL OF BIOCHEMICAL CHARACTERISTICS BY GENES

BEADLE has expressed in the following terms the generally held views today on the transmission of biochemical characteristics :

"In order to exist as such, genes obviously must be capable of inducing the formation of exact copies of themselves. . . . In addition to catalysing formation of more units like themselves, genes in general have hetero-catalytic properties, that is they catalyse the formation of other substances. . . . In determining the specific chemical and perhaps physical configuration of protein molecules, genes directly determine enzyme specificities and thereby control in a primary way enzymatic synthesis and other chemical reactions in the organism. . . ."

The colour of the fruit of the tomato *Lycopersicon esculentum* results from the presence of a series of carotenoids whose existence depends on at least three genes (T, R, B,). As far as the two genes T and R are concerned, Table XVIII shows the carotenoid pattern in four pure strains of *Lycopersicon* of the four genotypes RT, Rt, rT and rt.

TABLE XVIII

The carotene content of four strains of tomato

(Mackinney and Jenkins, 1952)

Carotene type	Micrograms of carotenoid per gramme of fruit			
	RT Red	Rt Orange	rT Yellow	rt Intermediate
All-*trans* Lycopene	70–130	—	0–0·5	—
cis Isomers of lycopene	—	40–55	—	10–15
β-carotene (all-*trans*)	5–10	3–12	1–3	0·5–1·0
poly-cis-carotene	—	8–15	—	—
all-*trans*-S-carotene	0–0·1	20–15	—	0·01
Phytofluene	3–5	4–7	Ca. 0·1	0·7–1·0
Total	80–150	75–150	3–7	15–20

The carotenoid concentration increases in the following order of genotypes

rT rt Rt RT

and it can be seen that the chief result of substituting R for r is an increase in the amount of carotenoid.

The flower pigments, which we described under the name anthocyanins and whose glycones are called anthocyanidins, have been the object of extensive genetic studies carried out at the John Innes Horticultural Institute. The anthoxanthins by their presence can modify the colour of a flower determined by the anthocyanins. A change in a single gene may markedly alter the colour of a flower. For example, in the snapdragon the yellow or white colour depends on particular combinations of the same pair of allelomorphs, *Y* and *y*. A yellow colour corresponds to the genotypes *YY* or *Yy*, whilst the recessive plants *yy* have white flowers. The reader will find a number of descriptions of biochemical characteristics controlled by genes in the work of Wagner and Mitchell (1955).

II. BIOCHEMICAL DIFFERENTIATION OF CELLS IN A SINGLE ORGANISM

In the course of the ontogenesis of a multicellular organism, the various cells, although characterized by having the same genotype, may be different biochemically. The process called "determination" by the embryologists causes one or other set of genes to act, the result being apparent in the differentiation of each class of cell, resulting from the influence of the cytoplasm on the activity of the genes or on the products of genes. The biochemical diversity of organisms is hence in fact a diversity of cell aggregates which are themselves biochemically differentiated.

The explanation of how cells coming from the same zygote are differentiated biochemically, belongs to the domain of chemical embryology and chemical genetics and is still largely conjectural.

In a remarkable series of studies on the content and history of the cell theory, John R. Baker (1948) has provided a modern formulation of the theory in the following seven propositions:

"I. Most organisms consist of a large number of microscopic bodies called 'cells', which, in the less differentiated tissues, tend to be polyhedral or nearly spherical.

"II. Cells have certain definable characters. These characters show that cells (*a*) are all of essentially the same nature and (*b*) are units of structure.

"III. Cells always arise, directly or indirectly, from pre-existing cells, usually by binary fission.

"IV. Cells sometimes become transformed into bodies no longer possessing all the characteristics of a cell. Cells (together with these transformed cells, if present) are the living parts of organisms : that is, the parts which accomplish the synthesis of new material. Cellular organisms consist of nothing except cells, transformed cells, and material extruded by cells and by transformed cells (except that in some cases water, with its dissolved substances, is taken directly from the environment into the coelom or other intercellular space).

"V. Cells are to some extent individuals, and there are therefore two grades of individuality in most organisms; that of the cells, and that of the organism as a whole.

"VI. Each cell of a many-celled organism corresponds in certain respects to the whole body of a simple protist.

"VII. Many-celled plants and animals probably originated by the adherence of protist individuals after division."

The fact that cells are all of essentially the same nature is described in the first part of this book under the heading of the biochemical unity of organisms, and this idea implies also for the biochemist the similarity of each cell of a multicellular organism to a monocellular organism. The idea that organisms are made up of cells and transformed cells, for the biochemist, corresponds to the concept of the biochemical diversity of the cells of the same organism, all having however the same genotype. To illustrate the great variety of biochemical differentiation in cells having the same genotype, we shall take as our example an adult mammal such as man. The cells of the ectoderm become differentiated into the cells of the epidermis, of the glands of the skin, of the adenohypophysis, into nerve cells and modified nerve cells such as those of the neurohypophysis or the suprarenal medulla, etc.

To the biochemist, the epiderm cell in mammals is characterized particularly by the biosynthesis of keratin, a protein rich in S–S linkages. This type of cell is also one of the sites of synthesis of cholesterol. The cells of the sebaceous glands are notable in bringing about the rapid transformation of the whole of their content into a mixture of many lipides, saturated alcohols, and hydrocarbons, etc.

Among the large polyhedral cells of the adenohypophysis we find several types : cells whose cytoplasm is only slightly chromophilic, acidophilic cells or eosinophils (α cells), and basophilic cells (β cells). The eosinophils are differentiated in that they synthesize two hormones, somatotrophic (growth) hormone, and the lactogenic hormone (luteotrophin). The basophilic cells biosynthesize thyrotrophic hormone, adrenocorticotrophic hormone (ACTH), follicle stimulating hormone and the luteinizing hormone. It was once believed that the hormones of the anterior hypophysis were all proteins, but this has been shown to be false for ACTH and is very doubtful where the thryotrophic hormone is concerned.

The neurones or nerve cells are characterized biochemically by the nature and concentration of the complex lipides they contain and by an exceptionally high concentration of the enzymes of the priming reactions which consume glucose, and notably of hexokinase. Also the concentration of the α-decarboxylase of glutamic acid (coenzyme: pyridoxal-5-phosphate) is particularly high in neurones. The system for the amidation of glutamic acid is also very abundant. The neurones are of two types. All the preganglionic fibres of the autonomic nervous system are cholinergic as also are the postganglionic fibres of the parasympathetic system and certain postganglionic fibres of the sympathetic system (those serving the sweat glands for instance). The motor nerves are also cholinergic. Besides the quantitative aspect of acetylcholine synthesis, the cholinergic fibres are characterized biochemically by the mechanism of the transport of this substance along the fibre and its liberation at the extremities. The adrenergic nerves synthesize noradrenaline, apparently by decarboxylation of dihydroxyphenylserine. The cells of the adrenal medulla synthesize noradrenaline and adrenaline, the latter from phenylalanine as has been proved by using phenylalanine marked with ^{14}C in the α-carbon, the isotope later appearing in the α-carbon of adrenaline.

The argentaffin cells of the intestine are differentiated in that they can synthesize 5-hydroxytryptamine, probably *via* 5-hydroxytryptophane. Another biochemical differentiation of nerve cells is observed in the dendritic melanocytes which, in the skin and the eye, are specialized for the

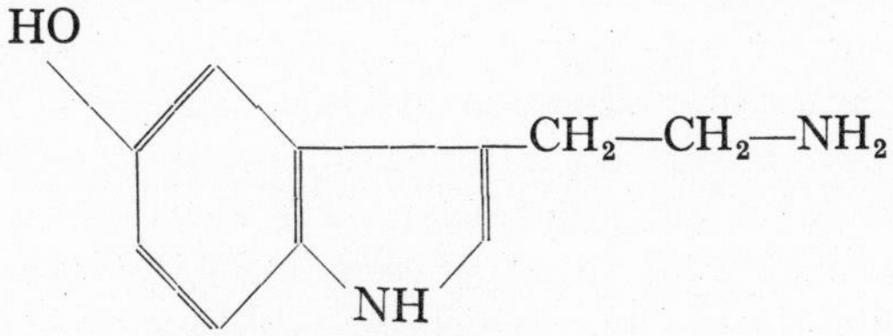

HO

$CH_2—CH_2—NH_2$

NH

5-hydroxytryptamine

biosynthesis of melanin. By means of their tyrosinase these cells transform tyrosine to dihydroxyphenylalanine, or DOPA, a substance similar in structure to noradrenaline. The cells of the neurohypophysis, another type of specialized nerve cell, perform a special synthesis, that of vasopressin and oxytocin.

The cells of the endoderm differentiate into the cells of the salivary glands, the mucous cells of the digestive tract, the exocrine pancreas, the hepatic parenchyma, the parathyroid, the insulin-producing tissue, the thyroid and the pulmonary epithelium.

The cells of the mucous membrane of the digestive tract and its neighbouring glands show many types of biochemical differentiation. The cells of the salivary glands are either of the mucous type or of the serous type.

These latter synthesize ptyalin, an endoamylase which is also an α-amylase. When we come to the gastric mucosa, besides mucous cells we find present parietal cells specialized for the secretion of hydrochloric acid by a mechanism of active transport, and peptic cells which can synthesize pepsinogen, from which an endopeptidase, pepsin, is formed.

The cells of the exocrine pancreas are remarkably specialized for the production of a whole series of enzyme proteins. Among these proteins we find a lipase, an amylase, a maltase, a lactase, invertases, an exopeptidase (carboxypeptidase) and various proenzymes, notably trypsinogen and chymotrypsinogen. These two latter substances are transformed in the intestinal lumen into two endopeptidases, trypsin and chymotrypsin. The secretory cells of the intestinal mucosa produce a series of exopeptidases: leucine aminopeptidase, glycyl-glycine dipeptidase, aminotripeptidase, glycyl-leucine dipeptidase, prolidase, etc. In addition they synthesize a maltase, an invertase, an enterokinase, nucleotidases and nucleosidases.

One of the biochemical characteristics of the cells of the hepatic parenchyma, in the domain of carbohydrate metabolism, is the presence of glucose-6-phosphatase. Its presence enables the liver cell to liberate glucose from G-6-P. The liver cell is also able to set free glucose from G-1-P and liver glycogen. The cells of the hepatic parenchyma are much more active than other cells in utilizing CO_2 for the synthesis of oxaloacetic acid from pyruvic acid and of malic acid from pyruvic acid. The carbohydrate metabolism of the liver cell is much more complex than that of other types of cell for a multiplicity of operations is involved: conversion of glucose into various hexoses, glycogenesis, glucose oxidation, synthesis of amino and fatty acids, glycogenolysis and gluconeogenesis. In the degradation of fatty acids, the liver cell is found to possess a special biochemical peculiarity; there is a check on the speed of entry of acetyl-CoA into the tricarboxylic acid cycle. Even under normal conditions, the stationary state of the cell in the hepatic parenchyma is characterized by a certain accumulation of acetyl-CoA due to the fact that its entry into the tricarboxylic acid cycle is less rapid than in other tissues. Associated with this peculiarity is another, which is the existence of a side reaction in which two molecules of acetyl-CoA condense together and lose a molecule of CoA to form acetoacetyl-CoA which is hydrolysed by a deacylase into acetoacetic acid and CoA. This reaction only occurs to a slight degree in most cells and the small amount of acetoacetic acid formed is reconverted into acetoacetyl-CoA, but in the liver cell this reconversion only occurs to a slight extent. The slowness of oxidation of acetyl-CoA, the concentration of which is maintained at a higher level than in other cells, leads to a greater production of acetoacetic acid which is only slightly reconverted to acetyl-CoA, and hence ketone bodies are formed. In fact, in the liver cell, the greater part of the acetoacetic acid formed is reduced to β-hydroxybutyric acid by butyric dehydrogenase. A small part of the acetoacetic acid decarboxylates spontaneously to form acetone. The name *ketone bodies* is given to the sum of acetoacetic acid, β-hydroxybutyric acid and acetone. Ketogenesis, although occurring to a slight extent in cells in general, is not accompanied by an accumulation of ketone bodies as takes place in the liver cell. The stationary state in normal liver is characterized by a higher concentration of these substances which then pass into the circulation. The conglomeration of cells of the liver parenchyma forms the chief site of synthesis of lipides from carbohydrate and the liver cell is responsible for the synthesis of the phospholipides of blood plasma.

When we come to consider protein metabolism, the cells of the hepatic parenchyma in mammals are seen to possess important biochemical characteristics. They are the principal site of deamination of amino acids due to their high concentration of glutamic dehydrogenase. This process also occurs in the kidney but the liver, which is also the site of ureogenesis, is distinguished by possessing the system of enzymes which operate the "ornithine cycle". In this cycle glutamic acid, ammonia and CO_2 combine to form carbamylglutamate, which in the presence of ATP and Mg^{++} combines with a further molecule of CO_2 and a further molecule of ammonia to give an intermediate whose nature is still unknown. This latter compound reacts with ornithine giving citrulline and regenerating carbamylglutamic acid.

$$\underset{\text{glutamic acid}}{HOOC—CH_2—CH_2—\underset{\underset{NH_2}{|}}{CH}—COOH} + CO_2 + NH_3 \xrightarrow{-H_2O} \underset{\text{carbamylglutamic acid}}{HOOC—CH_2—CH_2—\underset{\underset{\underset{\underset{\underset{O}{\|}}{C—NH_2}}{|}}{NH}}{|}}{CH}—COOH}$$

$$HOOC—CH_2—CH_2—\underset{\underset{\underset{\underset{\underset{O}{\|}}{C—NH_2}}{|}}{NH}}{|}}{CH}—COOH + NH_3 + CO_2 \longrightarrow \text{unknown intermediate}$$

$$\text{unknown intermediate} + \underset{\text{ornithine}}{NH_3—CH_2—CH_2—CH_2—\underset{\underset{NH_2}{|}}{CH}—COOH}$$

$$\xrightarrow{\text{enzyme}} \underset{\text{citrulline}}{NH_2—\underset{\underset{O}{\|}}{C}—\overset{H}{N}—CH_2—CH_2—CH_2—\underset{\underset{NH_2}{|}}{CH}—COOH} + \text{carbamylglutamic acid}$$

Under the influence of an enzyme system that functions in the presence of Mg^{++} and ATP, the citrulline reacts with aspartic acid forming arginosuccinic acid which is converted into arginine and fumaric acid in the presence of another enzyme system

$$\underset{\text{citrulline}}{H_2N\text{—}\underset{\underset{O}{\|}}{C}\text{—}\overset{H}{N}\text{—}CH_2\text{—}CH_2\text{—}CH_2\text{—}\underset{\underset{NH_2}{|}}{CH}\text{—}COOH} + \underset{\text{aspartic acid}}{HOOC\text{—}CH_2\text{—}\underset{\underset{NH_2}{|}}{CH}\text{—}COOH}$$

$$\xrightarrow[Mg^{++},\ ATP]{\text{enzyme}} HN{=}\underset{\underset{HN\text{—}\underset{\underset{\underset{\underset{COOH}{|}}{CH_2}}{|}}{C}\text{—}H\text{—}COOH}{|}}{C}\text{—}\overset{H}{N}\text{—}CH_2\text{—}CH_2\text{—}CH_2\text{—}\underset{\underset{NH_2}{|}}{CH}\text{—}COOH$$

arginosuccinic acid

$$\Big\downarrow \text{enzyme} \quad H_2O$$

$$\underset{\text{arginine}}{H_2N\text{—}\underset{\underset{NH}{\|}}{C}\text{—}\overset{H}{N}\text{—}CH_2\text{—}CH_2\text{—}CH_2\text{—}\underset{\underset{NH_2}{|}}{CH}\text{—}COOH} + \underset{\text{fumaric acid}}{HOOC\text{—}CH{=}CH\text{—}COOH}$$

The arginine is hydrolysed to urea and ornithine in the presence of arginase

$$\underset{\text{arginine}}{H_2N\text{—}\underset{\underset{NH}{\|}}{C}\text{—}\overset{H}{N}\text{—}CH_2\text{—}CH_2\text{—}CH_2\text{—}\underset{\underset{NH_2}{|}}{CH}\text{—}COOH}$$

$$\xrightarrow{\text{arginase}} O{=}C\begin{matrix} \diagup NH_2 \\ \diagdown NH_3 \end{matrix} \quad + \underset{\text{ornithine}}{NH_2\text{—}CH_2\text{—}CH_2\text{—}CH_2\text{—}\underset{\underset{NH_2}{|}}{CH}\text{—}COOH}$$

The fumaric acid passes into the tricarboxylic acid cycle or in the presence of fumarase it is transformed to malic acid which also enters the Krebs cycle.

In mammalian liver parenchyma cells, the synthesis of the steroid skeleton which was described on p. 236 is extended by acquisition of an enzyme system leading to the production of the substances known as bile acids. In man, this synthesis yields cholic acid, desoxycholic acid and chenodesoxycholic acid. The hepatic parenchyma in mammals also conjugates these bile acids with taurine and with glycine.

The pathway from cholesterol to cholic acid implies that there are a number of stages and a number of enzymes involved. Another characteristic of the liver cell is its ability to bring about detoxication reactions, in man the most important being conjugation with glucuronic acid. Liver contains UDP-glucuronate and an enzyme which catalyses its formation from glucuronic acid. This UDP-glucuronate appears to be one of the substances involved in the biosynthesis of mucopolysaccharides. In the

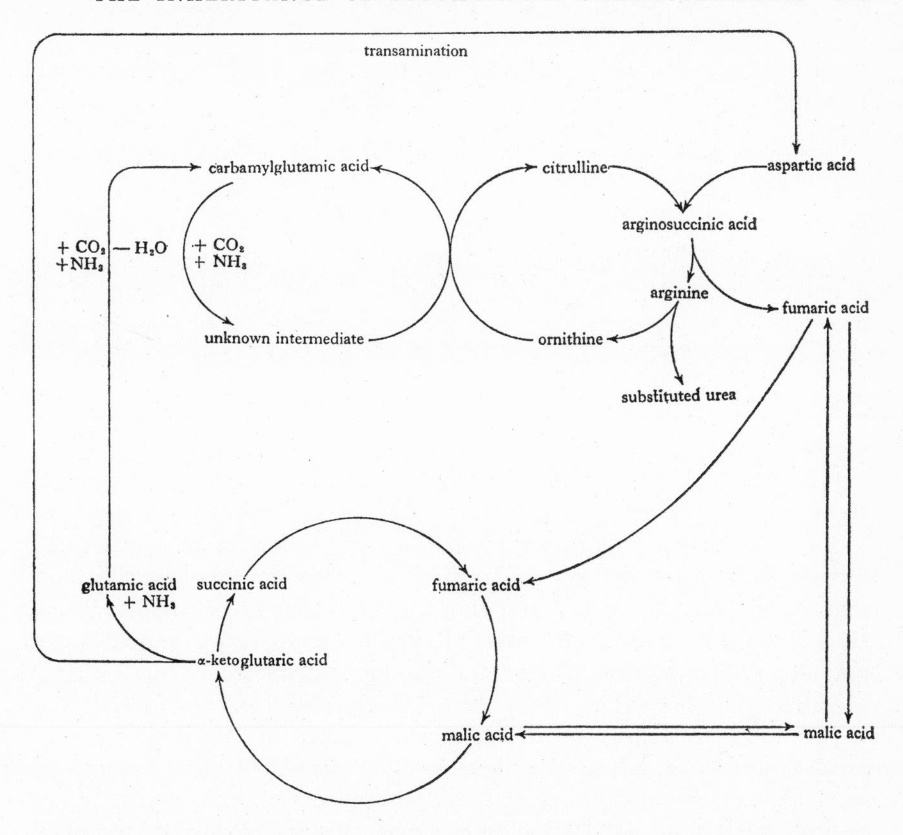

presence of alcohols, phenols, or aromatic acids, the UDP-glucuronate is diverted from its normal function and the foreign substance is excreted as a glucuronate formed in the following type of reaction

$$\text{UDP-glucuronate} + \text{ROH} \longrightarrow \text{UDP} + \text{R-O-glucuronate}$$

Bilirubin resulting from the breakdown of haemoglobin in the cells of the reticulo-endothelial system passes into the blood plasma where it circulates in combination with the α_1-globulin fraction; from there it passes into the cells of the hepatic parenchyma which conjugate the bilirubin with glucuronic acid and excrete the product in the bile. Furthermore the hepatic parenchyma is the site of considerable protein synthesis, that of the blood plasma proteins.

The cells of the parathyroid gland show a special type of biochemical differentiation in that they are able to synthesize parathyroid hormone, a true protein hormone which has so far not been isolated in a pure state.

The pancreatic islets consist of two types of cell differing in their biosynthetic characteristics: the α-cells which produce glucagon and the

β-cells which produce insulin. The latter hormone is a protein (see p. 107) whilst glucagon is a polypeptide in which the amino acid sequence is the following :

His. ser. glu. gly. thr. phe. thr. ser. asp. tyr. ser. lys. tyr. leu. asp. ser. arg. arg. ala. glu. asp. phe. val. glu. try. leu. met. asp. thr.

(Brower, Sinn, Staub and Behrens)

The cells of the thyroid gland fix I^- ions and oxidize them enzymically to iodine. They contain the specific enzyme systems for the formation of iodotyrosine and iodohistidine, and for the condensation of the iodotyrosines into iodothyronines, especially the two thyroid hormones, L-3:5:3′-triiodothyronine and L-3:3′-diiodothyronine. Another thyroid hormone and the most important quantitatively is L-thyroxine, derived from the coupling together of two molecules of L-3:5-diiodotyrosine.

From the mesoderm are formed the cells of the muscles, of connective tissue, the cells of the adrenal cortex, of the gonads and the urinary tract.

The cell of striated muscle is specialized chiefly for the biosynthesis of myosin, and in the non-myosin fraction of striated muscle fibres we find that the glycolytic enzymes predominate, hence the great importance of aerobic glycolysis in skeletal muscle. The fibres of the myocardium are better provided with mitochondria and the enzyme-systems for respiration and oxidative phosphorylation than those of skeletal muscle.

The internal framework in mammals consists of connective tissue, cartilage and bone. These structures contain and bound the groupings of specialized epithelial cells—which are localized into organs which is turn are integrated to form the complete organism. From a biochemical point of view, the body framework is a network of connective tissue modified in certain regions to form cartilage and bone.

The connective tissues are made up of three types of constituents : cells, fibres and ground substance. In ordinary connective tissue, the cells are of two types, histiocytes and fibrocytes. The histiocytes are provided with a number of special biochemical properties notably in the possession of a system able to rupture the α-methene bridge in the haemoglobin of senile (120–130 days old) erythrocytes which they have phagocytized.

The fibrocytes are differentiated so that they can perform the biosynthesis of connective fibres and the ground substance. The collagen fibres, produced by the fibrocytes, differ markedly from the other proteins in the mammalian organism in containing unusually large amounts of glycine and proline, a small amount of histidine and almost undetectable amounts of tryptophane and cystine. Also, collagen contains certain amino acids which are not present in other body proteins (elastin excepted): these are hydroxyproline and hydroxylysine. Collagen fibres have a special type of physical structure and under the electron microscope a transverse striation can be seen. Elastin fibres, also a product of the fibrocytes, like collagen, contain much glycine and proline, traces of tyrosine and no tryptophan. But whilst collagen is more or less "normal" in the amounts of arginine, lysine, aspartic acid and glutamic acid which it contains, elastin contains only very small amounts of these polar amino acids. The ground substance, also synthesized by the fibrocytes, consists of mucoproteins the prosthetic groups of which consist of chondroitin sulphate joined to galactosamine by a glycoside linkage. The ground substance also contains free mucopolysaccharides, the chief one being hyaluronic acid (acetylglucosamine + glucuronic acid).

In the type of connective tissue known as cartilage, the ground substance is more dense than that of ordinary connective tissue and besides collagen and elastin fibres it contains a chondromucoid the prosthetic group of which is chondroitin sulphate. In the case of bony tissue, its character is a result of the biochemical differentiation of the large cells of mesenchymatous origin, the osteoblasts. The beginning of this differentiation of a mesenchymatous cell into an osteoblast, depends on the position of the cell in the bone-forming region and is marked by the appearance of alkaline phosphatase in the nucleus and the accumulation of large amounts of glycogen in the cytoplasm. The mitochondria increase in number and the amount of RNA in the cytoplasm also increases. Between the cells, the interstitial substance is made up mainly of reticular fibres. As differentiation continues, phosphatase activity appears in the cytoplasm and finally reaches a maximum and so does the accumulation of glycogen. The number of mitochondria continues to increase. The basophilic character of the cytoplasm also increases. Bundles of osteogenous collagen appear in the interstitial substance, distinct from normal collagen in giving a positive reaction for alkaline phosphatase and in being highly metachromatic due to the presence of polysaccharides. The osteoblast having reached its final form the phosphatase activity in the nucleus and cytoplasm decreases sharply and the cytoplasmic glycogen disappears whilst the basophilia attains a maximum. The organic matrix of the bone, strongly metachromatic and later to be filled with bone salts, appears in the region of the non-nucleated extremity of the osteoblast. What we have just described is the most simple type of ossification and is known as the intramembranous type. In most bones, the production by the osteoblasts of the calcifiable matrix of the bone takes place on a cartilaginous former. The bone is constantly eroded and new osseous material laid down. The erosion is due to the activity of the osteoclasts, mesenchymatic cells differentiated to possess proteolytic activity. In fact, in the case of osteoblasts and osteoclasts, it would be preferable to speak of biochemical modification rather than of biochemical differentiation. In reality osteocytes, osteoblasts and osteoclasts are examples of reversible modifications of the same type of connective cell.

The mesenchymatic cells are not only transformed into fibrocytes, cartilaginous cells, osteoblasts and osteoclasts. They also give rise to the various types of blood cell. An erythrocyte begins as a reticulated cell in the bone marrow, and, from a biochemical point of view, we can recognize three phases in its differentiation. In the first stage, the cell contains a few mitochondria and a nucleus with a very distinct nucleolus. The cytoplasm, rich in RNA, is highly basophilic. The cell multiplies rapidly and an active synthesis of proteins and nucleic acids is going on. In the second stage the nucleus loses its nucleolus and the basophilia of the cytoplasm diminishes. During the third stage, that of the polychromatic erythoblast, we see a further diminution of RNA and at the same time the cell becomes acidophilic and is coloured by acid stains. This is the result of the biosynthesis of a new relatively basic protein, globin. At the same period, molecules of haem and haemoglobin are rapidly formed.

In the orthochromatic erythroblast, or normoblast, cell division does not occur. The mitochondria have disappeared and only traces of RNA remain in the cytoplasm. The nucleus is small. On the other hand, the haemoglobin concentration has increased from 1–2 parts per 100 to 20 parts per 100. The nucleus having disappeared, the cell flattens and becomes biconcave so that the red blood cell is nothing more than a bag of haemoglobin, only the cytoplasmic enzyme systems having been retained: those for glycolysis and the hexosemonophosphate shunt, reducing systems able to maintain the haemoglobin in the reduced state. The red blood corpuscle contains relatively large amounts of catalase. It protects the haemoglobin by decomposing the hydrogen peroxide which would otherwise form in the corpuscle.

The study of leucocytes is still in the hands of histologists. But a few results of a biochemical nature have been obtained and they show some aspects of differentiation. Neutrophil leucocytes, for example, show a high aerobic glycolysis and they contain esters of hyaluronic acid. The granules of the eosinophils are surrounded by an envelope of phospholipides and among their constituents there is an antihistaminic substance. From the megakaryocytes of the bone marrow are derived the blood platelets which are highly specialized biochemically. They contain, and liberate into the blood on clotting, a number of *platelet factors*, one activating thromboplastin, another accelerating the formation of thrombin from prothrombin, yet another accelerating the conversion of fibrinogen to fibrin, etc.

The most remarkable example of differentiation in cells of mesodermic origin is the metabolic series which continues the process of biosynthesis of the steroid ring (see p. 236). We have already described one of these continuations, the synthesis of bile acids by the liver cell. In the cells of the adrenal cortex and the gonads, other systems continue the biosynthesis of the steroid ring with the formation of steriod hormones.

It is generally accepted that the active cells in the adrenal cortex are those of the *zona fasciculata*, which secrete corticosteroids under the influence of ACTH. The secretion of the various corticosteroid hormones implies that a complex system of enzymes is involved which characterizes the biochemical differentiation of the cells of the *zona fasciculata*. The reader will find an excellent account of the biology of the adrenal cortex in the recent work of Chester Jones (1957).

When we come to consider the biosynthesis of the steroid hormones by the gonads, or by the placenta, here also we have enzyme systems special to these cells.

The preceding pages give only a slight idea of the biochemical diversity accompanying cellular differentiation in the organism of a mammal such as man. Also, the description of these differentiations has been made in an altogether too schematic manner without taking into account the variations existing from cell to cell in the framework of the same cellular differentiation.

Among the same class of differentiated cells we may also observe an individual biochemical variation depending on time, age and the reproductive cycle, etc. In the water flea *Daphnia*, for example, the haemoglobin content of the blood varies with the instar. The smallest concentration corresponds to the time when the eggs have reached the development of late-stage embryos ready to be released. After this the blood haemoglobin rapidly diminishes, passing from the blood into the ovaries before the eggs are laid. After the laying of the eggs the blood of the female gradually recovers its haemoglobin content (Fox, Hardcastle and Dresel, 1949).

III. PHENOTYPE AND "*MILIEU*"

Under given conditions of the *milieu*, cellular differentiation controlled by a given genotype can produce an extreme diversity of results in the way of biochemical systems. When to this is added the influence of the *milieu* even further differences in a given biochemical system may be produced.

Grasshoppers which have been raised at an elevated temperature are pale whilst those which have grown at a lower temperature are dark. This is because at temperatures higher than 40° the biosyntheses of melanin and of insectorubin are inhibited. Here we have a direct action on an enzymatic component of the existing phenotype, and we may call this a phenotropic action of the *milieu*.

A further example, the green pigment present in the tegument of solitary locusts is not present in the insects of the gregarious type. The haemolymph of the solitary form is a brilliant green whilst that of the gregarious form is a golden-yellow. The characteristic difference here is the production of mesobiliverdin in the solitary locust.

A remarkable example of the influence of the *milieu* on the biochemical form of the phenotype is provided by the influence of the partial pressure of oxygen in the *milieu* on the biosynthesis of haem derivatives. It has been shown in yeasts that the presence of air stimulates the synthesis of cytochromes *a*, *b* and *c* and that the absence of air inhibits this synthesis. On the other hand, it is well known that a fall in oxygen pressure increases the blood haemoglobin in man at high altitudes and in fishes living in waters poor in oxygen. In mammals, a fall in the external oxygen pressure also increases the cytochrome-*c* and myoglobin concentrations in muscles. Among the Cladocera, a subdivision of the Crustacea, a fall in the oxygen content of the medium increases the haemoglobin concentration in muscles, ganglia and blood. In *Daphnia pulex*, *D. magna* and *D. obtusa*, an increase in blood haemoglobin in poorly aerated water has been demonstrated by H. M. Fox. Fox and Phear also observed that the animals lost their blood pigment in well aerated waters.

Whatever the type of differences in the biochemical order which can be brought about by the influence of the medium on the biochemical phenotype, it is possible to determine the spectrum of possible phenotypes and so to find the limits set to the organism by its own genetic potential in the realization of the phenotype by the interaction of the environment and the genotype.

REFERENCES

BAKER, J. R. (1948). The cell-theory : a restatement, history and critique. Part I. *Quart. J. Micr. Sc.*, **89**, 103–125.

JONES, T. CHESTER (1957). *The Adrenal Cortex*. Univ. Press, Cambridge.

KNOX, W. E., AUERBACH, V. H. and LIN, E. C. C. (1956). Enzymatic and metabolic adaptations in animals. *Physiol. Rev.* **36**, 164–254.

PROSSER, C. L. (1955). Physiological variation in animals. *Biol. Rev.*, **30**, 229–262.

WAGNER, R. P. and MITCHELL, H. K. (1955). *Genetics and Metabolism*. Wiley, New York.

CHAPTER III

BIOCHEMISTRY AND TAXONOMY

I. BIOCHEMICAL DIVERSITY

"EACH species consists of groups of individuals with more or less similar gene combinations, optimally adapted for a given environment" (Mayr, 1949). This definition of species implies the existence of biochemical characters typical of the species and that these specific characters are adapted to the ecological niche in which the species prospers and dominates its competitors.

To illustrate this, let us consider the special properties of the haemoglobin in animals.

Typically, the respiratory function of the internal environment operates by means of a cycle in which the internal environment circulates around the organism between the various tissues and the point where it is equilibrated with the external environment or a continuation of the latter.

At the point of contact with the external environment the blood becomes charged with oxygen and gives up carbon dioxide. On reaching the tissues it loses oxygen and takes up carbon dioxide. This typical respiratory cycle requires the mediation of a physico-chemical system to bring about the transport of oxygen in one direction and of carbon dioxide in the other.

There are a number of properties of haemoglobin which are important when it functions as a carrier. It can be oxygenated and the degree of oxygenation is a function of the partial pressure of oxygen. Being a hetero-protein, it bears acid groups which can combine with bases, the dissociation of these groups varies with pH and cations are lost when the pH approaches the isoelectric point. The dissociation does not only vary with the pH but also according to the degree of oxygenation, and inversely, the degree of oxygenation at a given partial pressure of oxygen will vary with the dissociation of the acid groups in the neighbourhood of the oxygen-bearing groups. On the other hand, the carrier molecule bears free $-NH_2$ groups which are able to form compounds of the carbamate type with carbon dioxide.

We may plot the amount of absorbed oxygen as a function of its partial pressure for different bloods and coelomic fluids, the temperatures and carbon dioxide partial pressures being those existing in the arterial blood.

If we do this we obtain the series of curves shown in Fig. 89. These curves are very different one from another, one of the reasons for this being that the number of oxygen-binding groups varies from case to case. The oxygen capacity, i.e. the quantity of oxygen in volumes per cent corresponding to complete saturation of the carrier, in effect regulates the level at which the curve flattens out. In order to compare the different curves with profit, it is necessary to consider in each case, for different partial pressures, not only the amount of oxygen combined with the carrier, but also the degree of saturation of the latter. Thus, in Fig. 90 we have a series of curves whose positions can be related to each other by noting the value of the partial pressure of oxygen corresponding to 50% saturation (p_{50}). The position

TABLE XIX

	Raia ocellata	*Chelydra serpentina*	Duck	Goose	Man
O_2 total transported, vol. %	3·92	3·70	10·0	5·14	5·30
O_2 transported in dissolved form, vol. %	0·22	0·17	0·15	0·17	0·10

$p_{O_2} = \pm 150$ (in air, or in water in equilibrium with air)

TABLE XX

	Sipunculus nudus	*Urechis caupo*	*Busycon canaliculatum*	*Loligo pealeii*	*Raia ocellata*	*Chelydra serpentina*	Duck	Goose	Man	Horse
	Hr	Hb	Hcy	Hcy	Hb	Hb	Hb	Hb	Hb	Hb
p_{O_2} arterial	32	75	36	115	70	57	102	94	100	78
% sat. arterial blood	90	97	95	97	93	95	98	96	98	96

and the shape of the curves in Fig. 89 correspond, in each case, to the temperature and CO_2 partial pressure of the arterial blood. In the case of the ray the temperature is 10° and in man 38°.

The partial pressure of CO_2 is 8mm in the frog and 43mm in the case of the Urodel *Amphiuma*.

If the curves had been traced at the same p_{CO_2}, and at the same temperature, the p_{50} values would not have been those shown in Fig. 90. The particular shape and form which correspond to physiological conditions is

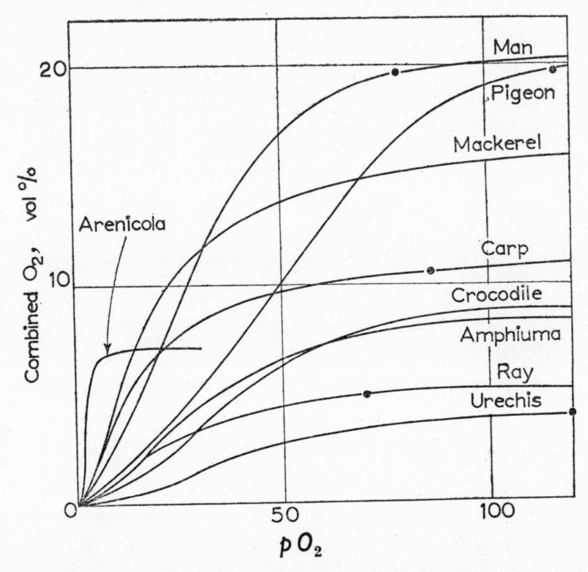

Fig. 89—Oxygen absorption curves for various bloods and coelomic fluids containing haemoglobin under "arterial" conditions reproduced *in vitro*. The black circles indicate the value of the arterial p_{O_2}.

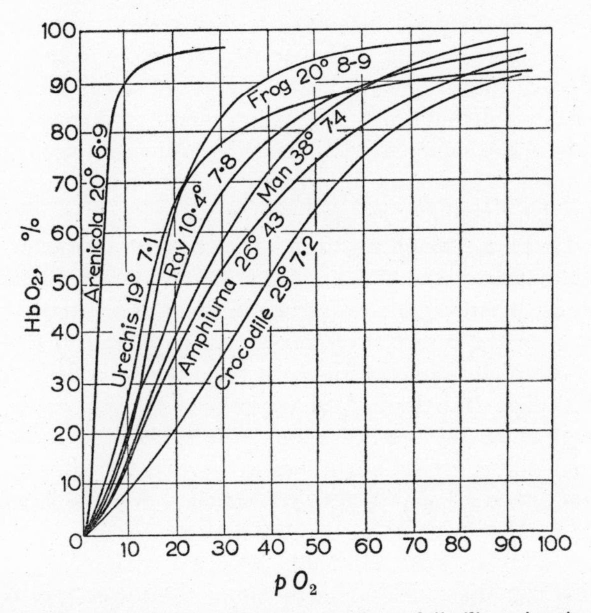

Fig. 90—Oxygen absorption curves for a number of "*milieux interieurs*" containing haemoglobin. The temperature is given and the pH except in the case of the Frog and Amphiuma, where the partial pressure of carbon dioxide is listed.

the result of the action of a multitude of factors such as the p_{CO_2} and temperature of the arterial blood, the affinity of the haemoglobin for oxygen, the intensity of the Bohr effect, etc.

Corpuscles containing haemoglobin are found in the blood of all Vertebrates, and since these animals have a well-defined respiratory cycle they are a useful starting-point for the study of the role of haemoglobin in the transport of oxygen by the blood.

The important part played by haemoglobin in oxygen transport is clearly shown by the values obtained for different bloods of the "transported oxygen", i.e. the difference in total oxygen between the venous and arterial blood less the difference in dissolved oxygen for these bloods.

The part played in oxygen transport by the sigmoid character of the dissociation curve is evident. With the partial pressures of oxygen occurring in arterial and venous blood, a hyperbolic curve would only allow the transport of a much smaller amount of oxygen. When the reduction of the blood is accompanied by acidification the Bohr effect also comes in, since the curve is displaced to the right, so that, at the same p_{O_2} there is a lower degree of oxygenation of haemoglobin.

Does the dissociation curve, as it exists under arterial and under venous conditions, show any characteristics parallel to the physiological or ecological character of the animal?

If, regardless of the particular oxygen carrier they contain, we examine the few animal species whose blood respiratory cycle is known, and if we note the values of the arterial p_{O_2} and the degree of saturation of the arterial blood, we shall find that from one case to another there exists, even for animals living in the same environment, very different gradients of oxygen pressures, contrary to what is found with CO_2 which is always, or nearly always, in the arterial blood, in equilibrium, with the external environment. Yet, whatever the p_{O_2} resulting from the particular character of the respiratory system, the arterial blood is always found to be 90 to 98% saturated. In other words, whatever the difference between the external p_{O_2} and the p_{O_2}, the point on the dissociation curve corresponding to the arterial p_{O_2} is always found to lie along the top right-hand portion of the curve.

Hence the shape and position of the dissociation curve are adapted to the respiratory needs of the organism. The slightest decrease in the p_{O_2} would immediately bring about a loss of oxygen from the haemoglobin. The fact that one is not justified in considering, even in aquatic animals, that the arterial p_{O_2} is equal to the external p_{O_2} has been verified by the observations of H. M. Fox (see Table XVII).

Despite the fact that we know little about the respiratory cycle of fish, it is possible to establish a relation between the more or less vertical shape of their dissociation curve and the concentration of oxygen in the external environment. First proposed in 1919 by Krogh and Leitch, this relation has been confirmed many times. As these authors pointed out, a strong affinity for oxygen allows a fish living in badly aerated water to charge its blood with oxygen more easily than could a fish possessing a haemoglobin of low affinity. Moreover, a high affinity, accentuated by a low temperature, would maintain the curve in the left-hand region between the axes, i.e. in the low-pressure region, and consequently the oxygen would be released to the tissues at a low pressure, unless the Bohr effect was to interfere and displace the curve to the right. Several workers have confirmed that in fresh-water fish the Bohr effect is more marked than in those living in deep cold waters and that the blood of these same fish also has a lower affinity for oxygen at low p_{CO_2} values. These two characteristics, feeble affinity and a relatively powerful Bohr effect, counterbalance the properties imposed on the blood by the low temperature. Various observations reveal the more or less marked "pumping action" due to the Bohr effect, in deep-water fish, in bringing about the liberation of oxygen in the swim-bladder. But if the Bohr effect is more marked in fresh-water Teleosts than in mammals, it is still more pronounced in the marine Teleosts which fits in with a characteristic property of the marine Teleosts, that of having a low arterial p_{CO_2}, corresponding to that of sea water. Here, the Bohr effect appears to be an effective correction of the almost hyperbolic character of the dissociation curve, without decreasing the efficiency of the charge mechanism as would be the case in a medium rich in CO_2.

Another example of a relation between the affinity for oxygen of the haemoglobin in the arterial blood and the oxygen level of the environment is provided by mammals living at high altitudes, such as the lama (*Lama huanachus*), the vicuna (*Lama vicugna*) and the viscacha (*Lagostoma* sp.), the haemoglobins of which have a higher affinity for oxygen than those of other mammals.

When the venous blood leaves the tissues on its way to the heart, the partial pressure of oxygen is 40mm Hg for man, 38mm in the horse, 56mm in the goose, 37mm in the duck, 15mm in the turtle *Chelydra serpentina*, 14mm in the ray *Raia ocellata*, and the corresponding degrees of saturation are 60%, 70%, 38%, 35% and 33% respectively. Thus, on the one hand a sufficient oxygen concentration gradient is assured, this being an important factor in the supply of this element to the cells, and on the other hand, the venous blood carries a reserve of oxygen which can be called upon if the rate of metabolism is increased, or if the supply of oxygen is curtailed.

The part played by this reserve is prominent in the seal which, during a dive, uses almost the whole of the oxygen in its blood. The almost total reduction of the venous blood has been reported to occur in other diving animals such as the duck and the musk-rat.

The use of haemoglobin to provide a reserve of oxygen can be observed during periods of suspension of the breathing mechanism. In an Invertebrate not provided with a circulation like *Urechis*, the functioning of this reserve can be clearly seen. The Echurian *Urechis caupo* is found along the Californian coast living in the mud and sand in a U-shaped tube through which it causes water to circulate during its periods of activity by the peristaltic action of its musculo-cutaneous tube. The continually renewed water brings food and oxygen to it. In fact by a peristaltic movement opposite in direction to that of the musculo-cutaneous tube, the animal can "inspire" the circulating water through its anus into its terminal intestine which is highly developed and the thin wall of which is in contact with the haemoglobin-containing corpuscles of the coelomic fluid. After a number of these inspiratory movements, a single expiratory movement follows expelling all the water in the intestine. In well-oxygenated water the haemoglobin of the coelomic fluid is almost completely saturated (97%) although the oxygen partial pressure is only 75mm Hg i.e. much less than in the surrounding water (around 150mm). If the animal is at rest under these conditions its haemoglobin will remain completely saturated and the dissolved oxygen will be sufficient for its needs. As we have said, the animal draws sea-water into its intestine and then expels it after having oxygenated its coelomic fluid at the expense of the oxygen in the sea-water. (In the expired water p_{O_2} = 100mm approx.) Under these conditions it does not use its haemoglobin at all. The volume of the coelomic fluid is about 20cm^3 and its oxygen capacity is 4 volumes per cent, so that the coelomic fluid contains 0·8 cm^3 of oxygen. The oxygen consumption of *Urechis*, on an average, is around 0·01cm^3/min. It is clear that only a small part of the oxygen has to be replaced each minute and for this the dissolved oxygen suffices. During its periods of activity which coincide with the periods of elimination of water, *Urechis* lives on the dissolved oxygen provided by its respiratory system. When the animal retires into the middle horizontal part of its tube after a period of activity, it remains motionless and ceases to cause the water to circulate or to be taken into its digestive tube.

The total amount of oxygen in the coelomic fluid and in the water of the intestine corresponds to the amount which it consumed in 70 min; if the coelomic fluid did not contain haemoglobin the oxygen would be used up after 14 min. Thus the presence of haemoglobin enables the animal to have a rest period between its periods of activity five times longer than would otherwise be possible.

When *Urechis* respires, the p_{O_2} of the water in its intestine is 100mm when the p_{O_2} of the outside water is 150mm.

Under these conditions the p_{O_2} of the coelomic fluid is 75mm. These conditions correspond to 97% saturation. The haemoglobin in the corpuscles remains saturated and the oxygen diffuses from the water in the intestine to the blood plasma and from there to the tissues. There is no evidence of the haemoglobin, which does not circulate, playing any part as a carrier. During the periods of rest, the animal stops breathing. The oxygen is not replenished from the water in the intestine and consequently the p_{O_2} of the coelomic plasma tends to fall, thus bringing about a liberation of oxygen from the haemoglobin because of the particular position of the dissociation curve.

II. DIVERSITY WITHIN SPECIES

To define a species as consisting of groups of individuals with more or less similar gene combinations means that there are genotype differences within the species itself. In the human species, which has a high variability, we may say that there are no two individuals, even twins, possessing the same assortment of genes. A large amount of data is available on individual variation in humans (see R. J. Williams, 1956). The water concentration in 18 normal men and 11 normal women was found to vary from 45·6% to 70·2%. We also have a number of results on the quantitative pattern of various enzyme systems. The plasma alkaline phosphatase concentration, is a characteristic of the individual and remains constant, but from one individual to another it was found to vary between 1·29 and 14·0 units (of 600 subjects examined by Clark and Beck). The cholinesterase of red blood corpuscles is constant for a given individual but varies considerably from one person to another, etc.

III. DIVERSITY BETWEEN SPECIES

It is to Aristotle that we owe the invention of the first practical system for the classification of living beings. More than 2000 years ago this naturalist of genius proposed to classify organisms according to the degree of similarity of their morphological and anatomical characteristics. Despite the appearance of other systems claimed to be more natural, but today forgotten, the system of Aristotle has survived and is referred to today as "the natural system". A certain number of species are collected together into a new group, defined by the possession of common characteristics, and several of these groups together form a more general category, etc. By the accumulation of taxonomic data it was possible to formulate a principle which was the subject of much admiration and satisfaction among naturalists; this was, that classification, based upon a few diagnostic characteristics, of a species and the placing of it in a given class enables one to forecast the existence of a whole range of morphological and biological traits in individuals of that same species. This idea, to which we are accustomed today and which appears self-evident and banal, must have stirred those few who glimpsed the possibilities which at that time were still unsuspected by the majority. When finally the merit of this system was admitted, it was recognized that an essential criterion was the existence of a fundamental similarity and not merely a superficial one it also led to the recognition of a common basic plan in the chief natural groups. During the first half of the 19th century, this idea appeared in numerous guises depending on the personal preferences of its protagonists. For the most theoretically inclined, like Goethe or Oken "these ideal patterns which the creative principle set before itself were, so to say, Platonic ideas in the mind of the creative spirit" (Sir Charles Sherrington. *Goethe on Nature and on Science*. Cambridge, 1949, p. 24). The more objective, as Julian Huxley said of Thomas Huxley, "simply *assumed* that structural homology (or common archetypal plan) was the right key to unlock classificatory secrets" (Julian Huxley. *Evolution. The modern synthesis*, London, 1942, p. 391). We might as well say that during the first half of the 19th century, the idea of a plan was purely descriptive and had no explanatory basis, and that Schiller was right when he replied to the exposition of Goethe: "Das ist keine Erfahrung; das ist eine Idee."

The publication of the great work by Charles Darwin changed all this. Since the advent and generalization of the Evolution Theory, the basic criterion for natural classification, which up till then was the degree of similarity, has become the degree of phylogenetic kinship. The aim of present day taxonomy is to build up a classification consisting of classes based upon phylogenetic relations. As Dobhzansky has pointed out, this new point of view has not led to any fundamental modification of classification. Here is an important point, the consideration of which leads to an increased confidence in the system established by taxonomists, which we shall use as our guide.

When discussing the significance of various characteristics of plants useful in their taxonomy at the supraspecific level, Erdtmann (1952) wrote: "Much attention is paid by taxonomists to minor characteristics such as the form, structure and arrangement of epidermal cells because they are essentially indifferent to external factors and consequently conservative. Such properties are therefore handed down from generation to generation and from species without suffering much change. Comparatively recent specializations possess little taxonomic interest."

From the biochemical aspect, as with other aspects, if it is true that the characteristics of the species and its sub-divisions are naturally inserted into the physiology of the organism and its relation with its ecological niche, it is to be expected that the biochemical traits which are transmitted from organism to organism and bear witness to a common line of ancestors will not be those of an essential physiological or ecological character. The utility of supraspecific categories is above all to enable us to express our *views on the probable nature of phylogeny*. As Calman (1949) says, "the characters most important in taxonomy are those which maintain themselves unchanged through the greatest range of variation."

The higher categories will thus indicate those limits within which characters common to a more or less broad range of species maintain themselves in spite of great species, physiological and ecological differences. The

TABLE XXI

The principal pigments of the different classes of algae

(compiled by G. E. Fogg, 1952)

	Chlorophyceae	Siphonales	Euglenineae	Phaeophyceae	Bacilliariophyceae	Chrysophyceae	Xanthophyceae	Dinophyceae	Rhodophyceae	Myxophyceae
Chlorophylls										
Chlorophyll *a*	●	●	●	●	●	●	●	●	●	●
Chlorophyll *b*	◑	◑	○	–	–	–	–	–	–	–
Chlorophyll *c*	–	–	–	○	○	·	–	○	–	–
Chlorophyll *d*	–	–	–	–	–	·	–	–	○	–
Chlorophyll *e*	–	–	–	–	–	·	○	–	–	–
Carotenes										
α-carotene	○	●	·	–	–	·	·	–	○	·
β-carotene	●	○	●	●	●	●	●	●	●	●
E-carotene	–	○	·	–	○	·	·	·	·	·
Xanthophylls										
Lutein	●	○	?	–	–	○	–	–	◑	?
Zeaxanthin	○	·	·	–	–	·	–	–	·	?
Violaxanthin	○	○	·	○	–	·	·	–	·	·
Flavoxanthin	?	?	·	○	–	·	·	·	·	·
Neoxanthin	○	◑	·	○	–	·	–	–	·	·
Siphonein	–	○	–	–	–	·	–	–	·	·
Siphonoxanthin	·	○	–	–	–	·	–	–	·	·
Fucoxanthin	–	–	–	◑	◑	○	–	–	?	·
Neifucoxanthin	–	–	–	○	○	·	–	–	·	·
Diatoxanthin	–	–	–	?	○	·	–	–	·	·
Diadinoxanthin	–	–	–	?	○	·	–	○	·	·
Dinoxanthin	–	–	–	?	–	·	–	○	·	·
Neodinoxanthin	–	–	–	–	–	·	–	○	·	·
Peridinin	–	–	–	–	–	·	–	◑	·	·
Myxoxanthin	–	–	–	–	–	·	–	–	·	◑
Myxoxanthophyll	–	–	–	–	–	·	–	–	·	◑
Unnamed	·	·	○	○	·	?	◑	·	?	?
Phycobilins										
r-phycoerythrin	–	–	–	–	–	?	–	–	●	–
r-phycocyanin	–	–	–	–	–	?	–	–	○	–
c-phycoerythrin	–	–	–	–	–	?	–	–	–	○
c-phycocyanin	–	–	–	–	–	?	–	–	–	●

phylogenetic implications of this concept, or at least, to be more cautious, its importance with respect to classification, is obvious.

Even as early as 1854 the Austrian chemist Rochleder clearly stated the taxonomic importance of the biochemical characteristics of plants, where the more general classes were concerned, thus : "Die Familienähnlichkeit

TABLE XXII

Biochemical characteristics of the algal classes

(compiled by G. E. Fogg, 1952)

Class	Reserve products	Cell wall constituents	Sterols
Chlorophyceae	starch fat	cellulose pectin	sitosterol fucosterol chondrillasterol ergosterol
Xanthophyceae	fat	pectin silica cellulose chitin (?)	sitosterol
Chrysophyceae	leucosin fat	pectin silica	fucosterol unidentified sterols
Bacillariophyceae	leucosin (?)	pectin	unidentified sterols
Cryptophyceae	starch	cellulose (?)	—
Dinophyceae	starch fat	cellulose pectin	— —
Euglenineae	paramylum	none	—
Phaeophyceae	mannitol laminarin	algin fucoidin cellulose	fucosterol
Rhodophyceae	floridoside mannoglycerate floridean starch	polygalactose-sulphate esters cellulose	fucosterol sitosterol unidentified sterols
Myxophyceae	myxophycean starch cyanophycin	pectin cellulose	none
Higher plants	starch fat	cellulose pectin lignin	sitosterol chondrillasterol stigmasterol

der Pflanzen is bedingt durch das gleichzeitige Vorhandensein mehrerer Stoffreihen". Much information on the relations between the biochemistry and the taxonomy of plants will be found in Molisch's *Pflanzenchemie und Pflanzenverwandschaft* and also in the *Handbuch der Pflanzenanalyse*. Some very interesting studies have been carried out by Erdtmann on the chemical taxonomy of the heartwood constituents of conifers.

The biochemical characteristics of various classes of algae are listed in Tables XXI and XXII. We can see that the biochemical diversity of these classes is clearly indicated. Moreover certain of these classes show biochemical similarities confirming the grouping of the Xanthophyceae, Chrysophyceae and Bacillariophyceae under the heading Chrysophyta while the affinities between the Dinophyceae and the Cryptophyceae justify their grouping in the Pyrrophyta.

When we come to the higher groups in animal taxonomy, the idea of biochemical character is by no means a new one. For a long time, the taxonomists have considered the siliceous skeleton of Radiolaria as a characteristic of that order, and within this order the presence of strontium sulphate in the skeleton as characteristic of the sub-order Acantharia. In the phylum Porifera, the class Calcispongiae have long been distinguished from other sponges by the calcareous nature of their spicules. The phylum Brachiopoda has been divided into the Ecardines, characterized by a calcareous shell, and the Testicardines. Similarly, the presence of chitin in the tegument of Arthropods has been considered as one of the characteristics of that phylum, and the possession of a calcareous shell as characteristic of the Mollusca.

Several biochemical characteristics of the sub-phylum Vertebrate can be enumerated :

(*a*) the biochemical system of bone, involving a number of functional subtances such as parathyroid hormone, vitamin D, etc.;

(*b*) the biochemical system of blood clotting, involving a protein characteristic of Vertebrates, fibrinogen, and a mechanism transforming fibrinogen into fibrin by the action of thrombin, resulting from the action on prothrombin of a number of substances present in plasma and blood platelets;

(*c*) the presence of keratin in the skin;

(*d*) the system of digestive enzymes in the form of a series of hydrolases, starting with pepsin and acting at different points;

(*e*) the presence in the blood of red cells containing a typical haemoglobin, characterized by its molecular weight and by certain definite proportions of arginine, cystine, histidine and lysine;

(*f*) the presence of a liver secreting a bile containing special steroids, the bile salts;

(*g*) the protein system of blood plasma;

(*h*) the presence of a carbohydrate metabolism involving insulin and systems sensitive to its action;

(*i*) the presence in the blood plasma of a system of inorganic bases and especially of a high level of sodium;

etc. . . .

Within the sub-phylum Vertebrates each class has its own biochemical peculiarities, some of which are of diagnostic value. The class Cyclostoma is so different from other Vertebrates in some of its biochemical characters that it deserves special mention. The biochemical mechanism for ossification is completely lacking from the Cyclostomes, and they show no sign of calcification. Another character distinguishing them from Vertebrates in general is the nature of the blood haemoglobin. Like the myoglobin of Vertebrates, the haemoglobin of the lamprey has a molecular weight of 17,000, its arginine and lysine content is similar to that of vertebrate haemoglobins whereas the histidine and cystine content as about the same as that of an invertebrate haemoglobin. The dissociation curve of lamprey haemoglobin is hyperbolic. The blood serum of Cyclostomes on electrophoresis gives a pattern which is very different from that of the other Vertebrates. But, in spite of the above differences, the Cyclostomes have a number of the biochemical characters of Vertebrates : a keratinized epidermis, a liver secreting a characteristic bile and specialized for the manufacture of glycogen, and their phosphagen is creatine phosphate as is general for Vertebrates.

Among Vertebrates, the class of fishes is distinguished by the complexity of their depot fats, the fatty acids in them covering a wide range of homologues in 14, 16, 18, 20 and 22 C atoms. The character of the depot fat is not only influenced by the character of the ingested fat, but also by the ability of the particular fish to hydrogenate or dehydrogenate the fatty acids presented to it.

In the fishes, as among most aquatic forms, xanthophylls are accumulated in preference to carotenes. But among the accumulators of xanthophylls, fishes form a special group since they accumulate only three : lutein, taraxanthin, and astaxanthin. These carotenoids are accumulated particularly in the chromatophores of the skin where they play a part in photo-response.

The role of the thryoid secretion in fishes is still unknown, but it can be said that, contrary to the case in the higher Vertebrates, the thyroid secretion of fishes has no action on metabolism and, contrary to its action in the Amphibia, it does not appear to influence metamorphosis.

Among the fishes, the sub-class Elasmobranchii, to which skates and rays belong, possesses certain special biochemical characters. The skeleton is essentially cartilaginous. It is calcified in some regions but properly speaking it is never bone tissue which is found only in the scales and teeth. Like all Vertebrates, the Elasmobranchii possess a liver secreting a bile which contains steroid substances. This bile contains a special bile salt, scymnol sulphate, a C_{27} steroid which has been detected in all Elasmobranchii studied so far, while in the true fishes cholic acid, a C_{24} steroid, is present in combination with taurine.

The organs and blood of the Elasmobranchii contain considerable quantities of urea. In the blood of marine Elasmobranchii, urea may attain a concentration of 26g/l and is never less than 18g/l. Here we are dealing with a case of selective retention of urea since the other nitrogenous compounds in Elasmobranch blood are no more concentrated than in the blood of other Vertebrates.

As in the case of the Cyclostomes, the biochemical characters of the Elasmobranchii are so clearly different from those of the teleost fishes that they are strong arguments in the support of those zoologists who favour the separation of the class of Elasmobranchii from the class of fishes.

Like the Elasmobranchii and unlike teleost fishes, Amphibia have bile salts of the C_{27} type. While the bile salts of teleost fishes are present in combination with taurine, those of Amphibia are always combined as sulphates as in the Elasmobranchii. Thyroxine has no action of the metabolism of Amphibia, as in the fishes, but the thyroid secretion has a very marked effect on their metamorphosis.

The Amphibia are uniform in their amino-nitrogen and purine catabolism which is always ureotelic.

Biochemical support for the separation of the Amphibia into the orders Anura and Urodela is found on comparison of the retinal pigments in the two. While the retina of Urodela contains mostly porphyropsin (p. 291) which is also present in Cyclostomes and is a derivative of vitamin A_2, the retina of the adult Anura contain only rhodopsin, a derivative of vitamin A_1. In this respect the Urodela are nearer to the Dipneusti which have porphyropsin as their retinal pigment. It can be pointed out here, that in the nature of their retinal pigment the class of fishes is very heterogeneous, as is the case for nitrogen metabolism and a number of other characters.

The nitrogen metabolism of the class Reptilia differs from that of fishes and Amphibia. They always have a uricotelic amino-nitrogen metabolism, a fact connected, as stated in Clementi's law, with the lack of arginase in the liver. Another interesting point is the fact that in terrestrial turtles, such as *Testudo graeca*, a more or less active system of ureotelic metabolism is present together with the enzyme system for uricotelic metabolism. With regard to their biliary steroids, the Reptilia show a systematic variation: among the sub-class Chelonia, the biliary steroids are derivatives of sterocholanic acid, while most of the members of the order Serpentes contain chloic acid. Among these, however, the family *Boidea* is characterized by pythocholic acid. Turtles and snakes contain C_{24} biliary steroids, while Haslewood has found in the sub-class Crocodilini that the alligator has a C_{27} steroid.

In all Reptilia examined so far, the biliary steroids are combined with taurine, as is the case with the teleost fishes, while in the Elasmobranchii and Amphibia the steroids are always in the form of sulphates. Reptilia, like all Vertebrates, have keratin in their integument, but in addition another keratin is found in their skin which is called "feather keratin" because it is also found in bird's feathers. This is not the only biochemical character that reptiles and birds have in common; both have a uricotelic nitrogen catabolism.

Although it is true that Reptilia and birds have many biochemical characters in common, there are also some peculiar to birds alone. Among them is the mechanism for the detoxification of benzoic acid by synthesis of ornithuric acid, a conjugate of benzoic acid and ornithine.

The biliary steroids of more than sixty species of mammal have been studied. In general, the characteristic biliary steroid is cholic acid. It is particularly interesting to find in groups of related species certain unique bile salts, although not necessarily as the principal constituents. For instance, in all members of the families Otaridae, Odobenidae and Phocidae (the seals and walruses) so far examined, a special bile acid, β-phocaecholic acid, has been found in addition to cholic acid. Certain genera too have bile salts of their own, for example the genus *Sus* which has no cholic acid but hyodesoxycholic acid instead. As already stated, biliary steroids are conjugated in the form of sulphates in the Elasmobranchii and Amphibia, and with taurine in the teleost fishes and reptiles. In mammals they are conjugated with taurine and glycine in varying proportions. The presence of glyco-acids is characteristic of mammalian biles.

The members of the sub-phylum Urochorda do not show the biochemical features we have described as being characteristic of Vertebrates but they have features of their own. They possess a cellulose coat and they accumulate vanadium in their tissues and blood cells. Although there is no thyroid secretion, they are sensitive to thyroxine which activates the development of the larvae. Also, their neural glands contain principles similar to the hypertensive, melanophore-expanding, oxytocic and gonadotrophic principles of the vertebrate hypophysis.

All the facts so far collected pertain to the Chordates, but many facts of a similar nature could be gathered through the study of each of the groups of the Metazoa. In what follows we shall limit our enquiry to just a few examples.

One of the oldest identified features of the phylum Arthropoda is the presence in their integument of a polyacetyglucosamine called chitin. In the integument the chitin is combined with protein. Another general character of Arthropods is the peculiar nature of their blood coagulation mechanism. The physiological phenomenon of blood clotting is found in Vertebrates and Arthropods and the two systems show certain similarities. The blood clotting mechanism in Vertebrates is summarized in Fig. 90a.

In Arthropods, the phenomenon of plasma coagulation depends upon the action of tissue coagulins on a coagulable protein. In the lobster, which

$$\text{Thromboplastin} + \text{prothrombin} \xrightarrow[\text{platelet accelerator}]{Ca^{++}} \text{thrombin}$$

$$\text{Plasma Ac-globulin} \xrightarrow{\text{thrombin}} \text{serum Ac-globulin}$$

$$\text{Thromboplastin} + \text{prothrombin} \xrightarrow[\substack{\text{platelet accelerator} \\ \text{serum Ac-globulin}}]{C_{++}} \text{thrombin}$$

$$\text{Fibrinogen} \xrightarrow{\text{thrombin}} \text{fibrin}$$

Fig. 90a (Ware, Fahey and Seegers). Events in clotting of vertebrate blood plasma

is the only case studied to date, this protein is quite different from the fibrinogen of Vertebrates. It is more soluble in salt solutions and moves faster in an electric field. An extract of Arthropod tissue coagulates an electrophorectically homogeneous preparation of lobster fibrinogen in the presence of calcium. During coagulation in Arthropods under physiological conditions, coagulin does not arise, as has long been believed, by an agglutination and disintegration of all blood cells, but from a special type of cell, the coagulocyte. Coagulocytes are homologues of the explosive cells described by Hardy (1892) in Crustacea.

The exocuticle of Arthropods is the result of the hardening of part of the endocuticle containing chitin in association with a water soluble protein to which Fraenkel and Rudall gave the name arthropodin. This hardening arises through the tanning of the arthropodin which is converted into sclerotin which is not soluble in water but is soluble in 5% sodium hydroxide at 50°. The tanning of arthropodin to sclerotin results from the action of a phenolase on a phenol, the resulting quinone combining with the amino-groups of the arthropodin. The classes Insecta and Crustacea although both conforming to the general biochemical plan of Arthropods, differ in the method of hardening of the exocuticle. In the Insecta this hardening is due to a tanning action, while in Crustacea it is due to calcification.

The Insecta definitely differ from the Crustacea as well as from other groups of animals in the composition of their blood plasma and particularly by having a high concentration of free amino acids in this plasma. While, in other groups, the plasma non-protein nitrogen does not exceed 10 mg per 100 ml, it may be as high as 300 mg per 100 ml in insects. Other characteristics of insect blood plasma are the high concentrations of trehalose, of uric acid and of non-fermentable reducing substances.

In the class Insecta, special biochemical characters of various subdivisions may be distinguished. As we have already stated, blood coagulation in insects is of the general type found in Arthropods depending on changes in special cells called coagulocytes, and the action of their coagulins on the fibrinogen of the plasma. The various visible stages of this coagulation show differences reflecting variations in the underlying chemical phenomena.

The first type of coagulation is characterized by the development around the coagulocytes of islands of coagulating material and the extension of the process to wider areas by the subsequent organization of this coagulum into a network. In a second type, the coagulocytes extrude threadlike pseudopodial extensions which form networks of varying complexity and on which veils of coagulated plasma often appear.

Orthoptera and Dermaptera are uniform in showing coagulation of the first type. The same type is found among Hemiptera, in the family Nepidae, the other families of the order lacking the ability to coagulate. The second type is found in all the Lepidoptera.

Other biochemical characters are peculiar to one or other order of insects. The plasma inorganic bases of Lepidoptera are characteristic in that there is a high percentage of magnesium and potassium and a low percentage of sodium.

Within the order Lepidotera, certain biochemical characters are typical of certain sub-divisions of the order as has been shown by E. B. Ford in his extensive studies on the wing pigments of butterflies.

The interest of comparative biochemistry springs from the fact that it is an extension of, and a support to, taxonomy, and thus it becomes possible to connect the study of biochemical diversity and the treasure of accumulated knowledge obtained by naturalists over several centuries.

REFERENCES

FOGG, C. E. (1953). *The Metabolism of Algae*. Methuen, London.

FLORKIN, MARCEL. (1944) *L'évolution biochimique*. Masson, Paris.

FLORKIN, MARCEL. (1952). Caractères biochimiques, des catégories supraspécifiques de la systématique animale. *Ann. Soc. Roy. Zool. Belg.*, **83**, 111–130.

HARRIS, H. (1953). *An Introduction to Human Biochemical Genetics*. Cambridge Univ. Press, London.

HASLEWOOD, G. A. D. (1955). Recent development in our knowledge of bile salts. *Physiol. Rev.*, **35**, 178–196.

KLEIN, G. (Editor). *Handbuch der Pflanzenanalyse*. Springer, Vienna, 1931–1933.

MOLISCH, HANS (1933). *Pflanzenchemie und Pflanzenwerwandschaft*. Fischer, Jena.

WILLIAMS, R. J. (1956). *Biochemical Individuality*. Wiley, New York.

CHAPTER IV

BIOCHEMICAL EVOLUTION

I. DEFINITION

BIOCHEMICAL evolution should not be considered as a fairy tale for grown-up biologists, but simply as a search for a natural order among the many diverse biochemical characters manifested in organisms. It simply means that when we notice a biochemical change along a branch of the taxonomist's phylogenic tree we shall call it a fact of biochemical evolution, meaning that in the two cases considered one is more specialized and the other more primitive. The identification of the primitive and of the specialized is decided, to start with, by the standards of the taxonomist, though not without taking into account the whole of biological knowledge. Biochemical evolution, as defined above, will be manifest by a change in the molecular structure of an organic compound or by changes in enzyme systems, these changes being either complications or simplifications as the case may be. There may also be changes in the steady states we commonly call the composition of the organism.

II. EVOLUTION OF BIOCHEMICAL CONSTITUENTS

Before considering the evolution of organisms from the biochemical angle, we must define a number of useful concepts.

Isology. The term *isologues* is applied to biochemical compounds, molecules or macromolecules, which show signs of chemical kinship. The cytochromes, peroxidase, catalase, haemoglobin, chlorocruorin, are isologues because they are haem derivatives. The maximum degree of isology occurs in the case of haemoglobins of two dogs from the same litter, it is less if we consider the haemoglobin of a dog and that of a jackal, still less if we consider that of a dog and that of a horse. In every case the haem, protohaem, is identical, the degree of isology depending on the nature of the globin. The degree of isology is still less in the case of a haemoglobin and of a catalase, the protein portions of the molecule being much more unlike than in the case of two haemoglobins. Another example of a lower degree of isology is provided by haemoglobin and chlorocruorin in which the haems are different. It is clear that there is a whole range of degrees of isology, always definable in organic chemical terms, for isology is a purely chemical concept.

Analogy. This term is applied to chemical units playing the same role in a biochemical system. Phosphocreatine and phosphoarginine in the muscles of mammals and crustaceans respectively, are analogues. Biochemical units may be both isologues and analogues, as is the case for a blood haemoglobin and a blood chlorocruorin : both serve as oxygen carriers. But this is not necessarily so : a blood haemoglobin and a haemocyanin are analogues, but they are not isologues.

When we have information about the relative positions in the classification of a number of species, and about the isologic relations of one or other of their biochemical constituents, then it becomes possible to draw conclusions about the biochemical evolution of these constituents. Consider, for example, chlorocruorin, the oxygen carrier in the Chlorhemians, in the Sabellidae and the Serpulidae. This carrier is present in the blood of three families of polychete Annelids. The Chlorhemians are Spionids, a classification which groups among the sedentary polychete Annelids, which are descended from the errant polychete Annelids, those forms whose preoral lobe is not sunk into the first segment of the metasome, and which feed on floating plankton gathered by means of posterior antennae in the form of long palps bearing a ciliated gutter. They live in sand or mud and secrete a membranous tube covered with a fine layer of slime. The Chlorhemians are Spionids which have lost the dissepiments and even the external segmentation. Their blood is green, and their palps are folded forward. Related to the Spionids are the cryptocephalic Annelids, having a preoral lobe sunk into the first segment of the trunk, but possessing furrowed appendages like those of the Spionids. Sedentary and tubicolous, the Cryptocephalae comprise two sub-divisions, the Sabellariides, which although sedentary and microphagic, have retained an uneven number of antennae, and the Sabelliforms which have even antennae and palps forming a multicoloured corolla. The Sabelliforms are divided into the Sabellidae, having a mucous tube, membranous or cornified, and the Serpulidae, possessing a calcareous tube.

The blood of Spionids other than the Chlorhemians is coloured red by haemoglobin. When we come to the Sabellariides, one of the genera of which is *Sabellaria*, their blood is charged with haemoglobin. In the Sabelliforms, sometimes called the Serpuliforms, chlorocruorin is the characteristic blood pigment. All the Sabellides so far studied contain it. Among the Serpulides blood of species in the genus *Serpula* contain both chlorocruorin and haemoglobin and in the genus *Spirorbis*, one species, *S. borealis* has a blood coloured by chlorocruorin, another, *S. corrugatus* contains haemoglobin and a third, *S. militaris* has a colourless blood. H. M. Fox (1949) did not find chlorocruorin in the tissues or in the coelomic fluid of the forms having chlorocruorin in the blood. No doubt, in those forms which contain it, the synthesis of chlorocruorin is a variant of haemoglobin synthesis as it was present in their Annelid ancestors possessing this synthetic mechanism. Also too, chlorocruorin is a close isologue of Annelid haemoglobin and possesses many similar properties. The haem of chlorocruorin, or chlorocruorohaem, differs from protoporphyrin in only a small detail, the oxidation of vinyl group 2. As for the protein portion, it is very similar to that found in Annelid haemoglobin as the data assembled in the following table show :

TABLE XXIII

	Iso-electric point	Molecular weight × 17000 (+)	*Containing amino acids* Cystine %	Arginine %	Histidine %	Lysine %
Haemoglobin of horse	6·78	4	0·74	3·57	8·13	8·31
Haemoglobin of lombric	5·28	192	1·41	10.07	4·68	1·73
Haemoglobin of arenicola	4·76	192	4·08	10·04	4·03	1·85
Chlorocruorin of *Spirographis*	4·3	192	1·64	9·64	2·38	3·64

In the case of chlorocruorin, we have a chemical entity isologous to haemoglobin and present in classes of our systematic classification and the comparative morphology of these classes shows their phylogenic relation to other classes the blood of whose members contains haemoglobin. Here we can speak of evolution of a biochemical component. In a case of this type there is not only isology, but phylogenic isology, or to use a term proposed by Lankester, *homogeny*.

Biochemical Parallelism

When isologous biochemical constituents are present in categories of the systematic classification not phylogenically related, we say that there is parallelism. The occurrence of haemoglobin in the Molluscs and in the Echinoderms is an example of parallelism. In fact, parallelisms are evidence for the unity of the general biochemical plan on which organisms are constructed.

REFERENCES

PEDERSEN, K. O. (1933). *Koll. Z.*, **63**, 268.

ROCHE, J. and JEAN, G. (1954). *Bull. Soc. Chim. Biol.*, **16**, 769; and ROCHE, J. and MOURGUE, M. (1941), *Bull. Soc. Chim. Biol.*, **23**, 1329.

SVEDBERG, T. (1933). *J. Biol. Chem.*, **103**, 311.

SVEDBERG, T. (1939), *Proc. Roy. Soc.*, *Ser. B.*, **127**, 1.

VAN SLYKE, D. D., HASTINGS, A. B., HEIDELBERGER, M. and NEILL, J. M., (1922). *J. Biol. Chem.*, **54**, 81.

Biochemical Convergence

When biochemical constituents are analogues without being isologues, as is the case for haemoglobin and haemocyanin, we say that there is biochemical convergence.

Heteromorphic Evolution

The phylogenic isology shown by the chlorocruorins and the haemoglobins of Annelids gives us an example of what can be called heteromorphic evolution, revealed by the acquisition of a modified constituent of a less complete isology. The haemoglobins with a strong affinity for oxygen appear to be more primitive than haemoglobins of weak affinity, and here we are dealing with a heteromorphic evolution of their protein component (molecule evolution).

In the higher animals, the dissociation of haemoglobin varies with its degree of oxygenation. The oxygenation of haemoglobin displaces the isoelectric point : in the horse for example, the isoelectric point of reduced haemoglobin is pH 6·78, and that of oxyhaemoglobin is pH 6·65. At the isoelectric pH, haemoglobin fixes small but equivalent amounts of acids and bases, but since the pH in red blood cells is on the alkaline side of the isoelectric point, the haemoglobin is present in combination with bases as the salt.

At the pH of blood, haemoglobin behaves like a polyvalent acid with at least five acid groups per atom of iron.

Horse oxyhaemoglobin whose isoelectric point is pH 6·65, contains, among others, an acid function (or groups of functions) which is weakly dissociated with a pK of 6·16. In the corpuscles of oxygenated horse blood the pH is 7·1 and this function for the most part is saturated with bases. The haemoglobin has a less acid character since its isoelectric point is at pH 6·8. This modification of the isoelectric point by a change in the oxygenation is due to a considerable decrease in the dissociation of the acid groups in the region of the oxygen-binding group, as we have described above. Their pK changes from 6·16 to 7·80. When such a change occurs in a medium whose pH varies hardly at all, there is a resulting liberation of the bases fixed to the acid function. The observation that reduction of blood raises the curve of CO_2 absorption is known as the "Haldane effect". It appears to be a character in the evolution of haemoglobin due to a modification of the protein moiety and consequently is an example of heteromorphic evolution. In fact the effect is not observed in the blood of the ray, of *Mustelus canis* or of *Urechis* all of which contain haemoglobins the dissociation of which does not vary with the degree of oxygenation.

The molecular evolution of proteins, as the above examples indicate, is evidently an essential facet of the evolution of organisms. Recent work has enabled us to obtain a clearer view of the heteromorphic aspects of proteins which are more or less isologous and new horizons have been opened up.

The molecular weights of Vertebrate haemoglobins are situated around 65,000–68,000. The molecules are apparently made up of two systems of three peptide chains. The N-terminal amino acid sequence of a number of haemoglobins is given in Table XXIV. There would appear to be a common basic chain in all cases.

TABLE XXIV

(Osawa and Satake 1955)

Species	*N–Terminal sequences*		
Horse, pig	Val. Leu.	Val. Gly.	Val Glu. (Leu.)
Dog	Val. Leu.	Val. Gly.	Val. Asp.
Bull, goat, sheep	Val. Leu.	Met. Gly.	
Cobaya	Val. Leu.	Val. Ser.	Val. Asp.
Rabbit, Snake	Val. Leu.	Val. Gly.	
Hen	Val. Leu.		

It would be extremely satisfying to be able to follow in homologous tissues, in every phyletic line, the stages in the biochemical evolution of each type of macromolecule in the cell. But our knowledge of the field of comparative biochemistry is still too sparse for such a task. On the other hand in the field of phylogeny, the gaps left in the explanation of the kinship between one class and the next are enormous, and living beings as we know them appear to possess such a continuity that certain writers have been led to deny the idea of evolution altogether. Frequently biochemical constituents are found in one group without it being possible to study biochemically a group that can be said, with certainty, to be the immediate predecessor in the phyletic series. The general outlines of phylogeny can however serve to define the more or less primitive or specialized character of a biochemical constituent.

Let us consider, for instance, the distribution of porphyropsin and rhodopsin (p. 290) in the visual organs of animals. A diagram systematizing the observations of different workers and particularly of George Wald and his school (Fig. 90b) shows, in the phylogenic series represented here, a definite chemical evolution in which porphyropsin appears to be more primitive than rhodopsin. At the present time it is generally agreed that Vertebrates originated in fresh water, and it is conceivable therefore that the early Vertebrates already possessed the porphyropsin system. This, of course, is not a matter open to direct investigation but we may notice that the African Lungfish *Protopterus*, which is believed to have descended

TABLE XXV

(W. Bergmann, 1949)

Distribution of the unsaponifiable portion of the lipids of animals

Phyla or classes	% of unsaponifiable in relation to the total lipids	Number of examples
Protozoa	35	2
Porifera	37	45
Coelenterata	35	16
Nemathelminthes	25	1
Annelida	22	7
Crustacea	16	14
Myriapoda	21	1
Insecta	7	31
Mollusca (marine)	13	18
Echinodermata	19	10
Chordata	1·2	50

TABLE XXVI

(W. Bergmann, 1949, 1952)

Phyla and Classes	Distribution of sterols in animals Principal sterols
Porifera	cholesterol, cholestanol, clionasterol, poriferasterol, chalinasterol, neospongosterol, chondrillasterol, halicionasterol, aptostanol and others.
Coelenterata	cholesterol, clionasterol, chalinasterol, palysterol and others
Annelida	cholesterol
Arthropoda	cholesterol
Mollusca	
Pelerypoda	cholinasterol, brassicasterol, corbisterol, cholesterol and others.
Castropoda	cholesterol
Cephalopoda	cholesterol
Echinodermata	
Asteroidea	stellasterols
Holothuroidea	stellasterols
Echinoidea	cholesterol
Protochordata	cholesterol
Chordata	cholesterol

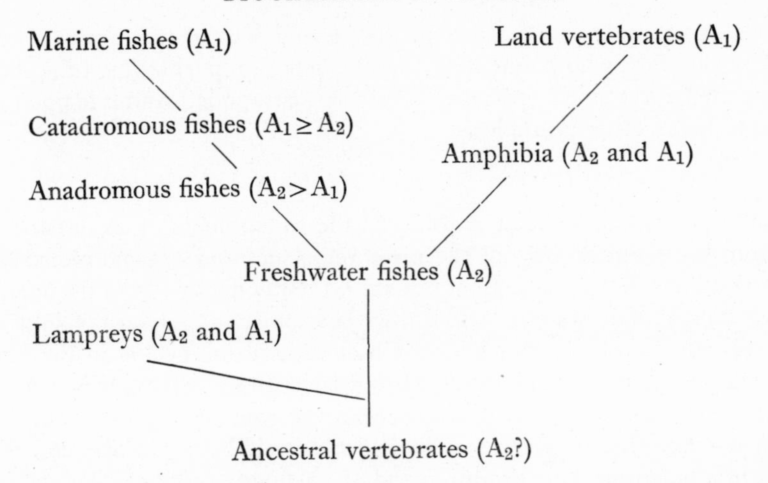

Fig. 90b—(Wald). Distribution of vitamins A_1 and A_2 in vertebrate retinas.

from a continuous line of fresh-water ancestors, possesses the porphyropsin system. The use of vitamin A_2 in the retina appears to be universal in fresh-water Vertebrates and to extend as far back to the origin of the Vertebrates as it is possible to penetrate.

W. Bergmann has emphasized that a marked difference exists, (which can be seen by reference to Table XXV) in the material extractable with fat-solvents when we compare the Vertebrates and the Invertebrates: there is a greater proportion of unsaponifiable matter in the latter.

Moreover, Bergmann noted that if we consider the distribution of sterols in animals, the greatest diversity of sterols is found in the most primitive groups while in the most highly specialized, cholesterol is almost the only one identified (Table XXVI).

Among the sterols of the least specialized animals we find C_{28} or C_{29} compounds. Sterols of this type differ in the type and degree of unsaturation, and in the nature of the radical attached at C–24, etc. (Bergmann, 1952). On the other hand, from a series of studies by Haslewood and co-workers, we see that in teleost fishes or Elasmobranchs, Amphibians, crocodiles and alligators, in a lizard, in Chelonians (turtles and tortoises) and in some birds, the bile salts contain C_{27}, C_{28} (or possibly C_{29}) alcohols and acids whilst in snakes and mammals, substances of this type are not found. But the presence of C_{24} bile acids has been demonstrated in snakes, teleost fishes, mammals and birds, but not in Elasmobranchs, Batracians or reptiles such as the Crocodilians and the Chelonians.

In general, the C_{27}, C_{28} and possibly the C_{29} bile salts go with a more primitive phylogenic status than with that of the more specialized animals which have C_{24} bile salts.

Another example connected with the general idea of phylogeny is one cited by Comfort, who pointed out that the depot uroporphyrin of the shelf occurs chiefly in the less specialized Archaeogastropoda. And it is possible to quote many other examples.

III. EVOLUTION OF BIOCHEMICAL SYSTEMS

In the preceding, we have considered the constituents of an organism, i.e. from the point of view of the macromolecules and organic molecules contained in it. But these compounds are evidently derived from the operation of biosynthetic systems, and thus, a heteromorphic evolution, such as the replacement of a haemoglobin by a chlorocruorin, occurs in the biosynthetic mechanism which produces that constituent. Hence this change is in an enzyme system, i.e. in a system of macromolecules the nature of which is controlled in every case by a gene, itself being on occasion the object of a heteromorphic evolution and of a reduction in the isology of its nucleic acids with those of its forbears. If we grant that the photosynthetic pathway (see Part Six) is a metabolic variant of the hexosemonophosphate shunt, then photosynthesis regarded as a reduction of CO_2 will be carried out by a system more specialized than the hexosemonophosphate shunt. On the other hand, if it is true that at the beginning the biosphere was lacking in CO_2, photosynthesis could only appear after the liberation of this substance from volcanoes and primitive forms of metabolism. If the presence of oxygen in the terrestrial atmosphere has depended on photosynthesis then that part of the overall metabolic schemes which concerns respiration is biochemically more specialized than that containing glycolysis and the hexosemonophosphate shunt. But all this lies in the domain of prehistoric biochemistry and consequently is of a highly speculative nature. In the biosphere at the present time we have before us what survives of many diversifications of the general plan of cellular biochemistry described in Part III, and evidently what remains has been preceded by more primitive systems which today have disppeared.

(*a*) *Specialization by Quantitative or Topographic Modifications*

Extracellular digestion compared to intracellular digestion implies that specialization has occurred in the sense of a relatively great biosynthesis of enzymes secreted into the lumen of the digestive tube and constantly renewed. Intracellular digestion is the primitive form. It is the only form of digestion in the Spongiae.

As Yonge has emphasized, an example that demonstrates very well the relation between the system of intracellular digestion and that of extracellular digestion is the Molluscs : among them we find all stages between an almost complete intracellular digestion and a totally extracellular digestion based on the secretion of enzymes into the lumen of the digestive tube. In general, Lamellibranchs feed by a ciliary mechanism which is responsible for the collection of fine particles, mainly of phytoplankton. The only extracellular phase of digestion they have is in the action of an amylase, all the other enzymes acting intracellularly. Among the herbivorous Gastropods (the Pulmonata excepted), like Yonge we can distinguish two groups : those possessing a crystalline style and those which do not. In the former, as for example the Streptoneura, conditions are very similar to those found in the Lamellibranchs, amylase being the only extracellular enzyme, the digestive diverticulae acting as organs of absorption and intracellular digestion, but never of secretion. The second group of herbivorous Gastropods, those not possessing a crystalline style, as is the case for the Tectibranchs and the Nudibranchs, show considerable diversity and in certain cases there is a proteinase in the juice in the digestive tube. When we come to the carnivorous Gastropods such as *Murex*, a proteinase actively secreted by the digestive diverticulae is always found in the digestive tube. Among them, too, there is also intracellular digestion. In addition, the salivary glands secrete amylase. Among the Pulmonata, such as the snail, the hydrolytic processes are almost completely extracellular. Only protein hydrolysis is intracellular.

In the Cephalopods, digestion is exclusively extracellular and intracellular digestion has disappeared.

(*b*) *Specialization by Acquisition of a New Constituent as a Result of Molecular Evolution*

During the course of the evolution of the cells that contain it, an enzyme system may become the object of a specialization of a new type. Snakes, for example, do not mix digestive secretions with their prey by a process of mastication. They swallow their prey after having injected it with a secretion which initiates hydrolysis. In the least specialized form, for example in *Colubridae opisthoglyphae*, a simple secretory tooth appears at the rear of the upper jaw and serves for the injection of a secretion whose function is purely digestive. In more specialized forms, this organ, following a decrease in length of the maxilla, approaches the anterior part of the buccal cavity and becomes an aggressive and defensive organ, as is the case in *Colubridae proteroglyphae* and even more so in the *Viperidae*.

The digestive origin of the secretion is further borne out by the presence in snake venoms of such hydrolases as proteases, peptidases, phosphatases, sterases, and lecithinases. The new specialization expresses itself by the presence of hyaluronidase, assuring the diffusion of the venom, and by the presence of substances of high toxicity (see Zeller, 1948).

Another example of modification of an old system by the addition of a new component is the urea-synthesizing system in the hepatic parenchyma

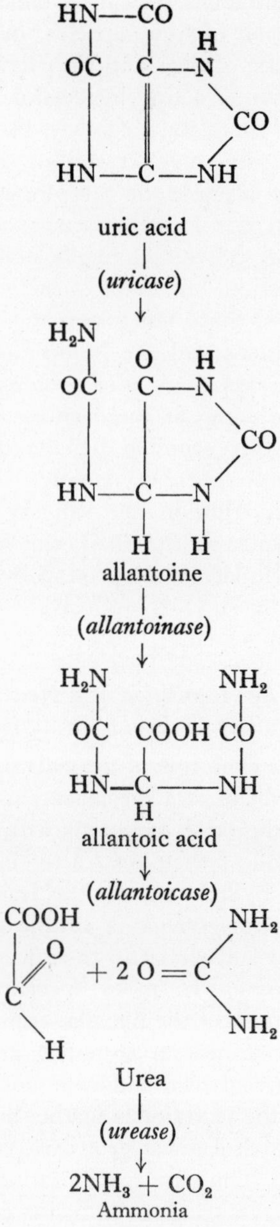

```
HN—CO
|    |    H
OC   C—N
|    ‖     \
|    ‖      CO
|    ‖     /
HN—C—NH
```

uric acid

|
(*uricase*)
↓

```
H2N
|    O    H
OC   C—N
|    |     \
|    |      CO
|    |     /
HN—C—N
     |    |
     H    H
```

allantoine

|
(*allantoinase*)
↓

```
H2N          NH2
|             |
OC   COOH   CO
|      |      |
HN—C ——NH
       H
```

allantoic acid

↓
(*allantoicase*)

```
COOH              NH2
|  O              /
| //   + 2 O = C
C                 \
  \               NH2
   H
```

Urea

|
(*urease*)
↓

$2NH_3 + CO_2$

Ammonia

Fig. 91—The uricolytic enzyme system.

of ureotelic Vertebrates (p. 309). The new function appears as the result of a specialization in which arginase has been added to the enzyme system bringing about the synthesis of arginine (p. 244).

(*c*) *Specialization by Loss of Constituents*

An enzyme system may be specialized not only by the acquisition of new enzymes, but also by the loss of certain existing ones. An example is the enzyme system of uricolysis. The most complete form of this system is found in marine Crustaceans and is shown in Fig. 91.

Most Insects only carry uricolysis to the stage of uric acid. The form of the uricolytic system in Insects compared to the most primitive form of the Crustaceans, is characterized by the disappearance of urease, allantoicase, allantoinase and uricase. The enzyme system for purine breakdown consists of uricase, allantoinase and allantoicase in the Batracians, it consists of only uricase in the Mammals, with the exception of the Primates who have lost the complete system of enzymes as likewise have the terrestrial Reptiles and Birds.

(*d*) *Specialization by Introduction of a Constituent of a Primitive System into a more Modern System*

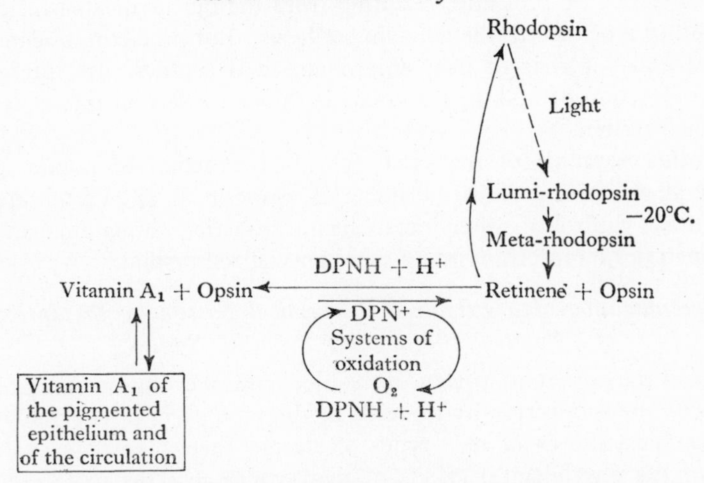

FIG. 92 (G. Wald).—The rhodopsin system.

A frequent form of evolution of enzyme systems and their associated systems (substrates, enzymes, coenzymes, hormonal regulators, etc.) is by the introduction of one or several of their components into a more specialized system. We have already noted (p. 290) the more specialized nature of rhodopsin, present in the retina of salt-water fish, reptiles, birds and mammals, compared to the more primitive porphyropsin of fresh-water

Vertebrates. Rhodopsin is a derivative of vitamin A_1 and porphyropsin is a derivative of vitamin A_2. The visual function of the A vitamins is the only one it has been possible to demonstrate in animals other than the mammals and birds. In the two latter, it plays the additional role of a vitamin essential for the normal function of epithelial tissue. This last fact shows us the development of a new biochemical system in which has been inserted a biochemical component already utilized in another system. The photoreceptor system of the rods in the retina of animals having a differentiated eye furnishes us with another example of this type of evolution in an enzyme system. Figure 92 indicates the changes taking place during photoreception in the rhodopsin of the eye. Retinene is produced by the reduction of vitamin A_1. The enzyme catalysing the transformation was first called retinene-reductase. We know today that it is alcohol-dehydrogenase (p. 162) as has been shown by Bliss. This universally distributed enzyme is found to have been inserted here into a new system that is extremely specialized.

The mechanisms of hormonal regulation provide us with many instances of insertions into new systems. The secretion of milk, due to the biochemical differentiation of one type of Mammalian cell (p. 306) is provoked and controlled by prolactin, resulting from the biochemical specialization of another type of cell, the adenohypophysis. But prolactin is secreted by the adenohypophysis of fish, amphibians and reptiles. Its intervention in the secretion of milk in mammals is thus an insertion into a new biochemical system.

Another example of the same type is the action of pitocin on the mammalian uterus. This hormone is present in all Vertebrates and acts in the control of water metabolism. Its action on mammalian uterus demonstrates its insertion into a more specialized system.

(*e*) *Specialization of a Primitive Biochemical System by the Introduction of a Constituent of another Primitive System*

One of the important aspects of the biochemical evolution of Vertebrates has been the acquisition by the cells of the mesoderm of enzyme systems for the biosynthesis of new types of steroid (heteromorphic evolution). One of the physiological effects of this evolution is the ionic regulation brought about by the action of the corticosteroid hormones at the urinary tube. In the Amphibiae this action is established in conjunction with a pre-existing system, that of the regulation controlled by the adenohypophysis.

The adaptation to terrestrial life in certain amphibians, such as the toad, in fact depends on the ability to reabsorb water controlled by the active principles of the hypophysis, and these substances are fundamental constituents in these animals (see Jones, 1957).

In many cases the biochemical systems characteristic of such and such a cellular differentiation appear to be biochemical inventions the past history of which we are so far unable to reconstruct. Such systems are to be found among the many different biochemical modifications in Vertebrates, for example, the complex enzyme systems for the degradation of haemoglobin present in histiocytes, the conversion of cholesterol to bile in the cells of the hepatic parenchyma, etc. The fact that we do not know the systems preceding them in phylogeny does not invalidate the fact that these biochemical inventions have evolved.

Scanty as it is at the moment, our knowledge of the biochemical diversity of organisms has indicated that more detailed studies could tell us much about the methods according to which the extension of the biosphere has been accomplished along the lines of biochemical evolution, the biochemical diversity being, as we shall see in Part VI, as essential as the biochemical unity, for the maintenance of the metabolism of the whole biosphere in extension.

REFERENCES

ANFINSEN, C. B. (1959) *The Molecular Basis of Evolution*, John Wiley, New York.

BERGMANN, W. (1949). Comparative biochemical studies on the lipids of marine invertebrates, with special reference to the sterols. *Sears Found. J. Marine Res.*, **8**, 137–176.

BERGMANN, W. (1952). Sterols. *Progr. Chem. of Fats and other Lipids*, **1**, 18–69.

FLORKIN, M. (1944). *L'évolution biochimique*. Masson, Paris.

JONES, I. C. (1957). *The Adrenal Cortex*. Cambridge Univ. Press.

WALD, G. 1951. The chemistry of rod in Fish. *Science* **113,** 287–291.

YONGE, C. M. (1937). Evolution and adaptation in the digestive system of Metazoa. *Biol. Rev.*, **12**, 87–115.

ZELLER, E. A. 1948. Enzymes of snake venoms and their biological significance. *Advanc. Enzymol.*, **8**, 459–495.

PART SIX

THE METABOLISM OF THE BIOSPHERE

INTRODUCTION

THE series of priming reactions and synthetic mechanisms described in Part Three of this book give some idea of the chemical processes occurring in the biosphere. Superimposed on this general background there are many variations, simplifications or amplifications arising from the differentiation, adaptation and evolution of both the cells and the organism. Without them life would become extinct.

Each organism is a link in a food chain whose beginning varies according to the particular association of living creatures. In a pond, bacteria and other micro-organisms are at the beginning of the chain. Crustaceans feed on the micro-organisms and themselves act as food for aquatic insects that, in turn, are eaten by fish. The dead bodies of the latter serve to nourish bacteria. Animals feeding on plants are the prey of carnivorous animals, that are themselves eaten by other carnivores. This concept of food chains demonstrates how the macromolecules in the cells of an organism can serve as food to other organisms which begin by hydrolysing them with the aid of the arsenal of hydrolases so liberally distributed throughout the biosphere. In this way one part of the biosphere serves to feed the other part. However, if each portion of the biosphere was nourished solely by the consumption of another portion, life would be progressively stifled and would disappear in a very short time. In the same way as for the metabolism of a single organism the metabolism of the biosphere implies an entry and an exit of matter and energy. This continuous exchange with the surroundings constitutes the general metabolism of the biosphere which is dealt with in Part Six.

CHAPTER I

ENTRY INTO THE BIOSPHERE

I. CARBON AND ENERGY

In addition to the priming and biosynthetic reactions described in Part Three we must consider the entry of energy and matter which occurs in certain regions of the biosphere. As we have pointed out, the priming reactions constitute a chemical machine which forms, at the expense of the chemical energy of nutrient molecules, energy-rich bonds of ATP, packets of energy which can be utilized for biosynthesis. Also, during the functioning of this chemical machine construction materials are produced which can be employed for biosynthetic purposes.

However organisms exist which are capable, by chemical mechanisms of their own, of introducing into their metabolism a supply of external energy, either chemical or electromagnetic in nature. Traditionally, the name chimiosynthesis is given to the synthesis of carbohydrates from CO_2 and chemical energy. In this sense, all organisms are chimiosynthetic. But, certain micro-organisms, during the synthesis of carbohydrates, introduce energy derived from the oxidation by oxygen (auto-oxidation) of a constituent of the external medium. Other organisms are capable of carrying out photosynthesis, i.e. synthesis of carbohydrates using electromagnetic energy derived from light. So, by the terms chimiosynthesis and photosynthesis we understand that sugars are synthesized. The term photometabolism refers to other types of metabolic action accomplished by light.

There are some micro-organisms who obtain all their energy and material from outside the biosphere. These are the autotrophes. They build up all their constituent organic material from CO_2, H_2O and other inorganic substances like ammonia, sulphates and phosphates. For energy they use that derived from the oxidation of substances in the surrounding medium. Photosynthesis, another form of autotrophism, occurs in certain bacteria, in algae, in diatoms, in green plants, etc.

A. Autotrophic Bacteria

These organisms do not obtain their nutrient from some other region of the biosphere: the flow of energy and matter through them is derived from the inorganic world. Examples are: the nitrous and nitric bacteria and the colourless sulphur bacteria.

The autotrophic bacteria are chimiosynthetic, that is, they synthesize sugars using the energy of oxidation of a constituent of the surrounding medium.

(*a*) *Nitrous Bacteria*

These bacteria accomplish a nitrosation (ammonium salts → nitrites). These bacteria are numerous and belong to the genera *Nitrosomonas* (aerobic, widely distributed in the soil of Europe and Asia, ovoid or spherical in shape, able to move in a liquid habitat by means of their flagellae they group themselves in mucilaginous zoogloeae) and *Nitrosococcus*, (in American soil, always non-mobile). The chimiosynthesis of carbohydrates in the nitrous bacteria consists of a transfer of hydrogen from ammonia to CO_2:

$$2NH_3 + 2O_2 \rightarrow 2NO_2H + 2H_2$$

$$2H_2 + CO_2 \rightarrow CH_2O + H_2O$$

(*b*) *Nitric Bacteria*

These oxidize nitrites to nitrates thus performing a nitration. Among the nitric bacteria are the *Nitrobacter* which are bacilliform, non-mobile, and aerobic (Fig. 93).

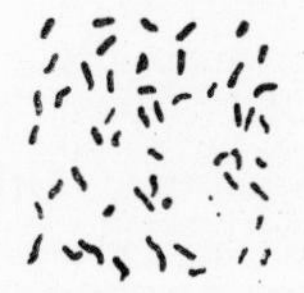

FIG. 93 (Winogradsky)—*Nitrobacter*

(*c*) *Colourless Sulphur Bacteria*

Certain of these are aerobic, others anaerobic. Among the aerobes are *Thiobacillus thioparus* and *Thiobacillus thiooxydans*. The former is present in soil in the form of small rods. It multiplies when the medium is neutral. It oxidizes thiosulphates (hyposulphites) or sulphides to sulphate and sometimes sulphur is deposited inside the cell.

$$2Na_2S_2O_3 + O_2 \rightarrow 2Na_2SO_4 + 2S$$

Thiobacillus thiooxydans is found in the soil in the vicinity of sulphur deposits. It produces large amounts of H_2SO_4 and only grows under acid conditions (pH 8 = 2·0–3·0). It oxidizes sulphur or thiosulphate to sulphuric acid:

$$2S + 3O_2 + 2H_2O \rightarrow 2H_2SO_4$$

$$Na_2S_2O_3 + H_2O + 2O_2 \rightarrow Na_2SO_4 + H_2SO_4$$

Certain other autotrophes which oxidize sulphur are anaerobic. This is the case with *Thiobacillus denitrifians* which oxidizes sulphur, H_2S, $Na_2S_2O_3$ (with formation of H_2SO_4), at the expense of oxygen derived from nitrates. It is widely distributed, being present in soils, water and muds.

$$5Na_2S_2O_3 + 8KNO_3 + 2NaHCO_3 \rightarrow 6Na_2SO_4 + 4K_2SO4 + 4N_2 + 2CO_2 + H_2O$$

In addition to the simple bacteria we have just considered, there are some morphologically more complex, such as *Thiothrix* and *Beggiatoa* who oxidize H_2S to H_2SO_4 using part of the energy from this reaction to synthesize carbon chains. They are aerobes containing particles of sulphur in their cells. In addition to CO_2 and oxygen they require the presence of H_2S. As long as H_2S is present, the sulphur particles remain in the cells. In the absence of H_2S, these bacteria can use their reserve of sulphur granules. When this reserve is exhausted, they die. The energy-yielding reactions are as follows:

$$H_2S + O \rightarrow H_2O + S$$

$$2S + 3O_2 + 2H_2O \rightarrow 2H_2SO_4$$

(*d*) *The Mechanism of Autotrophy*

The autotrophic bacteria pose the major problem of how the energy produced by an oxidation reaction is transferred and used for the synthesis of a sugar. In a general way the process can be represented as occurring in the following stages:

1. Activation by an enzyme of the oxidizable substrate (a thiosulphate dehydrogenase in *Thiobacillus*, an ammonium dehydrogenase in *Nitrosomonas*).
2. Oxidation by the cytochrome–cytochrome oxidase system.
3. Formation, during this oxidation, of energy-rich phosphate bonds.
4. Fixation of CO_2 by conversion to a carboxyl group, in the usual way.
5. Formation of a carboxyl phosphate.
6. Reduction of the latter by the enzyme of reaction 1, liberation of phosphate.

$$XCO—O \sim H_2PO_3 + RH_2 \rightleftharpoons XCHO + H_3PO_4 + R$$

However the above is almost entirely hypothetical.

B. Photosynthesis in the Green Algae and Green Plants

Photosynthesis by green algae and green plants is the major means of introducing carbon into the biosphere. The annual production of organic substances by photosynthesis in the biosphere is 2000 times greater than the annual production of steel throughout the world, which is 100 million tons per annum.

According to Loomis, photosynthesis produces 270,000,000,000 tons of glucose per annum and consumes 396,000,000,000 tons of carbon dioxide. Statistically, over 2000 years all the CO_2 molecules in the air will have been incorporated into the biosphere at some time or other.

In plants and algae, photosynthesis takes place in cytoplasmic inclusions, the chloroplasts.

(*a*) *The Chloroplasts*

The chloroplasts in green algae and plants are the seat of photosynthessi and producers of glucose-1-P. They are disc-shaped particles 3 to 10 μ in diameter and 1 to 2 μ in thickness. It is possible to isolate them from leaves and show that they are bounded by a definite membrane which is semi-permeable. The chloroplasts contain a number of *grana* whose diameter varies, according to the type of cell, from 0·2 to 2 μ. A chloroplast contains from 10 to 100 *grana* imbedded in a protein matrix. The electron microscope reveals that they have a laminar structure. They contain 33 to 50% protein and also contain lipides. The chloroplasts are auto-reproductive and can divide.

There are two types of pigments in the chloroplasts, chlorophyll and carotenoids. Besides chlorophyll, the chloroplasts of the red algae contain other tetrapyrrole pigments which are active in photosynthesis, these are the phycobilins. The leaves of green plants often contain in the vacuole (i.e. outside the cytoplasm), pigments such as the anthocyanins which do not play any part in photosynthesis.

(*b*) *History of the Ideas Relative to Photosynthesis*

It was not until 1727 that Stephen Hales expressed doubts about the correctness of the then current view that plants obtained all their nourishment from the soil. Hales suggested that air and light also played a part. The next step was due to Priestley who showed, in 1771, that green plants gave out oxygen. The following year Ingenhouz demonstrated the part played by light in this phenomenon. In 1782 Senebier discovered that CO_2 was also concerned in the production, in light, of oxygen by green plants. In 1804 quantitative methods of study were applied by Saussure. He showed that the weight gained by a plant over a given period during photosynthesis, plus the weight of oxygen liberated, is greater than the weight of CO_2 taken in. He suggested that water played a part. In 1941 Van Niel showed that the photosynthetic purple algae, the Thiorhodaceae, can multiply in an anaerobic inorganic medium provided that the medium contains H_2S. It was also shown that the amount of growth is proportional to the H_2S concentration. So photosynthesis must be considered as being linked to an oxido-reduction reaction, and in Van Niel's theory, which is generally accepted today, the hydrogen donor is always H_2O. Up to about 1935 studies of photosynthesis were concentrated on the effect of various factors on the rate of photosynthesis in the living plant. Much work has been done from this physiological aspect, the main result being only to underline the mystery of photosynthesis.

With the advent of methods employing radioactive isotopes and biochemical methods for the study of isolated systems, it became possible to penetrate into the intimate mechanism of photosynthesis. In 1940 the reaction of Hill (p. 357) was announced and the first experiment using isotopes (by Ruben, Kamen and Hassid, using ^{11}C, the only available carbon isotope at that time) was carried out. The presence of magnesium in chlorophyll had led, by a process of reasoning on chemical grounds, to the idea that the first step in biosynthesis was a photochemical reaction involving chlorophyll and CO_2. This idea stemmed from three observations: the presence of magnesium in chlorophyll, the reduction of CO_2 to formaldehyde by metallic magnesium in acid solution, and the feeble biochemical reactivity of CO_2.

Today, we know that on the contrary CO_2 is a metabolite of general importance. Facts obtained since 1940 lead us to believe that photosynthesis is a process in which the photochemical reaction is a photolysis of water preparatory to the transfer of hydrogen.

According to the ideas of Calvin, the priming reaction for photosynthesis, that is the transformation of water under the influence of light, furnishes much TPNH and ATP from the electromagnetic energy of the light. Also pyruvic acid is diverted to the photosynthetic cycle as a result of the presence of thioctic acid in its dithiol form.

By contrast, in the dark, oxidation takes place and the disulphide form is re-established; the carbon then takes a path required by respiration.

(c) *The Initial Stage of Photosynthesis*

The first stage is a process of quantum absorption converting water into a reducing agent and an oxidizing agent.

$$H_2O \xrightarrow{h\nu} [H] + [OH]$$

In green plants oxygen is liberated during this first stage. In phototrophic bacteria, the oxidizing radical [OH] must be reduced by a hydrogen donor which is specific in each case.

The second stage is a reduction

$$CO_2 + [H] \rightarrow (CH_2O)_x$$

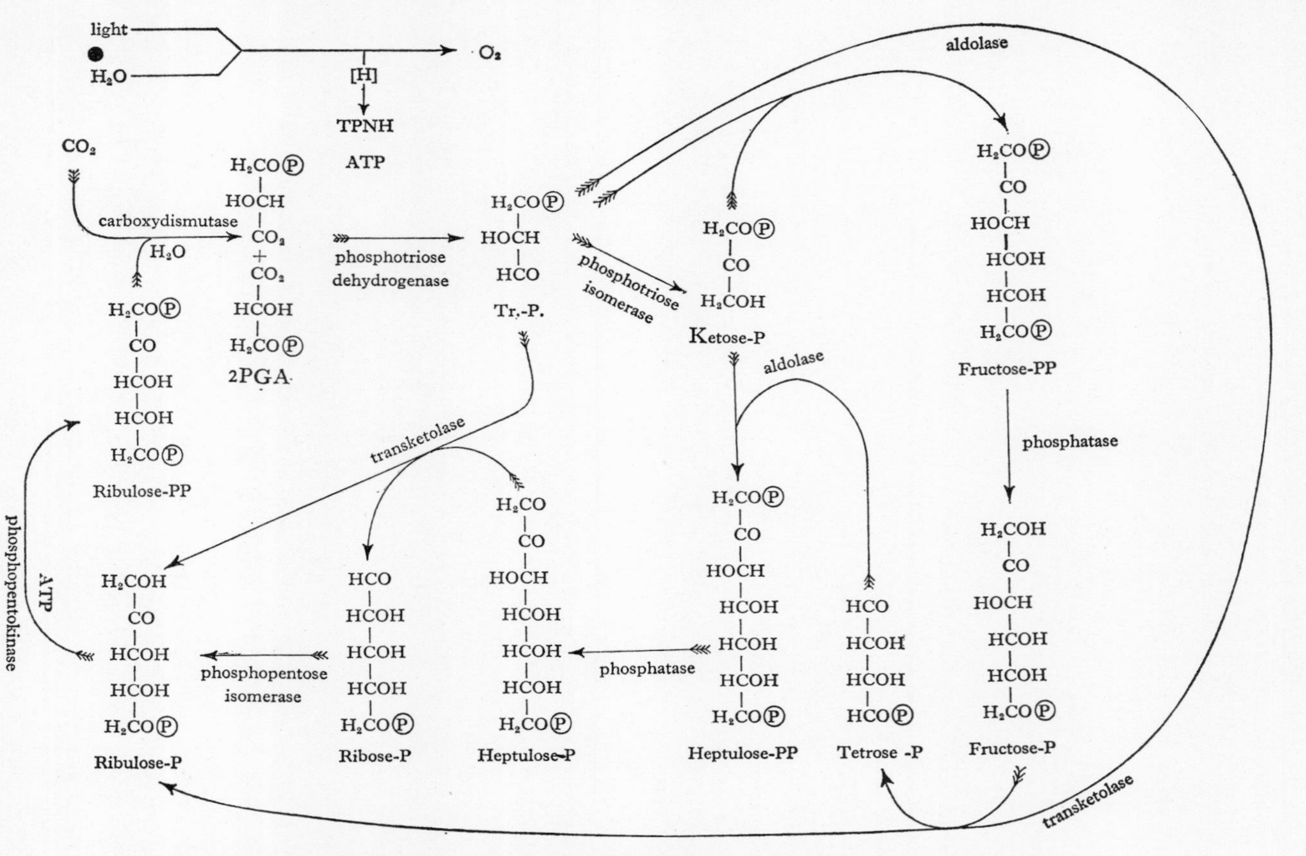

FIG. 94—The reductive cycle of photosynthesis and the pentose cycle according to Calvin.

This division into two stages is confirmed by the *Hill reaction*, i.e. the production of oxygen by isolated chloroplasts in the presence of a hydrogen acceptor such as benzoquinone or 2,6-dichlorophenol. By means of labelled oxygen it has been proved that the oxygen liberated in the Hill reaction is derived from the water.

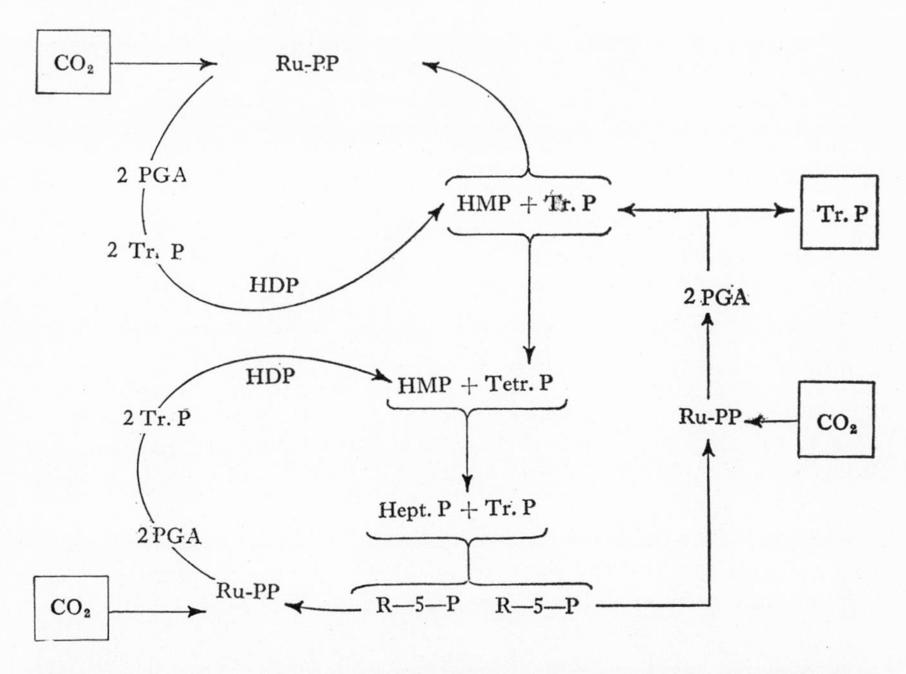

FIG. 95.—Racker's reaction scheme showing the formation of a molecule of triosephosphate from three molecules of CO_2 in the pentose phosphate cycle acting as a reductive cycle during photosynthesis.

(*d*) *The Reduction of Carbon Dioxide*

Second Stage of Photosynthesis

Carbon dioxide is first fixed in a carboxyl group, in the general way, the reverse of decarboxylation. This CO_2 appears in the carboxyl of 3-phosphoglyceric acid. Although the role of 3-phosphoglyceric acid is usually admitted, there is still much discussion as to the nature of the substance which first combines with the CO_2.

Calvin and his school believe that ribulose diphosphate is the immediate precursor of 3-phosphoglyceric acid. Thus the photosynthetic cycle would begin by a carboxylation of Ru-PP with formation ($C_5 + C = 2C_3$) of two molecules of phosphoglyceric acid (PGA). Starting with PGA, all the separate operations of the pentose cycle, and, according to Calvin (Fig. 94), of the associated photosynthetic cycle, have been reproduced *in vitro* using purified enzymes.

Aldolase catalyses the formation of heptulose diphosphate from a molecule of tetrose phosphate and a molecule of triose phosphate ($C_4 + C_3 = C_7$). Phosphatase converts the heptulose-PP to heptulose-P which, with a further molecule of triose-P, in the presence of transketolase, forms a molecule of ribose-P and a molecule of ribulose-P ($C_7 + C_3 = 2C_5$). The isomerase for pentose phosphates converts this mixture to ribulose-P which, in the presence of ATP and phosphopentokinase, gives ribulose-PP.

However it still remains, in this enzymatic scheme, to explain the fixation of CO_2 when entering this series of reactions. Calvin has isolated from spinach leaves and from ultrasonic macerates of the green alga *Chlorella* a soluble enzyme which, in the presence of bicarbonate, converts Ru-PP to two molecules of PGA. He has called it carboxydismutase, because the carboxylation depends on the oxidation of C-3 of ribulose to a carboxyl group.

The fact that all the necessary enzymatic tools have been isolated does not mean that the cycle actually does function. In fact for the reduction of PGA to a triose, a molecule of ATP and a molecule of TPNH are required. When we get to Ru-P, a further molecule of ATP is necessary for the formation of Ru-PP.

The cycle has been completely reconstructed *in vitro* by Racker (1955), who has thus achieved the reductive synthesis of a sugar from CO_2 and plant enzyme extracts. The sequence of reactions is as follows:

(1) 3 pentose-P + 3 ATP ⟶ 3 Ru-PP + 3 ADP
(2) 3 Ru-PP + 3 CO_2 + 3 H_2O ⟶ 6 PGA
(3) 6 PGA + 6 ATP ⟶ 6 DPGA + 6 ADP
(4) 6 DPGA + 6 DPNH + 6 H^+ ⟶ 6 triose-P + 6 DPN + 6P
(5) 4 triose-P ⟶ 2 HPP
(6) 2 HDP + 2 H_2O ⟶ 2 HMP + 2 P
(7) 1 HMP + 1 triose-P ⟶ 1 pentose-P + 1 tetrose-P
(8) 1 HMP + 1 tetrose-P ⟶ 1 heptulose-P + 1 triose-P
(9) 1 heptulose-P + 1 triose-P ⟶ 2 pentose-P

---

sum (1–9) 3 CO_2 + 9 ATP + 5 H_2O + 6 DPNH + 6H^+
⟶ 1 triose-P + 9 ADP + 6 DPN + 8 P
(10) 9 H_2O + 9 DPN ⟶ 9 DPNH + 9 H^+ + 9 O
(11) 3 DPNH + 9 ADP + 9 P + 3 H^+ + 3 O ⟶ 3 DPN +
9 ATP + 12 H_2O

---

sum (1–11) 3 CO_2 + 2 H_2O + P ⟶ 1 triose-P + 6 O

If we ignore equation (10) and (11) for the moment, we see that overall (reactions 1–9), to introduce a CO_2 molecule into a triosephosphate, three molecules of ATP and four reduction equivalents (4 electrons) are required. In nature, according to Calvin, they are provided by the conversion of electromagnetic energy. We require nothing more. The dynamo of photosynthesis (see p. 146) is therefore a means of providing ATP and TPNH. As for the reductive cycle of photosynthesis, according to this scheme it consists of a multienzyme system of which the hexosemonophosphate shunt is another variant.

It is only necessary to compare the pentose cycle of photosynthesis (Fig. 94) with the hexosemonophosphate shunt in Fig. 38 for their relationship to become apparent. Since the two mechanisms are still partly hypothetical, it is preferable to await further developments in our knowledge before attempting to establish a definite relation between respiration involving the hexosemonophosphate shunt and photosynthesis. The mode of formation of a triosephosphate molecule from three CO_2 molecules is shown graphically in Fig. 95.

According to the above views, photosynthesis appears as one aspect of intracellular regulation. A new stationary state is established when particles containing the electromagnetic dynamo are illuminated and a high reduction potential is produced due to a high concentration of TPNH, and there is an accompanying increase in the amount of ATP. In this manner photosynthesis is the opposite to respiration which continues again when illumination is stopped. Thioctic acid, inserted by Calvin into his description of the electromagnetic dynamo, appears to exert an additional regulatory action. Thioctic acid is one of the coenzymes for the oxidative decarboxylation of pyruvic acid and it functions thus in the disulphide form. When the photosynthetic cycle is functioning it is converted to its sulphhydryl form thus blocking the way to the tricarboxylic acid cycle, to the corresponding respiratory mechanism, and diverting the flow of carbon to photosynthesis. Inversely, in the dark, the disulphide form is re-established and the way is again open for the flow of carbon to the tricarboxylic acid cycle.

Thus from the above view-point photosynthesis can be regarded as being simply a special form of the priming reactions set out in Fig. 62. The pentose phosphate cycle is partly reversed and coupled to a reductive stage catalysed by triosephosphate dehydrogenase, thus replacing the oxidation catalysed by glucose-6-phosphate dehydrogenase. In the plant during photosynthesis, the decarboxylation of 6-phosphogluconic acid is replaced by the carboxylation of Ru-PP. However many of the ideas expounded in this chapter are hypothetical in nature and other theories of photosynthesis exist. No one theory can explain all the known facts and we must wait until the future for agreement to be reached upon the process which is the principal entry of inorganic carbon and energy into the biosphere.

C. Photosynthesis in the Purple, Brown, and Green Bacteria

The Rhodobacteriaceae are an extensive family of bacteria found in soil and water. Following Van Niel, they can be subdivided into three groups:

(*a*) *Chlorobacteriaceae*. Green sulphur bacteria not requiring organic growth factors.

(*b*) *Thiorhodaceae*. Purple sulphur bacteria not requiring organic growth factors but able to utilize as hydrogen donors various inorganic sulphur compounds, organic acids, and in certain cases hydrogen itself.

(*c*) *Athiorhodaceae*. Non-sulphur bacteria, purple, red or brown in colour, requiring various growth factors.

(*a*) *Chlorobacteriaceae*

These are anaerobic, and according to Van Niel, H_2S is the substance which reduces the oxidizing radical liberated by photolysis.

Sulphur accumulates in the culture in the form of globules.

(*b*) *Thiorhodaceae*

They are anaerobes which do not grow except in the presence of H_2S and light. Like the chlorobacteriaceae they use H_2S without oxidizing it since they are anaerobic, and also like them, they are photosynthetic without liberating oxygen. They do not release sulphur, but sulphuric acid.

$$H_2S + 2CO_2 + 2H_2O \xrightarrow{\text{light}} H_2SO_4 + 2(CH_2O)$$

In the place of H_2S, they can also utilize sulphite or thiosulphate.

$$4Na_2S_2O_3 + CO_2 + 3H_2O \xrightarrow{\text{light}} 2Na_2S_4O_6 + (CH_2O) + 4NaOH$$

The mechanism of this curious piece of photosynthesis is unknown.

(*c*) *Athiorhodaceae*

These bacteria assimilate CO_2 in the presence of light, but for this they require certain organic or inorganic compounds. Fatty acids are good substrates for their growth. A number of experimental facts indicate that they act as hydrogen donors, but this idea is still under discussion. The situation is clearer when we consider the utilization of isopropyl alcohol. Here, there is no doubt that the organic compound acts as a hydrogen donor to reduce the [OH] radical leaving acetone behind in the medium.

The overall equation for the reaction is:

$$CO_2 + 2CH_3CHOH.CH_3 \xrightarrow{\text{light}} (CH_2O) + H_2O + 2CH_3CO.CH_3$$

(*d*) *The Pigmentary System of the Green, Purple, and Brown Bacteria*

This is very similar to that in the green algae and green plants. The brown or purple colours are due to the presence of various carotenoids. It is likely that as in diatoms and the blue algae, the carotenoids play a part in the absorption of light, and transfer the energy thus accumulated to chlorophyll. The chlorophyll in the Thiorhodaceae and the Athiorhodaceae is bacteriochlorophyll-*a*, whilst the green bacteria contain a different chlorophyll.

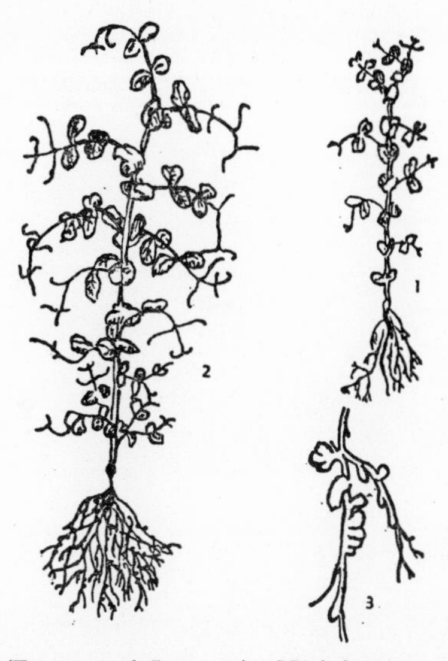

FIG. 96 (Errera and Laurent)—Nodules on pea roots.

1. A young plant which has remained stunted in sterilized sand containing neither combined nitrogen nor thinned with soil on which legumes have been grown; there are no nodules on the roots.
2. A young plant of the same age which has flourished in sterilized sand not containing combined nitrogen but thinned with soil in which peas had formerly grown; nodules are present on the roots.
3. A root bearing nodules.

II. PHOSPHORUS

The incorporation of phosphorus by green plants is the main means of entry of this element into the biosphere. If we consider a plant, the surroundings in which the roots live are very complex. Phosphorus is present in the form of sparingly, soluble calcium, iron and aluminium salts, as adsorbed anions on the soil particles and as organic compounds derived from the corpses of plants, animals and micro-organisms (iron, calcium or aluminium salts of phytin, and of nucleoproteins). In neutral or calcareous soils, the calcium salts of organic forms of phosphorus are more soluble and more available for bacterial decomposition. The soluble phosphates are concentrated by the roots and transported by the xylem in the plant to the active cells.

III. NITROGEN

In general, plants remove nitrates from the soil. Moreover the other forms of nitrogen in the soil, such as amino nitrogen and ammonia, are rapidly converted to nitrates by the action of numerous heterotrophic bacteria and autotrophic micro-organisms which derive their energy from the conversion of ammonia into nitrite (nitrous bacteria) or nitrite into nitrate (nitric bacteria). The absorbed nitrate can be accumulated by the plant, or reduced to nitrite and then to ammonia which the plant uses, notably for the formation of amino acid amino groups.

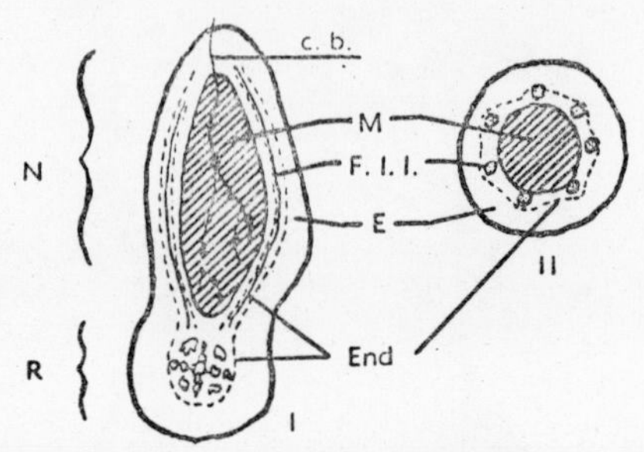

FIG. 97—(Guilliermond and Mangenot). Structure of a root nodule in a legume (*Vicia faba*).

I. A section along the long axis of the nodule.—R: a transverse section through a root; N : a longitudinal section of the nodule; c.b. : branched bacterial filament having infected the root.

II. A transverse section of the nodule. End : endoderm of the root (continuing into the nodule).

In addition, a limited number of organisms are able to utilize atmospheric nitrogen by reducing it to ammonia or amino groups.

The ocean is poor in nitrogen-fixing organisms. It receives its nitrogen from inflowing rivers. The Mississippi alone pours 360,000 tons of nitrogen per annum into the sea in the form of nitrates. The nitrogen of the land is therefore being continuously removed in this way. It is restored by putrefaction, by the conversion of the nitrogen of the air into nitrates by electric discharges during storms, and by the action of nitrogen fixing organisms, free bacteria or bacteria living in symbiosis with plants.

In fact, the fixation of nitrogen is a very common and wide-spread phenomenon in the biosphere. Still little is known about its mechanism, but it does not appear to be everywhere the same.

A. Fixation in the Root Nodules of Legumes

It is to Boussingault that we must give credit for having in 1838 established that Legumes fix the nitrogen of the air. After a period of great confusion, in 1885 Boussingault's views were confirmed by Atwater in America. Towards the middle of the nineteenth century a relationship was noticed between this phenomenon and the presence in legumes of the root nodules which had first been described by Malpighi in 1679. The presence in the nodules of rod-shaped bacteria associated into filaments had already been described in 1858, but their presence was incorrectly interpreted by the morphologists for over thirty years. It was not until 1888 that Beijerinck isolated these bacteria in a pure culture. The parasitic bacteria on the roots of legumes are very similar and they are collected together in

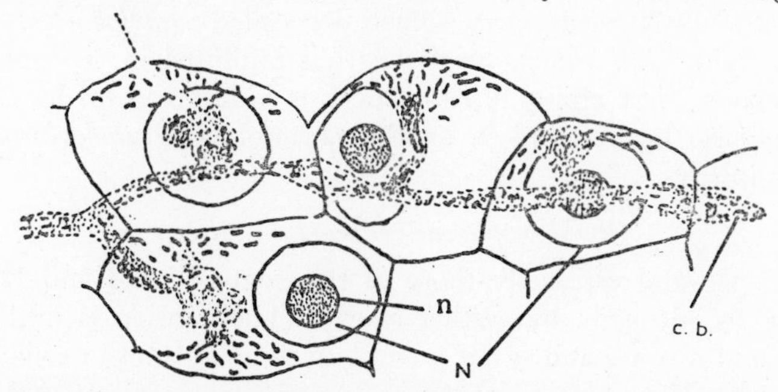

Fig. 98 (Guilliermond and Mangenot)—Contamination of cells in the region of a root nodule, by branches of the bacterial filament (c.b.).

Notice the bacteria contained in the mucilaginous mass of the filament whose branches insure the infestation of each cell; N and n, nucleus and nucleolus of the infected cells.

he genus *Rhizobium*. These bacteria do not contain cellulase and they apparently penetrate the plant at the extreme point of the root hairs which seem to be devoid of cellulose.

Neither the bacteria nor the plant, considered alone, fix nitrogen. In association, not only do they fix nitrogen but they excrete nitrogen compounds into the soil: aspartic acid, glutamic acid, oximino-succinic acid, etc.

These lead us to postulate the following mechanism:

$$\left.\begin{array}{l} N_2 \leftarrow NH_2OH \\ \quad + \\ CO—COOH \\ | \\ CH_2—COOH \end{array}\right\} \rightarrow \begin{array}{l} C = NOH—COOH \\ | \\ CH_2COOH \end{array} \xrightarrow{H_2O} \begin{array}{l} CHNH_2—COOH \\ | \\ 4(H)CH_2—COOH \end{array} \rightarrow \text{absorption into the plant}$$

Oxaloacetic acid oximino-succinic acid aspartic acid

There is no accumulation of hydroxylamine, so that it is probably rapidly reduced to ammonia when reacting with the ketonic acid. Alternatively, as believed by some workers, ammonia may be the first compound to be formed from the nitrogen of the air. The essential fact is the provision of oxaloacetic acid by the host plant.

The nodules contain a haemoglobin (leghaemoglobin) of low molecular weight (17,000), but is role in nitrogen fixation is unknown.

B. Fixation by Autonomous Organisms

In 1883, Berthelot showed that earth became enriched in nitrogen just by contact with the air, even if it was sterilized; he concluded that micro-organisms capable of fixing nitrogen were present in the soil.

(*a*) *Clostridium*

The first of these micro-organisms was isolated by Winogradsky in 1895, it is *Clostridium pasteurianum*, sometimes called *Amylobacter*. In this anaerobe, unlike *Rhizobium*, fixation is not inhibited in the presence of carbon dioxide. The ability to fix nitrogen is widespread in the *Clostridia* and it has also been found in another anaerobe, *Desulphovibrio*, which reduces sulphates.

(*b*) *Myxophycae* (*Blue-green Algae*)

These algae and especially those of the genus *Nostoc* and the genus *Anabaena*, fix nitrogen, but rather slowly. The fixation is inhibited by ammonia and nitrates and is not quantitatively important in soils.

(*c*) *The Purple Bacteria*

Many of the bacteria in the Athiorhodaceae group (non-sulphur purple bacteria) fix nitrogen. This fixation is coupled to growth and only occurs in the presence of light and oxygen.

(*d*) *Azotobacter*

These bacteria are exceptionally large and resemble the blue-green algae. They easily form gums and they are obligatory aerobes. Fixation of nitrogen only occurs in the presence of a source of carbon and is probably coupled to oxidation. A part of the nitrogen fixed is excreted into the medium in the form of amino acids. Again, ammonia itself or a precursor of it is combined with the dicarboxylic acid. As in the other cases of fixation, the mechanism of the process is shrouded in mystery.

IV. SULPHUR

Plants absorb and assimilate sulphates. Soil contains a great deal of calcium sulphate. Bacteria exist which reduce sulphates to H_2S. Such bacteria live in muds, animal intestines, etc., and everywhere where organic materials are putrefying.

$$SO_4^- + 4H_2 \rightarrow H_2S + 2H_2O + 2OH^-$$

The sulphides formed in the soil or in water can be again converted into sulphates, either by a purely chemical action or by the action of various bacteria, colourless sulphur bacteria, purple sulphur bacteria, etc.

REFERENCES

HILL, R. and WHILTINGHAM, C. P. (1955). *Photosynthesis*. Methuen, London.
LEES, H. (1955). *Biochemistry of Autotrophic Bacteria*. Butterworth, London.
BASSHAM, J. A. and CALVIN, M. (1957). *The Path of Carbon in Photosynthesis* Prentice-Hall, Englewood Cliffs, N.J.

CHAPTER II

DEPARTURE FROM THE BIOSPHERE

THE earth and the surface waters are the natural tombs of plants and animals. In these regions of the lithosphere and hydrosphere, the materials of the biosphere return to the inorganic world : the nitrogen of proteins becomes ammonia and nitrate, carbon is oxidized to carbonates and the other elements return to their inorganic forms. Elsewhere, too, living organisms are returning these elements by a continual rendering of respiratory carbon dioxide and metabolic excreta. The excreta and corpses are mineralized in the soil and in water by the action of micro-organisms. The latter, likewise, autolyse when unfavourable conditions interrupt their multiplication.

Particularly important are the processes by which nitrogen and carbon leave the biosphere to re-enter the inorganic world.

I. AMMONIFICATION IN THE SOIL

The dead bodies and excreta of living beings are attacked in the ground by the exoenzymes of many bacteria. For example, the exoenzymes of many *Clostridia* attack this dead matter and the proteins are converted to amino acids. Many bacteria release ammonia from these amino acids. The most active ammonifying organisms are *Bacillus mycoides*, *Proteus vulgaris* and various actinomycetes. Quantitatively the most important process is oxidative deamination (p. 210).

The bacteria of the soil can also accomplish a deamination by the removal of ammonia to produce a double bond

$$R\text{—}CH_2\text{—}CHNH_2\text{—}COOH \rightarrow R\text{—}CH = CH\text{—}COOH + NH_3$$

In this way bacteria of the *coli-typhosum* group can convert histidine to urocanic acid.

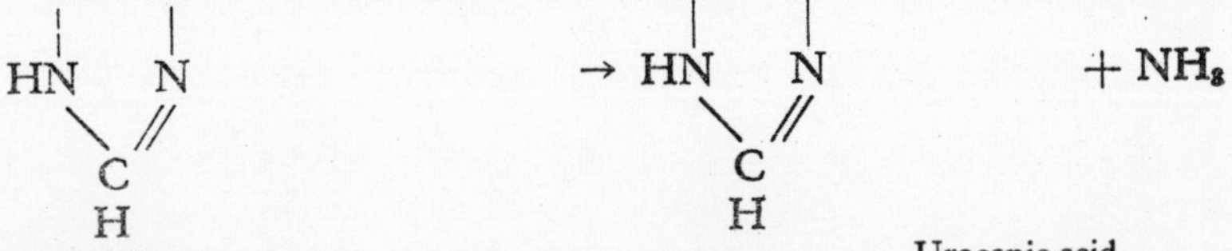

```
CH=CH—CH2CHNH2COOH    CH=CH—CH=CHCOOH
|    |                 |    |
HN   N              → HN   N              + NH3
 \  //                 \  //
  C                     C
  H                     H
Histidine                       Urocanic acid
```

In the same way aspartic acid is converted to fumaric acid by *E. coli.*

$$\begin{array}{l} CHNH_2\text{—}COOH \\ | \\ CH_2\text{—}COOH \end{array} \rightleftharpoons \begin{array}{l} CH\text{—}COOH \\ \| \\ CH\text{—}COOH \end{array} + NH_3$$

The removal of H_2S from cysteine is followed by the same process, which can be accomplished, in part, by *Proteus vulgaris.*

$$\begin{array}{l} CH_2SH \\ | \\ CHNH_2 \\ | \\ COOH \end{array} \xrightarrow{-H_2S} \begin{array}{l} CH_2 \\ \| \\ CNH_2 \\ | \\ COOH \end{array} \rightarrow \begin{array}{l} CH_3 \\ | \\ C{=}NH \\ | \\ COOH \end{array} \xrightarrow{H_2O} \begin{array}{l} CH_3 \\ | \\ C{=}O \\ | \\ COOH \end{array} + NH_3$$

Another type of deamination is reductive deamination as carried out anaerobically by the *Clostridia.* Glycine gives acetic acid, alanine and serine give propionic acid, etc. Although evidently hydrogen plays some part in the reaction, only amino acids are necessary. For example, two moles of glycine are reductively deaminated in the presence of *Cl. sporogenes* whilst at the same time a mole of alanine is oxidized to acetic acid.

$$CH_3\text{—}CHNH_2\text{—}COOH + H_2O \rightarrow CH_3\text{—}CO\text{—}COOH + NH_3 + 2\ (H)$$

$$CH_3\text{—}CO\text{—}COOH + H_2O \rightarrow CH_3\text{—}COOH + CO_2 + 2\ (H)$$

The hydrogen is then accepted by the glycine

$$2\ CH_2NH_2\text{—}COOH + 4\ (H) \rightarrow 2\ CH_3\text{—}COOH + 2\ NH_3$$

The amino group of amino acids is never hydrolysed directly by bacteria, but the latter can liberate NH_3 by hydrolysis of amides such as asparagine and glutamine.

$$R\text{—}CONH_2 + H_2O \rightarrow R\text{—}COOH + NH_3$$

A source of ammonia in the soil is the urea arising from the hydrolysis of arginine by various micro-organisms to ornithine and urea (micrococci, *Bacillus subtilis*). Certain bacteria (*Streptococcus fecalis*, *Streptococcus hemolyticus*, *Micrococcus aureus*; these organisms are parasites and play no part in the soil economy) contain an arginine-hydrolase and can perform a double hydrolysis of arginine to produce ornithine, two molecules of ammonia, and CO_2.

Certain other bacteria can form citrulline by a hydrolytic deamination of the =NH of arginine, but the citrulline formed is only metabolized very slowly.

Because they contain urease in their cells, many bacteria can hydrolyse urea, either derived as outlined above, or produced as an animal excretory product.

$$NH_2—CO—NH_2 + 2H_2O \rightarrow (NH_4)_2—CO_3 \rightarrow 2NH_3 + CO_2$$

If these above reactions are the source of ammonia in the soil, the degradation of amino acids and similar substances is complicated by the occurrence of numerous side-reactions which can inhibit ammonia production and consequently the nitrogen cycle.

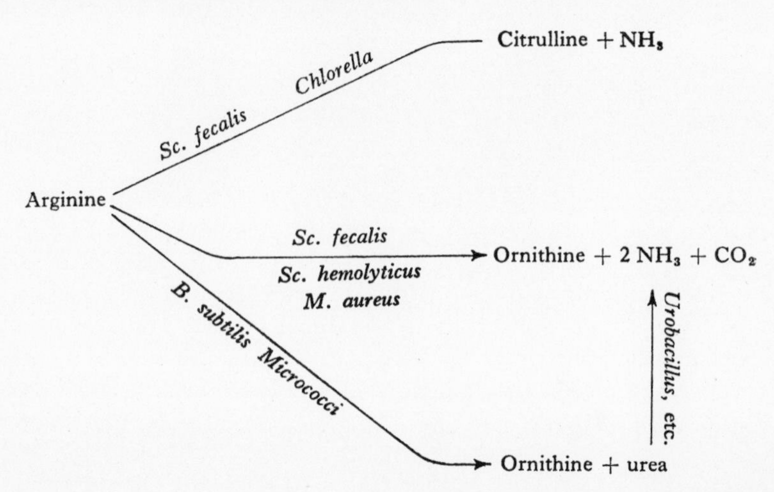

Examples are : the uptake of amino acids resulting from the hydrolysis of dead bodies by the protoplasm of bacteria, or by fungi; and in the soil, the formation of nitrogen-containing humus, by combination of carbohydrates and nitrogenous compounds.

But the most important side-reaction is bacterial decarboxylation, brought about by organisms of the *coli* group, by *Clostridia*, etc. and by fungi.

$$\underset{\displaystyle NH_2}{R—\underset{|}{CH}—COOH} \longrightarrow R—CH_2NH_2 + CO_2$$

The amines formed are basic, toxic to animals, and resistant to bacterial decomposition. Their oxidation only occurs in an alkaline medium and they are formed in an acid medium, so that the bacteria which produce them do not oxidize them.

II. THE EXIT OF CARBON FROM THE BIOSPHERE

Carbon disappears from the biosphere chiefly as CO_2 formed in the tricarboxylic acid cycle and eliminated by the organism. Equilibrium between this mechanism of loss and entry of carbon due to photosynthesis would not be maintained if there were not other ways in which CO_2 is lost.

The bacterial mineralization of corpses is partly responsible for filling the gap.

A. The Loss of Carbon present in Carbohydrate Macromolecules

(*a*) *Starch*

Bacteria and fungi are able to secrete α amylases into the surrounding medium and in particular this can be done by *Bac. subtilis*, *mesentericus*, *macerans* and *polymyxa.*

(*b*) *Pectins*

As we have already seen these are methylated polymers of D-galacturonic acid (polyuronides and not polysaccharides).

The chief organisms attacking pectin are found among the *Enterobacteriaceae* and such spore bearers as *Bac. macerans* and most of the *Clostridia.*

The breakdown of pectin is a complex process and takes place in several stages.

1. Conversion of protopectin to pectin (this occurs during the retting of flax). The enzyme responsible is protopectinase, which is present in *Aspergillus*, *Cl. felsineum*, etc.

2. Demethylation of pectin to pectin acid. The enzyme is pectase which is found in many bacteria.

3. Hydrolysis of the 1–4 linkage, splitting the macromolecule. Here the corresponding enzyme is pectinase which is present in *Asp. oryzae*, *Rhizopus tritici*, etc.

(*c*) *Cellulose*

Since cellulose constitutes the major part of the insoluble material in plants, the speed at which it is broken down is one of the important factors in the carbon cycle.

A number of micro-organisms capable of decomposing cellulose exist: myxobacteria, *Clostridia*, Actinomycetes and many fungi. The presence of a soluble cellulose has only been shown in a few cases. In other cases, the way in which the cellulose is broken down has not been decided.

B. The Loss of Carbon present in Amino Acids

The ketonic acids which result from the action of microbial proteases and the oxidative deamination of the resulting amino acids, can be directly reduced to hydroxy-acids

$$R—CO—COOH \xrightarrow{2H} R—CHOH—COOH$$

The ketonic acids can also be decarboxylated with the loss of one carbon atom to form an aldehyde.

$$R—CO—COOH \rightarrow CO_2 + R—CHO$$

The aldehyde may be dehydrogenated to an acid having one carbon atom less than the starting amino acid, or the aldehyde may be reduced to an alcohol

$$R—CHO + 2H \rightarrow R—CH_2OH$$

However most of the ketonic acids are oxidized by micro-organisms and CO_2 is formed. Soil consists of particles separated by water or a gaseous atmosphere. This atmosphere contains more CO_2 than the air. When the soil is poorly aerated and there is much organic matter present, bacterial action produces not only CO_2, but also some methane. The soil of rice-fields contains practically no oxygen but there is much hydrogen and methane present.

REFERENCE

THIMANN, K. V. (1955). *The Life of Bacteria*. Macmillan, New York.

CHAPTER III

THE CYCLES

I. THE CARBON CYCLE

DURING photosynthesis, CO_2 is removed from the atmosphere and from the hydrosphere. A part of this CO_2 is returned almost immediately during the respiration of plants. The remainder is, for the most part, returned indirectly by the respiration of animals and during the putrefaction of dead plants and animals. This is known as the biological carbon cycle.

The CO_2 content of the atmosphere hardly varies and this is due to the buffering of drastic fluctuations by the $CaCO_3$–$Ca(HCO_3)_2$–CO_2 system of the ocean. The main path of the carbon cycle is through the biosphere and the ocean. Carbonates are being continually diverted in the form of sediments, and organic carbon is being held up during its series of transformations in the form of fossilized carbon.

It is possible to calculate that since the start of the laying down of these two types of sediment, twelve times the total amount of CO_2 in the atmosphere has been trapped in the form of sediments. This removal of carbon has taken place gradually and has been compensated by CO_2 of volcanic origin.

The autoregulation of the carbon cycle, which maintains the CO_2 of the atmosphere at a constant level, depends on the one hand on the CO_2–bicarbonate–carbonate system of the air, seas and sediments, and on the other hand it depends on photosynthesis, the intensity of which is regulated by the concentration of available CO_2.

The carbon cycle is not at all dependent on the presence of animals or plants. It could continue in the presence of micro-organisms alone and with special intensity in the oceans where the photosynthesis is eight times more intense than that due to land plants. This marine photosynthesis is due to the presence of Diatoms and the Dinoflagellates of phytoplankton. Figure 100 shows a carbon cycle which is entirely microbial in character.

II. THE NITROGEN CYCLE

The main stages of this cycle are the fixation of nitrogen or nitrates by plants and certain bacteria, the mineralization of proteins to form ammonia and the conversion of this ammonia into nitrates. Fig. 101 shows the various stages of the cycle.

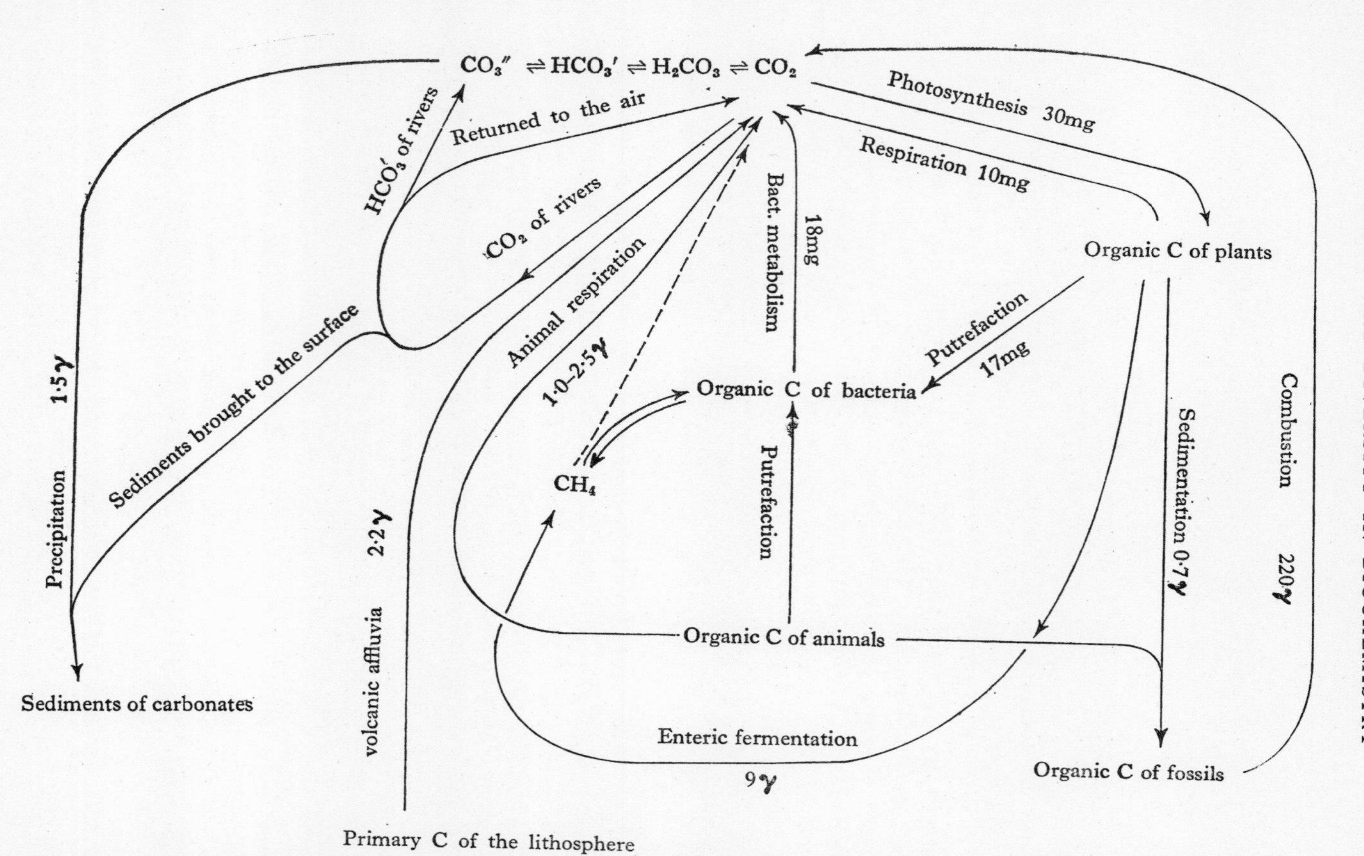

FIG. 99 (Hutchinson)—The carbon cycle. The amounts of carbon per square centimetre per year are indicated.

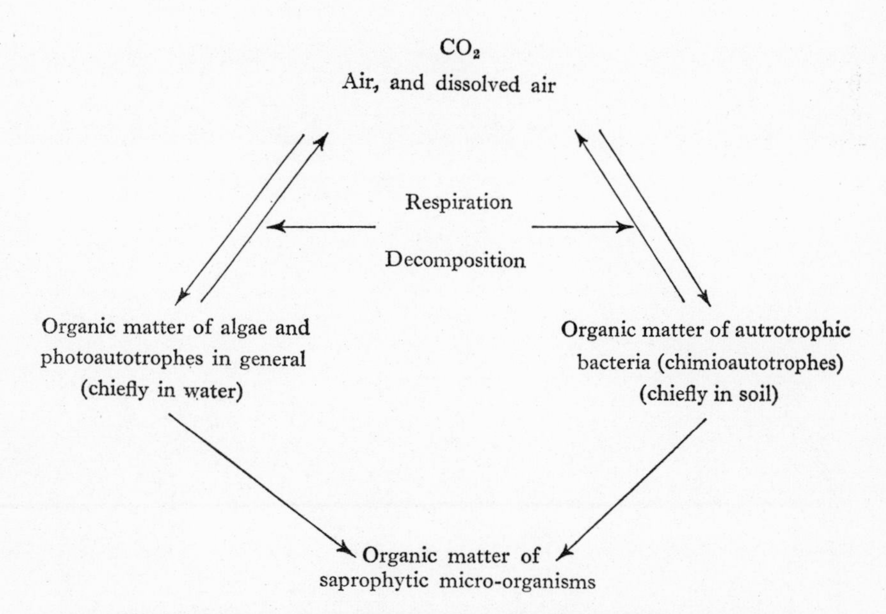

FIG. 100 (after Butlin and Postgate)—A microbiological carbon cycle.

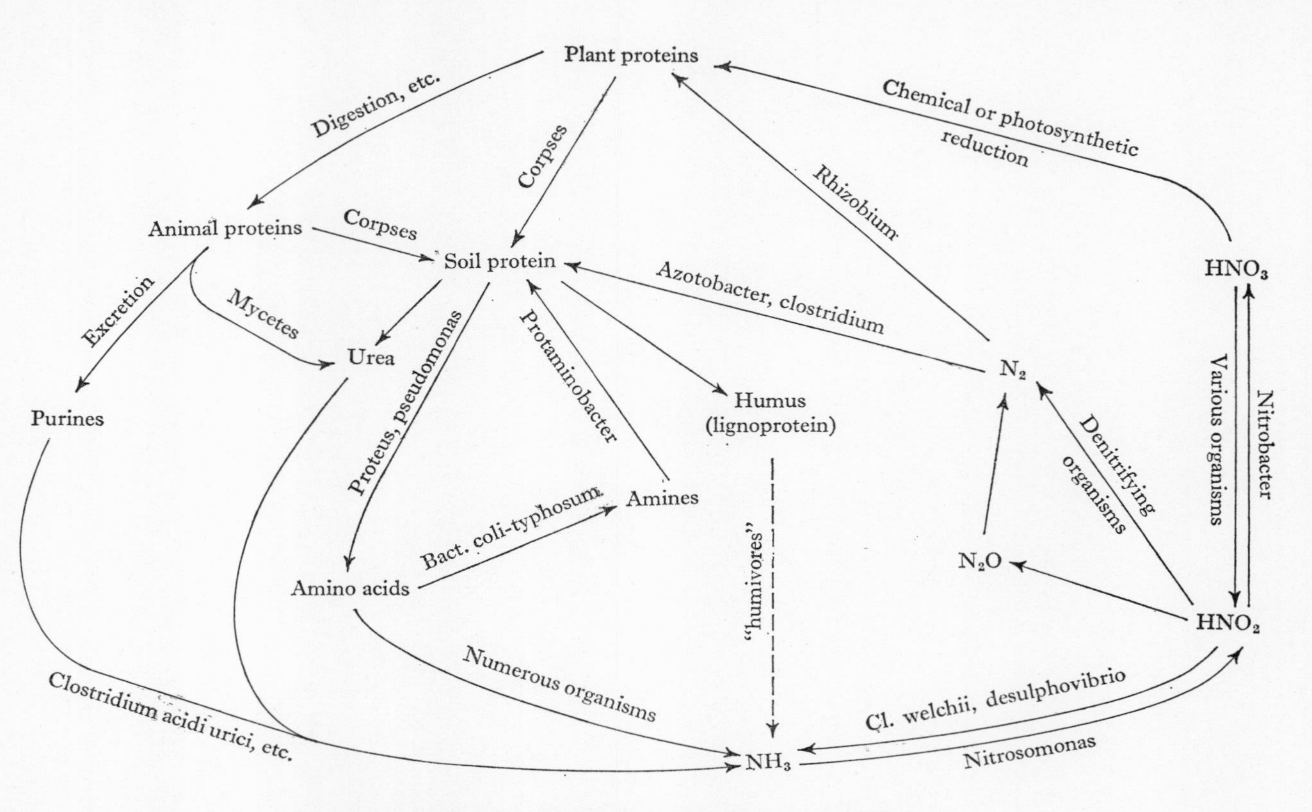

FIG. 101 (Thimann)—The nitrogen cycle in the biosphere.

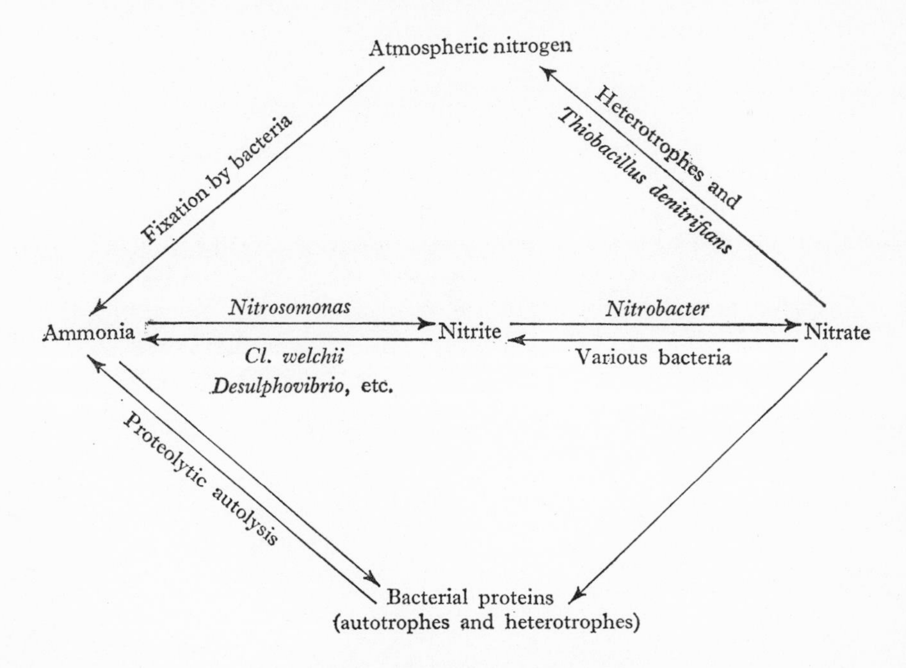

FIG. 102—Microbial nitrogen cycle.

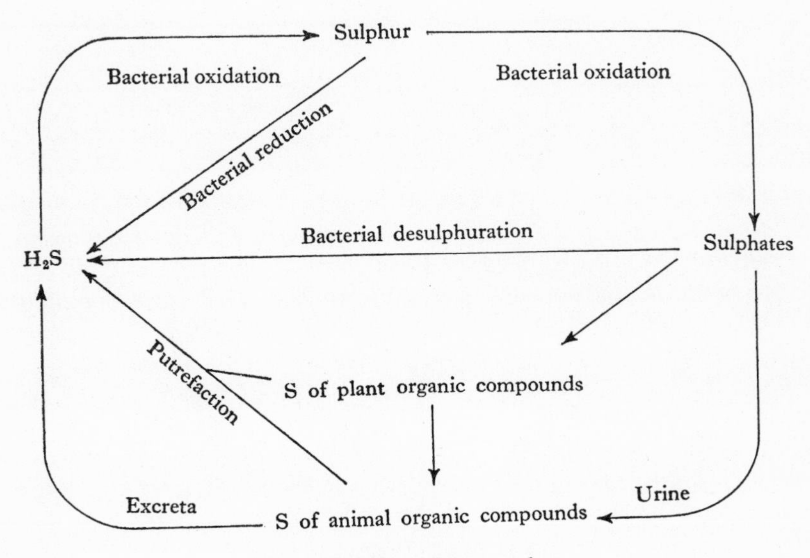

FIG. 103—The sulphur cycle.

If we have a heterogeneous microbial population, the cycle can operate without the intervention of animals, and even without that of plants, as Fig. 102 demonstrates.

III. THE SULPHUR CYCLE

This is somewhat analogous to the nitrogen cycle. Like nitrates, sulphates are utilized and reduced by plants. In its reduced form (—SH groups), like nitrogen in its reduced form as the amino groups of amino acids, sulphur plays a part in the construction of vegetable proteins, from whence it enters the animal organism. A part of this sulphur appears in the oxidized form in the urine (derived from sulphuric acid). When the plant

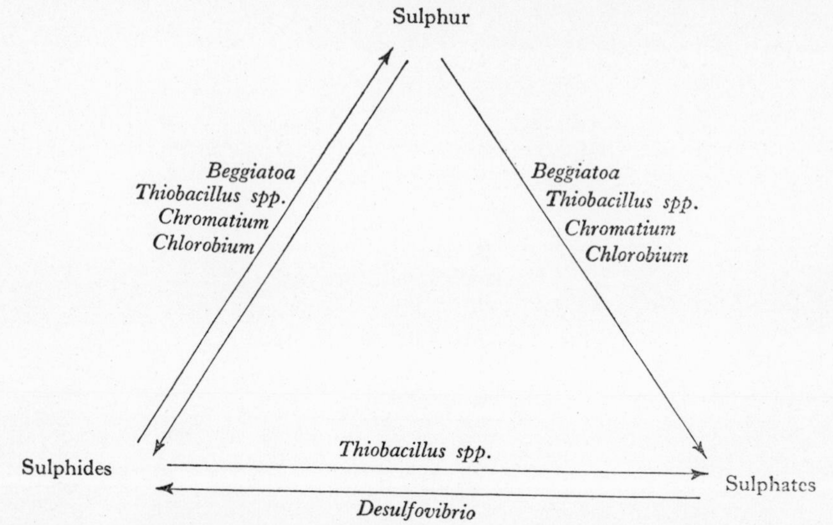

FIG. 104 (Butlin and Postgate)—A microbial sulphur cycle.

or animal putrefies, the sulphur is liberated by many aerobic and anaerobic bacteria as H_2S (analogous to deamination with the production of NH_3). Part of naturally occurring H_2S also comes from the removal of sulphur from sulphates by bacterial processes.

The opposite of the reduction of sulphates is a process corresponding to nitrification, by which bacteria convert H_2S and elementary sulphur to H_2SO_4. Other bacteria can reduce elementary sulphur to H_2S.

As in the case of the nitrogen cycle, animals and plants are not indispensable to the operation of the sulphur cycle. In nature one sometimes encounters this cycle maintained by a microbiological association of autotrophic bacteria, algae and protozoa, the name *sulphuretum* is applied to this community which can be found in clays, muds and in stagnant waters. Figure 104 shows a bacterial sulphur cycle.

IV. THE CIRCULATION OF PHOSPHORUS

The circulation of this element so necessary to life takes place exclusively by way of compounds in which the phosphorus is in its highest state of oxidation and hydration. Orthophosphoric acid, originating in the inorganic world, during its passage through the living world undergoes no chemical change apart from the formation of salts and esters (calcium phosphate in bones, phosphatides, nucleoproteins, sugar phosphates, etc.).

Before entering the living world, the phosphoric acid in inorganic compounds must first be mobilized. This is brought about by the liberation of various strong acids into the soil by numerous aerobic and anaerobic micro-organisms. The CO_2 liberated by the roots of plants and by bacteria also plays a part. Once rendered soluble the phosphates may be reprecipitated or assimilated by plants and then passed to animals in organic or inorganic combination. The excreta of animals and the dead bodies of plants and animals return to the soil the phosphates which have been removed. In this way a local accumulation of phosphate may be obtained and used as fertilizer.

One remarkable aspect of phosphorus metabolism in the biosphere is the increase in phosphate concentration with depth in the ocean. It appears that the phosphorus gradually passes into the sediment at the bottom and it can be calculated that several times the amount present in the ocean has been removed in this way and been replaced by phosphorus from the lithosphere brought down by the rivers. Compared to the removal of this element the return of phosphorus to the continents is very much in arrears since it depends on the uptake of food from the sea by animals, especially man and birds. The fishing industries of the world take around 60,000 tons of phosphorus (25 to 30 million tons of fish). Sea birds bring back to the land around ten times this figure.

Thus there is a considerable deficit between the 137×10^5 tons of phosphorus added to the ocean each year from the continents and the amount returned to the land by the feeding and excretion of marine animals. As a result there is a constant accumulation of phosphorus in the depths of the oceans and it can no longer be used to support terrestrial life.

V. THE METABOLISM OF THE BIOSPHERE

The cycles we have just described show, for the principal elements concerned, the entry of these elements into the biosphere from the inorganic world and their return to the inorganic world. Taken together these cycles describe the metabolism of the biosphere and they regulate its mass and distribution. Each region of the biosphere, made up of a community of organisms and their surroundings, is a functional unit and is termed an ecosystem.

From the biochemical point of view the organisms which make up an ecosystem are of four types: producers, consumers, those which bring about decomposition, and those which accomplish transformations of material. In the terrestrial region, for example in soil, the producers are mainly green plants although autotrophic bacteria also play a part. All the consumers are heterotrophes, i.e. herbivores consuming green plants (insects, rodents, ruminants, etc.), primary carnivores who consume the herbivores, and secondary carnivores who feed on primary carnivores, etc. Parasites are also consumers. The decomposing organisms are those that attack the dead bodies of producers and consumers and turn their substance into the inorganic state of CO_2, ammonia, H_2S, etc. This is accomplished by bacteria and fungi.

The transforming organisms alter the inorganic compounds resulting from the activities of the above and convert them to compounds which can be used by the producers; nitrates and sulphates for example.

It appears therefore that an ecosystem can exist very well if it is made up of producers and decomposing and transforming organisms. The consumers, including man, are only an unessential intermediate in the metabolism of the ecosystem.

The components of marine ecosystems differ from those of terrestrial ecosystems. In the open sea for example, the principal producers are the plankton, especially diatoms, which form what has been called "the ocean pasture". The amount of growth depends on seasonal conditions and photosynthesis only occurs where light is able to penetrate. Also, in addition to CO_2, nitrates, sulphates and phosphates are required. In winter when the ocean waters become agitated and are mixed, these salts are brought to the surface and rapid growth can begin as soon as there is a sufficient number of hours of sunlight. But gradually the inorganic salts are used up and the herbivorous consumers, especially the copepods, graze the ocean pasture and devour it. During the summer, owing to thermal stratification of the water and because the dead organisms sink into the depths, the situation remains stationary. When autumn comes, the surface temperature falls and agitation of the waters increases; the upper layers are resupplied with inorganic nutrients and a new growth of phytoplankton begins which is soon arrested by being consumed and by the fall in temperature and the amount of light. Winter brings about the great mixing of waters which, in the sea, corresponds to the tilling of the soil.

We have already listed the copepods among the marine herbivorous consumers. They are not the only examples, many molluscs and even certain fish belong to this group. But herbivorous consumers are less common than on land and they are almost always small in size (copepods, etc.). These small herbivores are eaten by numerous marine animals and notably by the whale. However most marine carnivores are dependent on the consumption of larger animals. The decomposing and transforming organisms in the marine habitat are, as on the land, micro-organisms.

Considered as a whole, the biosphere is nourished essentially by CO_2, nitrogen, water, sulphates, nitrates and phosphates. The greater part of the energy entering it is of solar origin.

One important aspect of the metabolism of the biosphere is the topography of its distribution. On land, the products of the activity of degrading organisms may be retained in the soil, although there is always a loss which may be considerable in acid soils or where there is excessive rain. In the sea, dead bodies end by sinking into the depths and they may be displaced by the currents so that the products of their transformation may be situated far away from the place where the macromolecules were synthesized. In the depths of the ocean phosphates and nitrates may be deposited far away from the places where photosynthesis is occurring but they may be brought to the surface again by vertical currents. Although during the year the displacement downwards and the displacement upwards may approximately cancel each other out, mineral salts are being continuously poured into the sea and a considerable amount is accumulated on the sea bottom and is inexorably removed from the terrestrial habitat.

On the other hand, the return to the inorganic form of what has been assimilated by the biosphere may be blocked by hold-ups in the mineralization process. The humus in the soil is one of these hold-ups and it is beneficial in its influence on the physical properties of the soil. But peat, lignite and coal show how there has been a long hold-up in the carbon cycle in certain areas. Chalk, coral, etc., are further examples of stagnation in the same cycle. Another example is the accumulation of guano in certain islands in Peru. No doubt the nitrogen of the atmosphere is an inexhaustible source, but the CO_2 of the air is not. Even in the equilibrium state of the biosphere at the present time, the low level of CO_2 in the atmosphere under bright conditions limits the intensity of photosynthesis which would be much greater if more CO_2 was available.

The low concentration of CO_2 in the atmosphere is the result of an equilibrium between producers and consumers. If this small amount was no longer present, life would stop.

As for phosphorus, it can only be liberated slowly from rocks and marine deposits. The most rapidly available source is provided by the decomposition of organisms. This is the vulnerable point in the metabolism of the biosphere. The increasing removal of phosphorus from the land to the sea is a menace to all terrestrial life, and it may make the colonization of the continents a mere episode between two eras of marine existence, unless the return of phosphorus to the land is increased by man, perhaps by the realization of his old dream of utilizing the vast resources of the oceans.

REFERENCES

Aller, W. C., Emerson, A. E., Park, O., Park. T and Schmidt, K. P., (1949). *Principles of Animal Ecology*. Saunders, Philadelphia.

Clarke, G. L. (1954). *Elements of Ecology*. Wiley, New York.

Index